THE BIOSYNTHESIS OF
STEROIDS, TERPENES, AND
ACETOGENINS

FRONTIERS IN CHEMISTRY

Ronald Breslow and Martin Karplus, Editors
Columbia University

THERMODYNAMICS OF SMALL SYSTEMS:
Parts I and II

T. L. Hill   *University of Oregon*

LECTURES ON QUANTUM THEORY OF MOLECULAR ELECTRONIC STRUCTURE

R. G. Parr   *The Johns Hopkins University*

OXIDATION MECHANISMS: Applications to Organic Chemistry

R. Stewart   *University of British Columbia*

THE BIOSYNTHESIS OF STEROIDS, TERPENES, AND ACETOGENINS

J. H. Richards   *California Institute of Technology*
J. B. Hendrickson   *Brandeis University*

THE BIOSYNTHESIS OF STEROIDS, TERPENES, AND ACETOGENINS

John H. Richards

California Institute of Technology

and

James B. Hendrickson

Brandeis University

W. A. BENJAMIN, INC.   1964

New York   Amsterdam

THE BIOSYNTHESIS OF STEROIDS, TERPENES, AND ACETOGENINS

Library of Congress Catalog Card Number 64–21233
Manufactured in the United States of America

*The manuscript was put into production on
9 July 1963; this volume was published
18 August 1964*

*The publisher is pleased to acknowledge the assistance of
William Prokos, who designed the dust jacket*

W. A. BENJAMIN, INC.
One Park Avenue, New York, New York 10016

Preface

In the last decade, acetate as a metabolic entity has assumed a position of central importance in biological processes, particularly as a prime substrate for the biosynthesis of a wide variety of natural substances. Indeed, the symbol adopted for the Fifth International Congress of Biochemistry, held in Moscow in the summer of 1961, was a somewhat stylized representation of an acetic acid molecule. As a result of this progress, acetate is now recognized as the common progenitor of a host of widely divergent structural types found in nature; e.g., terpenes, steroids, fatty acids, complex oxygen heterocycles phenolics, and even some alkaloids.

In every area of study there comes a time when hypotheses solidify into theory, when various, at one time independent, understandings merge into a clear and satisfying theoretical unity that generates predictions, the basic tenets of which are safe from experimental destruction. This is the propitious moment for a detailed exposition, since such an exposition may confidently be expected to remain substantially correct thereafter, while providing a useful condensation and organization that exposes the remaining areas of theoretical and experimental uncertainty, thus affording a springboard into future efforts. The study of biosynthesis from acetate seems to be at this stage; although many important questions still remain open, the theoretical outline is generally clear and is unlikely to undergo major revision in the future. We were therefore encouraged to undertake this summary of the field up to the end of 1962 and, in most cases, through 1963.

We should like to acknowledge that the original initiative for this work came from Professor Marshall Gates, who invited us to participate in a general volume on the biogenesis of natural substances. For reasons beyond his control (the life of an editor is not an easy one!), Professor Gates was

obliged to dissolve the enterprise.   This work represents the crystallization
of our manuscripts with considerable expansion, revision, and updating.

In order to identify ourselves as targets for criticism, one of us (J. B. H.)
claims primary responsibility for the first part of the book (Chapters 2
through 5) and the other (J. H. R.) is the principal author of the remainder.
J. B. H. would like to record his gratitude to Dr. David Dalton for assistance
in literature searching, and J. H. R. is grateful to an anonymous reviewer for
a great many very helpful criticisms.

J. B. HENDRICKSON
J. H. RICHARDS

Cambridge, Massachusetts
Pasadena, California
March 1964

Contents

Preface   v

one **Introduction**   1

    1–1 Acetogenins   1
    1–2 Biological Isoprene Unit   4
    1–3 Polymerization of Isopentenyl Pyrophosphate   6
    1–4 Cyclization   8
    1–5 Bile Acids and Steroids   9

two **Principles of Biogenetic Theory**   10

    2–1 Data   11
    2–2 Functional Group Pattern   11
    2–3 Economy   12
    2–4 Enzyme Control   13
    2–5 Nature of the Reactions   13
    2–6 Nature of the Starting Materials   14
    2–7 Limitations   14

three **Construction of the Acetate Hypothesis**   16

    3–1 Expansion of the Hypothesis   19
    3–2 Summary   26

four **Statistical Survey of Natural Compounds**   27

4–1   Linear Carbon Skeletons   28
4–2   Phenylpropanoid Skeletons   32
4–3   Acylphloroglucinol Derivatives (Cyclization Path A)   41
4–4   Orsellinic Acid Derivatives (Cyclization Path B)   62
4–5   More Complex Cyclizations   75
4–6   Miscellaneous Compounds   95
4–7   Correlation and Commentary   104
4–8   Alkaloids   116

five **Acetogenins: Experimental Verification**   121

5–1   Fatty Acids and Other Linear Carbon Skeletons   121
5–2   Aromatic Compounds   140
5–3   Phenylpropanoid and Flavonoid Compounds   155
5–4   Miscellaneous Compounds   164
5–5   Acetate Hypothesis: Final Summary   170

six **The Isoprene Unit**   173

6–1   Acetate → Mevalonate   175
6–2   Mevalonate → Isopentenyl Pyrophosphate   190
6–3   Polymerization of Δ^3-Isopentenyl Pyrophosphate   198

seven **Monoterpenes**   207

7–1   Acyclic Monoterpenes   207
7–2   Non-Head-to-Tail Monoterpenes   211
7–3   Monocyclic Monoterpenes   213
7–4   Bicyclic Monoterpenes   217
7–5   Cyclopentanoid Monoterpenes   221

eight **Sesquiterpenes**   225

8–1   Acyclic Sesquiterpenes   225
8–2   Bisabolene   226
8–3 β-Santalene and Cedrol   227
8–4   Longifolene   229
8–5   Helminthosporal   231

8–6   Santonin and Guaiazulene Skeletons   231
8–7   Vetivazulenes   235
8–8   Eremophilones   236
8–9   Sesquiterpenes with Medium-Sized Rings   236
8–10 Polygodial and Iresin   237
8–11 Trichothecin   238

nine **Diterpenes**

9–1   Linear Diterpenes   240
9–2   Cativic Acid, Sclareol, and Manoöl   241
9–3   Pimaranes and Abietanes   243
9–4   Phyllocladene-Type Skeletons   244
9–5   Stereochemistry   245
9–6   Diterpenes with Rearranged Skeletons   247
9–7   Diterpene Alkaloids   249
9–8   Experimental Biosynthetic Results   253

ten **Triterpenes**   257

10–1 Principles of Reaction Mechanisms   257
10–2 Olefin Cyclizations   259
10–3 Triterpene Rearrangements   263
10–4 Theoretical Postulates   264
10–5 Ambrein (Chair-Chair-Unfolded-Unfolded-Chair)   266
10–6 Onocerin (Chair-Chair-Unfolded-Chair-Chair)   266
10–7 Tetracyclic Triterpenes (Chair-Chair-Chair-Boat-
      Unfolded)   267
10–8 Pentacyclic Triterpenes (Chair-Chair-Chair-Boat-
      Chair)   268
10–9 Lanosterol (Chair-Boat-Chair-Boat-Unfolded)   273
10–10 Hydroxyhopenone (Chair-Chair-Chair-Chair-Chair)   277
10–11 Alternate Possibilities   277
10–12 Modified Triterpenes   278
10–13 Experimental Evidence for Mechanism of Squalene
      Cyclization   280
10–14 Experimental Studies of Triterpene Biosynthesis   285

eleven **Higher Terpenoids**   289

11–1 Carotenoids   289
11–2 Ubiquinones and Plastoquinones   302

twelve **Cholesterol Biogenesis**   305

    12–1   Origin of Carbon Atoms   305
    12–2   Conversion of Lanosterol to Cholesterol   311
    12–3   Ergosterol   324

thirteen **Further Transformations of Cholesterol**   326

    13–1   Reaction Types   326
    13–2   Bile Acids   329
    13–3   Corticoids   341
    13–4   Androgens   351
    13–5   Estrogens   357
    13–6   Summary   362
    13–7   Steroidal Alkaloids   363

    Appendix   365

    Index   387

THE BIOSYNTHESIS OF
STEROIDS, TERPENES, AND
ACETOGENINS

chapter one | Introduction

The role of acetate in the biosynthesis of almost all groups of natural products has received extensive theoretical and experimental consideration, especially within the last two decades. As a result the casual reader of this book may easily find himself inundated by the mass of structural correlations that is now apparent and by the large amount of detailed biochemical knowledge that is presently available on many aspects of this question. We propose, therefore, in this brief discussion to give a panoramic view of the role of acetate in the biosynthesis of natural products, and hope that it may serve as a gentle and concise introduction to the subject.

The importance of acetate as an intermediate in a host of biochemical processes has long been known. Acetate results from fatty acid breakdown, is a product of carbohydrate metabolism, and can be produced from certain amino acids. Acetate can also serve as a source of these substances and is thus a molecule that interconnects the three major classes of biological compounds: fats, carbohydrates, and proteins. Acetate can also serve as a source of energy through oxidation to carbon dioxide and water via the familiar Krebs cycle (or tricarboxylic acid cycle).

1–1 ACETOGENINS

The implication of acetate in the biosynthesis of a wide variety of straight-chain and aromatic natural compounds was first deduced on structural grounds; the acetate hypothesis stated that a linear polyketomethylene chain formed from head-to-tail self-condensation of acetate units could cyclize into a remarkable array of complex structures.

1

These deductions were subsequently confirmed by tracer and enzymatic studies.

The compounds encompassed by the acetate hypothesis are a broad group that has never, unfortunately, been graced with a generic name, so that, unlike the terpenes and alkaloids, no unified reviews of this group have been assembled. The group includes such categories as flavonoids, quinones, coumarins, chromones, depsides, benzophenones, and a host of others, all highly oxygenated compounds and about 85 per cent incorporating at least one benzene ring. Now that these compounds can be considered unified under the acetate biogenesis concept, it is appropriate that a generic name be given them; to this end it is suggested that they be called *acetogenins*.* It is hoped that future laboratory investigators of biogenesis will thus be dissuaded from concentrating solely on such biologically artificial groupings as flavones or xanthones and will consider the acetogenin group as a whole.

The conversion of acetate to the acetogenins is a process that possesses a close similarity to the construction of fatty acids (themselves acetogenins). New carbon-carbon bonds are formed in both cases by the addition of malonyl coenzyme A to an activated carbonyl group.

$$CH_3COSCoA + CO_2 \rightarrow CH_2\text{---}COSCoA$$
$$\qquad\qquad\qquad\qquad\qquad\quad |$$
$$\qquad\qquad\qquad\qquad\qquad COOH$$

$$\qquad\qquad\qquad\qquad\qquad\qquad\qquad O$$
$$\qquad\qquad\qquad\qquad\qquad\qquad\qquad \|$$
$$CH_3COSCoA + CH_2\text{---}COSCoA \rightarrow CH_3\text{---}C\text{---}CH_2\text{---}COSCoA + CO_2 \xrightarrow[\text{etc.}]{\text{redn.}}$$
$$\qquad\qquad\qquad\quad |$$
$$\qquad\qquad\qquad COOH$$

$$CH_3(CH_2)_{2n}COSCoA \rightarrow \text{Fatty Acid}$$

* The term *acetogenin* ("genesis from acetate") is intended to include compounds biogenetically derivable by the acetate hypothesis and its several variants discussed below, and to exclude the terpenes, which, although ultimately derived from acetate, are obviously themselves a homogeneous family arising more immediately from linear combination of isoprenoid units.

The term is clearly expressive of the biogenetic origin and unity of this diverse group of compounds, the suffix *-genin* defined[1] as "A termination denoting a substance formed from another substance, e.g., digitogenin from digitonin, etc." However, it has been criticized as implying "producing acetate" rather than "arising from acetate," especially in the adjectival form, and indeed the suffixes *-genic* and *-genous* are defined in both ways.[1] In order to avoid confusion with the *-genic* suffix, which is often used in the former sense, we have chosen to employ *acetogenous* as the adjectival form.

1. *Webster's New International Dictionary of the English Language*, unabridged 2d ed., 1960; 3d ed., 1961, Merriam, Springfield, Mass.

Malonyl coenzyme A is itself formed from acetate by carboxylation of acetyl coenzyme A.

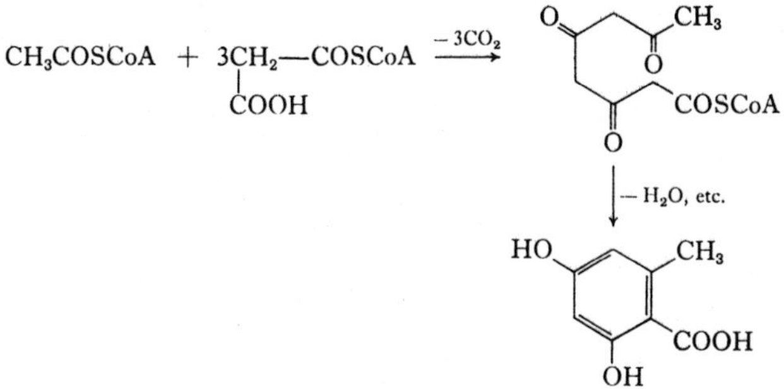

$$CH_3COSCoA \; + \; 3CH_2-COSCoA \xrightarrow{-3CO_2}$$

[1]

In the production of other natural products derived from acetate, it is useful to envision the intermediacy of an unreduced polyketo chain that can undergo internal, aldol-type reactions to yield cyclic products. The formation of orsellinic acid **[1]** points out two of the major features of acetogenins: first, they are derived from the appropriate folding of a chain whose backbone is composed of acetate units linked linearly head to tail; and, second, these substances often carry oxygen at those positions derived from the carboxyl group of the acetate precursor. In this fashion oxygen functions frequently mark the carboxyl carbons of acetate and so serve as an important key to the structural deduction of acetate biogenesis.

These comments apply to griseofulvin **[2]**, which also demonstrates another aspect of acetogenin biosynthesis: the acquisition of secondary substituents (in this case chlorine). These substituents can be of a wide variety and include halogen, oxygen, and carbon in various forms, e.g., methyl, formyl, carboxyl, or even isoprenoid chains.

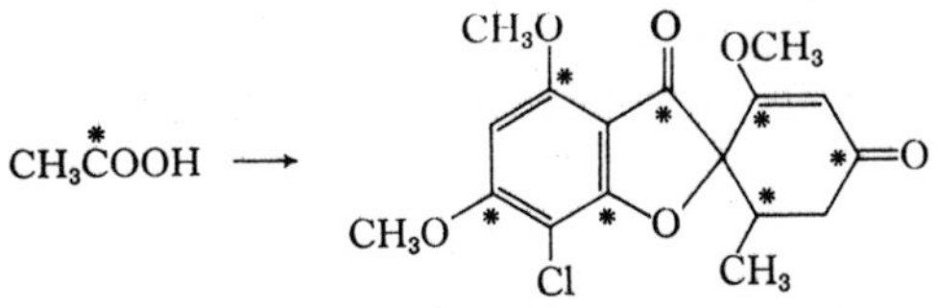

$$CH_3\overset{*}{C}OOH \longrightarrow$$

[2]

An additional secondary feature is further oxidation (or reduction) to give products in different over-all oxidation states from those of the formal polyketo-chain precursor. Cyclopaldic acid **[3]** demonstrates some of these features. Other modifications and variations of these few basic themes are possible and afford an extraordinarily wide

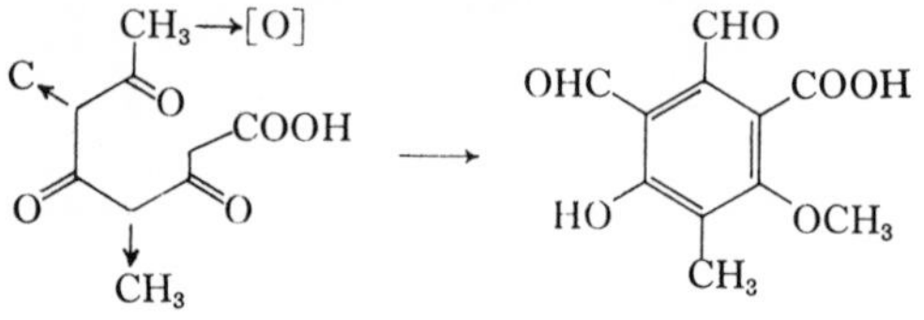

[3]

array of substances whose basic carbon skeleton is composed of a linear arrangement of acetate units. For example, such complex and apparently diverse substances as erythroaphin **[4]** and the alkaloid lycopodine **[5]** are probably derived directly from acetate.

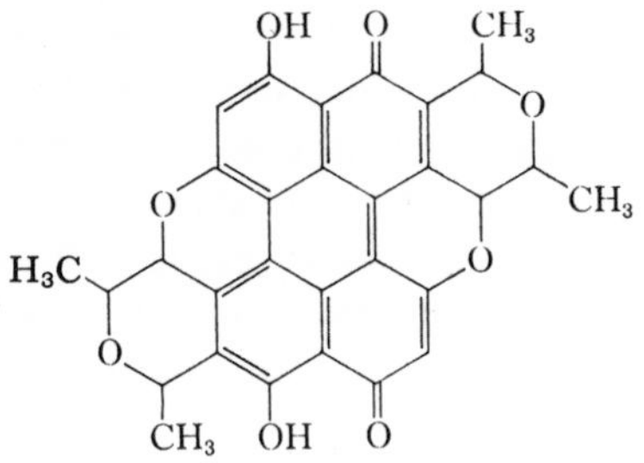

[4] 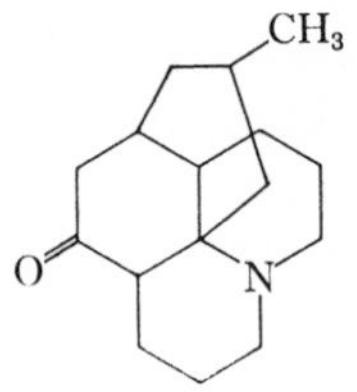   **[5]**

1-2 BIOLOGICAL ISOPRENE UNIT

For the incorporation of acetate into terpenes and their derivatives, a route is followed that differs at an early stage from that just discussed for the biosynthesis of the acetogenins. Whereas the acetogenins are formed by a linear linking of acetate units, the terpenes are generated by conversion of acetate to a branched-chain intermediate, Δ^3-isopentenyl pyrophosphate, the biological isoprene unit. The condensation of two moles of acetyl coenzyme A **[6]** produces acetoacetyl coenzyme A **[7]**, which, upon acquisition of another acetyl residue at the central carbonyl group, forms a branched, six-carbon substance, hydroxymethylglutaryl coenzyme A **[8]**. A stepwise reduction of the esterified carboxyl carbon of this substance produces mevalonate **[9]**.

The intermediates in the biosynthetic sequence prior to mevalonate are capable of interconversion to many other substances. However, the formation of mevalonate is an essentially irreversible process, and mevalonate once formed has essentially only one biochemical role—the production of isoprenoid substances. Its discovery was, therefore, one of the important breakthroughs in terpene biosynthesis.

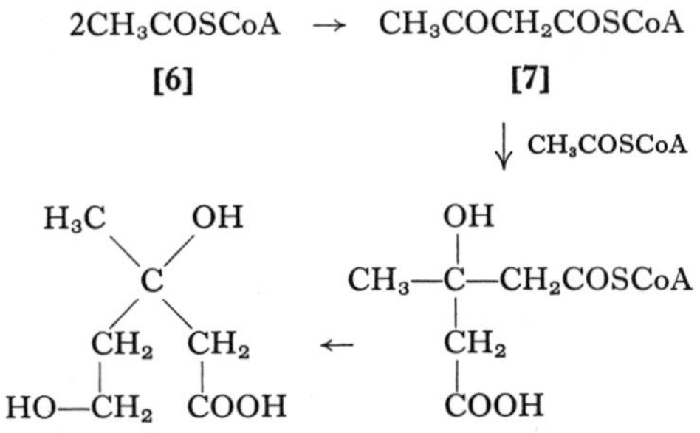

$$2CH_3COSCoA \rightarrow CH_3COCH_2COSCoA$$
$$[6] \qquad\qquad\qquad [7]$$

$$\downarrow CH_3COSCoA$$

[9]   [8]

The path after mevalonate commences with a series of stepwise phosphorylations ([9] → [10] → [11]) by which the terminal hydroxyl function of the mevalonate is activated as a pyrophosphate ester. The tertiary hydroxyl group is also phosphorylated ([11] → [12]), thus activating the resulting molecule for decarboxylation concerted with loss of phosphate and generation of Δ^3-isopentenyl pyrophosphate [13].

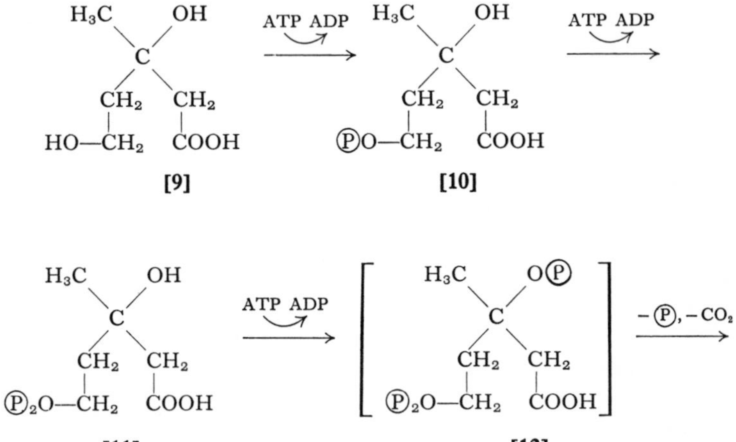

[9]   [10]

[11]   [12]

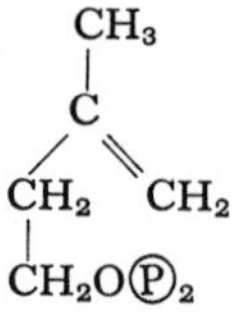

$$CH_3$$
$$|$$
$$C$$
$$CH_2 \quad CH_2$$
$$|$$
$$CH_2O\text{\textcircled{P}}_2$$

[13]

I-3 POLYMERIZATION OF ISOPENTENYL PYROPHOSPHATE

There now ensues a series of reactions by which this five-carbon intermediate (Δ^3-isopentenyl pyrophosphate) joins together with an appropriate number of its own kind to produce 10, 15, 20, 30, 40, or larger acyclic unsaturated molecules, which by further transformations can give rise to the many structural types found in terpenes. This polymerization process begins by an isomerization of Δ^3- to Δ^2-isopentenyl pyrophosphate **[14]**, which, being an allylic phosphate, can undergo a facile ionization, generating a cationic center that can then attack the double bond of a molecule of Δ^3-isopentenyl pyrophosphate. The loss of a proton leads to a 10-carbon product that, being itself an allylic phosphate, can react further to form higher multiples of the basic five-carbon unit. The ten-carbon intermediate (geranyl pyrophosphate **[15]**) is thought to be the precursor of the monoterpenes.

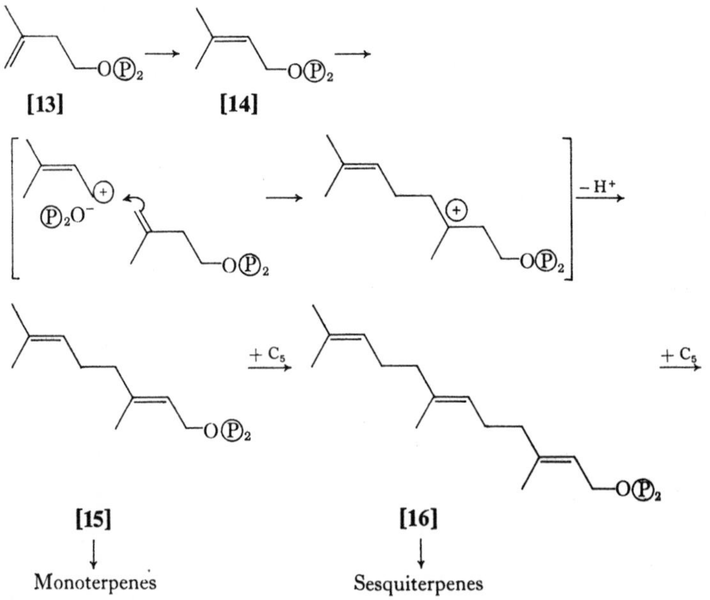

[13]   **[14]**

[15]   **[16]**

Monoterpenes   Sesquiterpenes

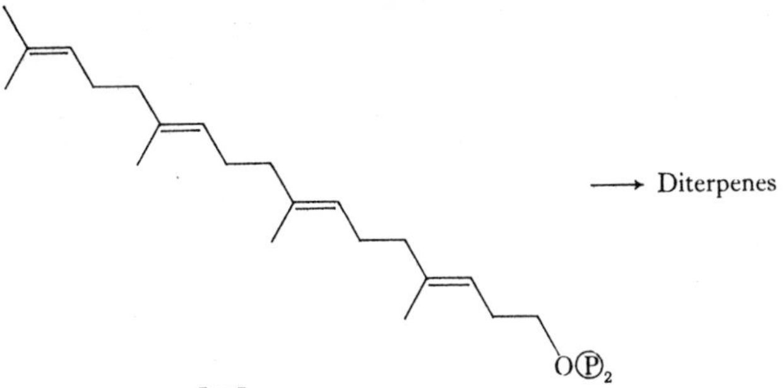

$\longrightarrow$ Diterpenes

[17]

$\downarrow + nC_5$

$C_{50} \longrightarrow$ Ubiquinones

$\downarrow$

Rubber

The 15-carbon farnesylpyrophosphate **[16]** produces the sesquiterpenes, the 20-carbon geranyl-geranylpyrophosphate **[17]** leads to diterpenes. Higher polymers give rise, for example, to the sidechains of the ubiquinones. If the process is repeated many times natural rubber is the result.

One will notice immediately that there are no 30- or 40-carbon intermediates supplied by the above scheme. Intermediates of this size are derived in a fundamentally different way—by dimerization of precursors of 15 and 20 carbons. Such a dimerization of farnesylpyrophosphate **[15]**, which involves a two-electron reduction, generates squalene **[18]**, a 30-carbon acyclic unsaturated hydrocarbon. This 30-carbon compound serves as the origin for the triterpenes. A slightly different type of dimerization of the C_{20} intermediate forms a 40-carbon substance that is the source of the tetraterpenes and carotenoids.

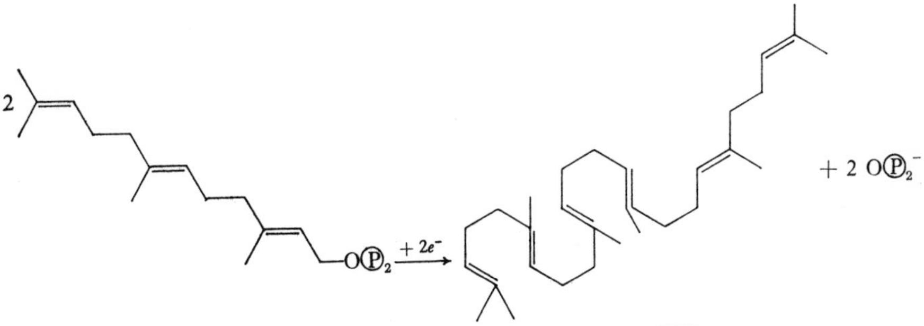

$+ 2\ O\text{(P)}_2^-$

[18]

I-4 CYCLIZATION

Although there are many types of cyclization processes of squalene that will hypothetically produce the many triterpenes, one of special interest is the oxidative cyclization of squalene to form lanosterol **[19]**.

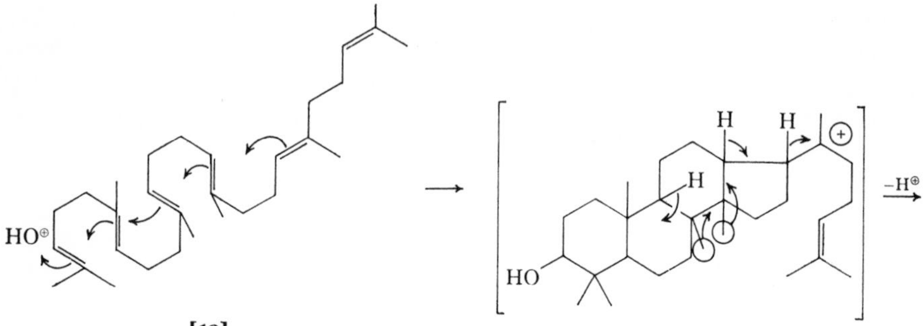

[18]

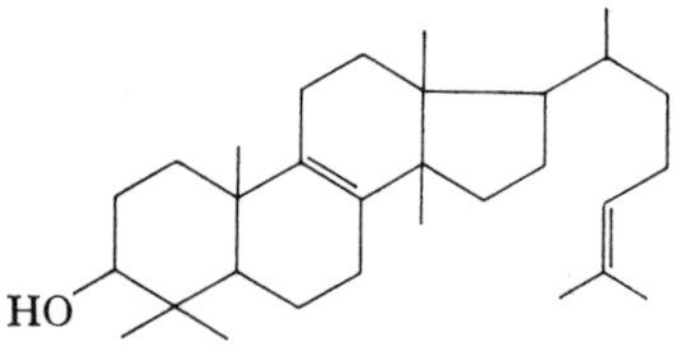

[19]

This cyclization is visualized as proceeding in a concerted fashion so that no stabilized intermediate exists between squalene and the final product, lanosterol. Although the theory accounts for the three-dimensional aspects of this cyclization, the process is shown, for simplicity, in only two dimensions (**[18]** → **[19]**).

There are a great many ancillary changes that can be brought about on the initial product of cyclization. In the case of lanosterol, these processes produce cholesterol **[20]** by a series of reactions that remove

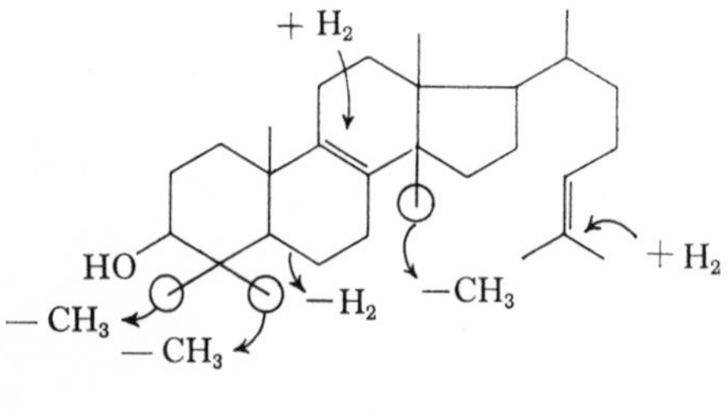

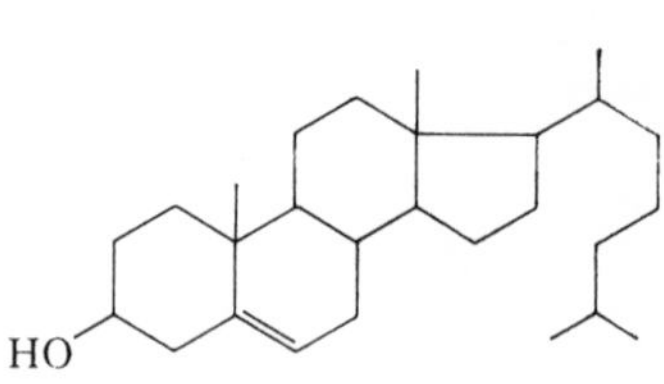

[20]

the three superfluous angular methyl groups, reorganize the unsaturation in the B ring, and reduce the sidechain double bond ([19] → [20]).

I-5 BILE ACIDS AND STEROIDS

Cholesterol furnishes other important biological substances by losing various fragments of itself and by undergoing oxidation or reduction at appropriate sites.   These conversions produce the bile acids, such as cholic acid [21], and the various hormones, such as progesterone [22], Δ^4-androstene-3,17-dione [23], and estrone [24].

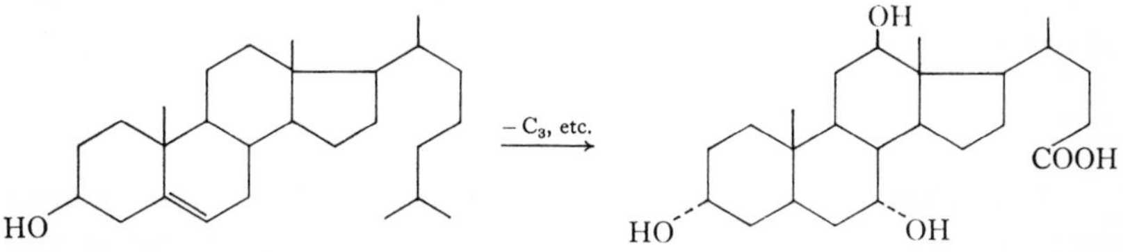

[21]

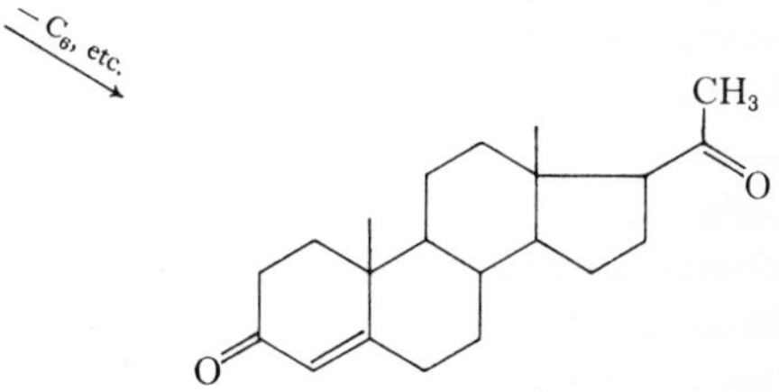

[22]

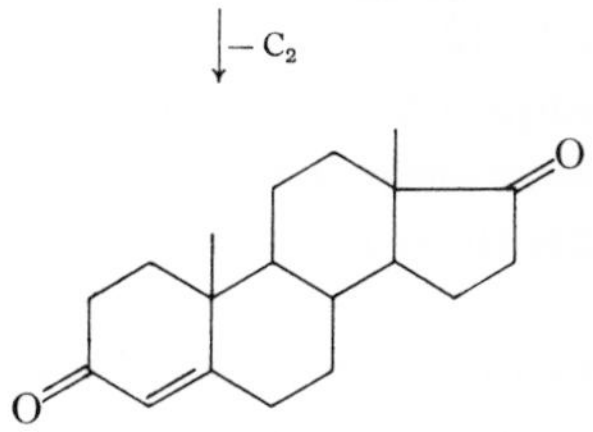

[23]

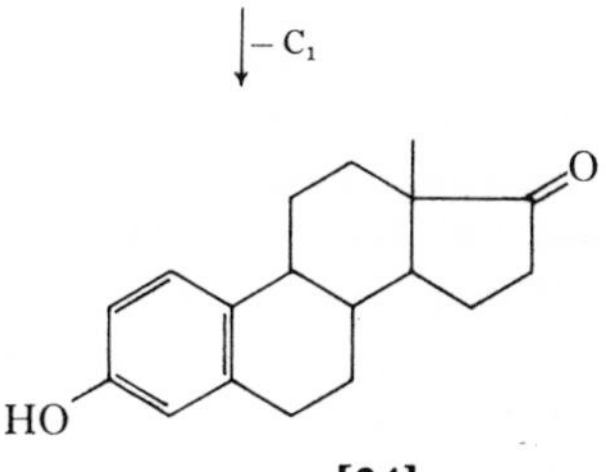

[24]

chapter two | Principles of Biogenetic Theory

The organic chemist has long been intrigued by the synthetic reactions used by living systems to produce the many interesting and complex organic molecules found in nature. The formulation of these biogenetic schemes has had a long and lively history, most notably in the extensive alkaloid speculations of Robinson[1,2] and Schöpf,[3-5] the isoprene rule of the Ruzicka school,[6] and the acetate hypothesis of Collie[7] and Birch.[8] The validity of these speculations as a scientific activity is certainly demonstrated by such results as the elegant syntheses of tropinone by Robinson[1] and the yohimbine skeleton by Hahn[9] and by the great use made of the isoprene rule in suggesting correct structures for many terpenes. More important, however, is the valuable function these hypotheses have served in recent years in providing a basis for the burgeoning activity of examining in vivo paths of biosynthesis with radioactive tracers and other techniques. Nevertheless, these schemes have often been criticized for lack of rigor and

1. Sir Robert Robinson, *J. Chem. Soc.*, **1917**, 762, 876.
2. Sir Robert Robinson, *The Structural Relations of Natural Products*, Clarendon, Oxford, 1955.
3. C. Schöpf, *Ann.*, **497**, 1 (1923).
4. C. Schöpf, G. Lehman, W. Arnold, K. Kach, H. Bayerle, K. Falk, F. Oechler, and H. Stever, *Angew. Chem.*, **50**, 779, 797 (1937).
5. C. Schöpf, discussion of paper by R. Robinson, *Congr. Intern. Quim. Pura Apl. Madrid*, **1934**, 153–173.
6. L. Ruzicka, *Experientia*, **9**, 357 (1953).
7. J. N. Collie, *J. Chem. Soc.*, **1893**, 63, 122, 329; *ibid.*, **1907**, 787, 1806.
8. A. J. Birch and F. W. Donovan, *Australian J. Chem.*, **6**, 369 (1953).
9. G. Hahn and H. Werner, *Ann.*, **520**, 123 (1935).

a naïveté concerning the mechanisms of living processes. In fact, since biogenetic speculations have been characterized by a lack of explicit criteria, these criticisms are too often valid and have lent disrepute to the whole field. Thus, it seems appropriate here to examine the bases for postulating biosynthetic pathways and such criteria as may be available to the modern practitioner.

2–1   DATA

The chief "data" serving as raw material for the construction of these hypotheses are a group of structures of natural products through which runs some thread of common feature. From this underlying similarity can be deduced a reaction scheme by which the entire group appears to have been produced in vivo. The reasoning has been aptly compared to that of comparative anatomy.[5] The greater the number of structures that support the biogenetic inferences derived in this way, the greater the confidence with which they may be regarded as an approximation of natural fact. Thus for statistical reasons a large number of structures are desirable, and the percentage correlation of these structures with a biogenetic scheme is a useful index of its validity when such a large number are available.

Furthermore, the source as well as the structure of the natural compounds can be important. Thus, the existence of several of these compounds in a single species, or a biological similarity among several species producing these compounds, is often presumptive evidence in favor of a common biogenetic pathway. Also any compound in the group with more striking ubiquity among these species may often be presumed to derive by the simplest, most direct path, with the fewest special variants (which are likely to be more species-dependent), as Paech[10] observed in his *Häufigkeitsregel*.

2–2   FUNCTIONAL GROUP PATTERN

In the "comparative anatomy" method of deducing biogenesis, it has always been taken as axiomatic that the skeletons of the compounds in a given group provide a primary clue to their mode of derivation in vivo. It is probable that the pattern of functional groups (or oxidized sites) on those skeletons also reflects their biogenesis, although to a lesser extent, since oxidized sites may also arise by secondary processes. Hence reliable deductions from functional group patterns should only

10. K. Paech, *Biochemie und Physiologie der Sekundären Pflanzenstoffe*, Springer Verlag, Berlin, 1950, p. 29.

be made statistically from a large group of compounds but can, as the ensuing pages will show, yield statistical distributions in remarkable harmony with a single biogenetic scheme.

2-3 ECONOMY

Considering the biogenetic pathways discussed in this book and elsewhere, one is commonly struck by the elegant economy with which organisms build up the complex skeletons of natural products. The great number of natural products in which organic chemists have traditionally been interested are of secondary, if any, metabolic importance to the organism that produces them (in fact, this may be one of the most comprehensive definitions of "natural products," as the term is commonly used by organic chemists).* Accordingly, it is reasonable to suppose that the organism uses the fewest possible reactions to produce them. Similarly, it is unwise to make biogenetic assumptions that rest on particular biological mysteries unique to a hypothesis concerned particularly with the production of such secondary materials. In violation of this principle of economy, it is, of course, easy to devise many biogeneses for any natural compound if only enough one- or two-carbon fragments are bonded together sufficient times until the right structure emerges!

---

* Most natural products (in the organic chemist's sense) serve no known function in the life of the organism that produces them and many have, by default, been described as "metabolic accidents." Indeed, as Birch has pointed out,[11] fungi often flourish without producing their characteristic metabolites at all. If such fortuitous metabolites really exist, their presence in the organism must put severe strictures of economy on any biogenetic scheme devised to explain their production. A number of natural products, however, likely serve the parent organism as poisonous protectors against predatory attack by other organisms (cf. the insecticidal phenols in pine heartwood or the antibiotics produced by molds) and have been referred to as weapons in the evolutionary "war of survival." However, even this neat explanation is far from clear; *Penicillium griseofulvum*, for example, produces mycelianamide, which is extremely toxic to the organism itself.[11] All such natural products, in any event, will not be likely to serve as food for further metabolic reactions and so will accumulate as end products; hence they are more available for isolation by the organic chemist than metabolic intermediates, which may never be present in quantity at any one time.

11. A. J. Birch and H. Smith, *Chem. Soc. (London) Spec. Publ.*, **12**, 1 (1958).

2-4 ENZYME CONTROL

It has occasionally been a deplorable feature of some biogenetic schemes to assume that enzymes can be invoked to carry out any desired reaction that, in their absence, would be unreasonable or unprecedented. One underlying feature of virtually all observed enzymes is that they merely catalyze reactions that are fundamentally sound mechanistically and are usually known to go in vitro (although often under rather more vigorous conditions). Furthermore, if a natural product is only a secondary metabolite, it is likely that most of the enzymes involved in its elaboration are of a low order of specificity and serve some more primary metabolic purpose as well. In general, a limited postulation of enzyme assistance, like a minimum number of reaction steps, is apparently more likely to prove correct.

2-5 NATURE OF THE REACTIONS

The reactions utilized in a biogenetic hypothesis should be reasonable ones from several points of view. Reactions known from in vitro experiments to be spontaneous under the conditions obtaining in a living cell (*physiological conditions*) are clearly tenable in a biogenetic hypothesis[1-5] and include examples such as the Mannich and aldol reaction and the cyclization of hydroxy-acids to lactones. Reactions depending on enzymes, on the other hand, are most defensible when they are simple, general reactions known from biochemical studies to be common in living organisms, e.g., reductions of ketones to alcohols, hydration of double bonds, methylation of phenols, etc. Furthermore, the limitations on the course of a reaction that are imposed by modern reaction theory cannot be overlooked in biosynthetic paths; violation of such principles as antiparallel additions to double bonds and Markownikoff orientation is rarely tenable. On the other hand, such consequences of modern theory often allow stereochemical as well as structural predictions in biogenesis and accordingly increase the rigor and usefulness of these speculations.[12,13]

Finally, although oxidation and reduction processes both appear to be of wide occurrence in the primary metabolic processes commonly examined in biochemistry, examination of the latter stages of most natural product biosyntheses suggests that oxidative processes are much

12. L. Ruzicka, in A. Todd (ed.), *Perspectives in Organic Chemistry*, Cambridge, New York, 1956, p. 265; A. Eschenmoser, L. Ruzicka, O. Jeger, and D. Arigoni, *Helv. Chim. Acta*, **38**, 1890 (1955).
13. J. B. Hendrickson, *Tetrahedron*, **7**, 82 (1959).

more widespread than reductive ones. Of the oxidations that occur, virtually all can be rationalized mechanistically as attack of the species $HO \cdot$ or $HO^{\oplus}$ (one- or two-electron oxidations) on an unshared pair of electrons (cf. $-\overset{|}{\underset{|}{N}}$: as in Wenkert's useful alkaloid conception [14] or the π electrons of a double bond or enol; cf. squalene cyclization, Chapter 12). It may well be that most or all these oxidations occur under the aegis of only a few oxidative enzymes of a rather low order of specificity, in keeping with the simplicity suggested in Section 2–4.

2–6 NATURE OF THE STARTING MATERIALS

Now that the over-all picture of intermediary metabolism has been fairly sketched in, it is possible to draw on the intermediates contained in it as available starting points for biogenetic pathways; thus it is no longer necessary and certainly not desirable to postulate unlikely materials such as ethylene and isoprene for this purpose. It is logical to assume, as starting materials, compounds such as amino acids or acetate, which are available in quantity in the mobile reservoirs at the heart of the primary metabolism of the organism.

2–7 LIMITATIONS

It is important to remember that this inferential approach to biogenesis has implicit limitations imposed by the nature of the reasoning. Thus, it is usually impossible to discern anything of the *sequence* of synthetic steps in the elaboration of a natural molecule, so that, although it is convenient to discuss these steps in a certain order, it must be understood to cast no demerit on the reasoning if this order is later rearranged. Similarly, it is not possible to discern the actual reagents used in many cases but only the effective structural element involved. Formaldehyde has frequently been postulated as a reactant and criticized on the grounds of its toxicity and the fact that it is rarely encountered free in nature,[2] but the inferential approach can only be responsible for observing the structural introduction of $-CH_2-$, whereas the actual reactant may be any species representing formaldehyde masked, for example, as an acetal or in some other condition as in folic acid. Accordingly, it is merely a structural convenience to speak of "formaldehyde or an equivalent" or of similar reactants in a biogenetic scheme.

14. E. Wenkert, *Experientia*, **10**, 346 (1954).

Furthermore, it is occasionally true that two schemes compete with more or less equal effectiveness as explanation of the production of a group of natural structures.   In such cases it is usually fruitless to press the utility of this reconstructive reasoning to distinguish between the two routes.   Several such cases exist in the following sections, and they can be finally settled only by direct experiment.

It must, of course, always be recognized that the biogenetic inferences derived by structural examination can never be more than hypothetical in any case and must ultimately be supported by direct experiment, using such tools as radioactive tracers or direct enzyme isolation.   Nonetheless, the two approaches to biogenesis—the direct and the indirect—complement each other, since the inferential hypotheses provide the basis for direct experiment as well as affording evidence for the *generality* of a scheme that may be thoroughly tested in only a few species.   The direct experiments serve, once they corroborate the general features of a biogenetic pathway, to amplify and modify the original.   The acetate hypothesis, discussed in the following chapters, provides an excellent instance of the operation of the tenets presented in the foregoing paragraphs as well as the complementary action of structural inference and direct experiment.

chapter three | Construction of the Acetate Hypothesis

It may be said at the outset that direct experiment has in recent years provided a very large measure of support for the acetate hypothesis. The approach taken in the subsequent sections to the presentation of this hypothesis is primarily historical with the details of the direct experimental corroboration reserved for the later part. The conception is developed first following the original lines laid down by Birch and stressing the application of the principles above; a statistical correlation of known chemical structures with the hypothesis is made in order that both the effectiveness and scope of the hypothesis may be clearly seen. This is then followed by a discussion of the experiments that derived from it and have served to confirm and amplify the general terms of the conception. In a few cases, however, the experimental results have somewhat altered the original conception, and in these cases it was deemed desirable to present the current view, based on direct experiment, in the earlier sections to avoid confusion. Such deviations from the inferential approach are pointed out in the text.

The biogenetic scheme currently referred to as the acetate hypothesis was first suggested by Collie [1] on the basis of some interesting transformations he had observed with polyacetyl compounds. Thus, he found that, in weak alkali, diacetylacetone [1] dimerized via aldol condensations and dehydrated to the naphthalene derivative [2], and that dehydracetic acid [3] (obtained from pyrolysis of acetoacetic ester), treated similarly, yielded orsellinic acid [4]. Struck by the similarity of [2] to natural naphthalenic compounds and by the presence of [4] in natural sources, Collie postulated that such compounds might be formed

1. J. N. Collie, *J. Chem. Soc.*, **1893**, 122, 329; *ibid.*, **1907**, 787, 1806.

in nature from polyacetic acids and emphasized the relative ease with which these condensations occurred. The idea lay fallow for many years until, in 1953, in a brilliant reexamination of the conception, Birch[2] laid down most of the modern view of the acetate hypothesis and pointed out its broad scope and great usefulness. His views were amplified in a later review.[3] Using radioactive tracers, Birch and his school have since investigated the conception experimentally with fruitful results, all of which tend to support the validity of the acetate hypothesis.

[1] $\xrightarrow{-OH}$ [2]

[3] $\xrightarrow{-OH}$ [4]

The primary building block of acetate biogenesis is a linear poly-acetic acid chain, CH_3—CO—$(CH_2$—CO$)_n$—CH_2—COOH, presumably formed by repeated head-to-tail condensations of acetate units. The biochemical rationale for this, based on a postulated fatty acid biosynthesis, has been that it represents the reverse of the oxidative degradation scheme for fatty acids in vivo. In detail, it was felt that acetic acid, activated as a thioester [5] (as of coenzyme A) could easily self-condense in a Claisen or aldol-like condensation to yield such β-keto acids [7]. More recently, direct investigation of the biosynthesis of these linear chains has shown that acetyl coenzyme A is first carboxylated with carbon dioxide to produce malonyl coenzyme A [6] with a more active methylene group that can then react with a second molecule of acetyl coenzyme A and decarboxylate to form a four-carbon chain. This compound may then react with another malonyl unit in the same way [8] to provide further linear extension of the chain. The process is summarized in formulas [5] through [8] and discussed at greater length in Section 5–1.

2. A. J. Birch and F. W. Donovan, *Australian J. Chem.*, 6, 360 (1953).
3. A. J. Birch, *Fortschr. Chem. Org. Naturstoffe*, 14, 186 (1957).

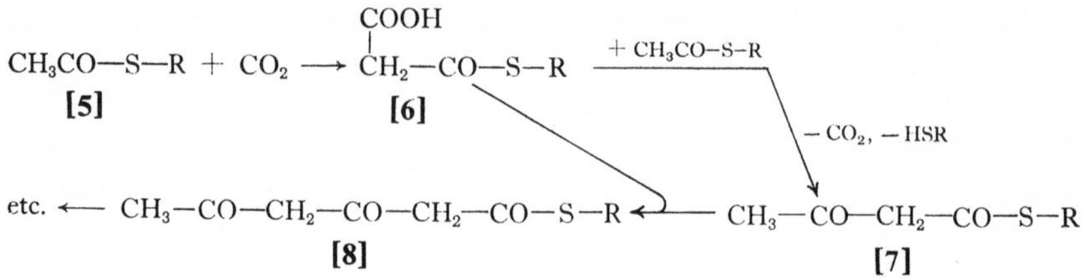

$$CH_3CO-S-R + CO_2 \longrightarrow \overset{\displaystyle COOH}{\underset{[6]}{CH_2-CO-S-R}} \xrightarrow{+ CH_3CO-S-R}$$

[5]

$-CO_2, -HSR$

$$\text{etc.} \longleftarrow CH_3-CO-CH_2-CO-CH_2-CO-S-R \longleftarrow CH_3-CO-CH_2-CO-S-R$$

[8]   [7]

This process has been studied in detail only for the biosynthesis of saturated fatty acids, in which case reduction of the β-ketone precedes further chain extension with malonyl units, so that the actual existence, in nature, of a polyacetyl chain as such remains an open question, discussed further in Section 5–1. However, as a formal convenience for the purposes of constructing the hypothesis, we shall consider the chains as poly-β-keto-methylenes, with the reservation that they may be masked, partially reduced, or cyclized *before* they reach their ultimate length; the inferential method cannot distinguish most of these possible modifications in any case.

The key reaction of the polyacetyl chain is cyclization. Thus an enolate anion may attack a keto group at another portion of the chain to yield cyclized products of either O or C acylation. Both reactions occur with facility in forming six-membered rings, the C alkylation

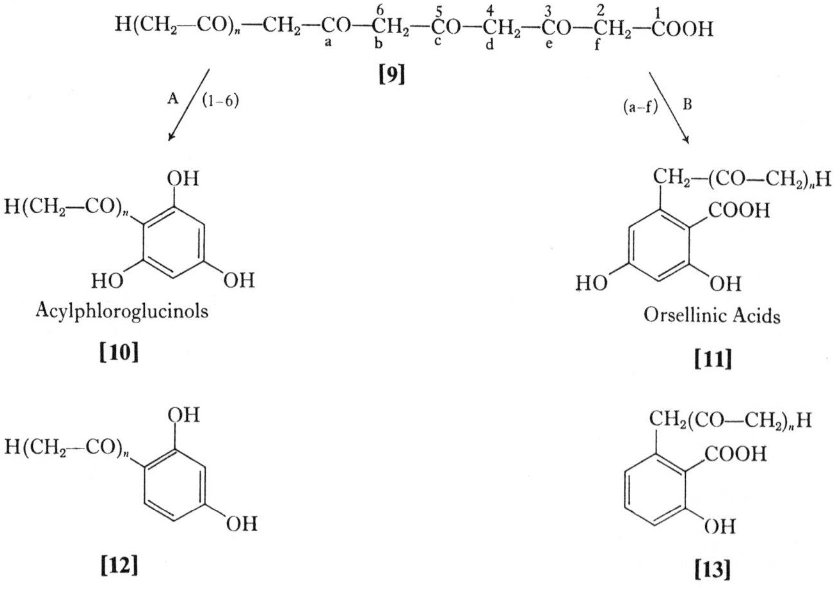

$$H(CH_2-CO)_n-CH_2-CO-\underset{a}{\overset{6}{C}H_2}-\underset{b}{\overset{5}{C}O}-\underset{c}{\overset{4}{C}H_2}-\underset{d}{\overset{3}{C}O}-\underset{e}{\overset{2}{C}H_2}-\underset{f}{\overset{1}{C}OOH}$$

[9]

A $(1-6)$ $(a-f)$ B

Acylphloroglucinols   Orsellinic Acids

[10]   [11]

[12]   [13]

(aldol or Claisen* condensation) in this case leading to a phenolic aromatic ring. Two major routes, paths A and B above, lead to two families of phenols, the acylphloroglucinol [10] and orsellinic acid [11] derivatives, respectively, distinguished by their aromatic substituent patterns. Reduction of an uninvolved ketone before cyclization can lead analogously to the generalized types [12] and [13]; such reduction finds support in the direct studies of fatty acid biosynthesis. In this connection, it would appear mechanistically much less likely to reduce a phenolic hydroxyl after the cyclization, and it is this unlikelihood that in turn lends credence to the belief that a site of aromatic oxygen is a fair indication of a site of ketone in the precursor polyacetyl chain. Decarboxylation of the β-keto acid at the terminus of the chain is a second mechanistic variant that would seem unexceptional and should give rise to decarboxylated varieties of the orsellinic acid derivatives.

3–I EXPANSION OF THE HYPOTHESIS

If we grant the capability of the polyacetyl chain for elaboration of complex aromatic structures, it is further instructive to examine three variants on the scheme suggested by the modes of reactivity mechanistically available to such a chain, such as the decarboxylation or ketone-reduction mentioned above.

Incorporation of Other Acids

The terminal acid of the polyacetyl chain $R—(CO—CH_2)_n—COOH$ need not always be acetic acid; it is as conceivable that another acid $R—COOH$ might initiate the extension of a chain with malonyl units. The variety of such acids actually observed is in fact severely limited in almost all acetogenins to a few benzoic and cinnamic acids with a very particular pattern of ring hydroxylation. The biosynthesis of these simple aromatic acids has been examined experimentally [4–6] in lower organisms and is summarized in Chart I.†

---

* The *keto* group of the terminal carboxyl is assumed capable of activation to undergo the same reaction, presumably as the thiolester.

† That shikimic acid is probably the source of these acids in higher plants is suggested by its wide occurrence and by some preliminary tracer studies.[5–7] Certain details of the chart are derived from studies described in Section 5–3 on the ϕ-C$_3$ compounds.

4. B. D. Davis, *Adv. Enzym.*, **16**, 247 (1955).
5. C. E. Dalgliesh, *Adv. Protein Chem.*, **10**, 31 (1955).
6. J. G. Levin and D. B. Sprinson, *Biochem. Biophys. Res. Commun.*, **3**, 157 (1960).
7. W. D. Ollis (ed.), *The Chemistry of Natural Phenolic Compounds*, Pergamon, New York, 1961.

The benzoic and cinnamic acids arising from this biosynthetic pathway are of course not acetogenins. They are readily distinguished from aromatic rings arising (vide supra) by polyacetyl cyclization, since the latter possess the characteristic resorcinol pattern of oxygenation on the ring; the aromatic acids derived from shikimic acid, however, have either no hydroxyl, 4-hydroxyl, 3,4-dihydroxyl, or 3,4,5-trihydroxyl substituency, referred to the carboxy or C_3-sidechain position. It may be taken as a reasonable variant of the acetate hypothesis that the shikimic-derived acids may be chain-extended by malonyl units, just as acetic acid is, to provide polyacetyl chains with aromatic terminals.

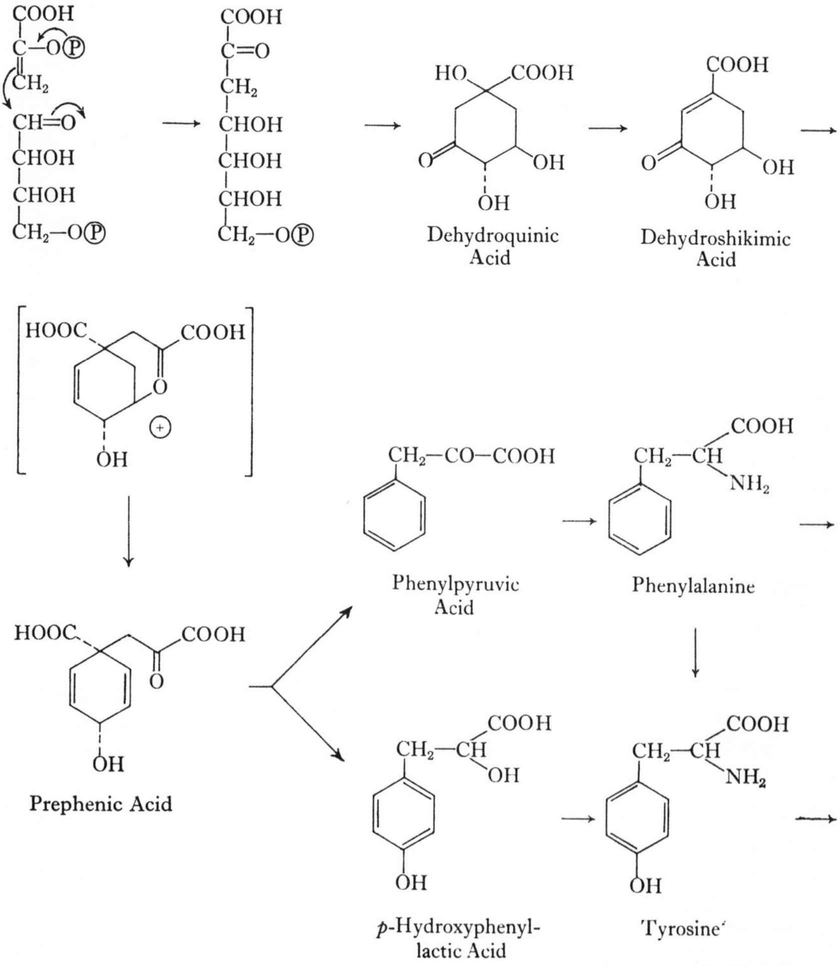

Dehydroquinic Acid

Dehydroshikimic Acid

Phenylpyruvic Acid

Phenylalanine

Prephenic Acid

p-Hydroxyphenyl-lactic Acid

Tyrosine

In fact it appears very likely that the large number of benzenoid compounds in nature almost invariably derive their aromatic rings by one of two routes: (1) via shikimic acid or (2) through polyacetyl-chain cyclization. Here is certainly a striking example of the principle of economy in biogenesis!

The only other acids that appear to be involved as chain terminals are various intermediate- or full-length, linear fatty acids, sometimes unsaturated but usually saturated. Since such acids are themselves of acetate origin, it is only a question of biosynthetic sequence rather than origin in such cases and usually it is impossible to discern from structural examinations anything about the sequence of steps (however, see page 62).

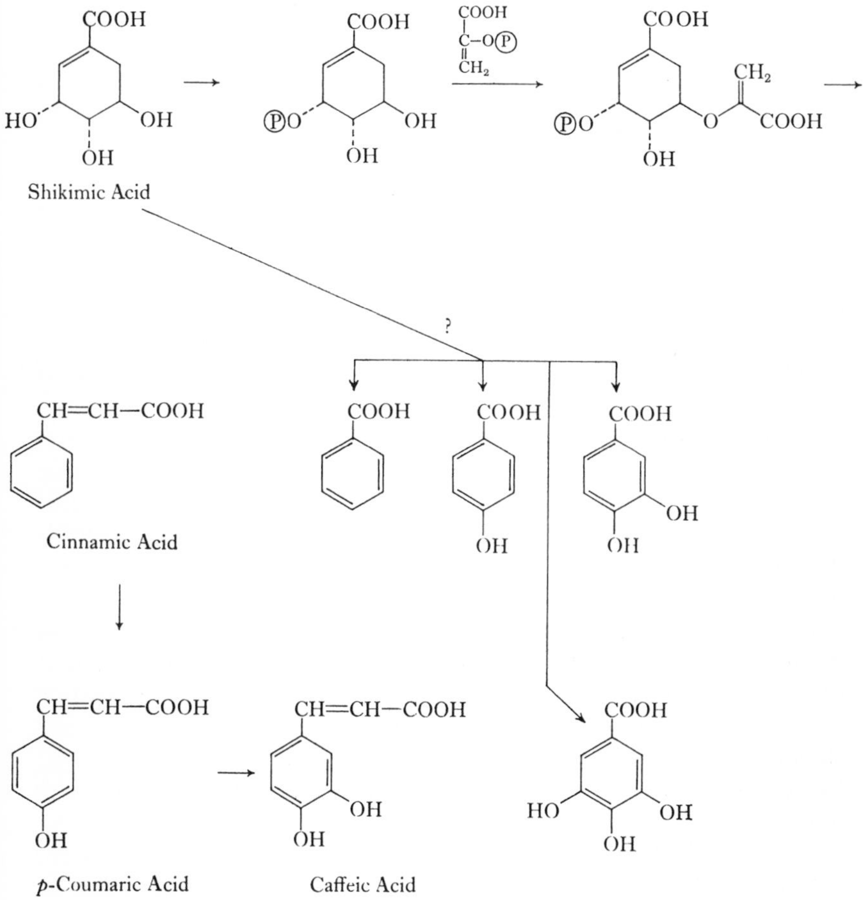

Chart I *The shikimic acid pathway to aromatic compounds*

Substitution at Methylene Carbons

Just as the enol of the β-diketone group of the polyacetyl chain may cause cyclization by intramolecular substitution (aldol), it may also be substituted intermolecularly by electrophilic reagents ($R^{\oplus}$) either at carbon or oxygen, as formalized in Equation (3–1). We may consider group $R^{\oplus}$ to be an alkylating agent or an oxidizing agent such as an equivalent of $HO^{\oplus}$.

$$\tag{3-1}$$

The same mechanism is formally available for nuclear substitution on the cyclized phenols, but is energetically favored if it occurs on the polyacetyl chain before cyclization, since substitution on the phenol requires destruction of the aromatic resonance energy in the transition state.   Hence it is likely that such substitutions often precede cyclization.   This argument is valid for the resorcinols but probably not for the phloroglucinols, since in the latter the aromatic resonance energy is largely cancelled by the energy required to maintain three keto groups in their enol form.   Thus, phloroglucinol itself readily forms a trioxime and probably differs little from the open polyacetyl chain in stability.

Examination of the structures of the acetogenins suggests that relatively few groups are commonly utilized in substitutions of this sort, these being methyl, methylene, isopentenyl, glycosidyl, and hydroxyl, with the methyl group predominating to a notable degree.   In a number of cases multiple methylations are in evidence, and, in a few cases where an isobutyryl group appears to be the terminal acid of the chain, it is likely that this arises by bis-methylation on a methylene carbon, followed by cleavage of the β-diketone as shown in Equation (3–2).   Mechanistically, this is supported by the destruction of the stabilizing conjugation in the enol form of the β-diketone that occurs on bis-methylation, for it is known that dialkylated β-diketones are much more susceptible to hydrolytic cleavage.

Enol alkylation by some equivalent of formaldehyde is apparent in some hydroxy-methyl compounds among the acetogenins and in some in which two enolic units are joined at carbon by —CH$_2$—

$$CH_3$$
$$|$$
$$R—CO—CH_2CO—\cdots \rightarrow R—CO—C—CO—\cdots \rightarrow$$
$$|$$
$$CH_3$$

(3-2)

$$CH_3$$
$$\diagdown$$
$$R—COOH + \quad CH—CO—\cdots$$
$$\diagup$$
$$CH_3$$

(methylenation). None of the substituting agents suggested in this section is biochemically unreasonable, in keeping with the criteria of Chapter 2.

A large number of acetogenins contain isopentenyl units consistent with their formation by O- or C-alkylation by a fragment such as isopentenyl pyrophosphate, derived from mevalonic acid (see Chapter 6). These units are found either as simple substituents or cyclized into fused heterocyclic rings and often appear in higher oxidation states. Oxidation of the isopentenyl residue often merely takes the form of simple epoxidation or hydroxylation of the double bond; it has been suggested, alternatively, that two-electron oxidation of the adjacent enol (viz. next section) could result in facile cyclization directly to the common dimethylchromene as shown below.[8] It may be noted that conjugate addition of water to the intermediate α,β-unsaturated ketone of this route provides a reasonable source of the oxygen often found on the 1 position of the isopentenyl substituent. The initial isopentenylation could also occur, although less easily for steric reasons, by S_N2' reaction on the allylic pyrophosphate, and a few 3-substituted isopentenyl groups are indeed found in natural compounds. Finally, since many natural structures are known that exhibit fused furan rings bearing no isopropyl residue, it has been suggested that they arise by cleavage of an isopropyl group after cyclization of the isoprenoid substituent.[9] These various possibilities are outlined in Chart II; more detailed structural correlations of the existing isoprenoid forms are offered in the correlation Section (4–7). For convenience in both places the polyacetyl chain or phenol is represented only by an enolic fragment.

Many phenolic compounds exist in plants as O-glycosides (most commonly with glucose), and these must also arise by the enol alkylation

8. W. D. Ollis and I. O. Sutherland, Ref. 7, Chap. 4.
9. R. Aneja, S. K. Mukerjee, and T. R. Seshadri, *Tetrahedron*, **4**, 256 (1957).

mechanism. Since such linkages are relatively unstable, many natural compounds, isolated as phenols, may have actually been O-glycosides in the plant; accordingly only the aglycones have been tabulated and discussed below. It has recently been observed also that certain natural products are C-glycosides as one would predict from the mechanism of enol alkylation.[10] Since the glycoside moiety represents part of the carbon skeleton of the molecule, the few cases known have been arbitrarily included in the subsequent discussions.

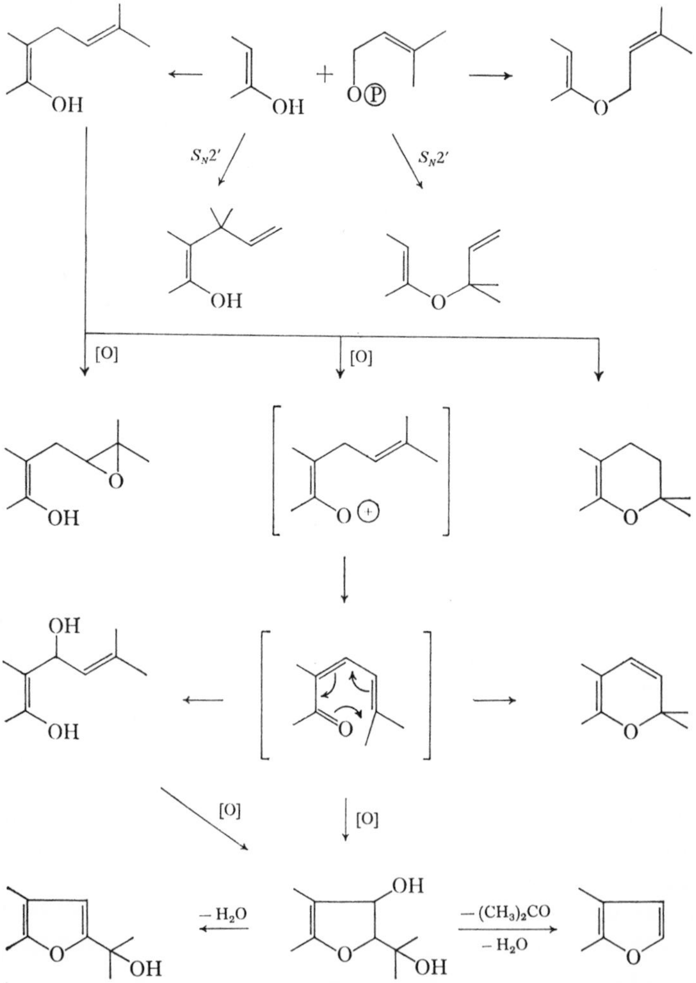

Chart II   *Variations in isopentenylation of polyacetyl chains*

10. L. Hörhammer and H. Wagner, Ref. 7, Chap. 10.

Oxidative Coupling

The oxidative procedure mentioned above as involving effectively an $HO^{\oplus}$ species is a two-electron oxidation; there exists also the possibility of a one-electron oxidation of the enol to a form such as

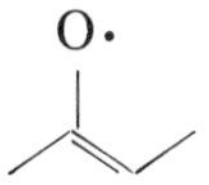

The radical thus formed may then couple with another such radical to yield a dimeric structure, as in the examples of Chart III. Such a dimerization may also occur by comparable oxidative coupling of two phenols, in which case both ortho and para positions, as well as the phenolic oxygen, are candidates for formation of the coupling bond as in the illustrations in Chart III.

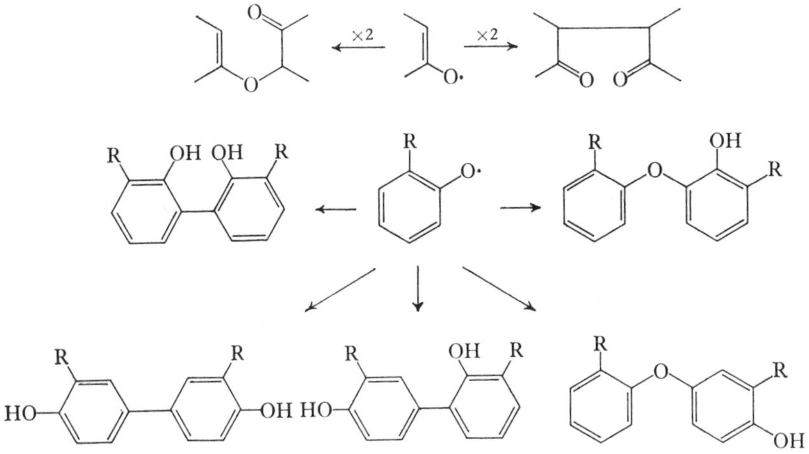

Chart III *Variations in oxidative coupling of polyacetyl chains*

The argument on energetic grounds that substitution precedes cyclization is perhaps also applicable: A number of structures that appear to arise by this oxidative coupling of phenols may owe their origin to oxidative dimerization of the enols of the antecedent polyacetyl chain, followed by aldol cyclizations (cf. usnic acid, Section 4–3). One-electron oxidation may be more common in nature than two-electron oxidation, but the method of structural inference does not permit a distinction in cases of simple hydroxylation, since coupling of the enol radical with HO· would produce the same product as the attack of an HO$^\oplus$ equivalent discussed already above. This may well be the type of process by which natural phenols are oxidized to hydroquinones or quinones, for this para-oxidation of phenols does appear to play a role in the elaboration of acetogenins.

The operation of the oxidative coupling variant of the acetate hypothesis may easily be inferred from structures containing two halves, each of acetate origin in itself, joined by a bond between methylene carbons of their original polyacetyl chains. The oxidative coupling reaction is, in fact, broader in scope than just the acetogenins, extending into alkaloid, terpene, and lignin examples; two excellent reviews of the operation of these oxidative couplings in biogenesis generally are available.[11,12]

3-2 SUMMARY

Biogenesis of natural compounds by the acetate hypothesis takes place by extension of a terminal acid with successive malonyl units into a linear polyacetyl chain. This chain may then cyclize in aldol-type condensations by virtue of its enolic reactivity; the latter also allows C- or O-substitution by methyl, methylene, isopentenyl, hydroxyl, or sugars, as well as oxidative coupling between two polyacetyl chains (or subsequent phenols) at methylene carbons. The notation used for polyacetyl precursors in the subsequent discussion is indicated in [14]. Occasional variants on this basic over-all pattern are separately discussed where they arise in the several subsequent sections.

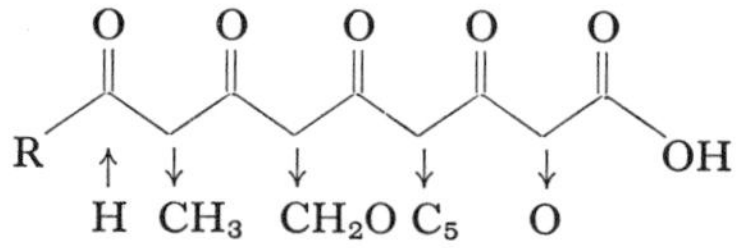

[14]

11. D. H. R. Barton and T. Cohen, *Festschr. Arthur Stoll*, **1957**, 117.
12. H. Erdtman and C. A. Wachtmeister, *Festschr. Arthur Stoll*, **1957**, 144.

Statistical

chapter
four

Survey of Natural Compounds

The acetogenins provide a fruitful group for examination by the method of structural inference, since there are a very large number of known structures as candidates, and most of these are sufficiently complex to provide clear inferences. For this purpose a compendium of natural products was assembled for examination; the intention has been to include all nonnitrogenous compounds except sugars and terpenes, the latter being considered separately in later chapters.* Needless

---

* Although a conscientious search for all relevant natural products was made, it cannot be claimed that none have been missed. It is hoped that this is justifiable in that the present work is not primarily an exhaustive compendium and that a few missing compounds are unlikely to alter the statistical treatment significantly in so large a sample. In any event, several excellent and very reliable compendia have become available in recent years, notably the superb Karrer encyclopedia,[1] the Pfizer Handbook,[2] Thomson,[3] and Geissman.[4] Most compounds included in these sources are not individually cited in the survey below. The literature was examined through 1961, and the compounds are listed in the Appendix, page 365.

1. W. Karrer, *Konstitution und Vorkommen der organischen Pflanzenstoffe (exclusive Alkaloide)*, Birkhäuser, Basel, 1958.
2. M. W. Miller, *The Pfizer Handbook of Microbial Metabolites*, McGraw-Hill, New York, 1961.
3. R. H. Thomson, *Naturally Occurring Quinones*, Butterworths, London, 1957.
4. T. A. Geissman (ed.), *The Chemistry of Flavonoid Compounds*, Pergamon, New York, 1961; see also the earlier review by T. A. Geissman and E. Hinreiner, *Botan. Rev.*, **18**, 77, 165 (1952).

to say, not all these compounds are likely to be acetate-derived, and there is danger in some cases of trying to fit intractable structures to the scheme. Nevertheless, a high proportion of these compounds appears to be acetogenous, and in the examination below a statistical survey is made of the correlation of these structures with the tenets of the hypothesis advanced above, in order to clarify the extent to which the inferential approach is valid as well as to show the great variety and scope of structures that can be derived from acetate by the simple construction discussed in Chapter 3.

The groups of compounds dealt with in the subsequent paragraphs are arranged primarily in accordance with the biogenetic mechanisms referred to above, where these are applicable, rather than in the traditional classifications by structure type or species source. Also, the structures of the examples used in this chapter are not always reproduced in the traditional manner; rather, they are consistently written so that the originating polyacetyl chain is seen with the terminal RCO··· at the left-hand side.

4–I LINEAR CARBON SKELETONS

The structures deriving most directly from the polyacetyl chain should have simple linear carbon skeletons with alternating sites of oxygen attachment.* Unfortunately, structural inferences concerning the biogenesis of the fatty acids and the many highly unsaturated linear compounds in molds and *Compositae* are usually tenuous, since the sites of oxygen attachment in a polyacetyl precursor are obscured by dehydration or total reduction in compounds of this kind. Nevertheless, the biosynthesis of these compounds has been examined directly in considerable detail, as recounted in Chapter 5, with the result that these compounds are now known to arise by the acetate-malonate pathway.

Macrolides

As Woodward has pointed out,[5] the macrolide antibiotics provide a superb set of structures for a statistical examination of the correlation of oxygenated sites with the alternating pattern of a polyacetic acid precursor. The structures of these interesting antibiotics, collected in Chart I, point up their skeletal similarity as linear acids closed into large ring lactones, with a sprinkling of appended methyl groups and oxygens. Magnamycin, however, has an aldehyde group as well,

* The attachment of oxygen refers equally to any functionality in which oxygen is bonded to a carbon of the chain, such as hydroxyl, ketone, methoxyl, or acyloxy.

5. R. B. Woodward, *Festschr. Arthur Stoll*, **1957**, 524.

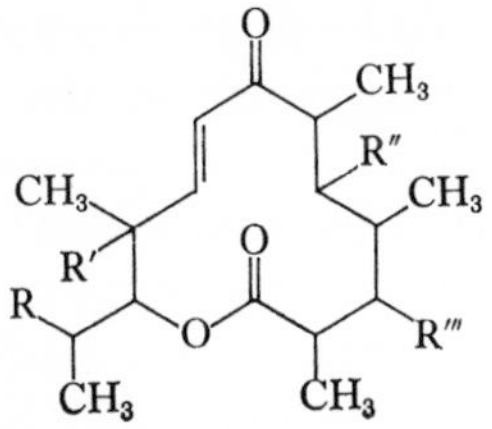

Methymycin (R = R″ = H;
R′ = OH; R‴ = O-sugar)

Neomethymycin (R = OH;
R′ = R″ = H; R‴ = O-sugar)

Picromycin (R = R″ = H;
R′ = OH; R‴ = O-sugar)

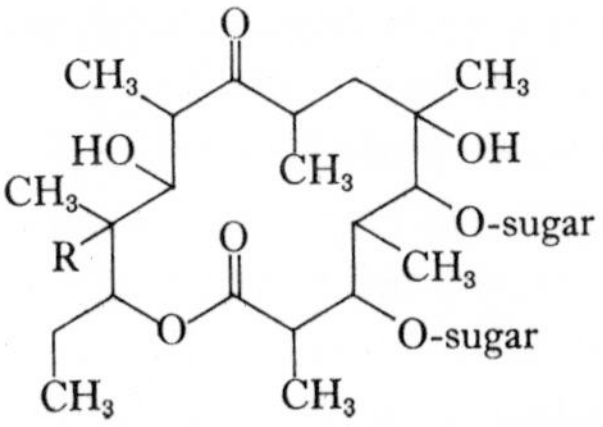

Erythromycin (R = OH)

Erythromycin B (R = H)

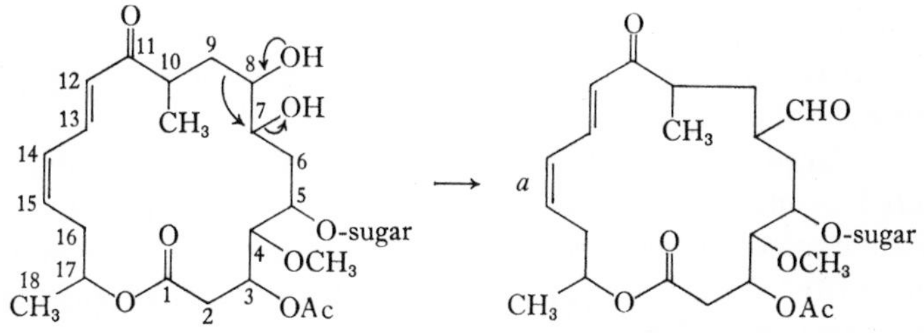

Protomagnamycin

$\longrightarrow$ *a*

Magnamycin B
Magnamycin = epoxide at *a*

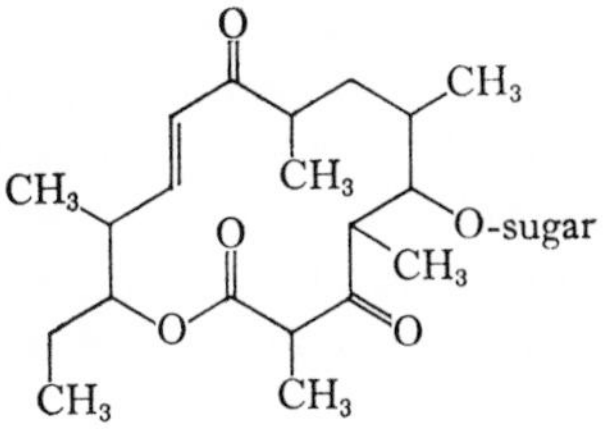

Narbomycin

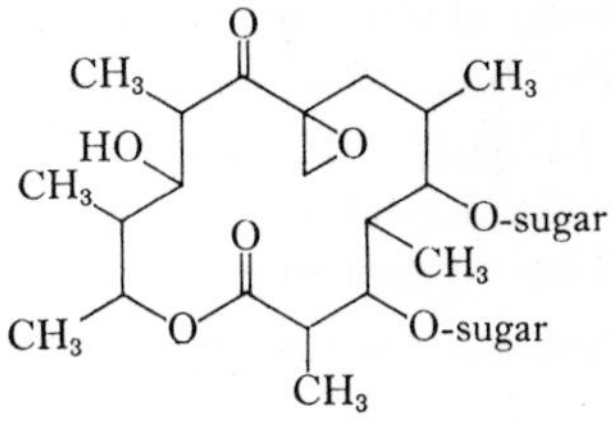

Oleandomycin

Chart I   *The macrolides*

which was thought[5] to arise by a pinacol-type rearrangement (cf. arrows) on the glycol system of a *protomagnamycin*, which has the same skeleton and absolute stereochemistry at C_{10} as tuberculostearic acid (10-methylstearic acid).   An examination of the positions of oxygen attachment* on the skeletons of the known macrolides may be made by

* Since all double bonds present are conjugated with carbonyl, hydration of these placing —OH at the β-position in the normal manner is assumed for the purposes of this correlation.

comparing each lactone with an ideal linear chain of alternating sites of oxygenation.[5] The correspondence is remarkable; in the eight known macrolides (counting protomagnamycin as the precursor of the magnamycins) there are a total of 110 skeletal carbons, of which 93 are either oxygenated or not in accord with polyacetyl prediction, a correlation of 85 per cent. The correlation is, of course, nearly perfect if substitution at methylene by OH^+ is accepted (Section 3–2). Recent work, described in Section 5–1, indicates however that although acetate is the source of most of the carbons of magnamycin, the several carbons around the aldehyde group arise from another source. The methyl groups, it should be noted, uniformly appear at methylene sites, as predicted for enol methylation. However, these sites are also correct for derivation of the methyl groups from propionate, rather than acetate, incorporation in the chain[5] and the inferential method allows no distinction. Present evidence, cited in Chapter 5, in fact favors the propionate variant. It is amusing to note in passing that parasorbic acid [1] is the simplest macrolide and clearly acetogenous as well.

Much larger lactone rings are apparently the hallmark of a newly discovered group of polyene macrolides, only a few of which have afforded complete structures to date. In the structures of pimaricin [2],[6] filipin [3],[7] and lagosin [3][7] one can see the familiar alternating sites of oxidation in general, but the correlation is less good and the skeletons are branched rather than linear, so that these molecules do not support the simple acetate hypothesis. The large majority (and the most common) of the fatty acids are linear chains with an even number of carbons, but a few are abnormal in having chain-branching [cf. alternaric [273] (p. 102) and corynomycolic (p. 140) acids, and the mold polyacids of Section 4–6] and are discussed below.

The natural musks[8] represent a small group of compounds with an apparent relationship to the fatty acids and macrolides in that they

CH₃

[1]

Parasorbic Acid

6. J. B. Patrick, R. P. Williams, and J. S. Webb, *J. Am. Chem. Soc.*, **80**, 6689 (1958).

7. M. L. Dhar, V. Thaller, and M. C. Whiting, *Proc. Chem. Soc.*, **1960**, 310.

8. E. Lederer, *Fortschr. Chem. Org. Naturstoffe*, **6**, 87 (1950).

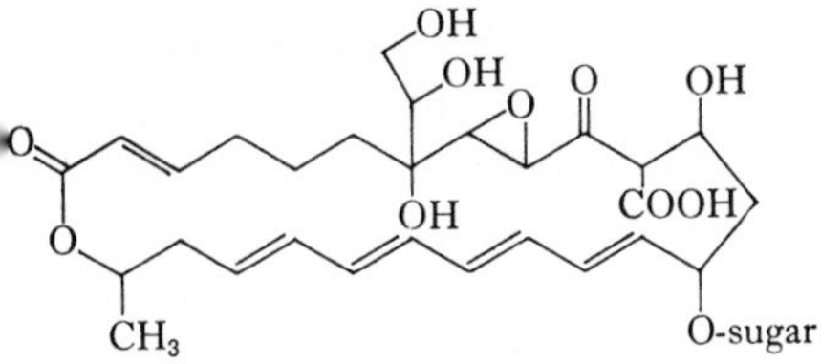

[2]

Pimaricin

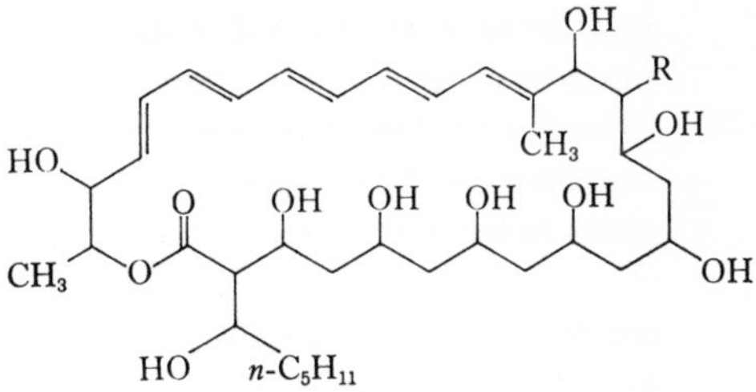

[3]

Filipin (R = H)
Lagosin (R = OH)

appear to arise by cyclization of long-chain acids; but again these molecules are so stripped of functionality as to provide no real basis for deduction.

Aromatic Variants

Among the variants on the acetate hypothesis is the provision that an acid other than acetic may terminate the polyacetyl chain (Section 3–1); such acids are almost invariably benzoic or cinnamic acids, either unsubstituted or bearing the shikimic-derived pattern of hydroxylation. The prototype of such products, then, is $(HO)_n\phi$—CO—CH$_2$—CO— CH$_2$···COOH, and will possess an odd-numbered sidechain if it is an acid or an even-numbered chain if decarboxylated to a methyl group at the chain end. Compounds with intermediate oxidation states at the terminal may have even- or odd-numbered chains without furnishing or denying any support to the hypothesis. Among the acids are cortisalin [4] and piperic acid [5], the latter coexisting with its tetrahydro derivative. More common than the free acids, however, are the enollactones obtained by cyclizing the carboxyl to an enolic oxygen on the δ-carbon, i.e., phenylcoumalin, paracotoin [6], and methoxy-paracotoin [6], in which the elements of the prototype polyacetyl chain are clear. An interesting alkaloid, found coexistent with methoxy-paracotoin, is anabine,[9] in which the methylenedioxyphenyl group of methoxy-paracotoin is replaced by β-pyridino, indicating analogous derivation from a polyacetyl chain terminating in nicotinic acid! Examples of the decarboxylated prototype are often partially reduced on the chain, reminiscent of the simple fatty acids. Thus, methyl-gingerol [7] retains only two oxidized sites on the chain, although they are found in positions

9. W. B. Mors, O. R. Gottlieb, and C. Djerassi, *J. Am. Chem. Soc.*, **79**, 4507 (1956).

consistent with the hypothesis; simpler examples are found in methyl phenethyl ketone, betuligenol [8], and zingerone [8], and, probably, in acetophenone, p-methoxyacetophenone, and acetovanillone, although compounds as uncomplicated as these acetophenones provide too few clues to be considered meaningful for deductive purposes.*

Cinnamic acids as terminals for the polyacetyl chain are evident in the structures of kawain [9], methysticin [9], yangonin [10], and their dihydro derivatives, all of which come from the same source (Kawa root) and retain intact all the oxygen markers of the presumed cinnamoyl-diacetic acid forerunners.

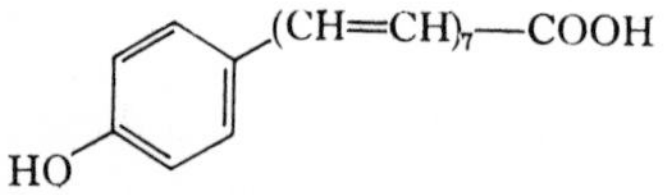

[4]
Cortisalin

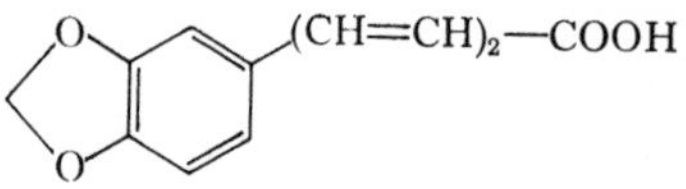

[5]
Piperic Acid

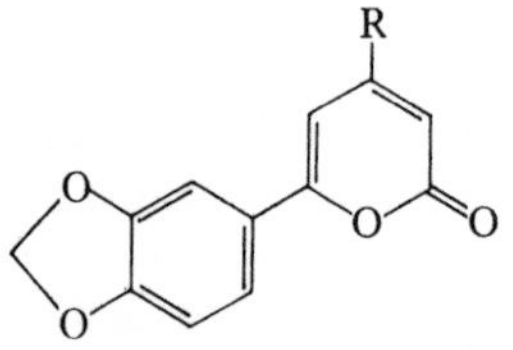

[6]
Paracotoin (R = H)
Methoxy-paracotoin (R = OCH₃)

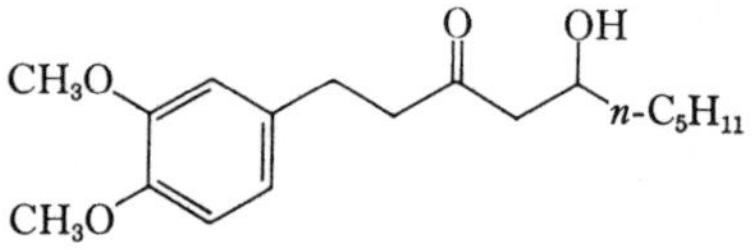

[7]
Methylgingerol

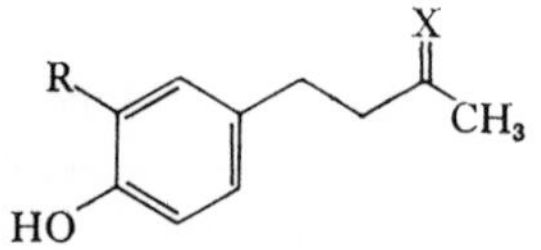

[8]
Betuligenol (R = H; X = H, OH)
Zingerone (R = OCH₃; X = O)

4–2 PHENYLPROPANOID SKELETONS

Compounds containing the 1-phenylpropane (ϕ-C_3) skeleton are virtually ubiquitous in the plant kingdom, ranging over a variety of

* The last compounds lend themselves most economically to the bio-genetic mode inferred here, but, as they are somewhat reduced chains in any case, the possibility of their arising entirely from acetate by an acylphloroglucinol cyclization accompanied by reductions cannot be excluded (see Section 4–3).

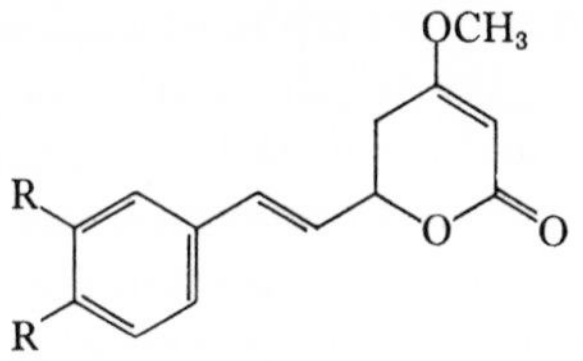

[9]

Kawain (R = H)

Methysticin (R = —O—CH₂—O—)

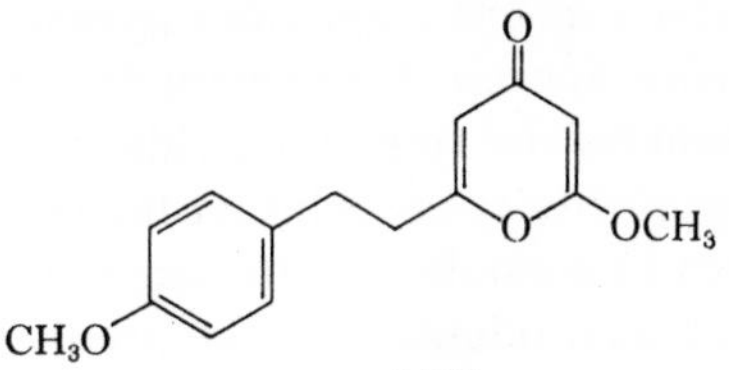

[10]

Yangonin

oxidation states in the C_3 chain from phenylpropanol and the allyl-benzenes to the cinnamic acids. Besides the simple phenylpropanes are the dimeric lignanes (discussed below), which are apparently derived from them. That the benzene rings of these compounds arise from shikimic acid is very likely in view of the overwhelming preponderance in the ϕ-C_3 compounds of the typical shikimic-derived oxidation patterns. Thus, in the 117 benzene rings in the simple ϕ-C_3 compounds (excluding coumarins, which are discussed below) and lignanes, the oxidation patterns are outlined in Table 4–1. Furthermore, the

Table 4–1 *Oxidation patterns in the benzene rings of ϕ-C_3 compounds*

No ring oxidation	= 10	
	4 = 13	Anticipated
Oxidation at	3, 4 = 70	from shikimic
position(s)	3, 4, 5 = 15	acid = 108 (92 per cent)
	2, 3, 4, 5 = 4	
Other patterns	= 5	
Total	117	

most widespread of these compounds (cinnamic and caffeic [11] acids, coniferyl [12] and syringyl alcohols [12]) possess the correct oxidation pattern for shikimic acid biogenesis.

The central question with regard to the acetate hypothesis is the origin of the three-carbon sidechain. Two possibilities present themselves, i.e., that the appropriate benzoic acid condenses with one malonyl unit to yield a ϕ-CO-CH₂-COOH starting material, or that the three carbons arise from pyruvic acid in the prephenic acid pathway, with appropriate oxidations supplying the requisite extra sites of oxidation on the ring and yielding the prototype acid $\phi CH_2COCOOH$. The simplicity of the relevant molecules makes a decision on inferential grounds impossible, but the accumulating evidence at present (Section 5–3) favors production by the prephenic acid pathway generally.

Several other groups of ϕ-C_3 compounds deserve attention. The lignanes are dimeric molecules, bearing the carbon skeletons of either pinoresinol ([13], 17 cases) or podophyllotoxin ([15], 13 cases), which indicates universal coupling of ϕ-C_3 units at the β-carbons of the side-chains. It has been suggested[10] that this dimerization occurs by oxidative coupling of the p-hydroxystyryl system ([16] → [17], cf. coniferyl alcohol [12]). This accords well with the low state of oxidation common in the C_3 units of the lignanes. Two dimers are known with the magnolol [18] carbon skeleton, which may also arise by this

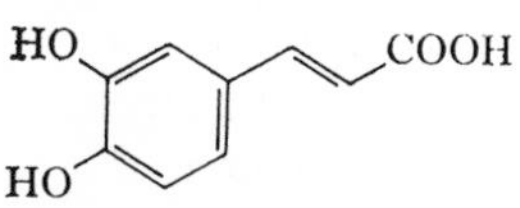

[11]

Caffeic Acid

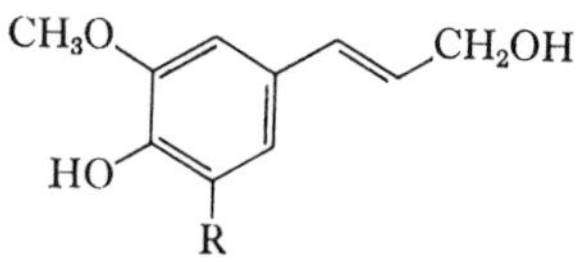

[12]

Syringyl Alcohol (R = OCH_3)
Coniferyl Alcohol (R = H)

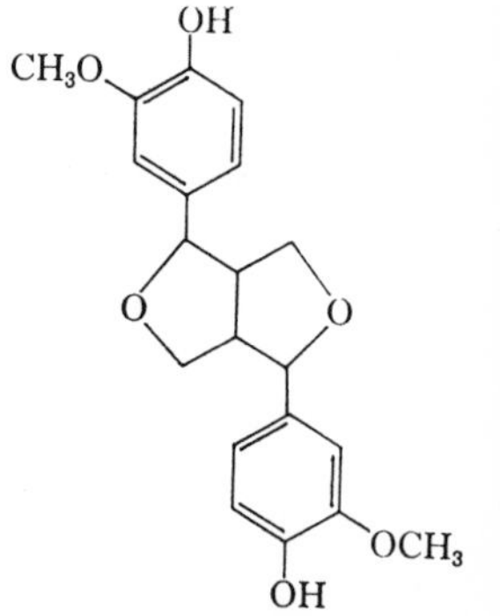

[13]

Pinoresinol

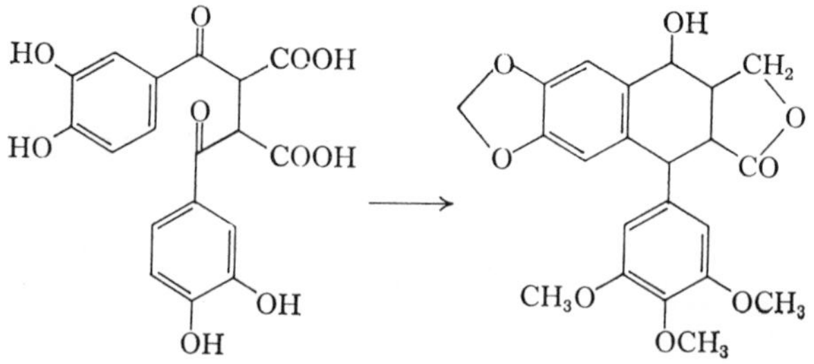

[14]

[15]

Podophyllotoxin

10. H. Erdtman and C. A. Wachtmeister, *Festschr. Arthur Stoll*, **1957**, 144.

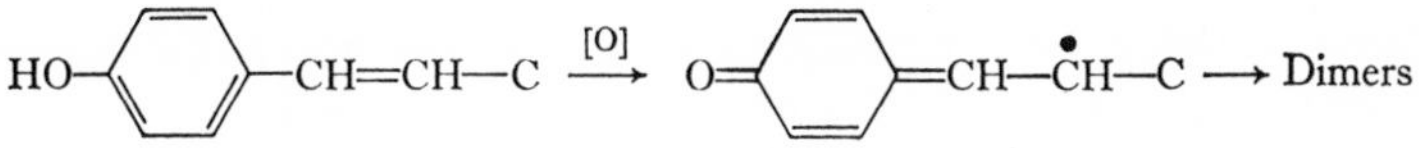

HO—⟨benzene⟩—CH=CH—C $\xrightarrow{[O]}$ O=⟨ring⟩=CH—ĊH—C → Dimers

[16]   [17]

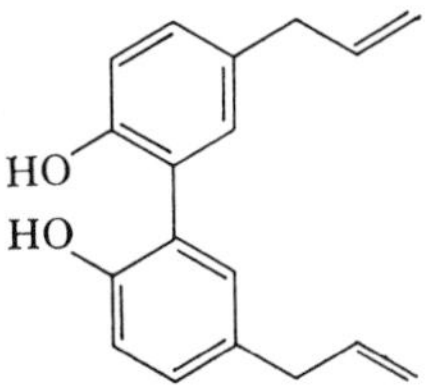

[18]
Magnolol

coupling. On the other hand, the $\phi COCH_2COOH$ precursor can dimerize by the oxidative coupling of its enol, as discussed in Section 3-1, page 25, to yield a dimer [14] more appropriate mechanistically for the requisite cyclization to the podophyllotoxin [15] skeleton.

The fungal terphenyls [20], [21], however, can be derived quite simply from the $\phi CH_2COCOOH$ precursors by simple Claisen-type condensations of the kind discussed in polyacetyl-chain cyclization in Chapter 3 (cf. [19]). Of the seven known terphenyls, five fit this pattern perfectly, the exceptions being volucrisporin (metahydroxy-phenyls, see Section 5-3) and muscarufin (structure and discussion, p. 171). An interesting suggestion has been made[11] that these terphenyls are in turn the precursors of the lichen pulvic acids [22], by an oxidative cleavage (dotted line in [20]) similar to the reaction of peroxide with these quinones in vitro.

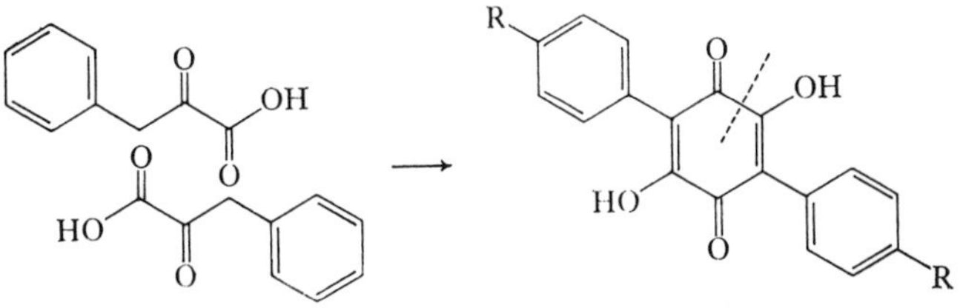

[19]   [20]

Polyporic Acid (R = H)
Atromentin (R = OH)

11. Y. Asahina and S. Shibata, *Chemistry of Lichen Substances*, Japan Society for the Promotion of Science, Tokyo, 1954.

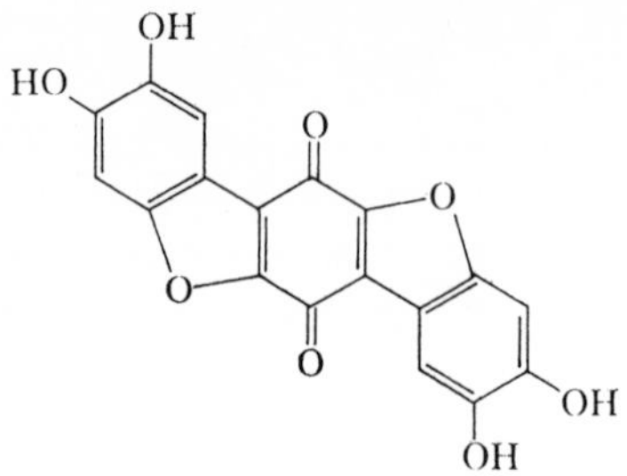

[21]

Thelephoric Acid

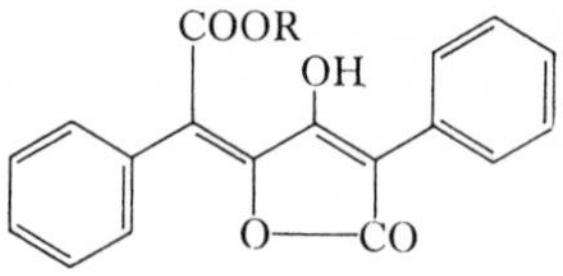

[22]

Pulvic Acid (R = H)

Vulpinic Acid (R = CH₃)

Coumarins

The biogenesis of the natural coumarins is somewhat resistant to elucidation by inferential means despite their essentially phenylpropanoid skeleton. The patterns of oxidized sites on the 80 known natural coumarins (excepting the five 4-substituted coumarins described later; aglycones only) are grouped as shown in Table 4–2. Several proposals for coumarin biosynthesis from cinnamic acids have been made. The first was offered by Haworth,[12] who postulated para-oxi-

Table 4–2 *Oxidation patterns in the natural coumarin aglycones*

Position	Number of examples
7	30
5, 7	17
6, 7	8
7, 8	8
5, 6, 7	3
5, 7, 8	6
6, 7, 8	4
Other (non-7)	5
	80

12. R. D. Haworth, *J. Chem. Soc.*, **1942**, 448.

dation of a *p*-hydroxy-cinnamic acid **[23]** to yield **[25]**, which could then cyclize by Michael addition of carboxyl (**[25]** → **[28]**), and dehydrate to yield a 7-hydroxycoumarin **[29]**; all but four of the known coumarins possess the 7-oxygen function. There is precedent for this mechanism in the biogenesis of homogentisic acid,[13] the first step of which is

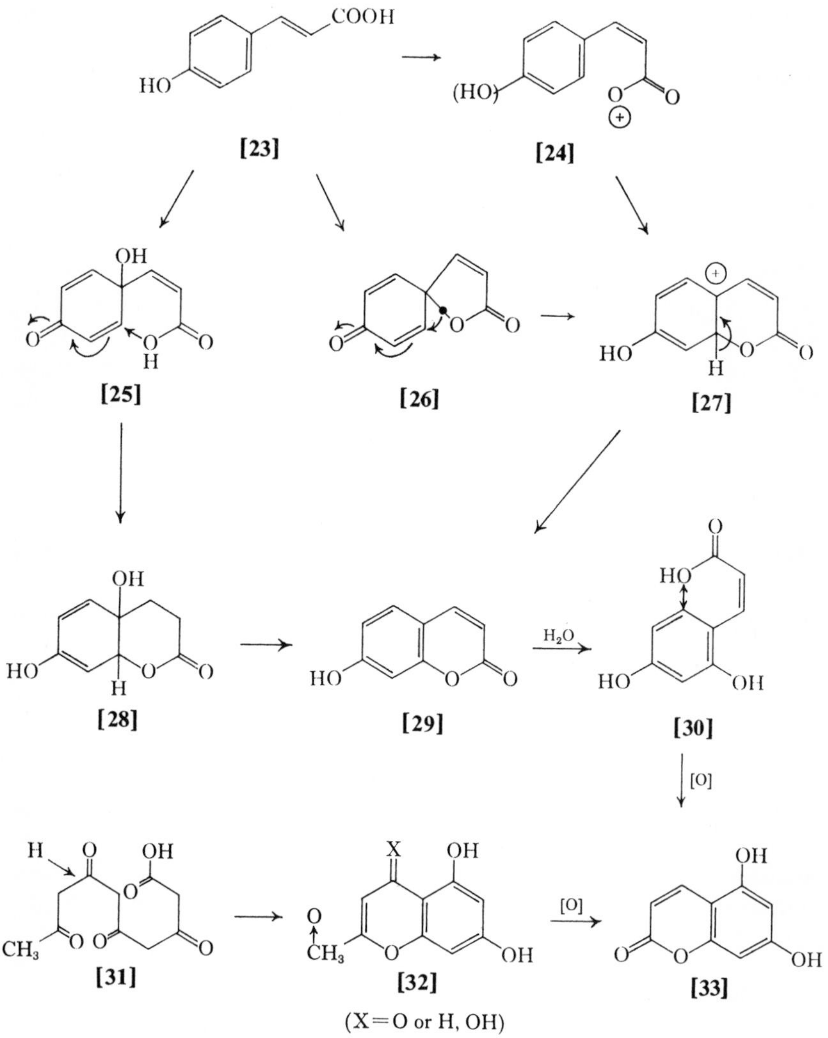

(X = O or H, OH)

13. B. N. La Du and V. G. Zannoni, *Nature*, **177**, 574 (1956); *J. Biol. Chem.*, **219**, 273 (1956).

a quite analogous para-oxidation of a phenol. In a variant on this proposal, Grisebach and Ollis[14] suggested the direct oxidative coupling of the para-position with the cinnamoyl carboxyl, as in [26], whereas Chambers et al.[15] have favored initial two-electron oxidation of the carboxyl (as in [24]) so as not to be dependent on the p-hydroxyl function. It is implied in these proposals that the benzene rings of the resultant coumarins largely bear hydroxylation patterns corresponding to their origin in the shikimic-prephenic biogenetic route, i.e., 7-hydroxy, 6,7-, or 7,8-dihydroxy, and 6,7,8-trihydroxy. The percentage of coumarins with this pattern of oxygen substitution is, however, only 64 per cent (46/72), which is significantly less than the value for their congeners, the simple ϕ-C_3 compounds. On the other hand, the offending coumarins almost always possess the phloroglucinol pattern characteristic of polyacetyl cyclization, suggesting that they may be true acetogenins. The biogenesis most simply implied is a path-A cyclization of the polyacetic acid [31] to yield a 2-methylchromone (more fully discussed in Section 4–3) or dihydrochromone [32], which must be oxidized to a phloroglucinol coumarin [33]. The difficulty in accepting this scheme lies in the rather unsatisfying oxidation required; clearly this approach lacks the simplicity of the other, and Whalley[16] has pointed out that hydrolytic opening of the coumarin [29] to [30] allows the oxidation process to repeat in the other ortho-position to afford the same 5,7-dihydroxycoumarin [33]. In favor of the acetate route from [31], however, it may be said that in the *Umbelliferae*, coumarins of this type often co-occur with 2-methylchromones [32] of like oxidation pattern and that some of these chromones are oxidized on the methyl group (cf. khellol [61], p. 45).[17]

Of the groups of coumarins listed in Table 4–2 by oxidation pattern on the benzene ring, those with the 6,7-, 7,8-, or 6,7,8-oxygens are most obviously of shikimic origin, but those with only 7-oxygen could arise by either of the above hypotheses, whereas the 5,7-oxygenated coumarins may be better fitted by a polyacetic derivation. A number of the coumarins, such as the chromones, also possess carbon sidechains attached to the benzene ring, either as isoprene units or as fused furans. These are reminiscent of the same groups commonly found in normal

14. H. Grisebach and W. D. Ollis, *Experientia*, **17**, 4 (1961).
15. K. Chambers, G. W. Kenner, M. J. T. Robinson, and B. R. Webster, *Proc. Chem. Soc.*, **1960**, 291.
16. W. B. Whalley in Ref. 17, Chap. 2.
17. W. D. Ollis (ed.), *The Chemistry of Natural Phenolic Compounds*, Pergamon, New York, 1961.

acetogenins and are thought to arise by C-alkylation of the β-diketone group; furthermore, one would expect C-alkylation of the phenols and catechols of the benzene rings from shikimic acid to be energetically more difficult, and indeed such benzofurans and C-isoprenes are virtually unknown on benzene rings clearly derived from shikimic acid (cf. the ϕ-C$_3$ compounds).

A statistical examination is interesting in this connection: The benzene rings of clear shikimic acid origin show less C-alkylation (9/19 = 47 per cent) than those with the 5,7-oxygenated pattern (14/16 = 88 per cent; if 5,6,7- and 5,7,8- are included, then 23/26 = 89 per cent). The simple 7-hydroxycoumarins show an intermediate incidence of C-alkylation (20/30 = 67 per cent). Thus there is a statistical implication that the coumarins with phloroglucinol nuclei may arise from acetate rather than shikimate and that some simple 7-oxycoumarins may share this alternative origin as well.* The ambiguity can ultimately be resolved only by tracer studies.

Only two coumarins have aliphatic substituents at C-3; these are 4-hydroxycoumarins and hence possess the β-ketolactone system for ready C-alkylation.† In dicoumarol [34] [18] two 4-hydroxycoumarins are joined at C-3 by methylene, whereas in ammoresinol [35] [19] alkylation by a farnesyl group has occurred.

[34]   [35]

Dicoumarol   Ammoresinol

* The argument based on C-alkylation may be spurious, since the increased proportion of ring substituency in the 5,7-dioxycoumarins could arise simply from the more facile alkylation of the phloroglucinol ring (see Section 3–2) in [33] from whatever source (as via [30]). Nevertheless, the higher proportion in the simple 7-oxycoumarins is not explainable in this way. Most C-alkylations are isoprene units or fused furans, more examples of which are cited in Section 4–7.

† The several 3-phenylcoumarins are considered under isoflavones in Section 4–3.

18. M. A. Stahmann, C. F. Huebner, and K. P. Link, *J. Biol. Chem.*, **138**, 513 (1941).
19. E. Späth and F. Kesztler, *Ber.*, **70**, 1255, 1679 (1937).

Five coumarins are carbon-substituted at C-4, one by n-propyl (mammein [37]),[24] and four by phenyl groups ([39],[23] inophyllolide [40],[20] calophyllolide [40],[21,22] and dalbergin [41][23]). It has been suggested[25] that the last four arise by double phenyl migration from a flavonoid via an isoflavonoid (Section 4–3), but the existence of mammein and the co-occurrence of [39] and mammein [37] in *Mammeaamericana* strongly suggest origin from a cyclization of a phloroglucinol ester[16,26] either of a linear acetogenin acid [36] or of a

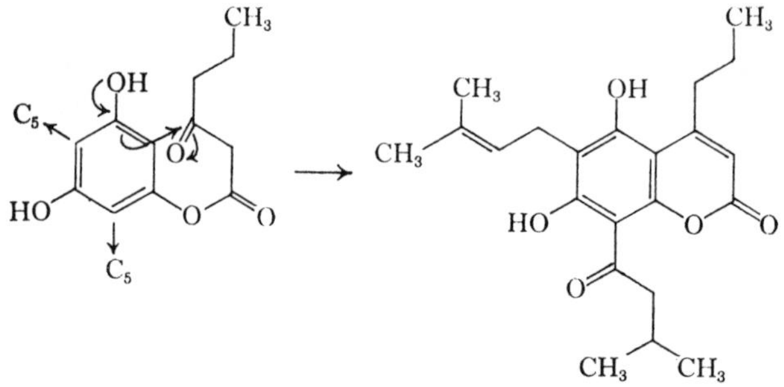

[36]

[37]

Mammein

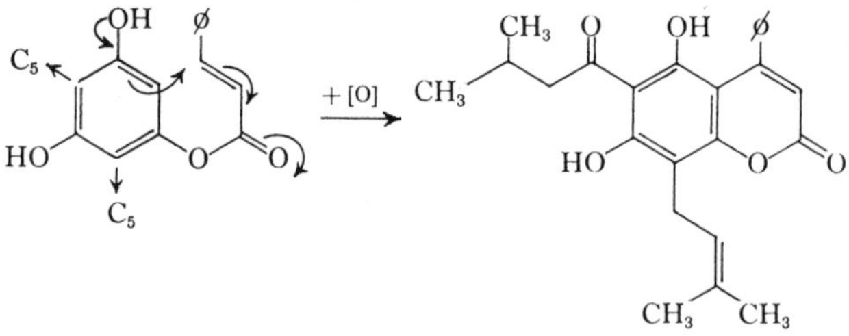

[38]

[39]

20. J. Polonsky, *Bull. Soc. Chim. France*, **1958**, 929.
21. J. Polonsky, *Bull. Soc. Chim. France*, **1956**, 914.
22. V. K. Ahluwalia, A. C. Mehta, and T. R. Seshadri, *Tetrahedron*, **4**, 271 (1958).
23. C. Djerassi, E. J. Eisenbraun, R. A. Finnegan, and B. Gilbert, *J. Org. Chem.*, **25**, 2165 (1960).
24. C. Djerassi, E. J. Eisenbraun, R. A. Finnegan, and B. Gilbert, *Tetrahedron Letters*, **1959**, 10.
25. H. Grisebach in Ref. 17, this chapter.
26. T. R. Seshadri, *Current Sci. (India)*, **26**, 239 (1957).

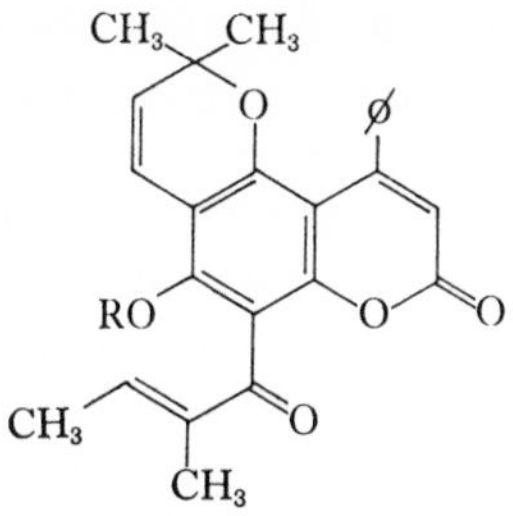

[40]

Calophyllolide (R = OCH₃)
Inophyllolide (R = H and cyclized by Michael addition)

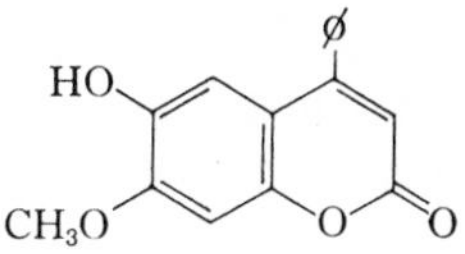

[41]

Dalbergin

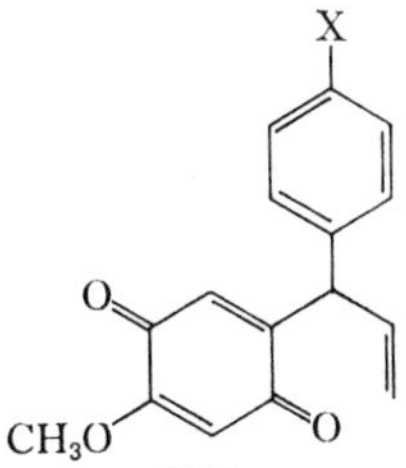

[42]

Dalbergiones (X = H or OCH₃)

phenylpropanoid **[38]**. Whatever the biogenesis of the 4-aryl-coumarins, it is likely that the newly discovered dalbergiones **[42]** represent variants of the same pathway because of their close structural as well as toxonomic relationships.[27]

4-3 ACYLPHLOROGLUCINOL DERIVATIVES

Among the acetophenone derivatives found in nature, virtually all have the 2,4,6 or 2,4 patterns of oxidation indicative of path-A cyclization of a polyacetic acid chain. Methylation is very common, occurring on oxygen or carbon in accordance with the previous discussion of enol alkylation. Thus mono-, di-, and tri-methyl ethers of phloroacetophenone are known, as is the parent compound; and in *Xanthorrhea* species, peonol and hydroxy-peonol **[43]** exist together.[28] Methylation on carbon is illustrated by clavatol **[44]**, whereas bis-methylation,

27. W. B. Eyton, W. D. Ollis, I. O. Sutherland, L. M. Jackman, O. R. Gottlieb, and M. T. Magalhaes, *Proc. Chem. Soc.*, **1962**, 301.
28. A. J. Birch and P. Hextall, *Australian J. Chem.*, **8**, 263 (1955).

which destroys the aromatic system, occurs in angustione and dehydroangustione [45] (such compounds are always represented here as
their keto-tautomers). A more striking set of methylated compounds
([46]–[48]), which represent the next higher "acetylog" of phloroacetophenone, are all found in the single species *Eugenia caryophyllata*,
providing a very clear demonstration of the possible varieties of enol
alkylation.[29] Angustifolionol [46] also coexists in another plant with
angustione and dehydroangustione [45]. Complete methylation and
isoprenylation of either phloroglucinol or an acylphloroglucinol later
deacylated is apparent in the structure of torquatone [66][30] (page 47).

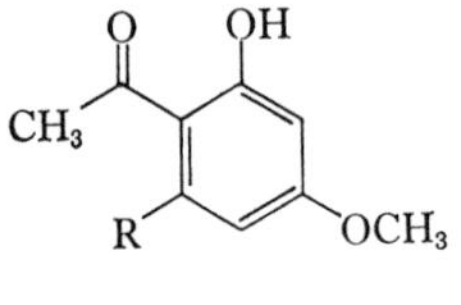

[43]

Peonol (R = H)
Hydroxy-peonol (R = OH)

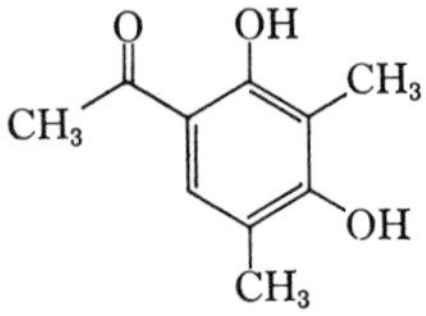

[44]

Clavatol

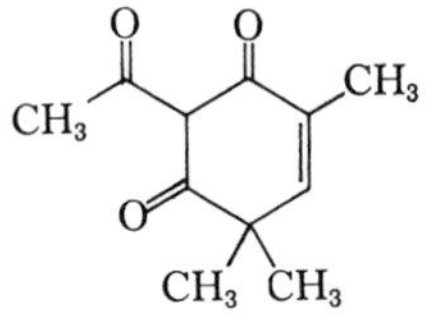

[45]

Dehydroangustione
Angustione: no double bond

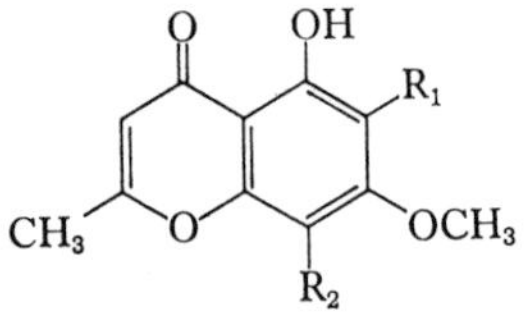

[46]

Constituents of *Eugenia carophyllata*

Eugenin ($R_1 = R_2 = H$)
Eugenitin ($R_1 = CH_3$; $R_2 = H$)
Isoeugenitin ($R_1 = H$; $R_2 = CH_3$)
Angustifolionol ($R_1 = R_2 = CH_3$)

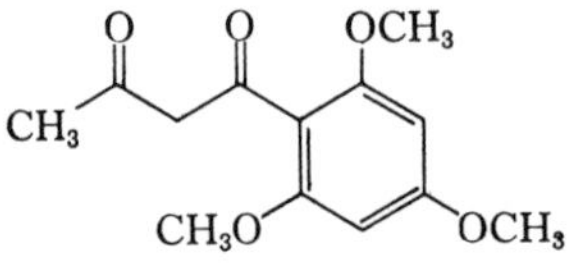

[47]

Eugenone

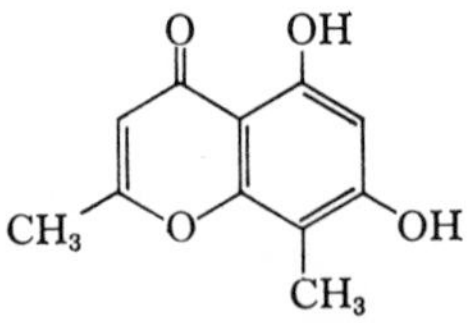

[48]

Isoeugenitol

29. A. J. Birch, P. Elliott, and A. R. Penfold, *Australian J. Chem.*, **7**, 169 (1954).
30. R. C. Bowyer and P. R. Jeffries, *Australian J. Chem.*, **1959**, 442.

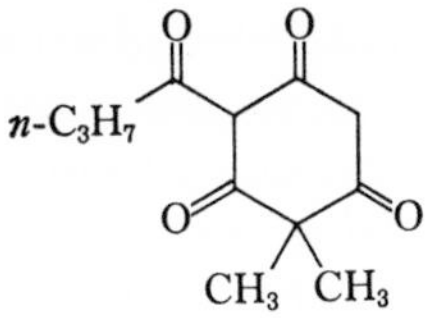

[49]
Aspidinol

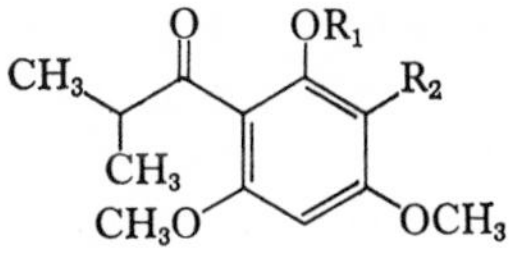

[50]
Baeckeol (R_1 = H; R_2 = CH₃)
Conglomerone (R_1 = CH₃; R_2 = H)

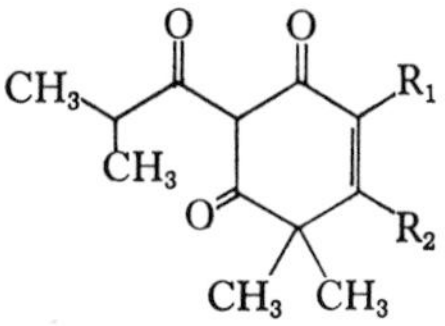

[51]
Xanthostemone (R_1 = R_2 = H)
Tasmanone (R_1 = CH₃; R_2 = OCH₃)

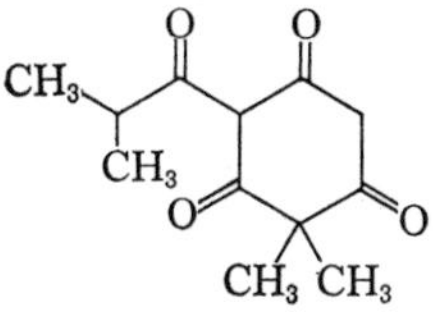

[52]
Butanofilicinic Acid

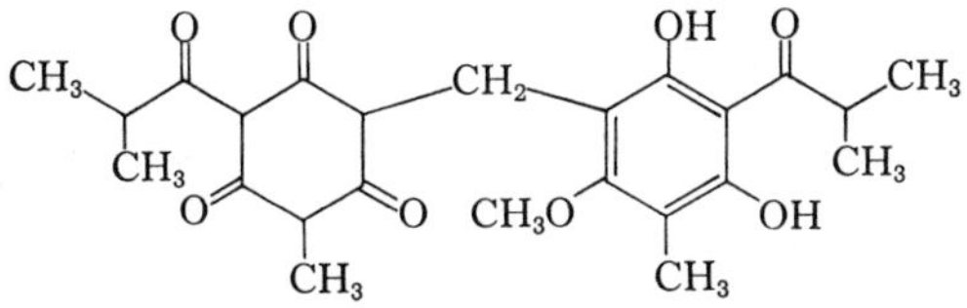

[53]
Protokosin

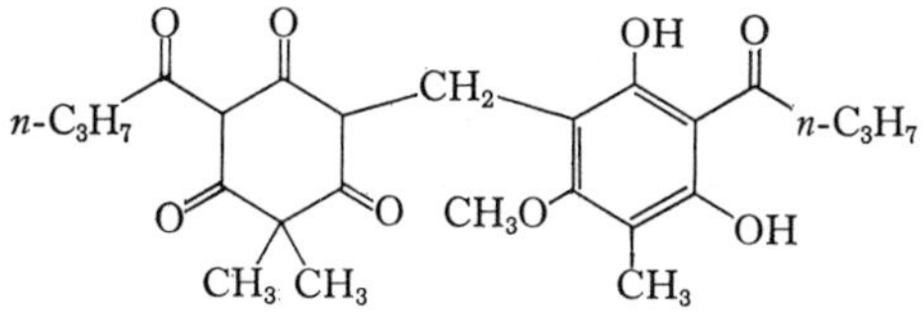

[54]
Flavaspidic Acid

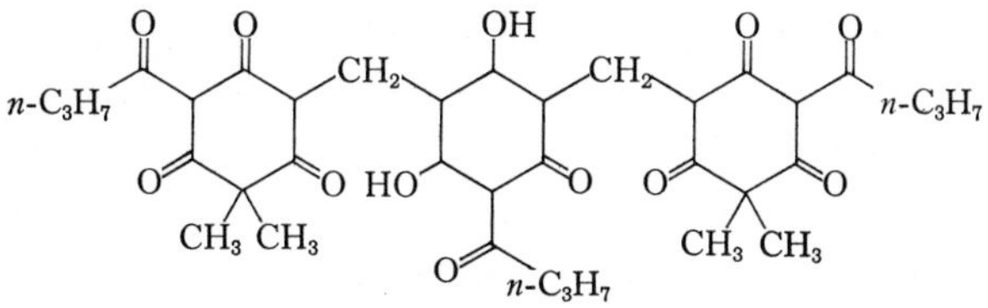

[55]
Filicin

In aspidinol [49][29] we observe bis-methylation on the ring; should bis-methylation occur on the sidechain, it is reasonable to expect cleavage of the terminal acetic acid as discussed in Chapter 3, and, in fact, highly methylated ketones of this form are known in a variety of compounds, e.g., baeckeol [50], conglomerone [50], xantho-stemone [51],[31] tasmanone [51],[32] and butanofilicinic acid [52].[32] It may be argued that these arise by substitution of isobutyric acid for the terminal acetic in the initial polyacetyl chain, but, in view of the high incidence of extensive methylation in the compounds of this series and the general rarity of isobutyryl residues (as distinct from true isoprene units) in secondary metabolites, this seems a less likely route.

Enol alkylation by a formaldehyde equivalent is not uncommon in the acetogenins and is handsomely represented in the phloroaceto-phenone series by the fern constituents [33] (*Aspidium* and *Hagenia* spp.), which are variously methylated derivatives of methylene dimers, cf. protokosin [53] and flavaspidic acid [54]. Filicin [55] is a felicitous example of the complexity of structure derivable by this essentially simple biogenetic scheme. Enol alkylation by an isoprene unit is also a common occurrence, leading either to isopentenyl ethers (O-alkylation) or to isopentenylated skeletons (C-alkylation). Thus the hop constituents include colupulone [56], whereas the *Evodia* species produce a series of phloroacetophenone chromenes, of which evodionol [57] and its methyl ether are representative. Analogously, peucenin [58] and visnamminol [59] are chromones that exemplify the process. Finally, enol substitution may lead (Section 3–1) to a benzofuran, many examples of which are found in natural sources (e.g., euparin [60]). The fruit of *Ammi visnaga* provides us not only with visnam-minol but also with visnagin, khellin, ammiol, and khellol [61], and the series as a whole serves as evidence for the origin of the fused furans in isoprene alkylation (Sections 3–1 and 4–7).

Oxidation of the enol to provide a new hydroxyl group at the methyl-ene site is operative not only in the above *Ammi* constituents, but also in the hop components, humulone [62] and cohumulone [56]. The structure of muellitol [63][34] also suggests this origin coupled with reduction of the ketones. On the other hand, an example of oxidative coupling of the methylene sites of two methyl-phloroacetophenone units is to be found in usnic acid [64], the most common constituent of

31. A. J. Birch and P. Elliott, *Australian J. Chem.*, **9**, 238 (1956).
32. A. J. Birch and P. Elliott, *Australian J. Chem.*, **9**, 95 (1956).
33. C. H. Hassall, *Progr. Org. Chem.*, **4**, 115 (1958).
34. F. N. Lahey, personal communication.

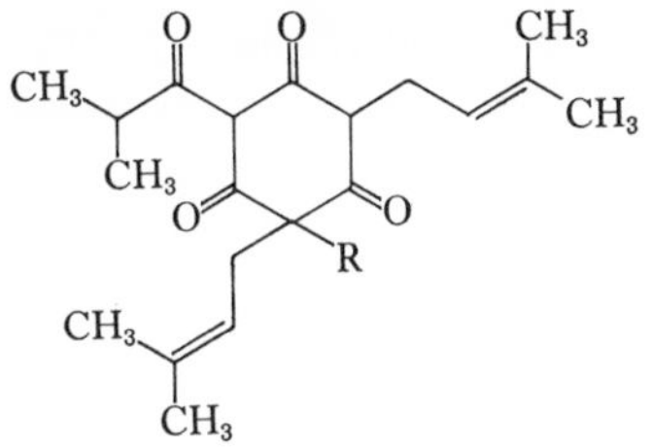

[56]

Colupulone (R = (structure))
Cohumulone (R = OH)

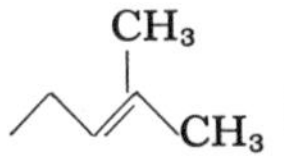

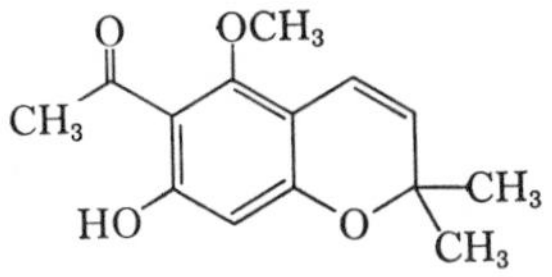

[57]
Evodionol

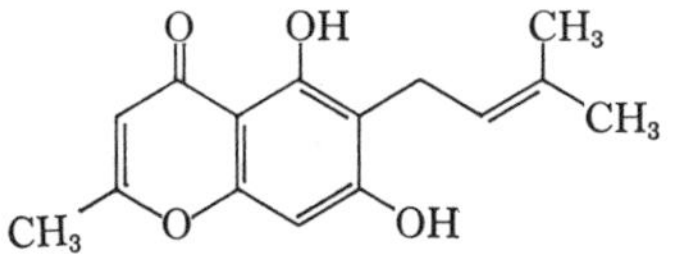

[58]
Peucenin

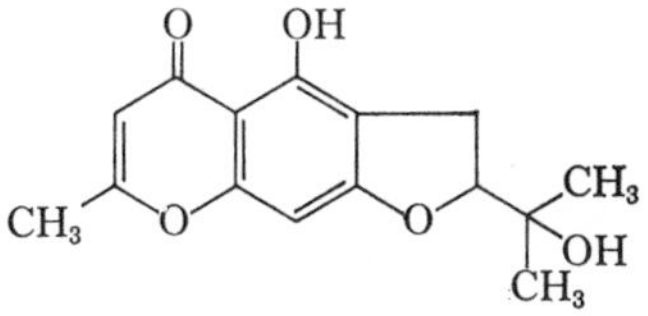

[59]
Visnamminol

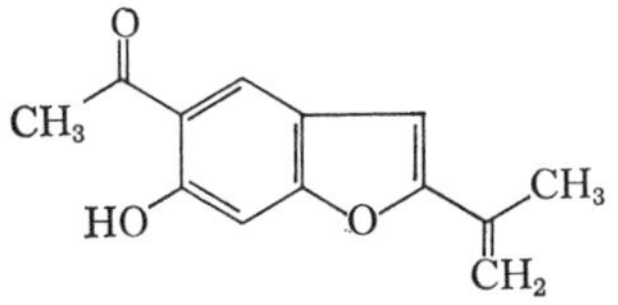

[60]
Euparin

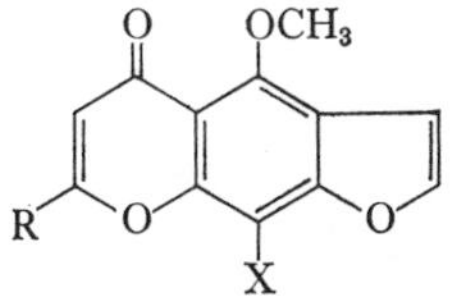

[61]
Visnagin (R = CH_3; X = H)
Khellin (R = CH_3; X = OCH_3)
Khellol (R = CH_2OH; X = H)
Ammiol (R = CH_2OH; X = OCH_3)

lichens. Usnic acid has been synthesized by Barton,[35] utilizing a one-electron oxidative-coupling reaction that elegantly simulates the biogenesis in vitro. It is, however, quite possible that the order of biogenetic steps may be different, and that the ether link is formed prior to coupling, or even that the phloroglucinol rings are cyclized last, only after initial oxidative coupling of open chains.

35. D. H. R. Barton, A. M. Deflorin, and O. E. Edwards, *J. Chem. Soc.*, **1956**, 530.

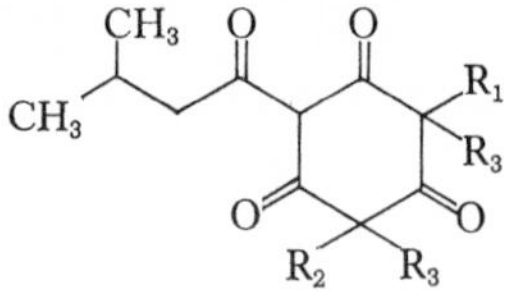

[62]

Leptospermone ($R_1 = R_2 = R_3 = CH_3$)

Lupulone ($R_1 = H$; $R_2 = R_3 = $![structure])

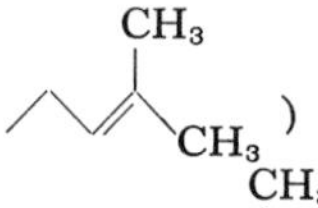

Humulone ($R_1 = H$; $R_2 = OH$; $R_3 = $![structure])

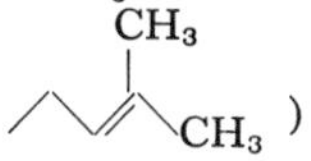

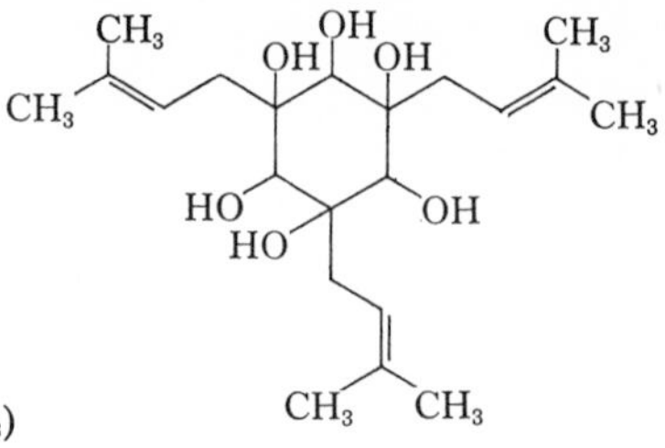

[63]
Muellitol

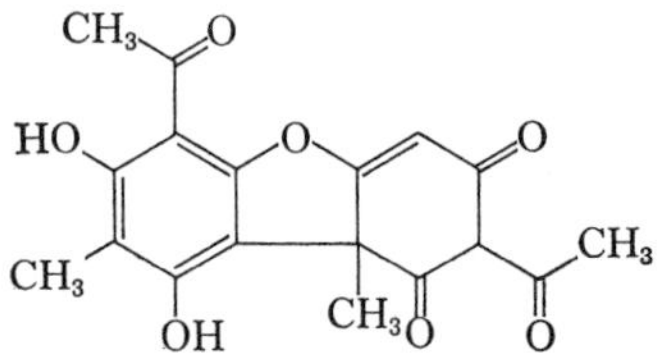

[64]
Usnic Acid

The extent to which the known structures of the natural aceto-phenones correlate with the predictions of the acetate hypothesis is dependent on the assumptions that are considered allowable. If we accept, as support for the hypothesis, those structures that lack no more than one of the oxygens at the predicted sites and are in complete har-mony with the discussions of Chapter 3, we find that, of 66 natural acetophenones, 58 are consistent with these conditions—a correlation of 88 per cent in support of the acetate hypothesis. Furthermore, the eight misfits are all simple molecules, such as acetophenone or *ortho-* or *para*-hydroxyacetophenone, and at least five of these probably derive by decarboxylation of a molecule such as ϕ—$COCH_2COOH$, since they possess the familiar hydroxylation patterns of shikimic acid origin. Therefore, a correlation of 96 per cent consistency with the acetate hypothesis is probably acceptable.

In considering the type-A cyclization to an acylphloroglucinol of a polyacetyl chain terminating in an acid other than acetic, we may expect natural products of the form **[65]**. In the case of the isoprenoid acid $(CH_3)_2CHCH_2COOH$ acting as $RCOOH$, we find leptospermone, humulone, and lupulone [62], the analogs of xanthostemone [51] and the other hop constituents, respectively. Alternatively, in view of their close relation to the other hop constituents, it is more likely that these few ketones are merely isoprenylated phloroglucinols with later oxidation of one isopentenyl group. Favoring this view are the apparent absences of any other acetogenins with clear isovaleryl terminals and a close correspondence in structure to torquatone [66] and muellitol [63].

Benzophenones and Xanthones

If the various shikimic-derived benzoic acids serve as RCOOH, benzophenones result. Ten benzophenones are known, and all but three conform in detail to the acetate hypothesis (cf. protocotoin [67]). Two inconsistent structures are p-hydroxybenzophenone, probably of acetate origin despite two missing phloroglucinol oxygens, and sulochrin [68]. One benzophenone[35] (griseophenone, pp. 80, 82) derives entirely from a polyacetyl chain by extended cyclization. Another, griseophenone Y [192] (page 84), formed in the same mold,[36] is identical except for a methyl group at a ketonic site and hence is inconsistent with the hypothesis.

The xanthones might reasonably be expected to arise by intramolecular oxidative coupling of benzophenones, but only three xanthones,

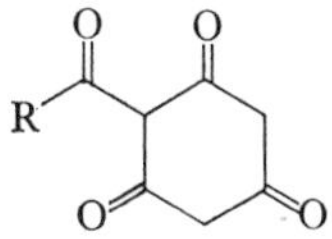

[65]

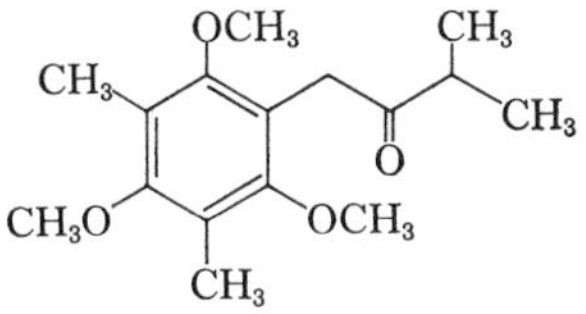

[66]

Torquatone

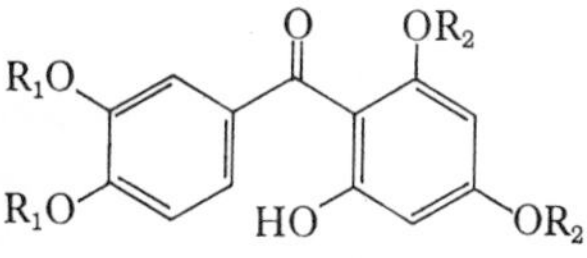

[67]

Protocotoin (R₁ = —CH₂—; R₂ = CH₃)
Maclurin (R₁ = R₂ = H)

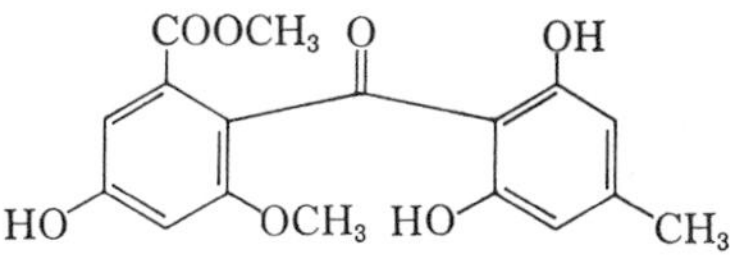

[68]

Sulochrin

36. A. I. Scott in Ref. 17, Chap. 6.

jacareubin [69],[37] mangiferin [70],[38] and mangostin [71],[39] appear to derive in this way from a normal acetogenin benzophenone (i.e., maclurin [67]). Another possibility is that the xanthones are formed by dehydrative rather than oxidative closure from a benzophenone bearing ortho-OH on each ring. Of the 15 xanthones of known

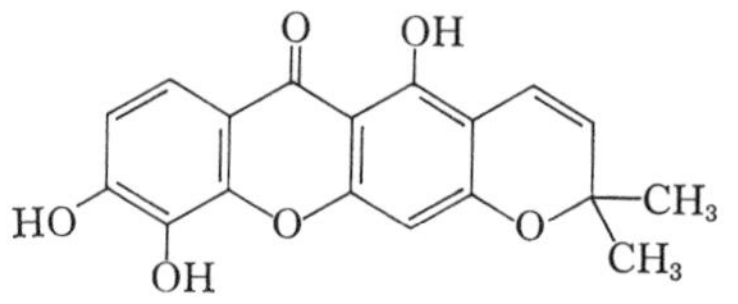

[69]
Jacareubin

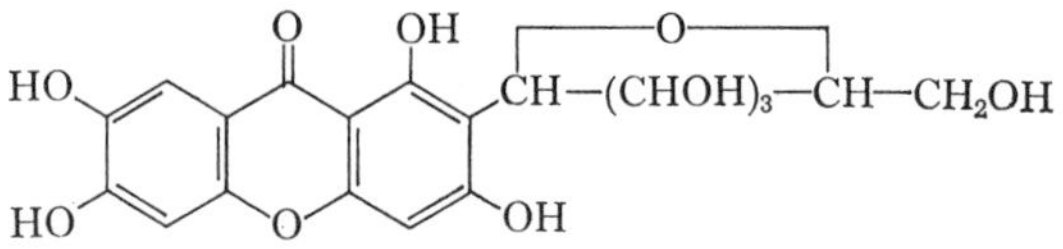

[70]
Mangiferin

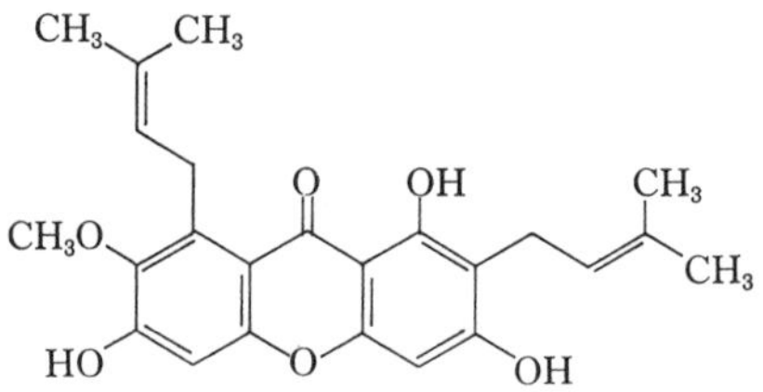

[71]
Mangostin

structure, nine appear to form a unified group; seven of these are found in *Swertia* or *Gentiana* spp. (*Gentianaceae*). All afford the open form [72] upon formal hydrolysis of the ether link. Ring B is apparently acetogenous, but ring A has a form inconsistent with shikimic acid origins. It is perhaps significant that gentisic acid [73] and the corresponding alcohol are known in nature, since this acid, as an extension

37. F. E. King, T. J. King, and L. C. Manning, *J. Chem. Soc.*, **1957**, 563.
38. J. D. Ramanathan and T. R. Seshadri, *Current Sci.* (*India*), **29**, 131 (1960).
39. P. Yates and G. H. Stout, *J. Am. Chem. Soc.*, **80**, 1691 (1958).

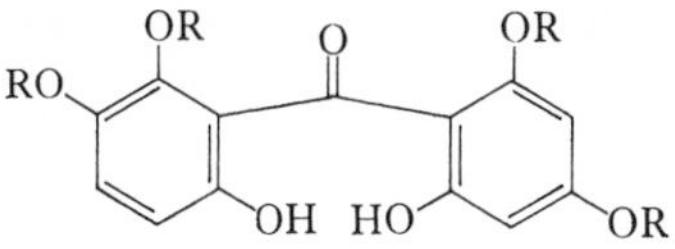

[72]

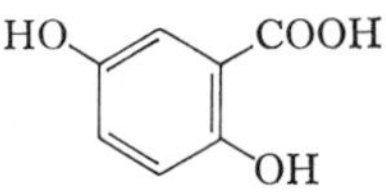

[73]
Gentisic Acid

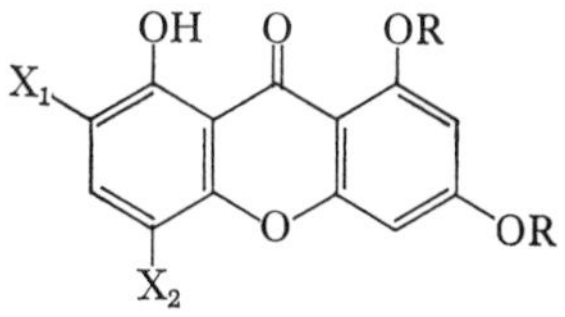

[74]
Swertianol (X_1 = H; X_2 = OCH_3; R = H)
Decussatin (X_1 = OCH_3; X_2 = H; R = CH_3)

of the polyacetyl chain, would provide a reasonable biogenesis for all nine xanthones. Among these gentian xanthones, swertianol and decussatin [74] are instructive examples, for it is clear that they may both derive from [72] (R = H) by dehydration, whereas an oxidative coupling would require two precursors; hence the principle of economy suggests preference for the dehydrative ring closure, as does a comparison of the known benzophenone sulochrin [68] with the xanthone pinselin [75], both of which are fungal metabolites. Their structures strongly indicate a common benzophenone precursor that is subsequently either methylated or dehydratively cyclized, respectively; the relation of sulochrin to some other fungal metabolites is discussed below (page 81). Lichexanthone, discussed in Section 4–5, also cyclizes by dehydration rather than by oxidative coupling. In this light, significant correlations of xanthone structure with the acetate hypothesis are difficult, but of 18 xanthone B-rings, 16 may be considered consistent with polyacetyl origin, the exceptions being the pinselins.

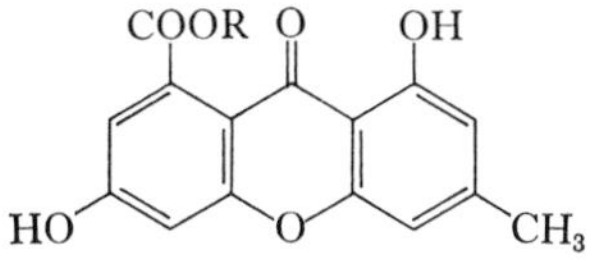

[75]
Pinselin (R = CH_3)
Pinselic Acid (R = H)

Flavonoids

The flavonoids **[77]** are a widely distributed group of plant pigments, characterized by a ϕ-C_3-ϕ skeleton, which contains a great number of examples. These compounds, the subject of much study for many years, are now well reviewed.[4] The various kinds of flavonoid compounds are usually distinguished by the functionality and state of oxidation of the central C_3 chain (viz. examples in Chart II). It is very likely on inferential grounds that the entire flavonoid group of natural products **[77]** arises by an acylphloroglucinol cyclization of a polyacetyl chain with one phenyl-propionic acid as terminal, cf. **[76]**. If this biogenetic hypothesis is correct, the flavonoid A rings should

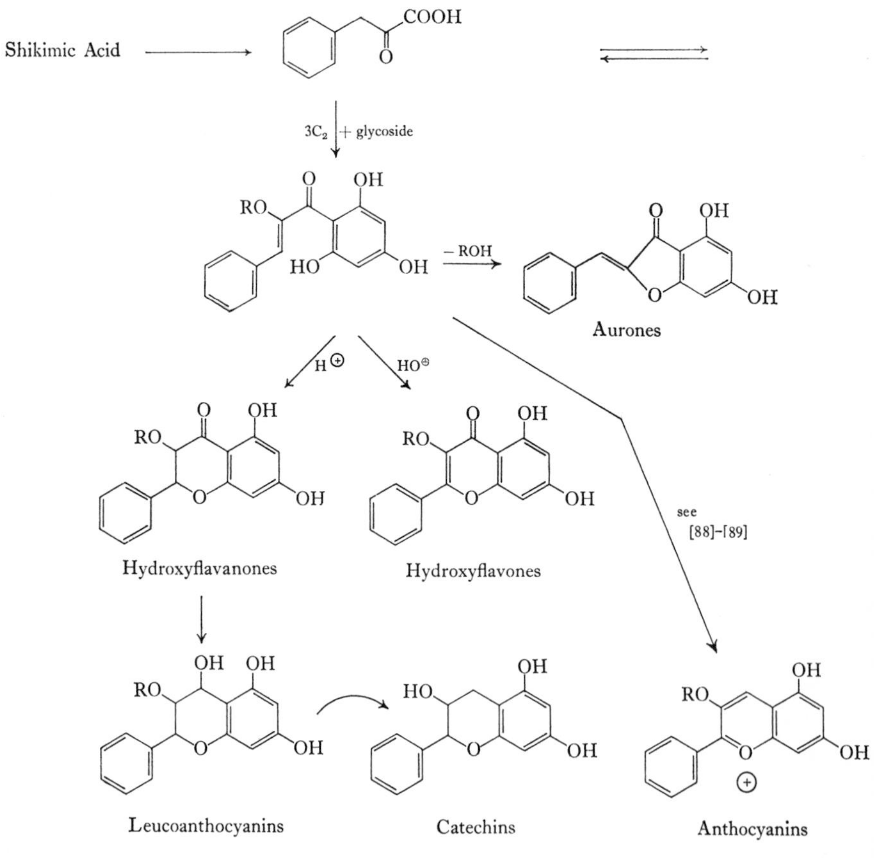

Shikimic Acid ⟶

3C$_2$ + glycoside

− ROH

Aurones

H ⊕   HO⊖

Hydroxyflavanones

Hydroxyflavones

see [88]-[89]

Leucoanthocyanins

Catechins

Anthocyanins

always display oxygen at both positions 5 and 7 (or one of these if only one oxygen), and the B rings should display the typical shikimic-derived patterns of ring hydroxylation. These criteria are the basis for the last columns of Table 4–3, in which are listed the frequencies of occurrence of oxygen and carbon substituents on the flavonoid nuclei in the various naturally occurring examples. It is evident that the detailed breakdown of oxygen positioning affords overwhelming statistical support for the origin of flavonoids postulated above. Furthermore, it is clear from an examination of the actual examples that, in general, the "misfits" are of far less common occurrence in natural sources.

The table also includes the number of C-alkylations to be found on

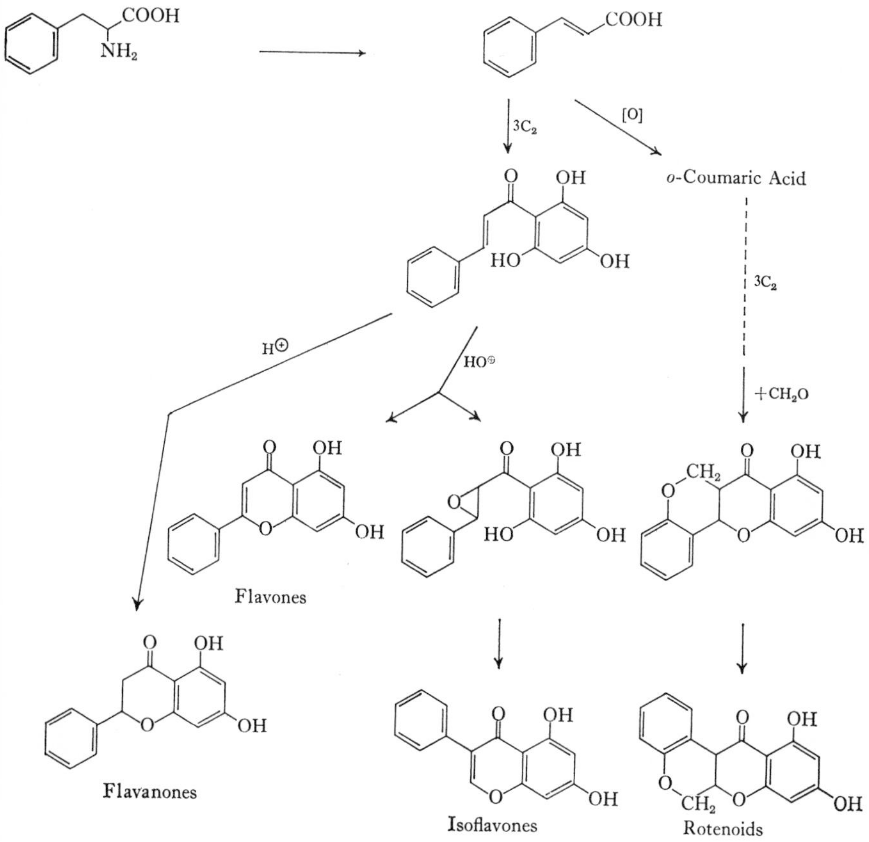

Chart II *Flavonoid biogenesis*

Table 4-3 *Frequency of occurrence of flavonoid substituents*[a]

Flavonoid type	No. of examples[a]	Frequency of oxygen attachments										C-alkyl-ations		Correlation with theoretical		
		Ring A					Ring B					Ring A	Ring B	Ring A	Ring B	Both Rings
		5	6	7	8	9	2′	3′	4′	5′	6′					
Open-chain ϕ-C_3-ϕ[b,c]	23	14(61)	6(26)	23(100)	6(26)	23(100)	0	5(22)	13(57)	0	0	7	0	19(83)	23(100)	19(83)
Aurones[d]	8	3(38)	0	8(100)	2(25)		0	7(88)	8(100)	0	0	0	0	6(75)	8(100)	6(75)
3-Hydroxy-flavanes[e,f]	16	11(69)	0	16(100)	2(12)		0	13(81)	16(100)	3(19)	0	0	0	14(88)	16(100)	14(88)
Anthocyanins	12	11(92)	0	12(100)	0		1(4)	7(58)	12(100)	4(33)	0	0	0	12(100)	12(100)	12(100)
Flavanones	28	22(79)	2(7)	28(100)	5(18)		0	11(39)	18(64)		0	14	0	25(89)	27(96)	24(86)
3-Hydroxy-flavanones[e]	15	13(87)	0	15(100)	0		0	5(33)	9(60)	2(13)	0	4	0	15(100)	15(100)	15(100)
Flavones[f]	51	49(96)	12(24)	46(90)	5(10)		5(10)	13(25)	36(71)	2(4)	0	14[g]	0	47(92)	46(90)	43(84)
3-Hydroxy-flavones	69	58(84)	21(30)	67(97)	19(28)		4(6)	43(62)	62(90)	7(10)	0	10	1	65(94)	64(93)	61(88)
Other flavo-noids[e,f]	6	5(83)	1(17)	6(100)	0		1(17)	1(17)	3(50)	0	0	2	1	6(100)	4(67)	4(67)
Totals	228	186(82)	42(18)	221(97)	39(17)		11(5)	105(46)	177(78)	18(8)	0	51	2	209(92)	215(94)	198(87)
Isoflavonoids[h]	42	17(40)	7(17)	42(100)	0		19(45)	11(26)	39(93)	9(21)	0	12	1	40(95)	23(55)	22(52)
Rotenoids	14	4(29)	0	14(100)	1(17)		14(100)	0	14(100)	14(100)	0	12	0	14(100)	0	0

[a] O-glycosides are not separately included; figures in parentheses are percentages.
[b] Includes chalcones, dihydrochalcones, etc., as well as rottlerin [83] and hyssopin [90]; see discussion in text.
[c] A-ring correlation: 3 or more oxygens with intact phloroglucinol pattern, or only two oxygens at 2,4- or 2,6-.
[d] Includes hydrated aurones, cf. maesopsin.
[e] In cases of several stereoisomers, only one is included.
[f] Includes bisflavonoids, each flavone moiety counted once; the bond adjoining the halves is not considered under C-alkylations.
[g] Includes one isopentenyl substituent at C_3 (in artocarpin).
[h] Includes angolensin and ononetin [101].

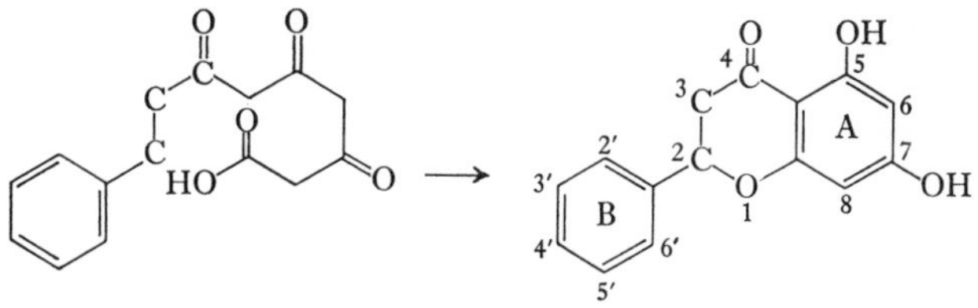

[76]   [77]

Flavonoids: common and typical examples

B ring:	no OH	4'-OH	3',4'-(OH)$_2$
Flavanone	Pinocembrin	Naringenin	Eriodictyol
3-Hydroxyflavanone	Pinobanksin	Aromadendrin	Taxifolin
Flavone	Chrysin	Apigenin	Luteolin
3-Hydroxyflavone	Galagin	Kaempferol	Quercetin

each ring in each body of compounds. These data admirably support the contention (cf. the discussion of coumarins above) that only the acetogenin ring should bear such substituents; thus, only two B rings (derived from shikimic acid in the flavonoid biogenesis) display this C-alkylation, whereas the 51 examples of C-alkylation on the A ring always bear the substituent at positions 6- or 8-, as anticipated for an acetate origin. These C-substituents are all methyl, methylene, isopentenyl, or C-glycosides, several examples of which are illustrated ([78] through [84]). Several bis-flavones [21] are now known that illustrate oxidative coupling of two flavonoid residues, cf. gingketin [80].

Enol methylation in the flavonoids is a very common biogenetic step that may be illustrated by the series of flavanones [84], many from *Pinus* spp., which includes the interesting C-dimethylated ceroptene

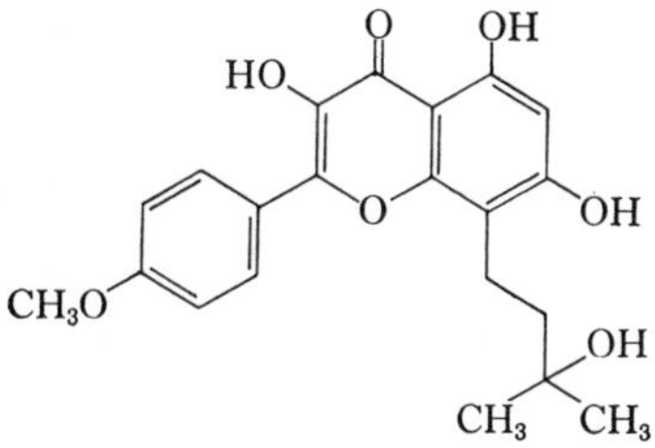

[78]   [79]

Icaritin   Orientin

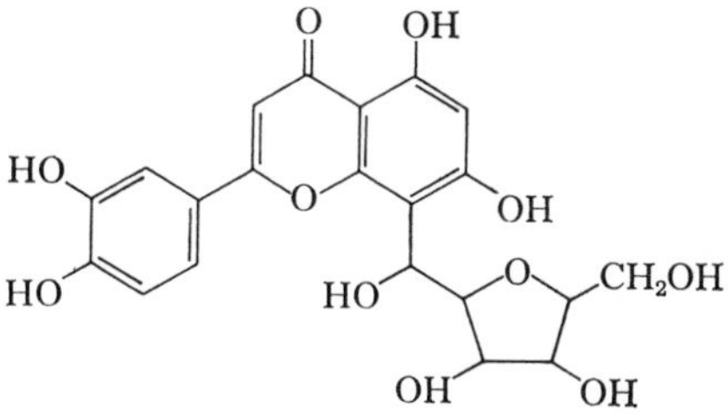

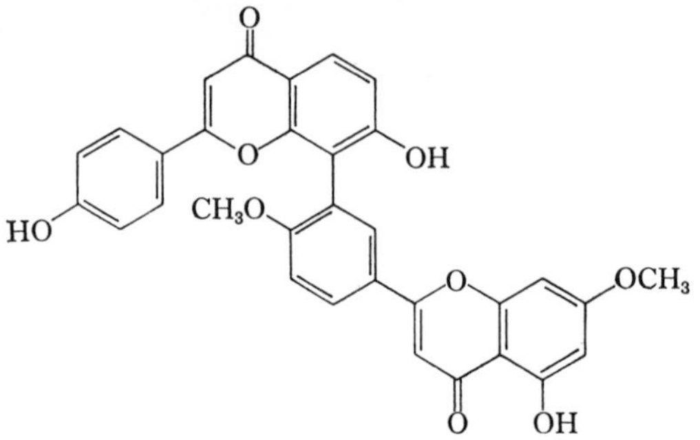

[80]

Gingketin

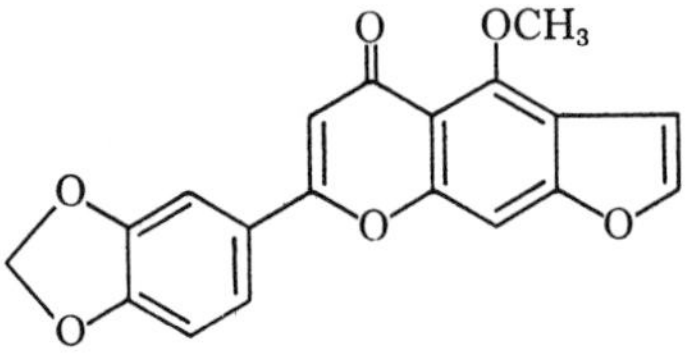

[81]

Gamatin

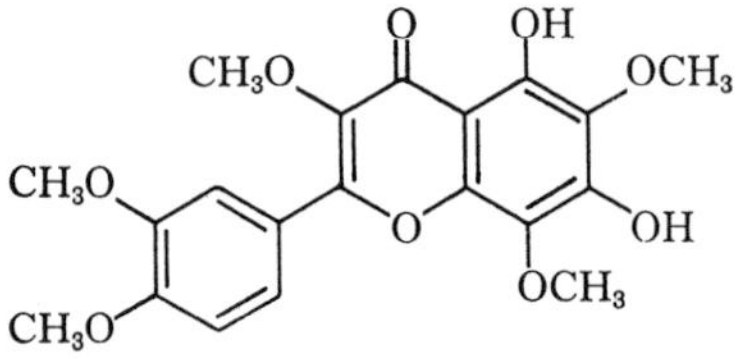

[82]

Erianthin

[85] recently isolated from a fern.[40]   The quaternary center in ceroptene recalls this common feature of the acylphloroglucinol fern constituents, mentioned above.   A handsome example of the variations possible in the acetate hypothesis is evident in the structure of rottlerin [83], in which a flavonoid chalcone is joined to a typical phloroacetophenone (the same one that produces usnic acid) by methylenation similar to that in the fern constituents.   Isorottlerin is a corresponding flavanone.

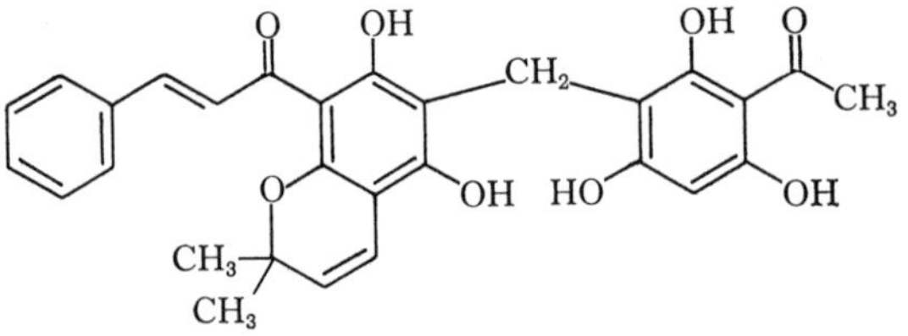

[83]

Rottlerin

40. S. Forsen and M. Nilsson, *Acta Chem. Scand.*, **13**, 1383 (1959).

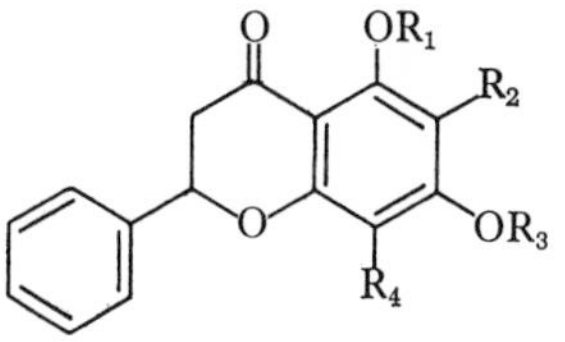

[84]

Flavanones	R_1	R_2	R_3	R_4
Pinocembrin	H	H	H	H
Alpinetin	CH_3	H	H	H
Cryptostrobin	H	CH_3	H	H
Pinostrobin	H	H	CH_3	H
Strobopinin	H	H	H	CH_3
Desmethoxy-matteucinol	H	CH_3	H	CH_3

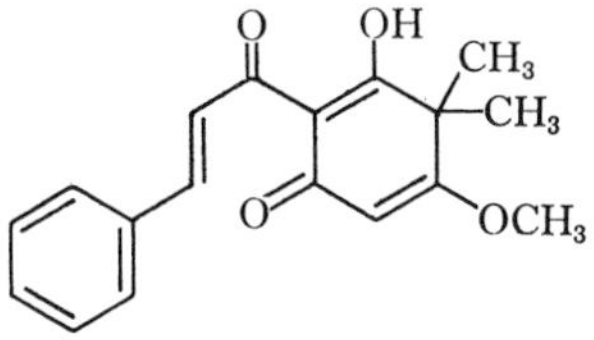

[85]
Ceroptene

Although the statistical approach gives eloquent testimony on the origins of the aromatic rings, it has little to say of the three-carbon central chain, which exists in practically all possible states of oxidation in these compounds. Carbon 4 is virtually always ketonic, as required for acetogenous entry into ring A. The three central carbons may presumably arise from a benzoic acid plus one malonate to a benzoylacetic acid or from the pyruvate portion of the common phenylpropanoid acids via prephenic and phenylpyruvic acids, and it is clear that structural inference cannot differentiate these routes. Experimental evidence (Section 5–3) favors the phenylpyruvic origin and allows the construction of a simple hypothetical scheme, shown in Chart II, for the origins of the various flavonoid compounds. In this scheme malonate-chain extension is envisioned either for the phenylpyruvic acid or for the cinnamic acid, each leading to a subfamily of flavonoids. It is interesting to observe that virtually all flavonoids with the 3-hydroxyl exist in nature as 3-glycosides, which may suggest that this glycosidation is an intimate biogenetic process, occurring early, as shown, to bind the 3-ketone as an enol-glycoside. This may then react in a manner analogous to that of the cinnamoyl-terminated chain, cyclizing either in a normal conjugative addition to the double bond or in an oxidative one (initiated, say, by attack of $HO^{\oplus}$ at C-3) to produce flavanones and flavones, respectively. In support of these subfamilies, it may be submitted that the hydroxyflavones and hydroxyflavanones more commonly cooccur than do flavones and hydroxyflavones.[4]

The origin of the anthocyanins and catechins is of special interest, since it involves loss of the characteristic 4-oxygen. Reduction of the 4-ketone and dehydration is the simplest route, and in this connection it is interesting to note that the 7-OH (or -OR) important for facilitating this dehydration is present in all catechins and anthocyanins and that

[86]

Dracorhodin ($R_1 = H$; $R_2 = CH_3$)
Carajurin ($R_1 = OCH_3$; $R_2 = OH$)

the intermediate quinone types are known, cf. dracorhodin and carajurin [86]. These compounds and the closely related *Gesneria* anthocyanins (cf. gesneridin) are unusual in lacking the 3-OH group typical of other anthocyanins and catechins. It has, however, been argued[41] on morphological grounds that the leucoanthocyanins (3,4-dihydroxyflavanes) cannot be direct precursors of anthocyanins, which suggests an alternative view of their biogenesis. Since the phenylpyruvic precursor and the anthocyanins are in the same oxidation state, a pathway involving no oxidations or reductions is reasonable, and the enol glycoside again provides for acceptable mechanisms as shown in [87] through [89].

The possibility that some flavonoids arise, alternatively, from a benzoylacetic terminal acid may not, however, be excluded without direct experiment, and indeed there is strong suggestion for such an origin in several structures. Two chalcones, hyssopin [90] and [91],

41. W. J. C. Lawrence, J. R. Price, (Mrs.) G. M. Robinson, and R. Robinson, *Phil. Trans. Roy. Soc. (London), Ser. B*, **230**, 149 (1939).

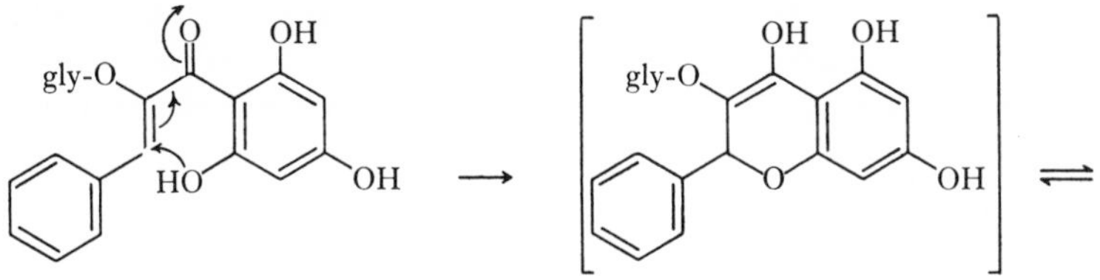

[87]   [88]

3-Hydroxyflavanones

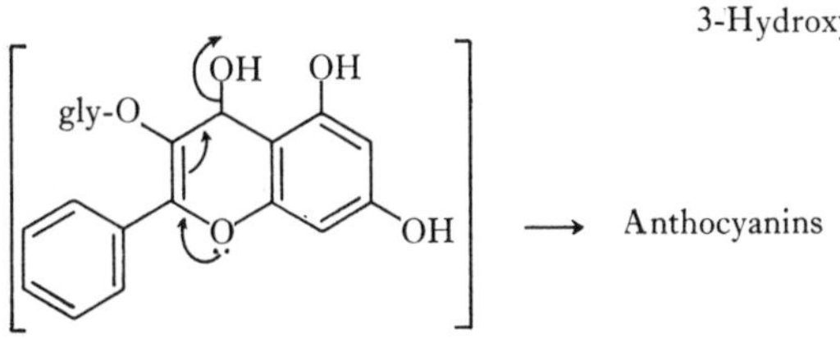

[89]   Anthocyanins

are patently reversed* in their ring patterns so that a ketone function
is present at C-2 as in a benzoyl-acetic precursor.   The same is true of
pongamol (lanceolatin C, [92]) which in fact coexists with the flavone
lanceolatin B [93] in *Tephrosia lanceolata*.   Although it must be noted
that the cooccurrence suggests a flavone origin here from a benzoic
rather than prephenic acid, it is also true that the coincidence may be due
merely to secondary oxidation-state changes in the C_3 link of a cinnamoyl
precursor.

Isoflavonoids and Rotenoids

Turning to the isoflavonoids (isoflavones [95], and others of like
skeleton, e.g., [97]–[98] and [100]–[102]), one is first struck by the great
similarity of the aromatic-ring-hydroxylation patterns to those of the
flavonoids, as summarized in Table 4–3.   These lend detailed credence

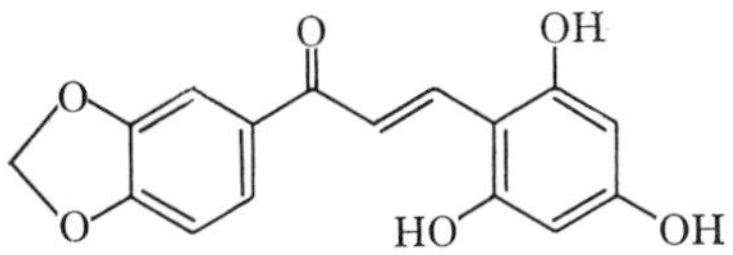

[90]   [91]

Hyssopin

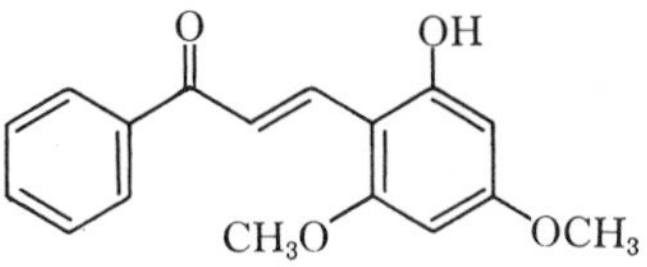

* These chalcones were counted in the correlation as having correctly
  derived A and B rings.

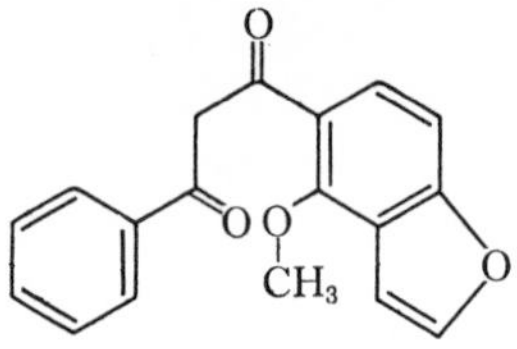

[92]
Pongamol

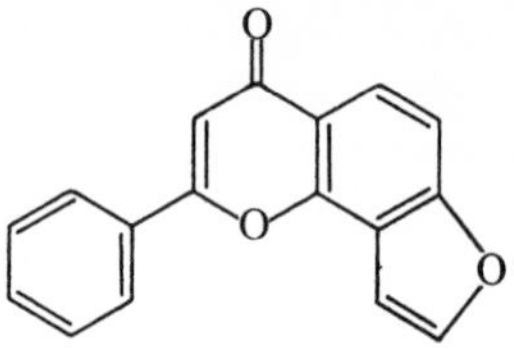

[93]
Lanceolatin B

to the intuitive sense that the isoflavonoids must arise by some variant in the flavonoid biogenetic pathway, and two such variants are immediately apparent. Either the B ring must migrate from carbon 2 to carbon 3 as in **[94]** or a phenylacetic acid (from phenylpyruvic by oxidative decarboxylation?) must act as chain terminal in order that an analogous malonate extension and cyclization be coupled at some stage through introduction of a C_1 unit as in **[96]**.

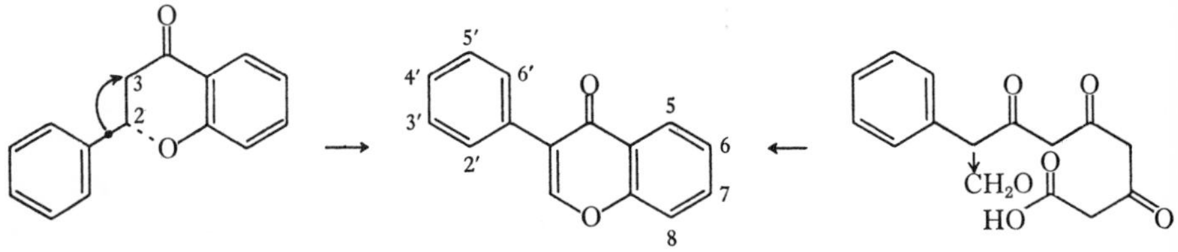

[94]

[95]
Isoflavones

[96]

	3′	4′	5	7
Genistein	H	OH	OH	OH
Orobol	OH	OH	OH	OH
Prunetin	H	OH	OH	OCH_3
Santal	OH	OH	OH	OCH_3
Biochanin-A	H	OCH_3	OH	OH
Pratensein	OCH_3	OH	OH	OH

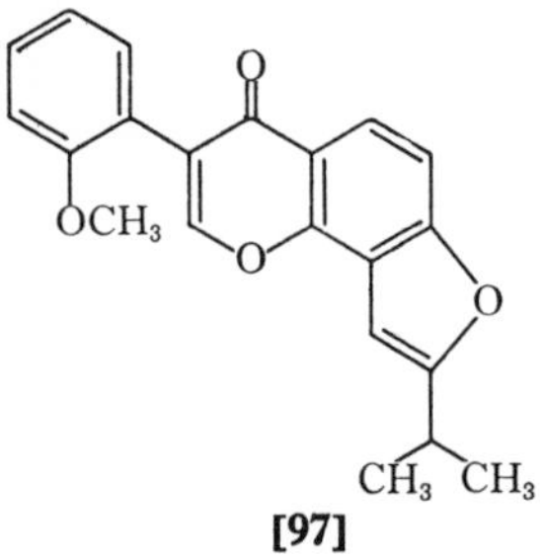

[97]
Munetone

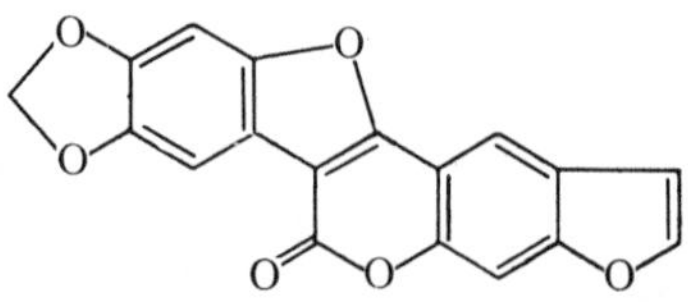

[98]
Erosnin

There is little inferential evidence to distinguish these paths. A few phenylacetic acids are known in nature, notably tropic acid [99], which is known [42] to arise from phenylalanine apparently by rearrangement with no one-carbon fragment involved. The species *Ononis spinosa* produces both formononetin [100] and ononetin [101], identical except in the matter of the added carbon, whereas *Pterocarpus* species

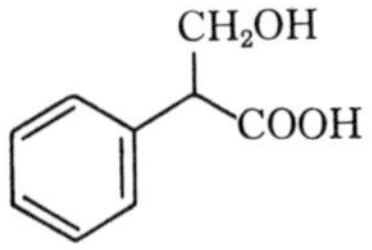

[99]
Tropic Acid

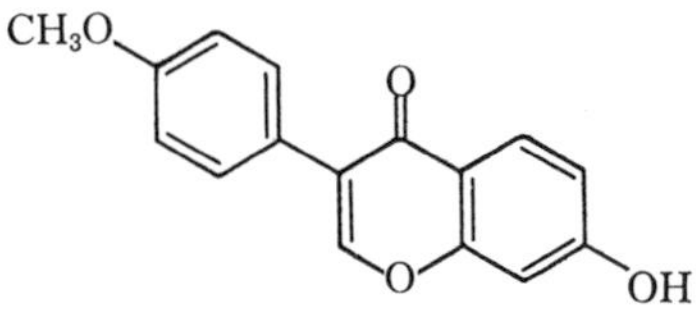

[100]
Formononetin

produce homopterocarpin [102] and angolensin [101], the latter apparently having been methylated rather than methylenated. However, in the cases studied to date (Section 5–3), the direct evidence substantiates

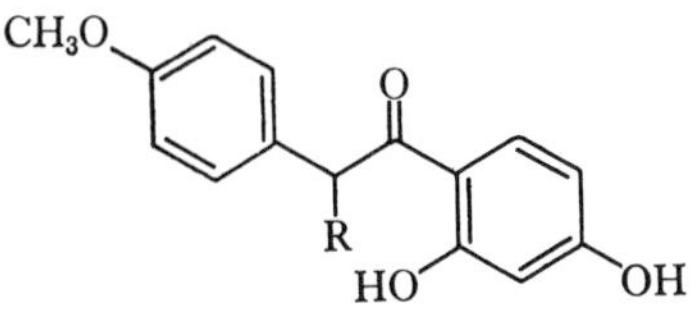

[101]
Ononetin (R = H)
Angolensin (R = CH₃)

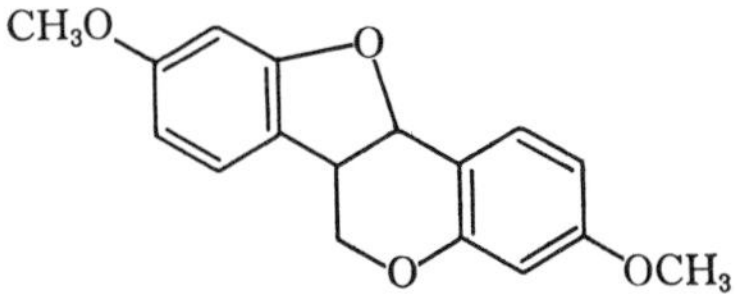

[102]
Homopterocarpin

the rearrangement pathway. Detailed discussions of this rearrangement have been presented by Ollis and Grisebach,[14,25] who envision oxidation of a chalcone to its epoxide followed by aryl migration with concomitant epoxide cleavage, as outlined in [103] → [104] and incorporated in Chart II.

The rotenoids ([105]–[108]) are a complex but remarkably uniform group of polycyclic chromanes that incorporate the isoflavonoid

42. E. Leete, *J. Am. Chem. Soc.*, **82**, 612 (1960); M. L. Louden and E. Leete, *J. Am. Chem. Soc.*, **84**, 1510 (1962).

skeleton with an extra skeletal carbon; the biogenesis of these compounds is discussed by Ollis.[14]   They all exhibit substitution patterns on the aromatic rings (detailed in Table 4–3), which are unmistakably

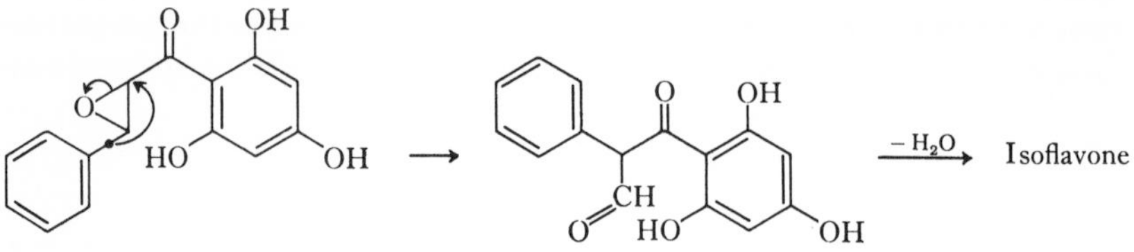

[103]   [104]   → Isoflavone

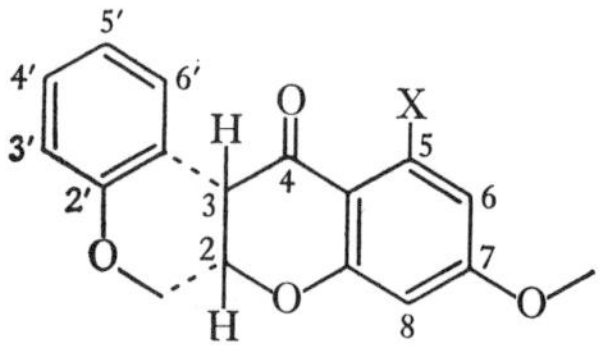

[105]
Rotenoids (X = H or O)

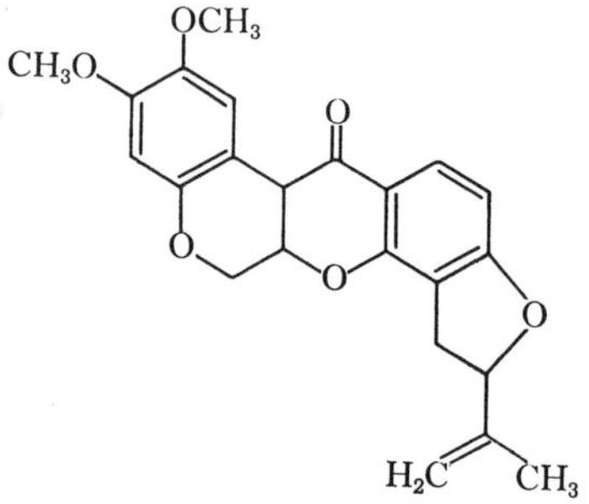

[106]
Rotenone

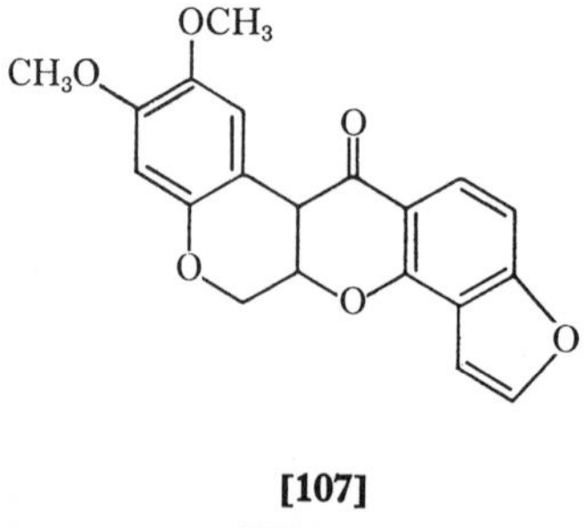

[107]
Elliptone

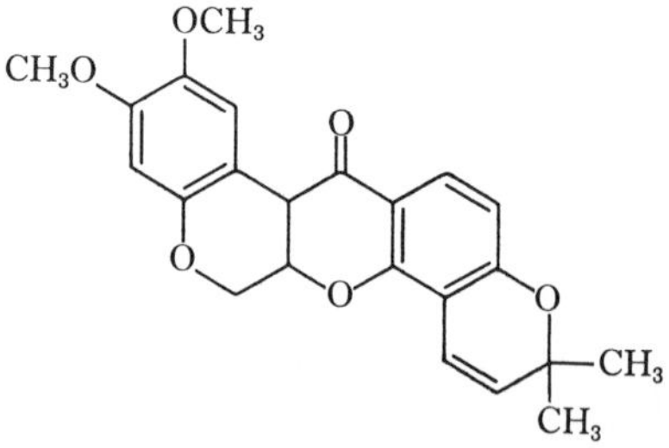

[108]
Deguelin

flavonoid.   Furthermore, one peculiarity of the isoflavonoids is the high instance of the "abnormal" 2′-oxygen on ring B (cf. munetone [97]), and it is just this oxygen that forms an integral part of the rotenoid skeletons; the correlation of isoflavonoid and rotenoid hydroxylation patterns is particularly close.   It is reasonable to suppose that the

2'-oxygen arises from incorporation of an *o*-coumaric acid from the coumarin biogenetic route, cf. [25]–[29], as the terminal acid of the polyacetyl chain, replacing the cinnamic acid of the normal route (Chart II). The presence of the 2'-oxygen presumably creates a mechanistically more favorable environment for the subsequent biogenetic reactions peculiar to isoflavonoids and rotenoids. Thus it may, for example, electronically assist the phenyl migration of the former. Should this oxygen be methylenated [109], cyclization (cf. [110]) to close a flavanone could be concerted with a second ring-closure to the methylene. To gain the rotenoid skeleton, compound [110] must undergo one of the rearrangements indicated in arrows, e.g., to [111] and hence to the rotenoids [112]. The other possible biogenetic route,

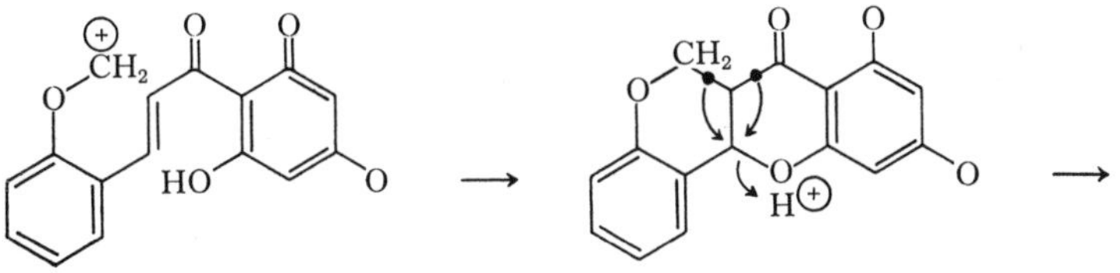

[109]   [110]

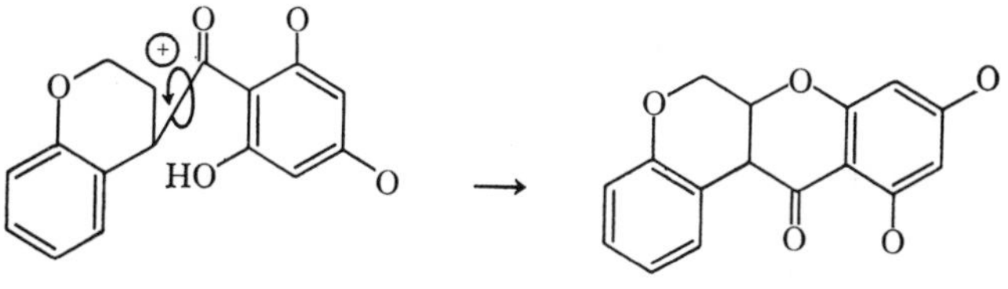

[111]   [112]

Rotenoids

involving preliminary rearrangement to an isoflavone followed by methylenation at C-3, is mechanistically less satisfactory, and it has been pointed out [14] that the 2,3-dehydrorotenoids that would reasonably result from such a mechanism are rare if not artifacts in nature. The stereoelectronic requirements of the rearrangement [110] are consistent with the known stereochemistry of the flavonoids and rotenoids.[43]

43. W. D. Ollis, Phytochemistry Symposium, Hong Kong, 1961; C. Djerassi, W. D. Ollis, and R. C. Russell, *J. Chem. Soc.*, **1961**, 1448; G. Büchi, L. Crombie, P. J. Godin, J. S. Kaltenbronn, K. S. Siddalingaiah, and D. A. Whiting, *J. Chem. Soc.*, **1961**, 2843.

4–4 ORSELLINIC ACID DERIVATIVES
(CYCLIZATION PATH B)

A number of simple benzene derivatives, mostly the metabolites of fungi (or lichens), fall into this pattern, the prototype being found in orsellinic acid (cf. [11], Chapter 3). Decarboxylation or loss of a ring hydroxyl by prior reduction are also unexceptional processes, and are simply represented in orcinol and 6-methylsalicyclic acid, respectively. The next higher "acetylog" is represented by the mold metabolite ([113], R = H_2), and various prior reductions are evident in [114], [125], and mellein [115], the correct formula of which was first proposed on biogenetic grounds.[44,45]

A number of closely related long-chain compounds found in the *Anacardiaceae* are relevant; all may be considered as derived from path-B cyclizations of a long polyacetyl chain, since they all have the requisite odd-membered linear sidechain characteristic of [12] in Chapter 3. Ginkgolic acid, ginkgol, and bilobol [116] are all found in *Ginkgo biloba* and illustrate the action of the decarboxylation or prior reduction variants. Similarly, the several sidechains (variously unsaturated) in samples of anacardic acid [117] are identical to those in cardol [117] and to those in the poison ivy catechols[46] and urushiol [117], wherein it is likely that the carbon adjacent to carboxyl is hydroxylated before cyclization, thus facilitating decarboxylation with aromatization. Renghol [117] and laccol [118] are other sidechain variants of urushiol, whereas pelanjuaic acid [118] is a variant of anacardic acid with a C_{17} sidechain rather than C_{15}. The interesting cases, campnospermol [119] and [120], coexist in *Campnosperma brevipetiolata* with oleyl methyl ketone, $CH_3(CH_2)_7CH{=}CH(CH_2)_7COCH_3$.[47,48] This set of compounds in the single species strongly suggests chain extension of oleic acid, first with one, then with four malonyl units with reduction at one ketone site before cyclization since it appears in the hydroxyl oxidation state (as an olefin) in the prearomatic [120]. Although it is a priori never possible to discern whether the entire acetogenin chain is built at once or the oleic acid is formed first and later extended by malonate, these cases all provide strong presumption of separate initial biosynthesis of the common fatty acids.

The action of the familiar methylation and hydroxylation variants

44. A. J. Birch and F. W. Donovan, *Chem. & Ind. (London)*, **1954**, 1047.
45. J. Blair and G. T. Newbold, *J. Chem. Soc.*, **1955**, 2871.
46. C. R. Dawson, *Record Chem. Progr. (Kresge-Hooker Sci. Lib.)*, **15**, 39 (1954).
47. L. K. Dalton and J. A. Lamberton, *Australian J. Chem.*, **11**, 46 (1958).
48. J. A. Lamberton, *Australian J. Chem.*, **11**, 73 (1958).

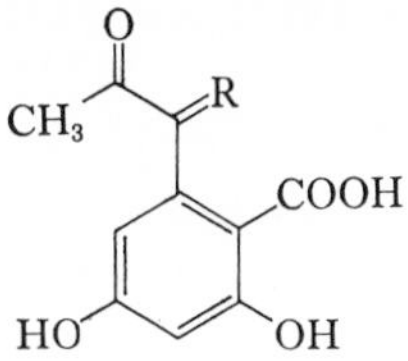

[113]
R = H$_2$
R = H, OH
R = O

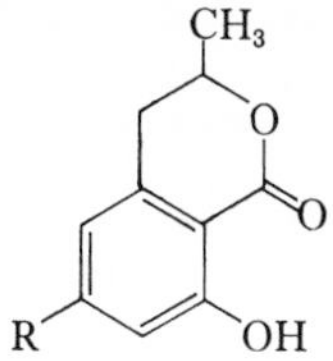

[114] (R = OCH$_3$)
[115] Mellein (R = H)

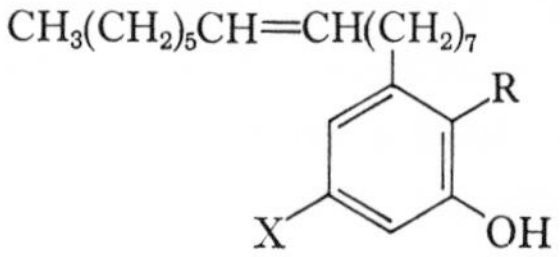

[116]
Bilobol (R = H; X = OH)
Gingkol (R = X = H)
Gingkolic Acid
(R = COOH; X = H)

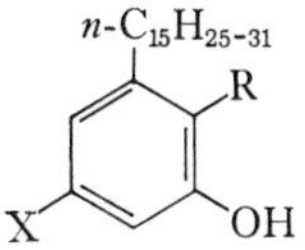

[117]
Anacardic Acid (R = COOH; X = H)
Cardol (R = H; X = OH)
Urushiol (R = OH; X = H)
Renghol (R = OH; X = H)

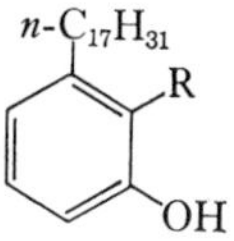

[118]
Pelanjuaic Acid (R = COOH)
Laccol (R = OH)

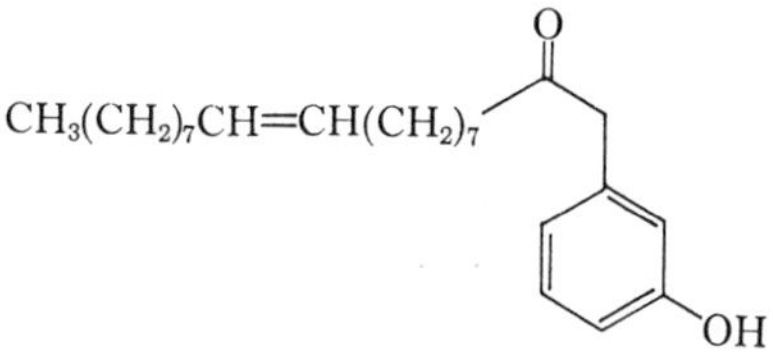

[119]
Campnospermol

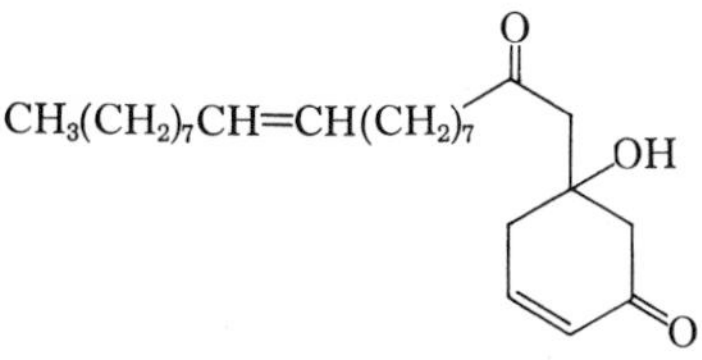

[120]

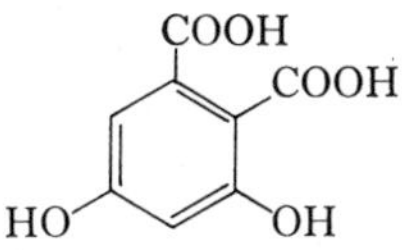

[121]

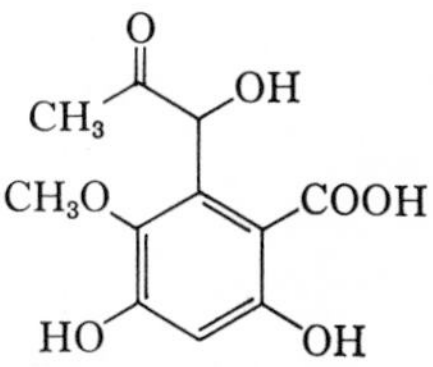

[122]
Ustic Acid

can be readily discerned in the four metabolites **[113]** and **[121]** of
Penicillium brevi-compactum and in ustic acid **[122]**, meconin **[123]**, and
the fungal constituents **[124]** to **[126]**. A number of simple benzoquinones illustrate the extent to which further oxidation may obscure
the familiar pattern of path-B cyclization. Of these, fumigatin and

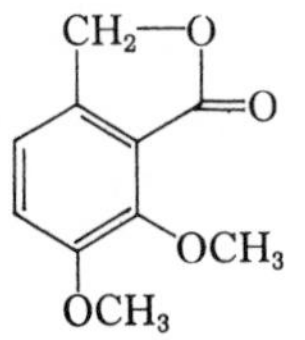

[123]
Meconin

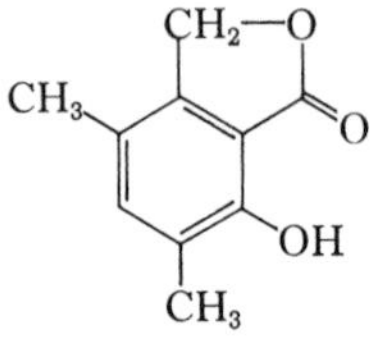

[124]

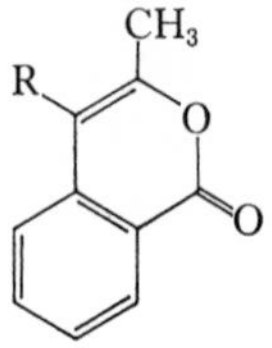

[125] R = H
[126] R = CH₃

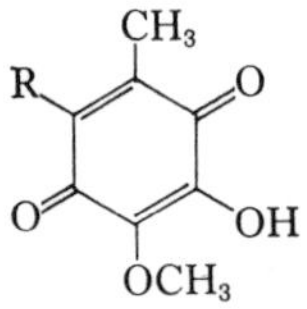

[127]
Fumigatin (R = H)
Spinulosin (R = OH)

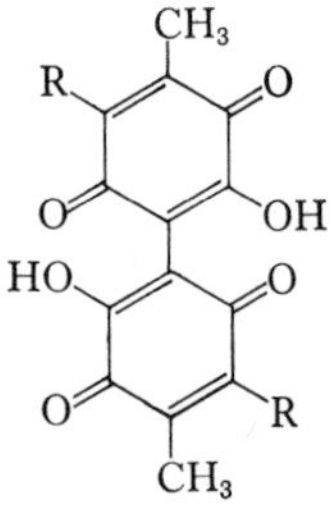

[128]
Phoenicin (R = H)
Oösporein (R = OH)

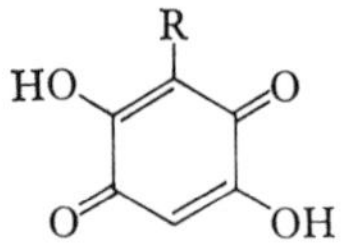

[129]
Rapanone (R = C₁₃H₂₇)
Embelin (R = C₁₁H₂₃)

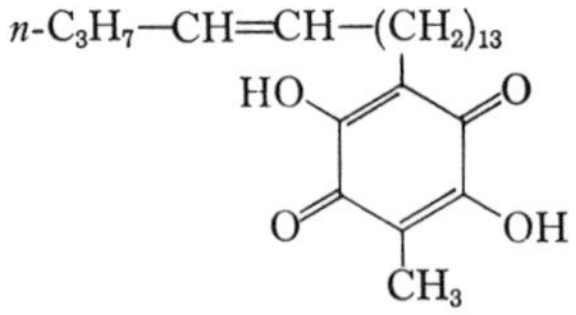

[130]
Maesaquinone

spinulosin **[127]** are typical, as are the oxidative coupling products,
oösporein **[128]** and phoenicin **[128]**. Embelin and rapanone **[129]**
exhibit the characteristic odd-membered sidechain, and maesaquinone
[130] may be wrongly formulated with an even-membered one.

Depsides and Depsidones

By far the largest group of acetogenins of this type are the depsides and depsidones as well as a few cognate lichen products.[11] The depsides (e.g., evernic acid [131]) are simply esters of two or more orsellinic-type units, and their correlation with acetogenesis is excellent. Following Birch's analysis,[49,50] if we examine the units obtained on hydrolysis of the depside bonds, we find that all have the acetogenin form shown in Table 4–4, in which $n = 1, 3, 5, 7$. Of the 64 units from 26 didepsides and four tridepsides, 34 are duplicates (by far the most common unit being orsellinic acid itself, which accounts for 13 of the 34 duplicates). The remaining 30 different units are analyzed in Table 4–4.

Table 4–4 *Depside units*

Position

R_1	R_2	3	R_4	5	6
27 H	27 H	15 H	18 H	26 H	17 CH_3
2 CH_3	3 CH_3	4 OH	12 CH_3	3 OH	1 CH_2OH
1 Erythritol		5 CH_3		1 Cl	4 n-C_3H_7
		5 CHO			4 n-C_5H_{11}
		1 COOH			1 $CH_2COC_3H_7$
					1 n-C_7H_{15}
					2 $CH_2COC_5H_{11}$

Thus, every depside is consistent with the acetate hypothesis if one allows that methyl or hydroxymethyl substituents may be further oxidized to —CHO or —COOH (namely position 3). It is of interest to note that the Cl— present in one depside (chloroatronorin) at C_5 must have been introduced onto that site via an oxidative process.

The depsidones (e.g., [131]–[133] and physodic acid, Chart III) are merely depsides with an ether link generated by oxidative coupling between a phenolic oxygen of one ring and a position ortho or para to a phenolic group on the other, as indicated at the top of Chart III

49. A. J. Birch and F. W. Donovan, *Australian J. Chem.*, **6**, 360 (1953).
50. A. J. Birch, *Fortschr. Chem. Org. Naturstoffe*, **14**, 186 (1957).

for the formation of physodic acid (analogous also to the xanthones jacareubin [69] and mangostin [71]). Correlation of the depsidones with the acetate hypothesis requires that we first formally separate the orsellinic units by reversing this process. Of the 42 units thus obtained (Table 4–5) from the 21 known depsidones, 26 are different from each

Table 4–5 *Depsidone units*

Position

6	1	R_2	3		R_4	5
11 CH_3	15 COOH	22 H	10 H		20 H	20 H
1 CH_2———O———CO		2 CH_3	2 Cl		4 CH_3	3 Cl
2 CH(OH)———O———CO			6 CH_3			1 CHO
2 $C(CH_3){=}CHCH_3$	3 H		2 CH_2OH			
2 $CO(CH_2)_3CH_3$	3 Cl		1 CH_2OAc			
4 n-C_5H_{11}			1 CH_2O-fumarate			
2 $CH_2CO(CH_2)_4CH_3$			2 CHO			

others (cf. Chart III)

2 CH_3	3 COOH	5 H	6 H		5 H	6 H
1 CH_2———O———CO	2 H	1 CH_3			1 CH_3	
1 n-C_3H_7						
2 n-C_5H_{11}						

other and two of these do not fit the orsellinic pattern. Of the remaining 24, all are consistent as acetogenins and some show features not found in the depsides. Thus, several of the depsidones are decarboxylated, and in others the carboxyl is lactonized to an oxidized methyl at C_6 as in meconin [123]. In the three nidulins [133] [51] the chain is methylated at a methylene site of the polyacetyl precursor. The two depsidones, which do not entirely fit the acetogenous pattern, are psoromic acid [134] and gangaleoidin [135]. The four related dibenzofurans shown in [136], [137], and Chart III, as well as picrolichenic acid,[52] are similarly broken down into substituents (cf. *others* in Table 4–5) to show their similarity to the depsidones and consistency with the acetate hypothesis.

51. F. M. Dean, D. S. Deorha, A. D. T. Erni, D. W. Hughes, and J. C. Roberts, *J. Chem. Soc.*, **1960**, 4829.
52. H. Erdtman and C. A. Wachtmeister, *Chem. & Ind.* (*London*), **1957**, 1042.

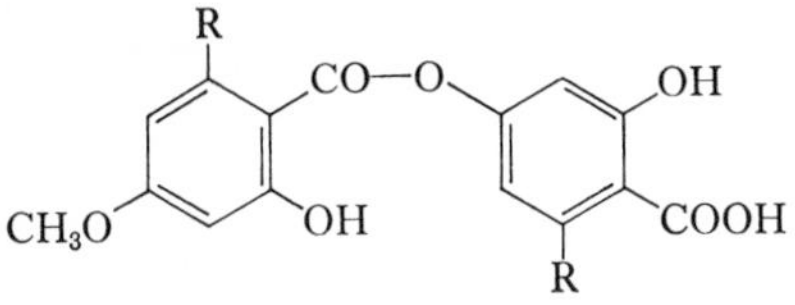

[131]
Evernic Acid (R = CH₃)
Microphyllic Acid (R = CH₂CO(CH₂)₄CH₃)
Perlatolic Acid (R = n-C₅H₁₁)

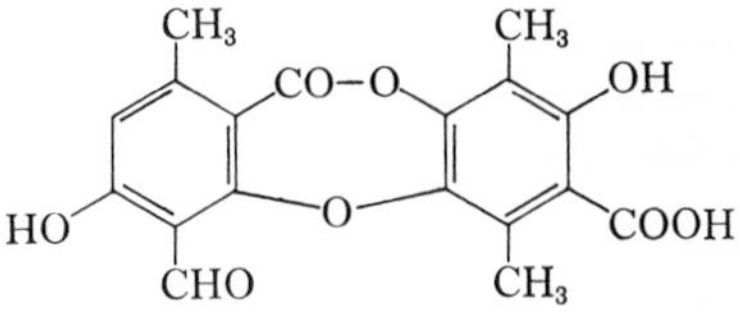

[132]
Virensic Acid

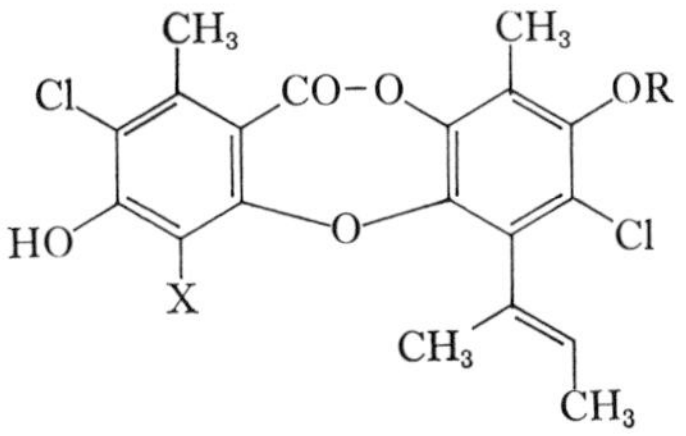

[133]
Nidulin (R = CH₃; X = Cl)
Nornidulin (R = H; X = Cl)
Deschloro-nornidulin (R = H; X = H)

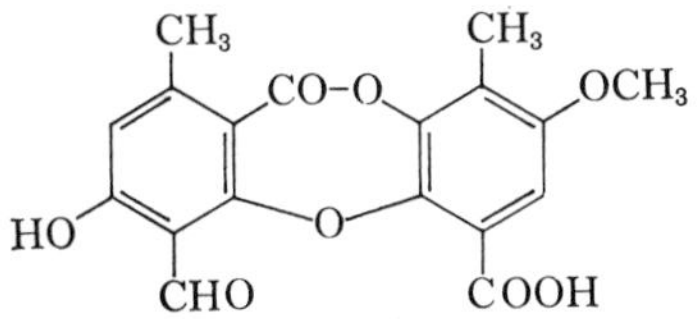

[134]
Psoromic Acid

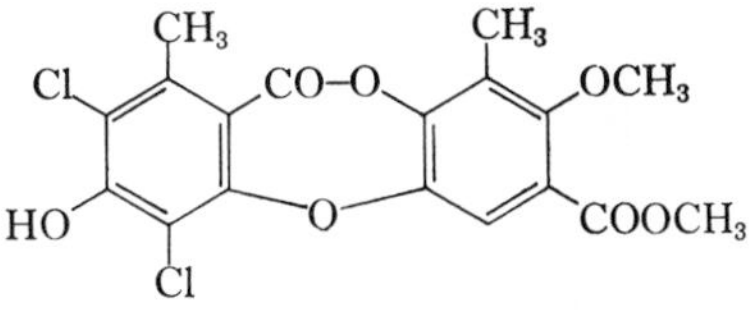

[135]
Gangaleoidin

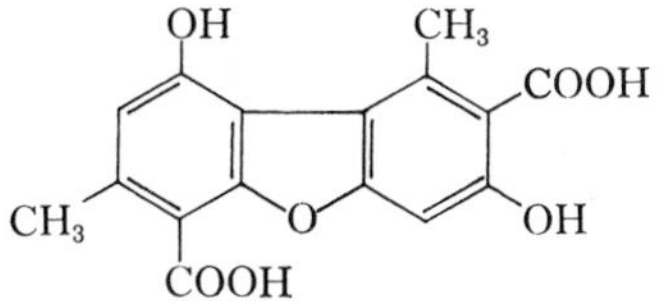

[136]
Pannaric Acid

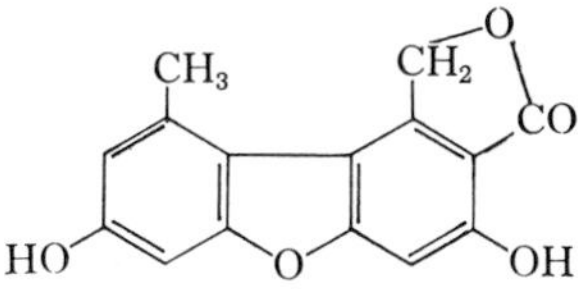

[137]
Strepsilin

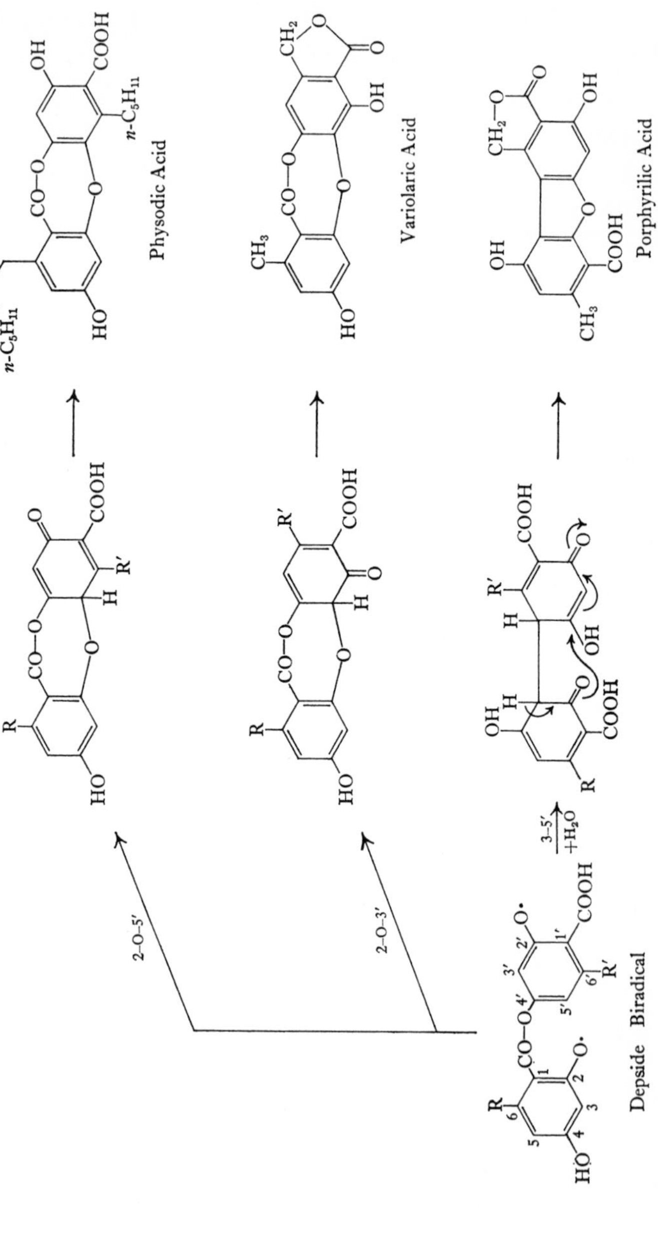

Physodic Acid

Variolaric Acid

Porphyrilic Acid

Depside Biradical

68

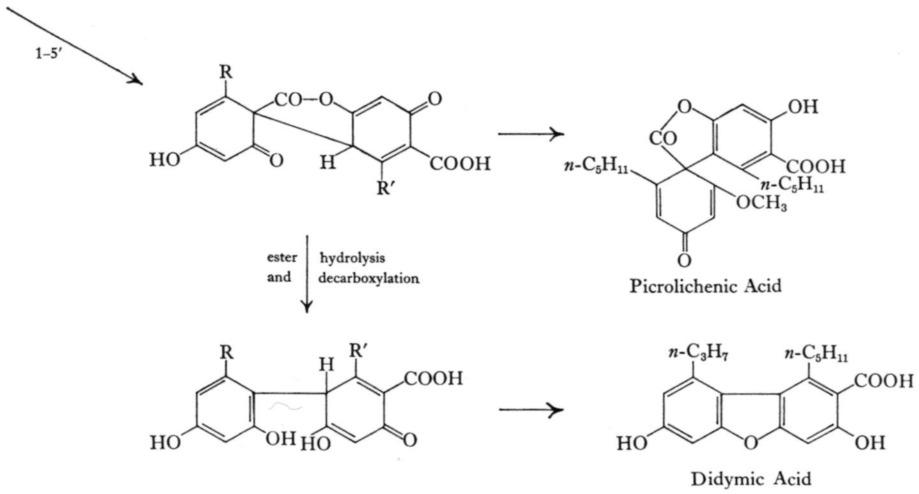
1–5′
R
CO—O
O
HO
O
H
R′
COOH
ester and hydrolysis decarboxylation
O
OH
CO
n-C_5H_{11}
COOH
n-C_5H_{11}
OCH_3
O
Picrolichenic Acid
R
H
R′
COOH
HO
OH
HO
O
n-C_3H_7
n-C_5H_{11}
COOH
HO
O
OH
Didymic Acid

Chart III *Oxidative coupling of depsides*

Several other compounds provide support for the postulation of oxidative coupling in depsidone formation. Since the free electron in a phenolic radical is available by resonance for coupling at the ortho and para positions as well as at oxygen, several possible coupling products are possible, as illustrated in Chart III starting with a generalized

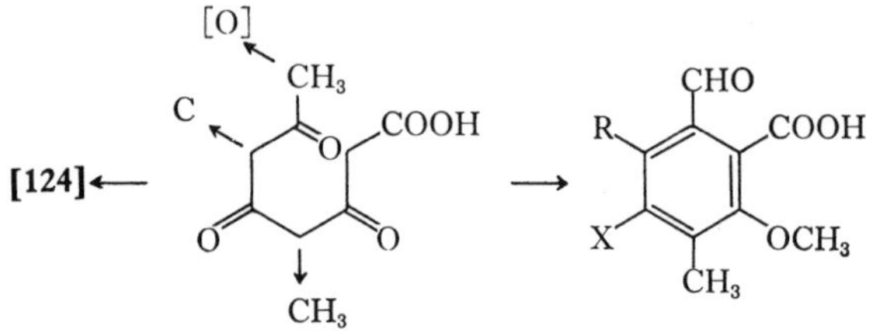

[138]

[139]

Gladiolic Acid (R = CHO; X = H)
Dihydrogladiolic Acid (R = CH$_2$OH; X = H)
Cyclopaldic Acid (R = CHO; X = OH)
Cyclopolic Acid (R = CH$_2$OH; X = OH)

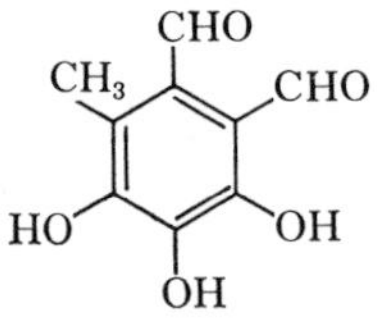

[140]
Flavipin

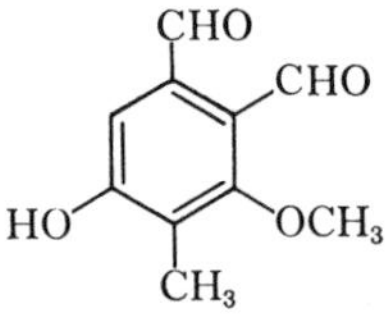

[141]
Quadrilineatin

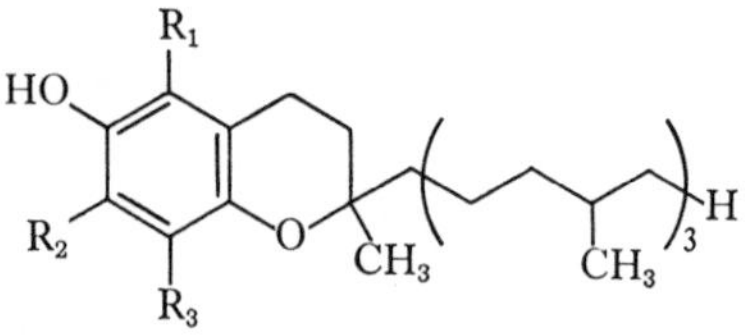

[142]

	R$_1$	R$_2$	R$_3$
α-Tocopherol	CH$_3$	CH$_3$	CH$_3$
β-Tocopherol	CH$_3$	H	CH$_3$
γ-Tocopherol	H	CH$_3$	CH$_3$
δ-Tocopherol	H	H	CH$_3$
ε-Tocopherol	CH$_3$	H	H
ζ-Tocopherol	CH$_3$	CH$_3$	H
η-Tocopherol	H	CH$_3$	H

depside biradical. The various possible products are indicated as their actual representatives among lichen products. It is noteworthy that variolaric and porphyrilic acids are both constructed from the same pair of phenolic precursors, whereas one C_5H_{11} precursor is present in the other three. This aptly illustrates the principle of economy in nature wherein a variety of structures all arise from a single biogenetic mechanism.

Among the products of simple path-B cyclization, a much more extensive tendency appears toward oxidation of methyl or methylene sites than among the acylphloroglucinols (path A). The existence of the series [113], of [121] and [124], and the common appearance of the series CH_3, CH_2OH, CHO, COOH as alkylated groups in the depsides and depsidones are examples (the latter may alternatively represent not oxidation but only a series of alkylating agents such as CH_2O or HCOOH equivalents). This same tendency to obscure the initial oxidation state of the orsellinic precursor also appears in a number of other benzene derivatives. Thus, whereas two *Penicillium* molds produce cyclopolic, cyclopaldic, dihydrogladiolic, and gladiolic acids [139], which appear to be derived from [138] (this is supported by the coexistence of [124] in *P. gladioli*), the *Aspergillus* metabolite flavipin [140] succeeds in completely obscuring its origin; quadrilineatin [141] [53] may be considered a link to flavipin, illuminating some intermediate changes. Alkylation by isoprene units is, on the other hand, much less common among orsellinic- than acylphloroglucinol-cyclization products. The widespread quinones of the tocopherol [142] and coenzyme Q [143] variety contain long polyisoprene chains on an obscured, presumably orsellinic nucleus, but the structures do not afford much correlation with theory. The same may be said of the simpler auroglaucin and flavoglaucin [144] and of mycophenolic acid [145] with the mutilated geranyl sidechain (oxidative loss of acetone). Alkylation of *n*-pentylorcinol or its acyclic polyacetyl precursor with a geranyl group would afford the intermediate [146], oxidation of which can yield cannabidiol [147]. Cyclization to tetrahydrocannabinol [148] and aromatization to cannabinol [149] are then unexceptional so that a reasonable origin of this group of coexistent *Cannabis* phenols may be seen in this sequence.

It is more difficult to assess in detail the correlative support afforded the acetate hypothesis by the compounds considered above. The depsides and congeneric compounds number 56 examples with one bad half in each of two examples, allowing a 98 per cent consistency with acetate origin. As to compounds containing a single phenyl or

53. J. H. Birkinshaw, P. Chaplen, and R. Lahoz-Oliver, *Biochem. J.*, **67**, 155 (1957).

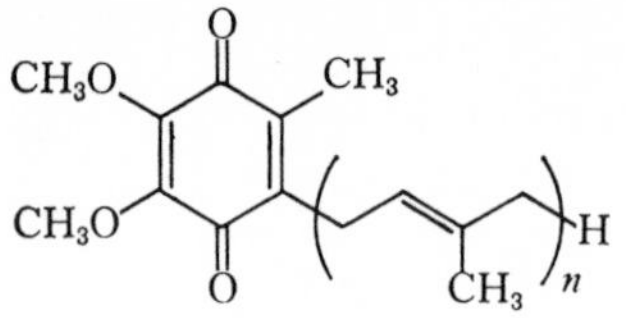

[143]

Coenzymes Q ($n = 6$–9)

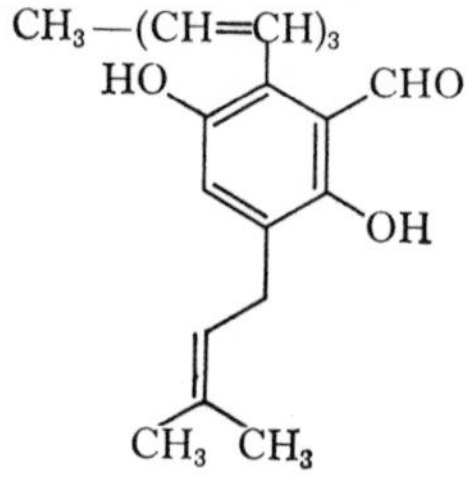

[144]

Auroglaucin

Flavoglaucin = Hexahydroheptyl
Analog

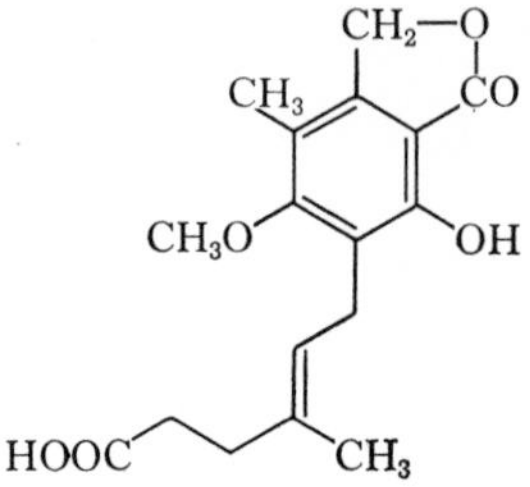

[145]

Mycophenolic Acid

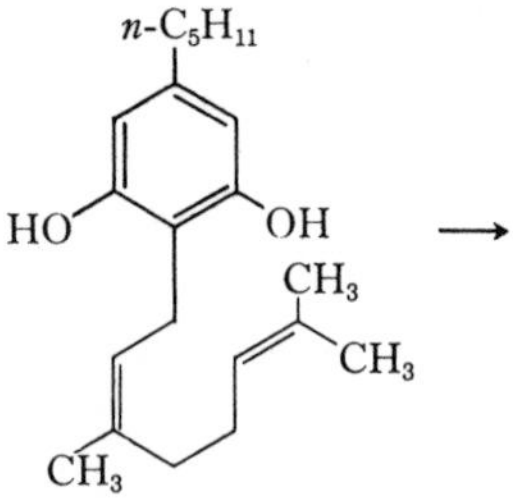

[146]

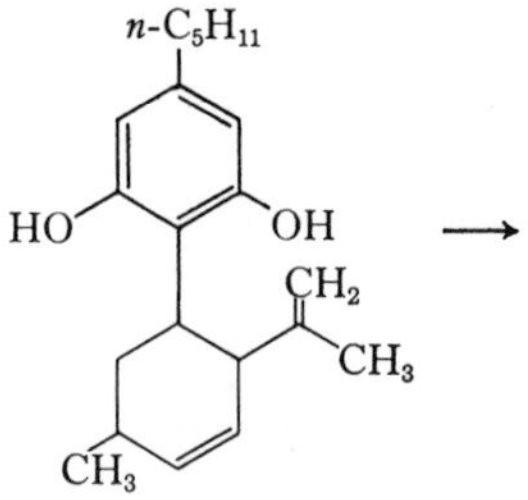

[147]

Cannabidiol

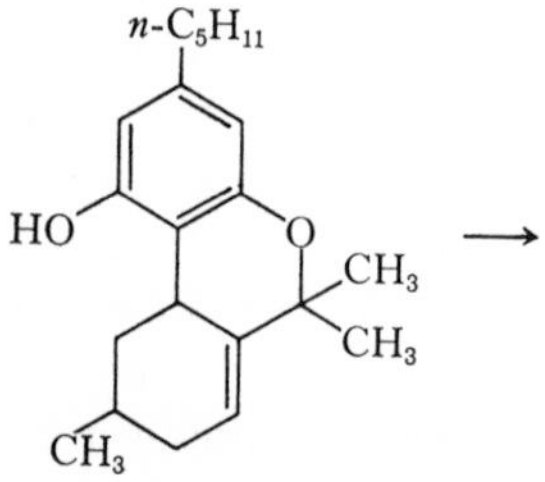

[148]

Tetrahydrocannabinol

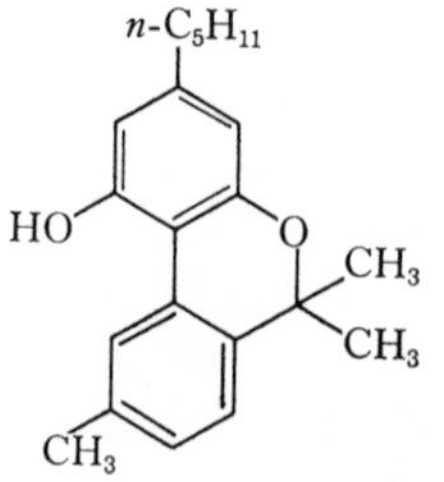

[149]

Cannabinol

hydrophenyl ring with sidechains and not specifically discussed elsewhere, there are about 74 examples; the number is rather uncertain because of the uncertainty in the number of double-bond isomers in the urushiol series. Of these compounds, 37 (50 per cent) can be said to provide support for the acetate hypothesis directly. Another 8 are the gladiolic acid polysubstituted aromatics, and 17 are more highly oxidized simple benzoquinones of the fumagatin variety. If these are taken as consistent with acetogenesis, the correlation is 84 per cent. The remaining compounds include the *Cannabis* phenols, palitantin [150][54] and frequentin [150],[54] and the simple *Ligusticum* root derivatives, ligusticumic acid [151] and its dihydrolactone. None is seriously incompatible with the acetate hypothesis.

[150]
Palitantin
Frequentin: double bond at ...

[151]
Ligusticumic Acid

Stilbenes

Turning now to those variants of cyclization "B" in which another acid terminates the chain, one is struck first by the absence of any examples of the simple biphenyl form [152] in which a benzoic acid replaces the anterior acetic. Replacement by a cinnamic (or dihydrocinnamic) acid, however, results in the family of natural stilbenes, common in pine heartwoods, none of which is a mold metabolite. In hydrangeol [153] and phyllodulcin [153], the carboxyl is retained and lactonized, but in the common stilbenes (e.g., pterostilbene [154] or pinosylvin [154]) decarboxylation is invariably the case. Agrimonolide [155][55] is a similar compound having one more acetate unit in the skeleton. Among the 18 examples, the A ring corresponds to a shikimogenic pattern of oxidation in 16 cases (89 per cent), the B ring to an acetate pattern (only one or two oxygens, placed correctly) in 16 cases

54. K. Bawden, B. Lythgoe, and D. J. S. Marsden, *J. Chem. Soc.*, **1959**, 1162.
55. M. Yamato, *Yakugaku Kenkyu*, **79**, 129, 1069 (1959).

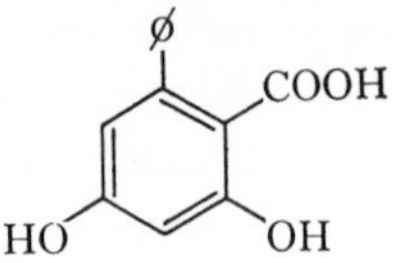

[152]

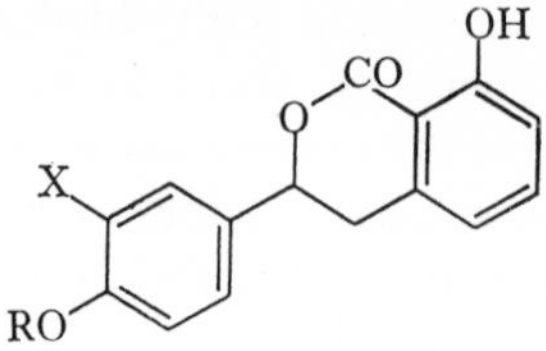

[153]

Hydrangeol (R = X = H)
Phyllodulcin (R = CH₃; X = OH)

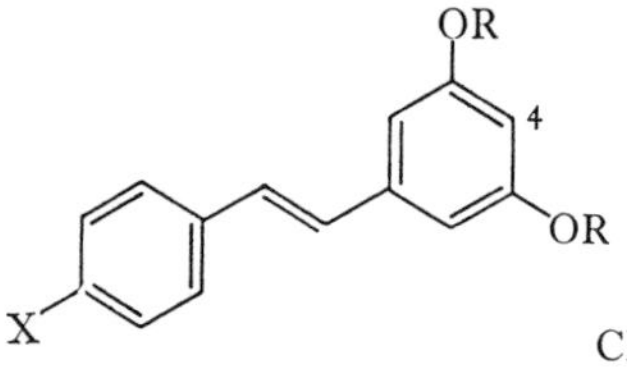

[154]

Pinosylvin (R = X = H)
Pterostilbene (R = CH₃; X = OH)

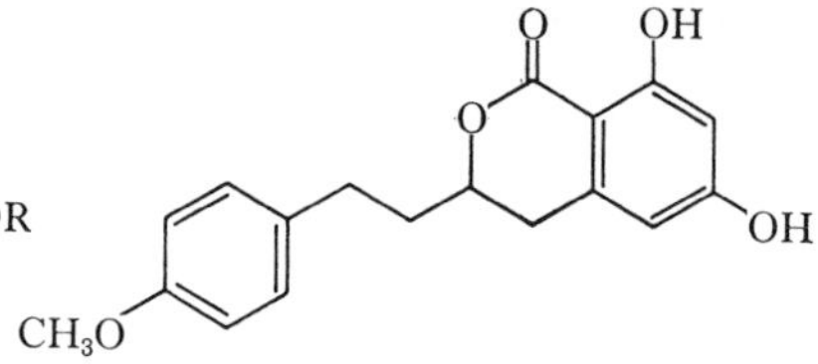

[155]

Agrimonolide

also.   One stilbene, chlorophorin, is alkylated (geranyl group at position 4 in [154]).   It is noteworthy that no flavonoids are known that could be said to arise by path-B cyclization in the B ring, as in [156].   As mentioned, only two flavonoids have C-alkylated B rings, and neither (peltogynol [157] [56] and distemonanthin [158]) bears a close resemblance to the B ring of [156], although such a biogenesis is not out of the question.

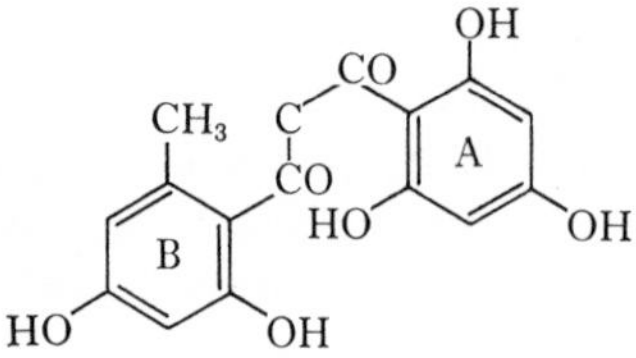

[156]

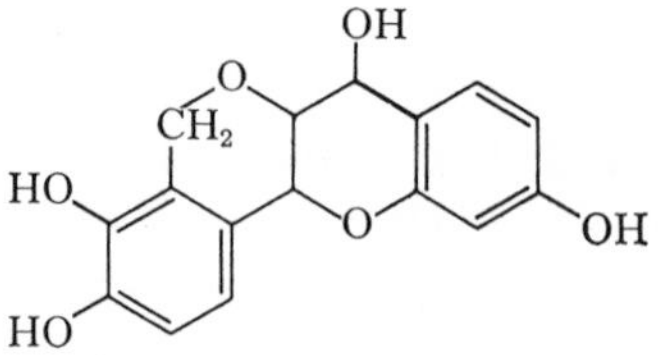

[157]

Peltogynol

56. W. G. C. Forsyth, C. H. Hassall, and J. B. Roberts, *Chem. & Ind.* (*London*), **1958**, 656.

[158]

Distemonanthin

4-5 MORE COMPLEX CYCLIZATIONS

It is reasonable to expect that a polyacetyl chain of sufficient length may cyclize in more complex ways than those already considered, giving rise to polycyclic aromatic systems, a number of which are found in nature. In the compounds discussed only three or four linear acetyl units have actually been involved in the cyclizations, so that no more than one phenolic ring was attainable in this way. In this section we shall examine the multiple possibilities for folding and cyclizing longer polyacetyl chains. Following the discussion of Chapter 3, it is assumed that alkylation or oxidation at methylene is acceptable, and that decarboxylation of the ultimate carboxyl is unexceptional.

Derivatives of Five- and Six-Acetyl Units; Naphthalenes and Naphthoquinones

Two cyclizations of the pentaacetyl chain may be considered, leading as shown ([159]-[164]) to the fungal products fuscin [159] [57] and citrinin [162], [58] both of which involve reduction of the C-2 carbonyl and have undergone substitution (methyl, isoprene, or oxygen) at the methylene sites. Three products [161] recently isolated [59] from *Curvularia* also conform to the fuscin mode of cyclization; of these, curvulol is also reduced at the terminal carbon.

In the case of citrinin [162] it may be noted that the terminal carboxyl appears reduced to the aldehyde state. This may have arisen from a chain of one more acetyl unit in which the β-keto acid is reduced to a β-hydroxy acid and cleaved to acetic acid and a terminal aldehyde by retroaldol reaction. Another possibility may be alkylation by formaldehyde (or formic acid) of the methylene adjacent to the

57. D. H. R. Barton and J. B. Hendrickson, *J. Chem. Soc.*, **1956**, 1028.
58. D. H. Johnson, A. Robertson, and W. B. Whalley, *J. Chem. Soc.*, **1950**, 2971.
59. A. Kamal, M. Ali Khan, and A. Ali Qureshi, *Tetrahedron*, **19**, 111 (1962).

terminal carboxyl, followed by decarboxylation. The hypothesis allows these variants but inspection of structures cannot distinguish them. However, it is interesting to observe that a mutant of the organism that produces citrinin produces instead the variant [164] with the terminal carboxyl intact.[60]

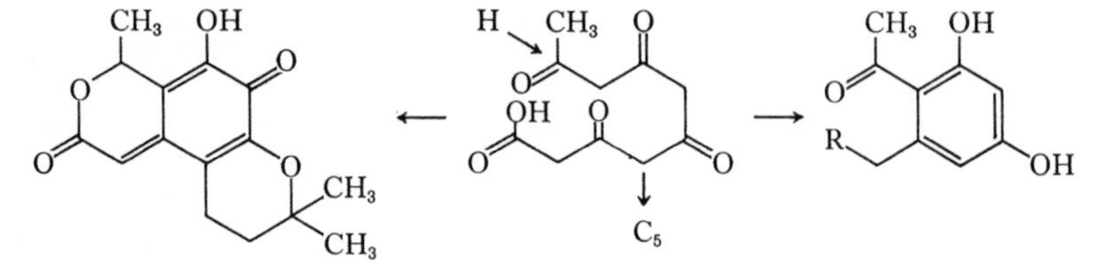

[159]	[160]	[161]
Fuscin		Curvulin (R = COOC$_2$H$_5$)
		Curvulinic Acid
		(R = COOH)
		Curvulol (R = CH$_2$OH)

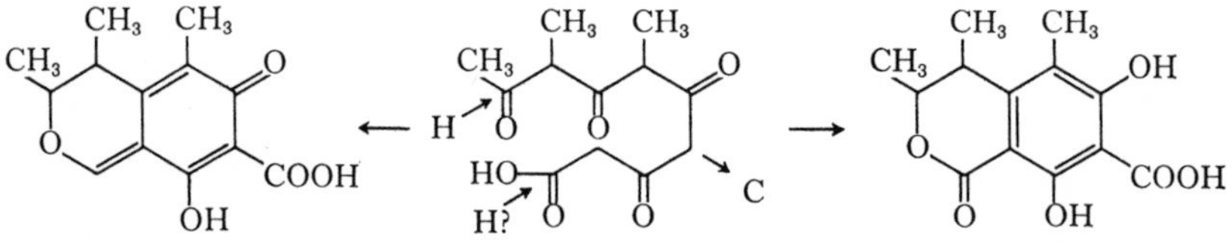

[162]	[163]	[164]
Citrinin		

Several other quinonoid pyrans in which the final carboxyl of the chain appears reduced are to be found. Thus the pigments of *Monascus* fungi, monascorubin[61] and rubropunctatin [167],[62] appear to be derived from a hexaacetyl chain (monascin also, which is a tetrahydro-rubropunctatin) as shown ([165]–[167]). It has been argued[63] that the skeletal branching here arises from the esterification of the fore-runner [165] to [166], which would probably cyclize spontaneously in an aldol reaction. In sclerotiorin [203],[63] from the same species (considered later), the same oxygen is merely acetylated and no aldol cyclization has occurred.

60. C. H. Hassall and D. W. Jones, *J. Chem. Soc.*, **1962**, 4189.
61. B. C. Fielding, E. J. Haws, J. S. E. Holker, A. D. G. Powell, A. Robert-son, D. N. Stanway, and W. B. Whalley, *Tetrahedron Letters*, **1960**, 24.
62. E. J. Haws, J. S. E. Holker, A. Kelly, A. D. G. Powell, and A. Robertson, *J. Chem. Soc.*, **1959**, 3598.
63. F. M. Dean, J. Staunton, and W. B. Whalley, *J. Chem. Soc.*, **1959**, 3004.

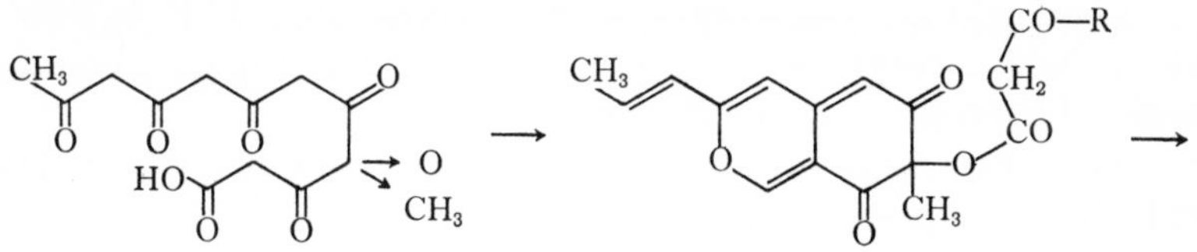

[165]

[166]

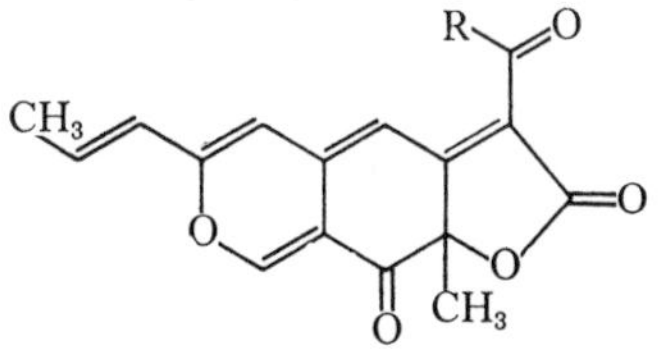

[167]
Monascorubin (R = $n\text{-}C_7H_{15}$)
Rubropunctatin (R = $n\text{-}C_5H_{11}$)

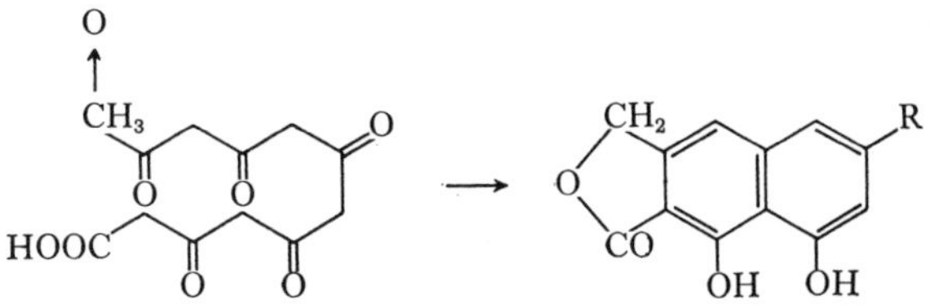

[168]

[169]
α-Sorigenin (R = OCH_3)
β-Sorigenin (R = H)

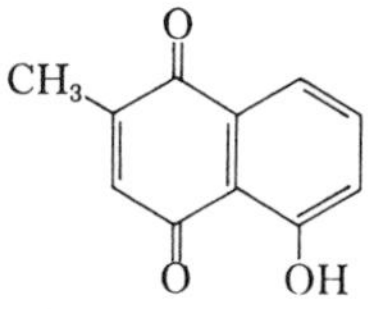

[170]
Plumbagin

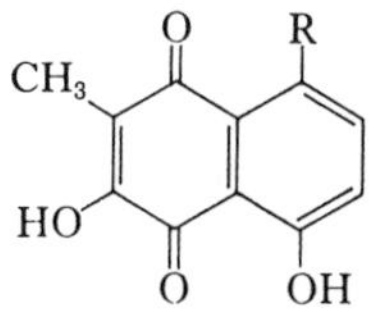

[171]
Droserone (R = H)
Hydroxydroserone (R = OH)

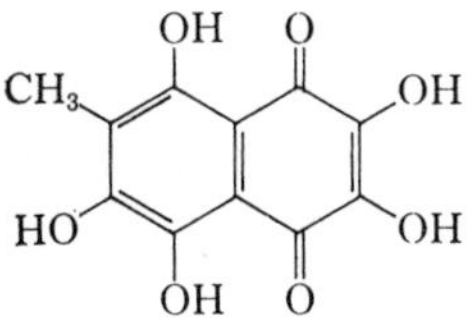

[172]
Spinochrome D

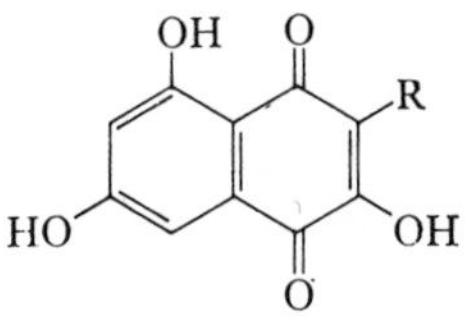

[173]
Flaviolin (R = H)
Spinochrome N (R = OH)

A different cyclization **[168]** of the six-unit chain is discernible in the sorigenins **[169]**; an incorrect formula for α-sorigenin was first corrected on this biogenetic basis.[64]

There are a great many naphthalenes and naphthoquinones (e.g., **[170]**–**[173]**) in nature; they are generally characterized by no carbon substituents or only a single carbon at the β-position. The biogenesis of naphthalenes may proceed from either a pentaacetyl **[174]** or hexaacetyl **[177]** chain, the extra carbon in the first case arising by enol alkylation.

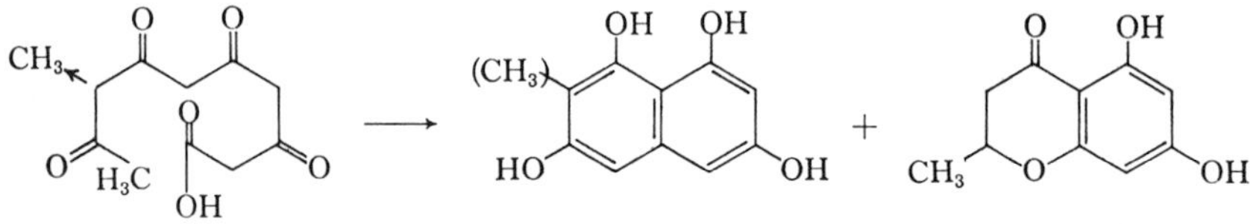

[174]
Pentaacetyl

[175]

[176]

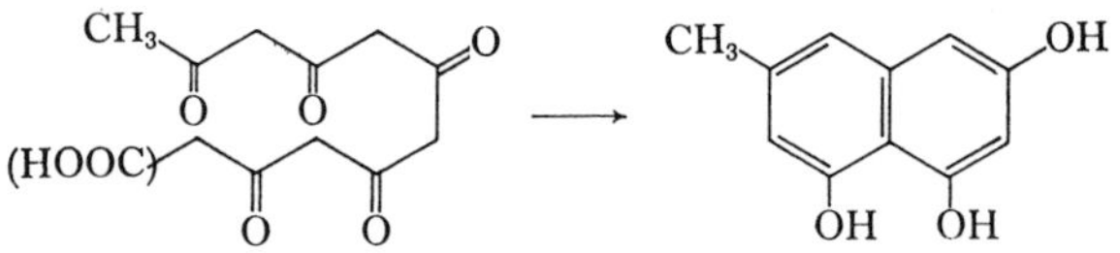

[177]
Hexaacetyl

[178]

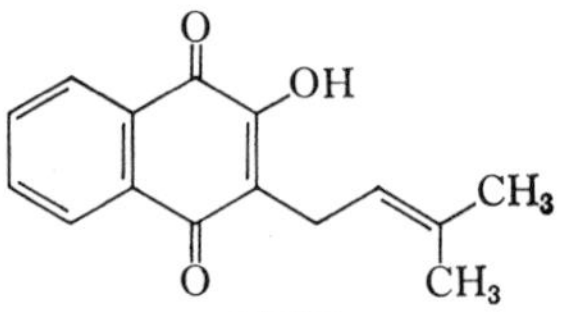

[179]
Lapachol

In principle the two routes are distinguishable by substituent patterns, but in fact most of the naphthalenes show a very poor correlation with either prediction (compare the continuous attrition of expected features exhibited by the series plumbagin **[170]**, the droserones **[171]**, and spinochrome D **[172]**). Furthermore, a number of naphthoquinones in nature lack the β-carbon; they have in its place oxygen or an

64. R. G. Haber, J. Nikuni, H. Schmid, and K. Yogi, *Helv. Chim. Acta*, **39**, 1654 (1956).

isoprene unit, as in spinochrome N [173] and lapachol [179], or no substituent as in flaviolin (the correct choice [44,65] for the final structure [173] was dictated by the acetate hypothesis). Other naphthoquinones with attached isoprenoid units are recorded in Section 4–7. Methyl ethers of 1,8-dihydroxynaphthalene cooccur in *Daldinia concentrica* with the chromanone [176] of much more obvious acetate origin; a slight variation on the above mode of folding the pentaacetyl chain can produce both compounds as indicated in [174].[66] Oxidative coupling is also operative in the same mold, which produces the tetrahydroxybinaphthyl [180] and the perylene-quinone [181], although the latter may be an artifact of aerial oxidation, known to occur readily in vitro. A similar circumstance is provided by species of *Diospyros*, which produce plumbagin [170], the naphthoquinone [182], and diospyros [183].

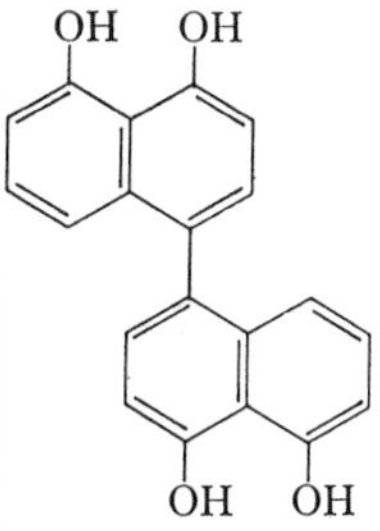

[180]	[181]	[182]	[183]
			Diospyros

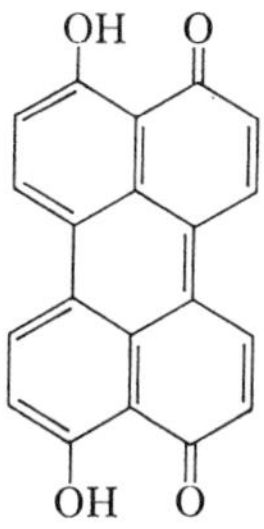

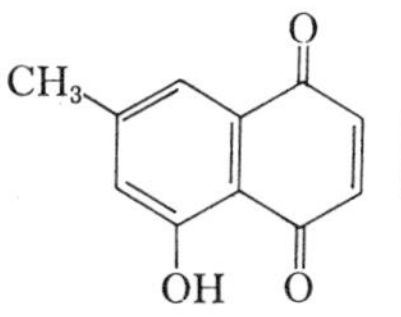

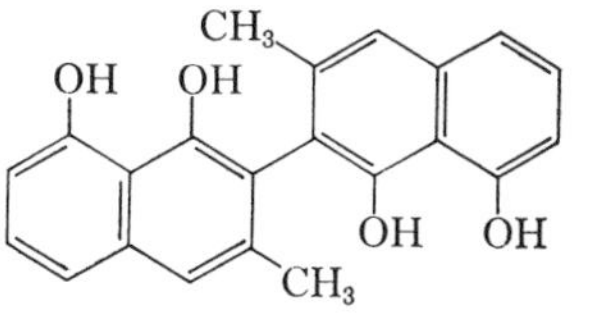

The formulas of the several aphid pigments [67] provide a spectacular set of naphthalenes oxidatively coupled into very complex quinones, the parent pigment protoaphin [185] being formed however by an entirely unexceptional cyclization [184] and oxidative coupling as in [180]. In series of subsequent changes that are simply internal aldol dehydrations, [185] is transformed into the pigments xanthoaphin [186] and erythroaphin [187]; the series aptly demonstrates the potential for biosynthesis of very elaborate molecules by the operation of the few basic operations of Chapter 3.

65. A. J. Birch and F. W. Donovan, *Australian J. Chem.*, **8**, 529 (1955).
66. D. C. Allport and J. D. Bu'Lock, *J. Chem. Soc.*, **1958**, 4090; *J. Chem. Soc.*, **1960**, 654.
67. A. R. Todd, *Experientia*, **18**, 433 (1962).

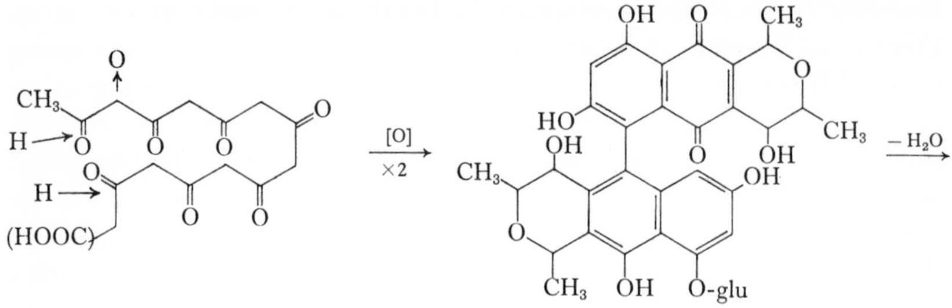

[184]

[185]
Protoaphin

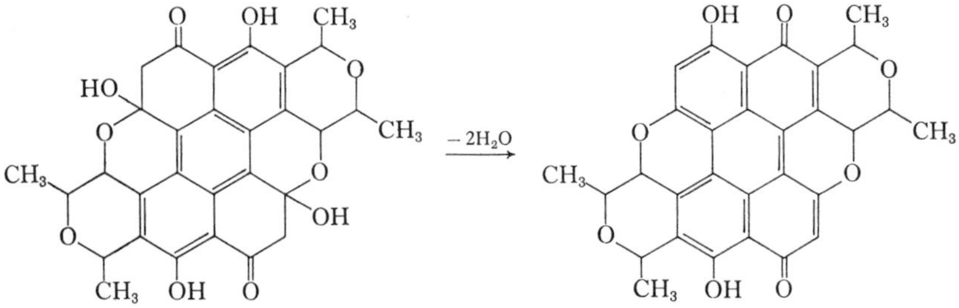

[186]
Xanthoaphin

[187]
Erythroaphin

The correlation of the naphthalene derivatives (including the bis-naphthoquinones and perylene-quinones, which apparently arise by oxidative coupling) with the acetate hypothesis is, however, only about 35 per cent in the 42 cases known (excluding the few naphthalenes discussed below).

Derivatives of Seven- and Eight-Acetyl Units; Anthraquinones

Probably the greatest variety of natural polycyclic compounds is to be found in the products of cyclization of the seven-unit polyacetyl chain indicated in Chart IV. Thus, one folding of the chain yields lichexanthone without modification and deschlorogriseofulvin from a modification involving reduction at C-13 and hydroxylation at C-8. A number of other compounds recently isolated[36] from the same mold that produces griseofulvin support this biogenesis admirably, [e.g., griseoxanthone, griseophenone, and dehydrogriseofulvin (no reduction at C-13 in biogenesis)]. The oxidative step leading to griseofulvin may occur on the griseophenone instead of earlier on the polyacetyl chain, and Scott has succeeded in an elegant and simple synthesis of griseofulvin that employs this biogenetic path.[68] Another mode of folding leads directly to the mold biphenyl, alternariol[69]; another, with decarboxylation, yields cordeauxiaquinone,[70] eleutherol,[71] and musizin (nepodin),[72,73] involving some secondary but ordinary modifications. The linear folding that yields purpurogenone (an alternate formula is derived the same way)[74,75] involves the same changes of C-8 and C-13 required for deschlorogriseofulvin; the marked similarity of purpurogenone and citrinin [162] tends to support this biogenetic route for both. Finally, if we modify the normal chain by oxidative decarboxylation of C-1, hydroxylation at C-4, and methylation or hydroxymethylation at C-10, three different coilings of this chain (A, B, C) each cyclize to yield the mold metabolites fusarubin, javanicin, fulvic acid, and citromycetin, in one of the most marvelous demonstrations of the versatility of this concept.[76] It is significant, furthermore, that a simple change of the medium on which the *Penicillium griseofulvum* is grown suffices to cause the mold to produce fulvic acid instead of griseofulvin![77] The mold products geodin and erdin [189],[78] which, although very similar to griseofulvin, do not conform with the formal requirements as acetogenins. Hassall[79] has pointed out the close structural similarity of geodin with the benzophenone sulochrin [188] and has isolated two more derivatives from the geodin-forming fungus *Aspergillus terreus*, (see asterric acid [190] and geodoxin [191], which serve to suggest a reasonable biogenetic interconversion among the four, as on page 84).

68. A. C. Day, J. Nabney, and A. I. Scott, *Proc. Chem. Soc.*, **1960**, 284.
69. H. Raistrick, C. E. Stickings, and R. Thomas, *Biochem. J.*, **55**, 421 (1953).
70. J. H. Lister, C. H. Eugster, and P. Karrer, *Helv. Chim. Acta*, **38**, 215 (1955).
71. H. Schmid, A. Ebnöther, and M. Burger, *Helv. Chim. Acta*, **33**, 609 (1950).
72. C. J. Covell, F. E. King, and J. W. W. Morgan, *J. Chem. Soc.*, **1961**, 702.
73. T. Murakami and A. Matsushima, *Chem. Pharm. Bull.* (*Tokyo*), **9**, 654 (1961).
74. R. G. Cooke and R. H. Thomson, *Rev. Pure Appl. Chem.*, **8**, 85 (1958).
75. J. C. Roberts and C. W. H. Warren, *J. Chem. Soc.*, **1955**, 2992.
76. A. J. Birch, R. J. English, R. A. Massy-Westropp, M. Slaytor, and H. Smith, *J. Chem. Soc.*, **1958**, 365.
77. F. M. Dean, R. A. Eade, R. A. Moubasher, and A. Robertson, *Nature*, **179**, 366 (1957).
78. D. H. R. Barton and A. I. Scott, *J. Chem. Soc.*, **1958**, 1767.
79. C. H. Hassall, Ref. 17, Chap. 6.

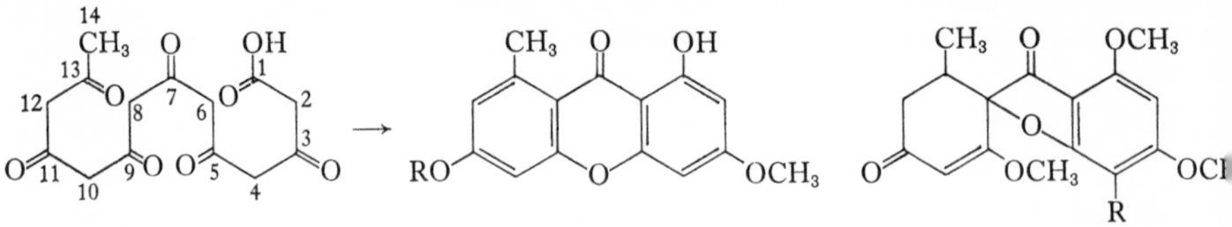

Lichexanthone (R = CH₃)
Griseoxanthone (R = H)

Deschlorogriseofulvin
(R = H)
Griseofulvin (R = Cl)

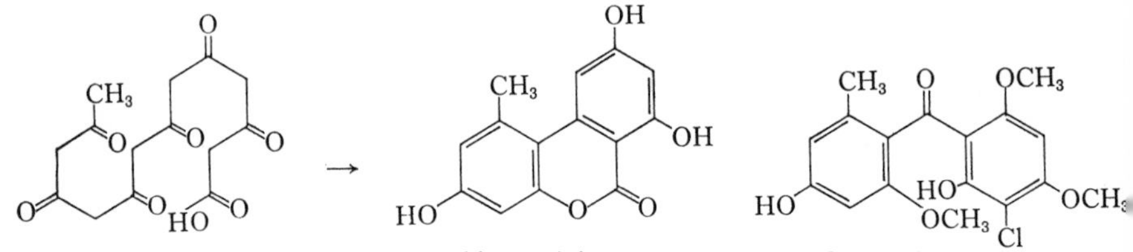

Alternariol

Griseophenone

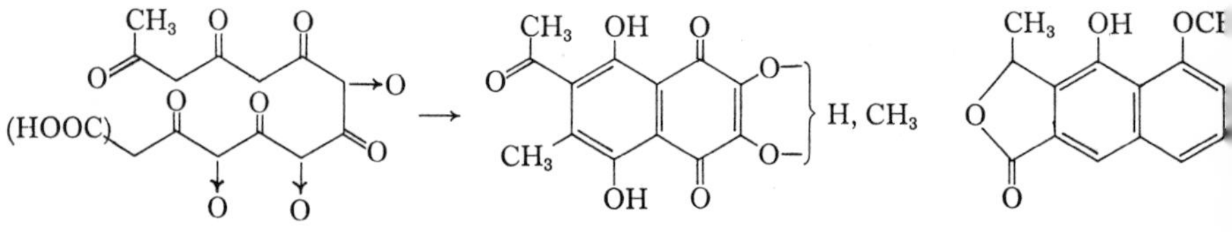

Cordeauxiaquinone

Eleutherol

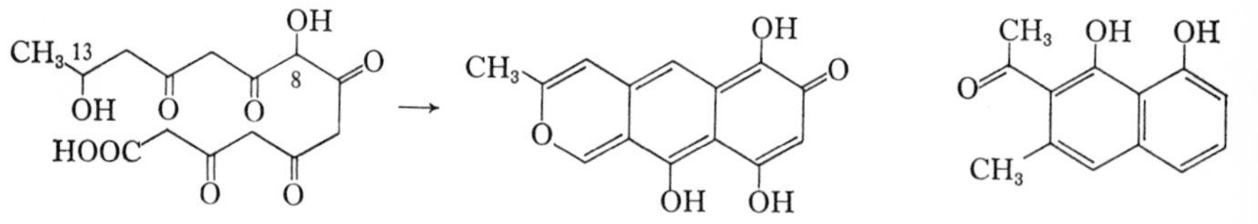

Purpurogenone

Musizin

The similarity of sulochrin with griseophenone Y [192] suggests that the ester in the former is an oxidized methyl group of orsellinic origin. However, the *para*-methyl group on the other ring of each is unusual in that it appears to occupy a ketonic site of the initial polyacetyl chain. The chlorines that appear variously in these compounds always occupy methylene sites.

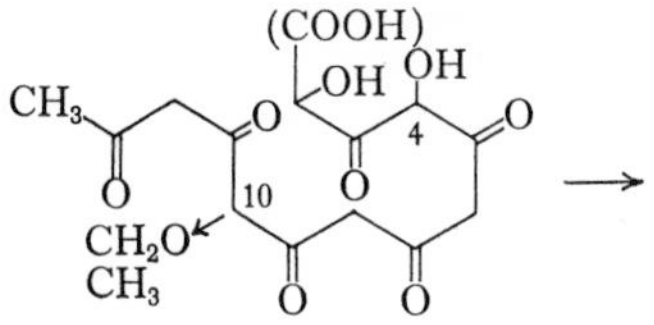

(A)

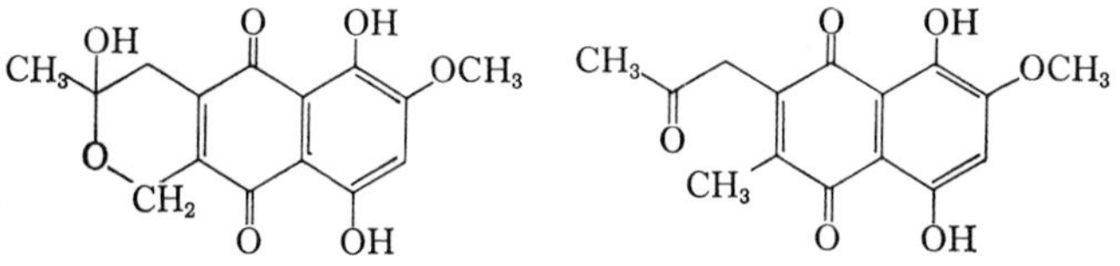

Fusarubin

Javanicin

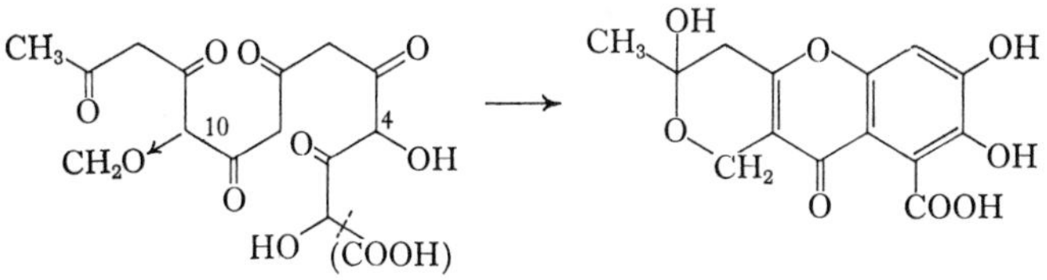

(B)

Fulvic Acid

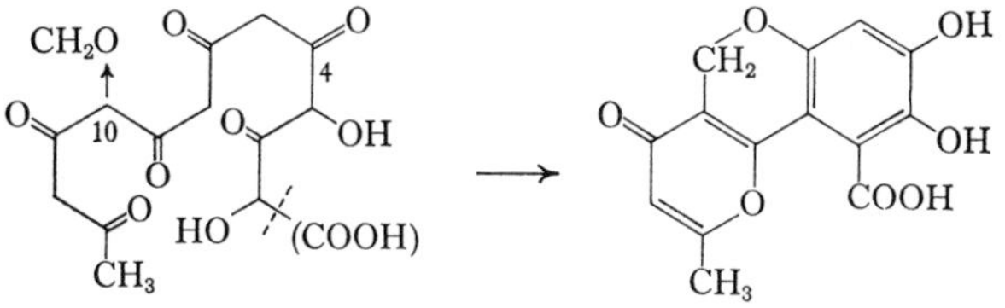

(C)

Citromycetin

Chart IV

The structure of mollisin **[194]** [80] may be dissected as shown **[193]**, whereas folding the heptaacetyl chain in other ways produces either rubrofusarin **[195]** [81] or, via **[196]**, the perinaphthenone pigments

80. G. J. M. van der Kerk and J. C. Overum, *Rec. Trav. Chim.*, **76**, 425 (1957).
81. G. H. Stout, D. L. Dreyer, and L. H. Jensen, *Chem. & Ind. (London)*, **1961**, 289.

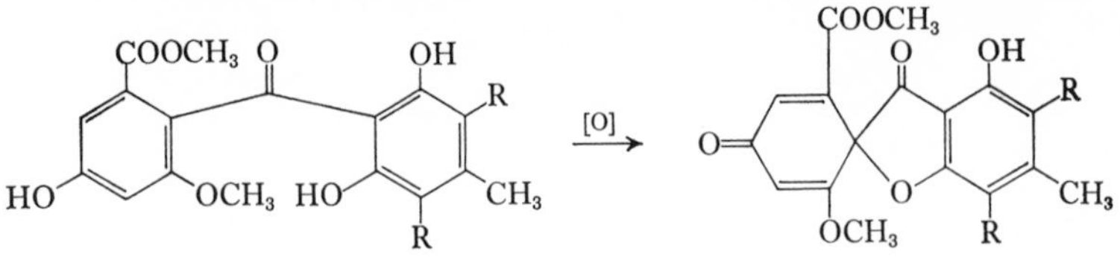

[188]
Sulochrin (R = H)

[189]
Geodin (R = Cl)
Erdin = corresponding acid

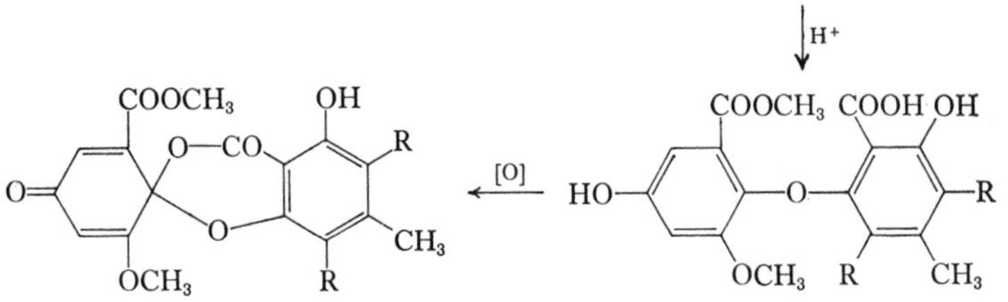

[191]
Geodoxin (R = Cl)

[190]
Asterric Acid (R = H)

atrovenetin[82] and (with a benzoyl terminus) haemocorin **[197]**.[72] Structure **[199]** has been offered[82] for the former, but it is notable that this exhibits an isoprenoid group attached at a ketonic site of the precursor; since no other examples of such isoprenylation exist,

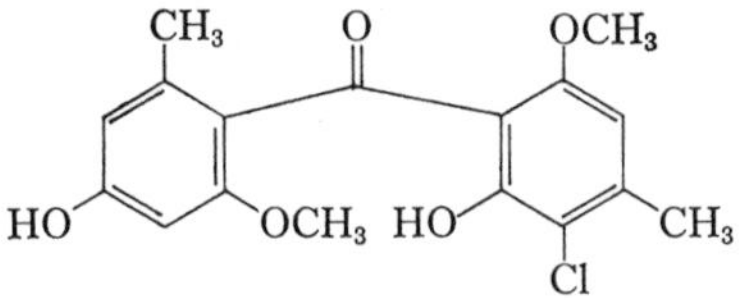

[192]
Griseophenone Y

there is a strong presumption that structure **[198]** is the correct representation.*

* Since this was written, X-ray evidence[83] has confirmed the correctness of **[198]**.

82. D. H. R. Barton, P. de Mayo, G. A. Morrison, and H. Raistrick, *Tetrahedron*, **6**, 48 (1959).
83. I. C. Paul, G. A. Sim, and G. A. Morrison, *Proc. Chem. Soc.*, **1962**, 352.

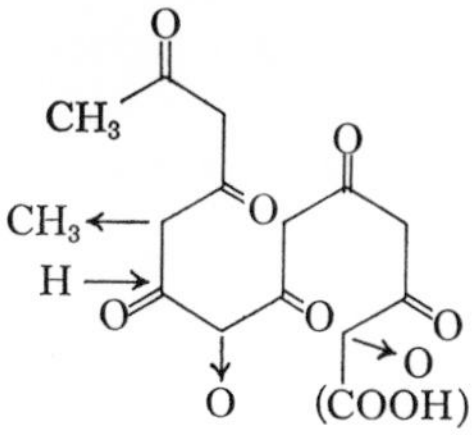

[193]

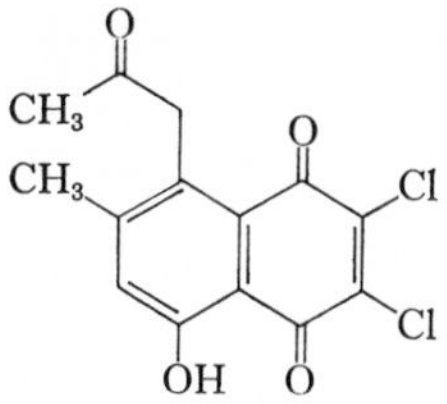

[194]
Mollisin

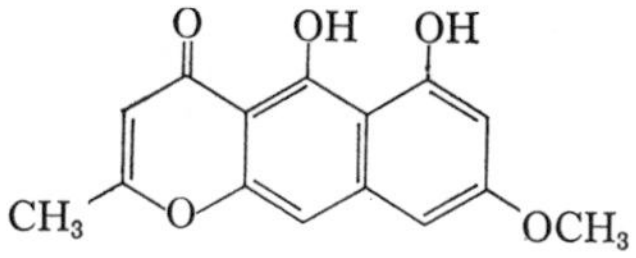

[195]
Rubrofusarin

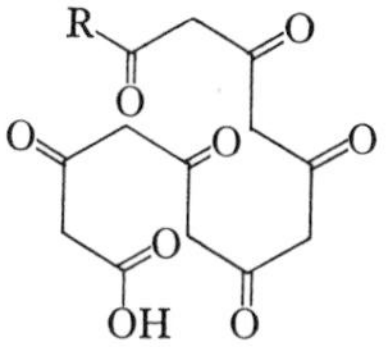

[196]

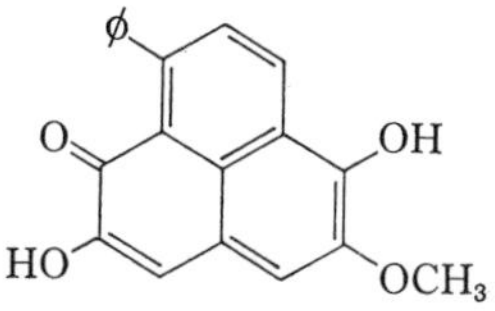

[197]
Haemocorin

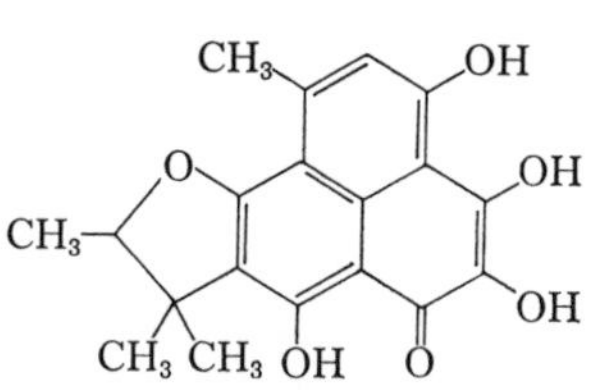

[198]
Atrovenetin

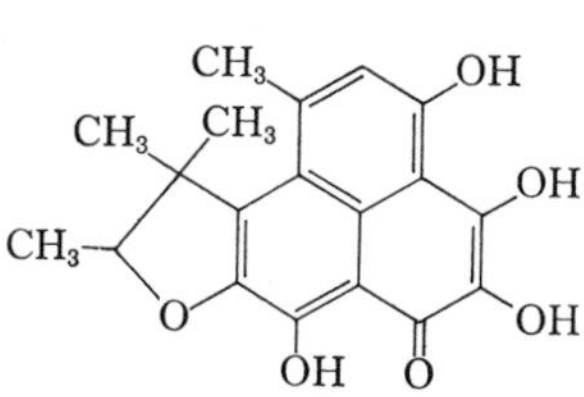

[199]

Eight acetate units comprise the chain that cyclizes to eleutherin **[200]** [84] and eleutherinol **[201]**, which coexist with eleutherol (Chart IV) in *Eleutherine bulbosa*. The correction of an early formula for eleutherinol

84. H. Schmid and A. Ebnöther, *Helv. Chim. Acta*, **34**, 1041 (1951).

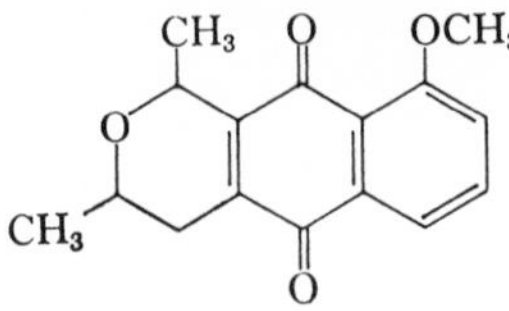

[200]
Eleutherin

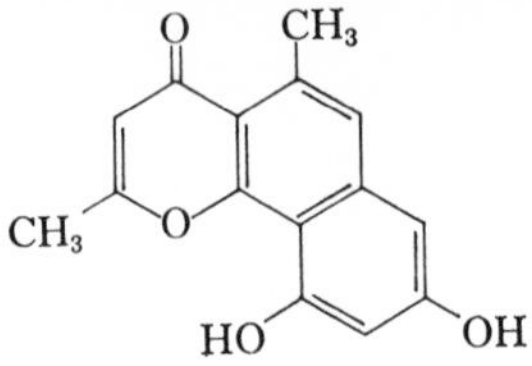

[201]
Eleutherinol

by Birch[85] constituted one of the first demonstrations of the usefulness of the acetate hypothesis. The octaacetyl chain **[202]** also provides the skeletons of the coexistent sclerotiorin **[203]**[63] and rotiorin **[204]**[63]; in the former, acetylation of the hydroxyl has occurred; in the latter, acetoacetylation followed by aldol cyclization accounts for the branched skeleton as in rubropunctatin **[167]**. Curvularin **[205]**[86] represents a large-ring lactone reminiscent of the macrolides, but in this case one that has undergone an internal cyclization and some stripping of functionality.

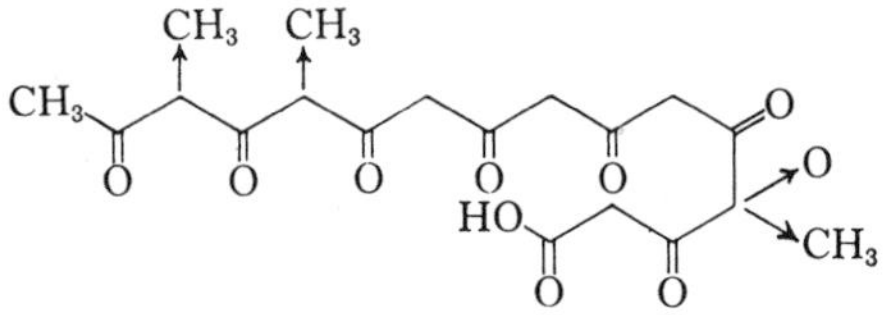

[202]

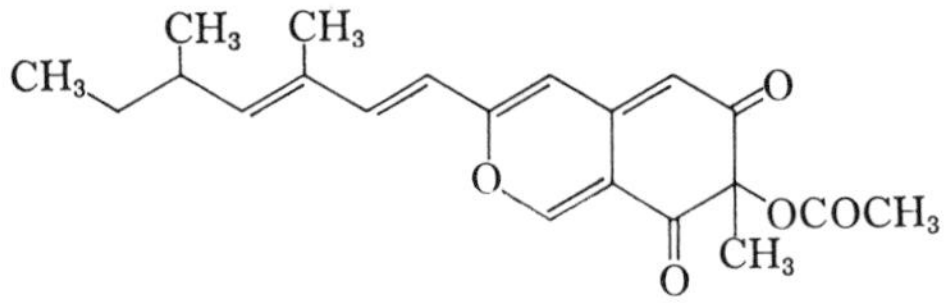

[203]
Sclerotiorin

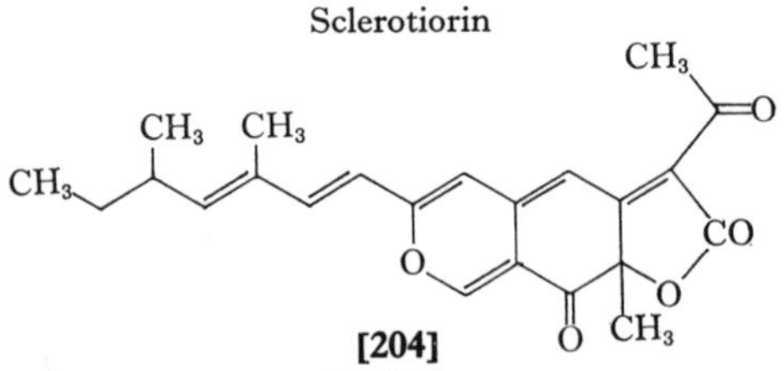

[204]
Rotiorin

85. A. J. Birch and F. W. Donovan, *Australian J. Chem.*, **6**, 360 (1953).
86. A. J. Birch, O. C. Musgrave, R. W. Rickards, and H. Smith, *J. Chem. Soc.*, **1959**, 3146.

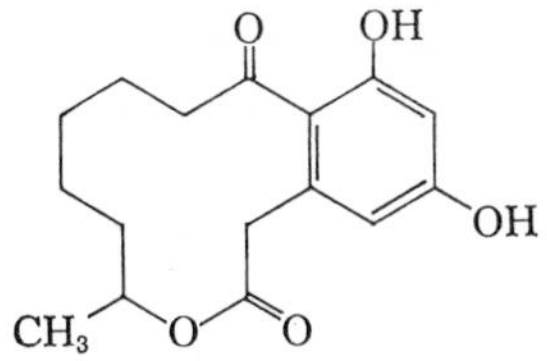

[205]

Curvularin

Certainly the most widespread of the acetogenins in this group, however, are the anthraquinones.[3] The same problem of origin exists here as in the naphthalenes, namely, the choice of cyclization of seven (**[206]** → **[207]**) or eight (**[208]** → **[209]**) acetate units.

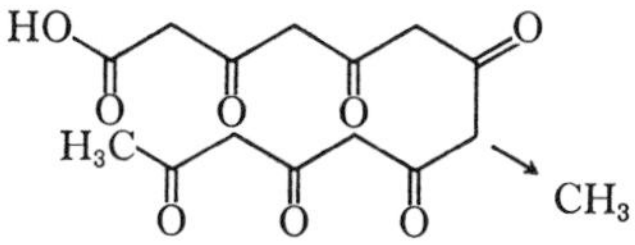

[206]

Heptaacetyl

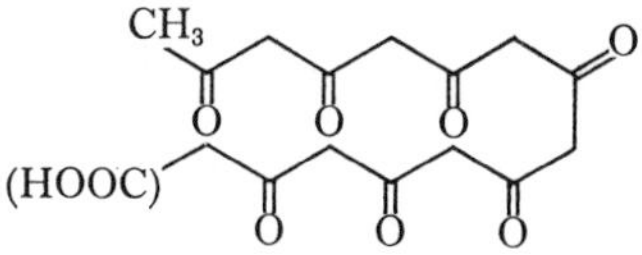

[208]

Octaacetyl

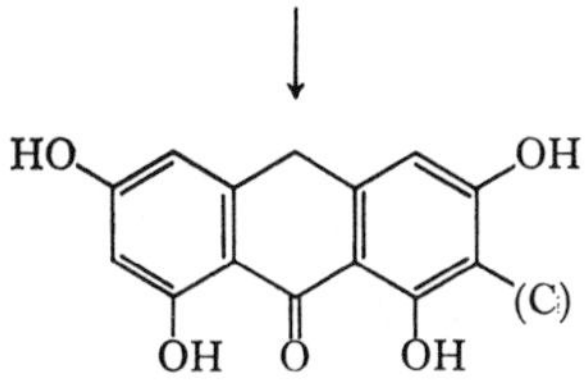

[207]

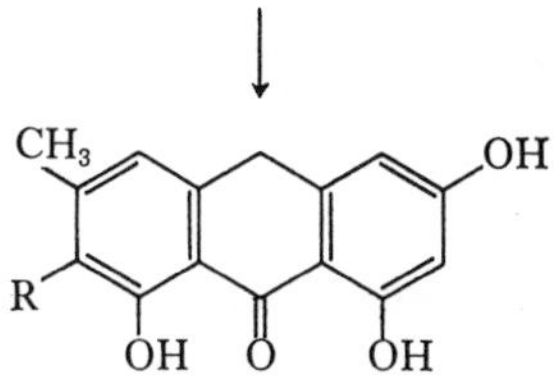

[209]

Emodin 9-anthrone (R = H)

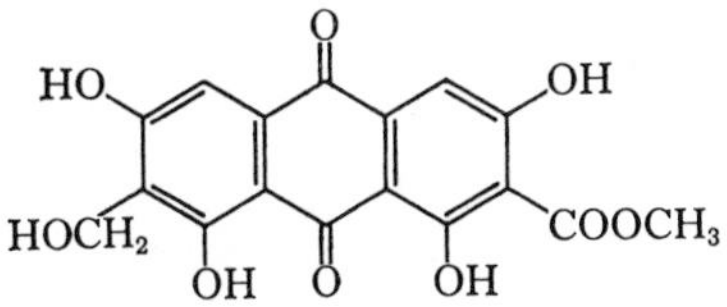

[210]

Rhodocladonic Acid

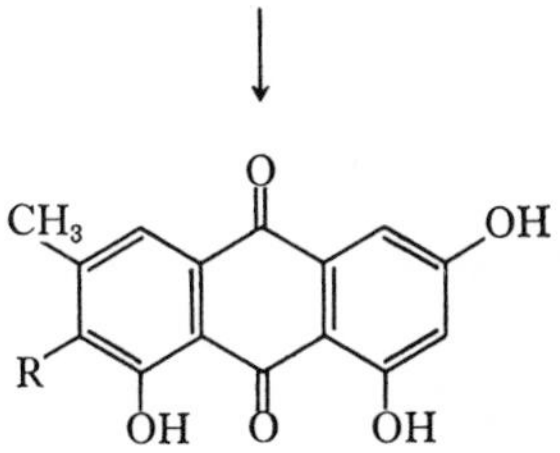

[211]

Emodin (R = H)
Endocrocin (R = COOH)

The 2-methyl group characteristic of so many anthraquinones would represent a methylation in the former case [206], whereas an anthraquinone with no carbon substituents could arise from an octa-acetyl cyclization and subsequent loss of the initial methyl by stepwise oxidation (vide infra) and ultimate decarboxylation. The two choices are theoretically distinguishable, as in the naphthalenes, by substitution patterns. The most common pattern appears to be the octaacetyl condensation to an anthrone that would be readily oxidized and decarboxylated to emodin ([211], frangula-emodin); significantly, the emodin 9-anthrone [209] has also been found in nature as have several other acetate-pattern anthrones. The anthraquinone retaining the carboxyl

[212]

[213]

Parietin (R = CH₃; R′ = CH₃)
Teloschistin (R = CH₂OH; R′ = CH₃)
Fallacinal (R = CHO; R′ = CH₃)
Parietinic Acid (R = COOH; R′ = CH₃)
Citrorosein (R = CH₂OH; R′ = H)
Emodic Acid (R = COOH; R′ = H)

Teak Constituents
(R = CH₃, CH₂OH,
CHO, COOH)

is endocrocin [211], found both in fungi and lichens. This mode of cyclization corresponds to path B for simple benzene derivatives and characterizes a large number of examples. In common with the path-B products, the emodin kind of anthraquinone also exhibits the same series of increasing oxidation of the sidechain as appears among the depsides and others, viz. the compounds [212] parietin (physcion), teloschistin, fallacinal, which are all found in one lichen, *Xanthoria fallax*, and parietinic acid [212] in another *Xanthoria* lichen. A similar series [213] is found in teakwood.[87]

Birch[88] has pointed out that different coiling of the octaacetyl chain ([215], with decarboxylation and one ketone reduction in each case) can produce either chrysophanol [214] or the phenanthraquinone

87. P. Rudman, *Chem. & Ind. (London)*, **1960**, 1356.
88. A. J. Birch and H. Smith, *Chem. Soc. (London)*, *Spec. Publ.*, **12**, 1 (1958).

denticulatol [216], which occur together in the same plant; denticulatol is the only phenanthraquinone found in nature to date.

The heptaacetyl chain condensation [206] to anthraquinones is less common; rhodocladonic acid [210] appears to be a bis-alkylated example. Twelve anthraquinones from the *Rubiaceae* are characterized by the pattern [217], some examples being shown here, but the lack of two "marker" oxygens in these cases makes them poor evidence to support this biogenetic mode.

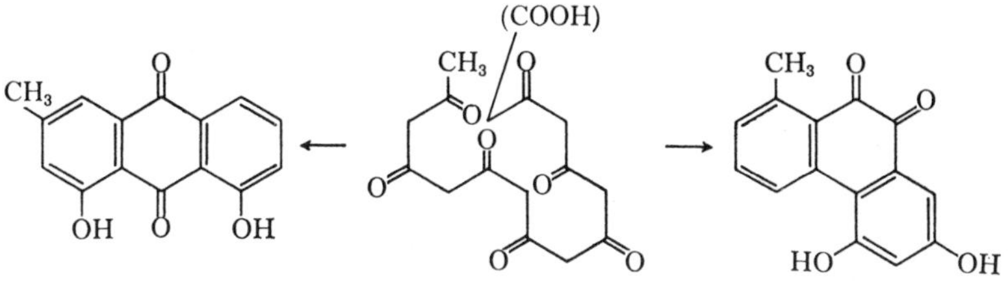

| [214] | [215] | [216] |
| Chrysophanol | | Denticulatol |

Among these anthraquinones are also found a most illuminating group of products resulting from oxidative coupling. The intermediate anthrones [209] of biogenesis are highly susceptible to oxidation at the 10-position, which is normally assumed to pick up oxygen and yield an anthraquinone. Should it instead undergo a dimeric coupling, it would yield a 10,10'-bis-anthrone. The pigments of *Hypericum performatum* provide a fine example of successive coupling stages in the protohypericins and hypericin [218].[89] Emodin anthrone [209] itself has also been isolated from the same plant and yields the first proto-hypericin on aeration in vitro! The sennidines [219] provide another example, this time of the first coupling stage. These dimeric anthra-quinone series recall the corresponding series of aphid pigments in the naphthalene section ([184]–[187]).

Shibata[90–92] has isolated nine such dimers (the skyrins [220]), mostly pigments of *Penicillium islandicum*, all of which are coupled at the

89. H. Brockmann, *Fortschr. Chem. Org. Naturstoffe*, **14**, 141 (1957).
90. S. Shibata, *Chem. Pharm. Bull. (Tokyo)*, **4**, 303 (1956); *ibid.*, **8**, 889 (1960).
91. S. Fujisi, S. Hishida, S. Shibata, and S. Matsueda, *Chem. & Ind. (London)*, **1961**, 1754.
92. S. Shibata and I. Kitagawa, *Chem. Pharm. Bull. (Tokyo)*, **8**, 884 (1960).

1-position.   A particularly interesting example from the point of view of intermediates in the biosynthetic process is the dimer rubroskyrin [221],[92] in which one can observe ketone reduction in the precursor without dehydration to an aromatic ring; the example is analogous to the cyclic ketone [120] of *Campnospermum* (Section 4-4) and the hydrated rings of xanthoaphin [186].

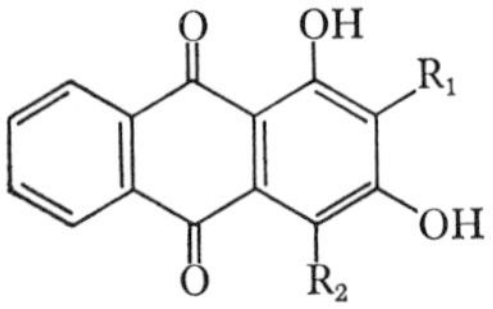

[217]

Xanthopurpurin ($R_1 = R_2 = H$)
Rubiadin ($R_1 = CH_3$; $R_2 = H$)
Lucidin ($R_1 = CH_2OH$; $R_2 = H$)
Anthragallol ($R_1 = OH$; $R_2 = H$)
Purpurin ($R_1 = H$; $R_2 = OH$)

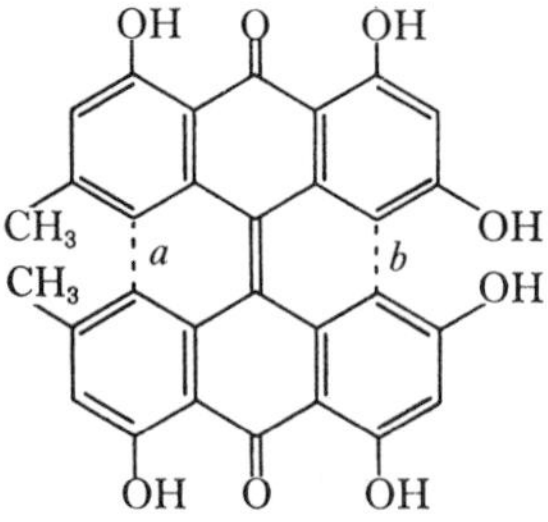

[218]

Protohypericin I (no bonds at *a* or *b*)
Protohypericin II (no bond at *a*; bond at *b*)
Hypericin (bonds at *a* and *b*)

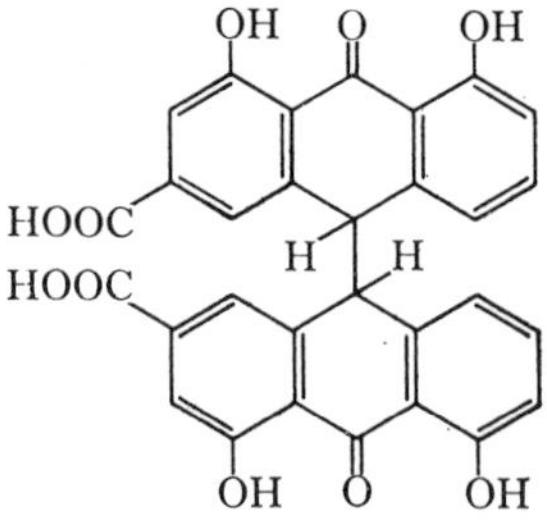

[219]

Sennidines A and B
(stereoisomers)

Several cases have recently been elucidated in which the intermediate anthrone is alkylated instead of oxidized at the 10-position. The examples to date are all C-glycosidations, as in the case of homonataloin [222].[93]   Another C-glycosidation, this time at a β-position, is evident in the insect pigment carminic acid [224],[94] which apparently

93. L. J. Haynes and J. L. Henderson, *Chem. & Ind.* (*London*), **1960**, 50.
94. M. A. Ali and L. J. Haynes, *J. Chem. Soc.*, **1959**, 1033.

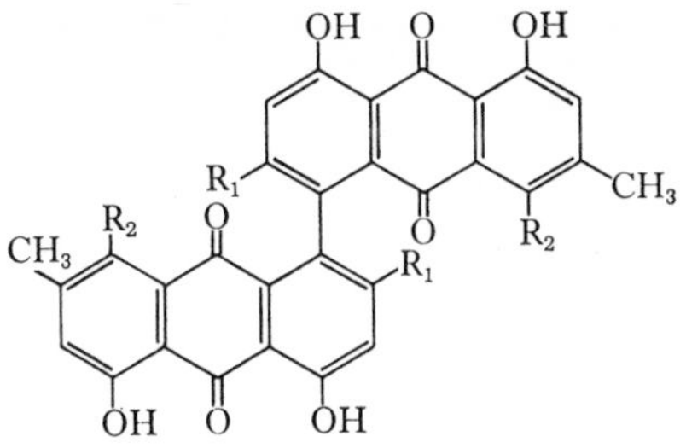

[220]

Skyrin (R_1 = OH; R_2 = H)
Iridoskyrin (R_1 = H; R_2 = OH)
Fusaroskyrin (R_1 = OCH$_3$; R_2 = OH)

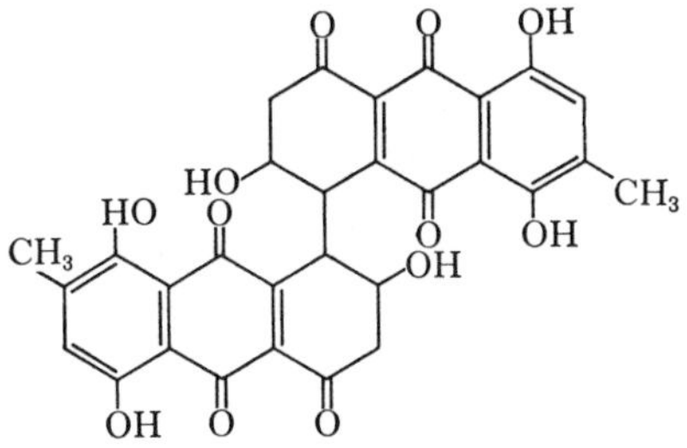

[221]
Rubroskyrin

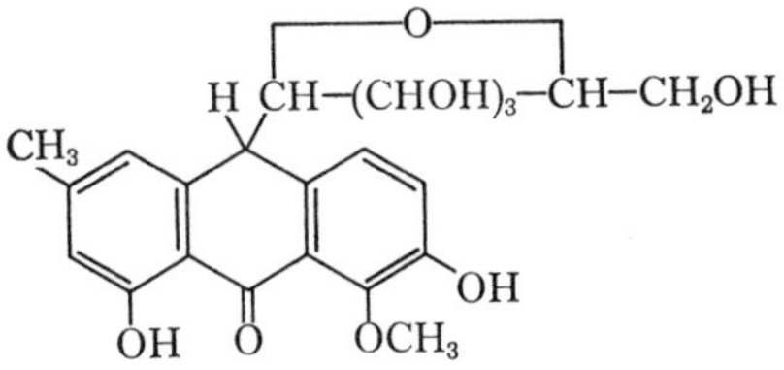

[222]
Homonataloin

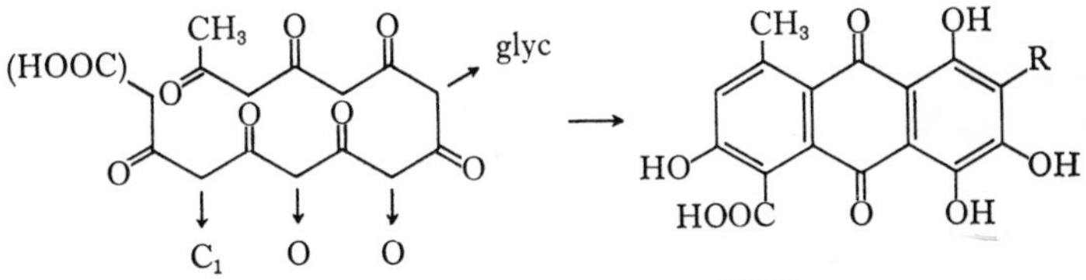

[223]　　　　　　　　**[224]**

Carminic Acid (R = —CH—(CHOH)$_3$—CH—CH$_2$OH)
Kermesic Acid (R = COCH$_3$)

arises by the uncommon condensation [223]; kermesic acid [224] is another insect pigment.

In order to examine the correlation of the 82 natural anthraquinones of known structure * with the acetate hypothesis, the assumption is made as before that one marker oxygen may be missing without impairing validity and that the other variants of Chapter 3 are also allowable. In these terms there are 51 (62 per cent) anthraquinones consistent with the hypothesis. Among the 40 anthraquinones found in lichens and fungi, however, 38 (95 per cent) are consistent and the other two are found in higher botanical orders of fungi. There seems here an implication that in the lower organisms the acetate biogenesis operates in a simple way, whereas in the higher plants it is either obscured or supplanted by other modes. As with the naphthoquinones, many anthraquinones that are inconsistent are found to have the A ring completely unsubstituted.

Derivatives of Nine- and Ten-Acetyl Units

Nine acetates comprise the chain that condenses to the quinones nalgiovensin and nalgiolaxin [225], early formulas for which were

[225]

Nalgiovensin (R = H)
Nalgiolaxin (R = H and Cl)

[226] (R = n-C$_3$H$_7$; R$_2$ = H)

[227] Solorinic Acid (R$_1$ = n-C$_5$H$_{11}$; R$_2$ = CH$_3$)

corrected by application of the acetate hypothesis.[95] The anthraquinones of the last section are generally formed by condensation analogous to the path-B (orsellinic acid type) in simple aromatics. Examples analogous to path-A (acylphloroglucinol) cyclization are apparent in the structures of the rhodocomatulins,[96] which are methyl ethers of [226], and solorinic acid [227].

* No O-glycosides or corresponding anthrones are included; dimers are counted once only, since in all cases both moieties are identical. Anthraquinones described in the following section are not included.

95. A. J. Birch and R. A. Massy-Westropp, *J. Chem. Soc.*, **1957**, 2215.
96. M. D. Sutherland and J. W. Wells, *Chem. & Ind. (London)*, **1959**, 291.

More complex examples are to be found in the "mycinone" antibiotics ([229]–[230]) from actinomycetes.[97] The nine cases presently known provide a satisfying set of variations on a single acetogenous theme [228], showing marker oxygens at all expected sites except one. The naphthacene skeleton of these antibiotics is also found in the tetracycline compounds [232] from streptomyces. The structure recently assigned to terramycin-X [233][98] may provide the clue since, except for the dimethylamine group, it represents a clear

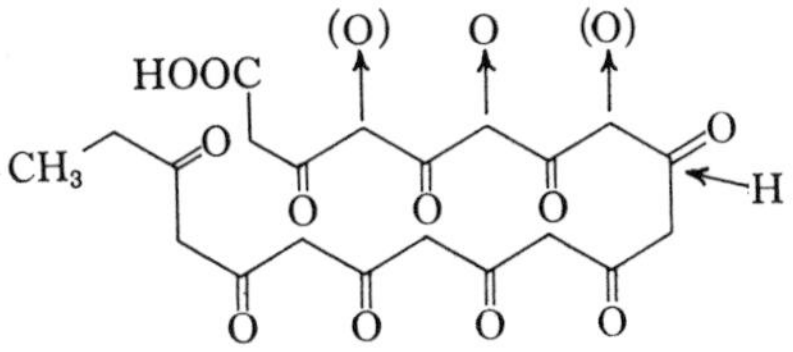

[228]

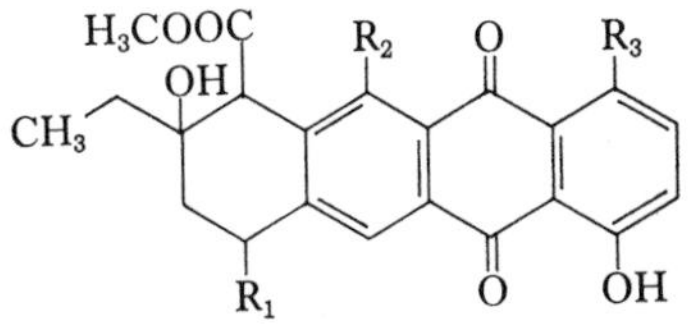

[229]

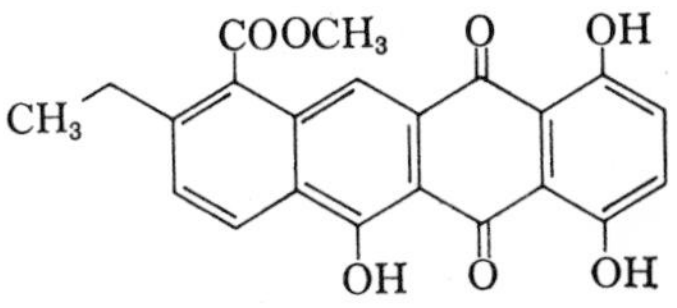

[230]

η-Pyrromycinone

	R₁	R₂	R₃
Aklavinone	OH	H	H
Deoxyaklavinone	H	H	H
δ-Rhodomycinone	H	OH	H
ε-Rhodomycinone	OH	OH	H
δ-Pyrromycinone	H	H	OH
ε-Pyrromycinone	OH	H	OH
δ-Isorhodomycinone	H	OH	OH
ε-Isorhodomycinone	OH	OH	OH

decaacetyl condensation product as indicated in [231] (ketone groups are all shown in their ketonic tautomers). The other tetracyclines all possess carboxamido groupings in place of the chain-terminal acetyl

97. W. D. Ollis and I. O. Sutherland, Ref. 17, Chap. 13.
98. F. A. Hochstein, M. S. von Wittenau, F. W. Tanner, and K. Murai, *J. Am. Chem. Soc.*, **82**, 5934 (1960).

group of terramycin X; this can arise by successive oxidations of the α-methyl. The added substituents at methylene sites are the major cause of variation in the tetracyclines [232]; 6-demethyltetracycline is, however, largely free of these and so may be considered the nearest to the parent acetogenin. Glutamic acid chain initiation (in ring A) has also been considered to explain the source of the dimethylamino and carboxamido functions (Section 5–2).

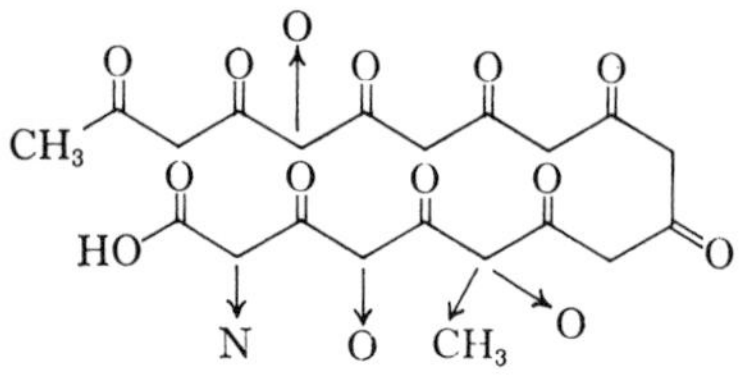

[231]

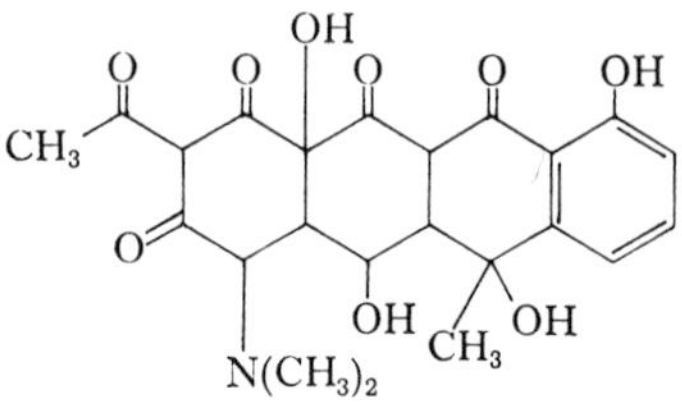

[233]

Terramycin X

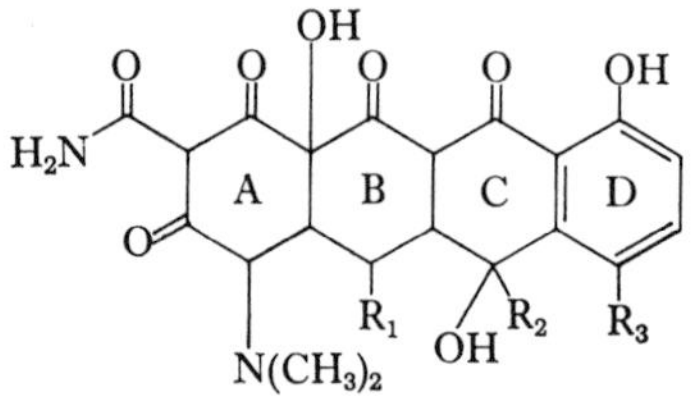

[232]

Tetracyclines

Terramycin (R_1 = OH; R_2 = CH_3; R_3 = H)
Aureomycin (R_1 = H; R_2 = CH_3; R_3 = Cl)
6-Demethyltetracycline (R_1 = R_2 = R_3 = H)

Resistomycin [235][99] is a very complex example of the potentialities implicit in the decaacetyl precursor, which may be dissected as shown [234] with perfect correlation of substituents; however, the folding [236] that produces siphulin [237][100] from a dodecaacetyl chain is apparently unique. The latter compound may arise from a chain terminating in a medium-length preformed fatty acid, as from octanoic

99. H. Brockmann, quoted in Ref. 3, page 266.
100. T. Bruun, *Tetrahedron Letters*, **1960**, 1.

acid extended by eight malonates. It is noteworthy that this is the *only* example of a clear polyacetate chain nominally longer than ten acetyl units. It is quite likely that this represents an upper limit of size for the acetogenins.

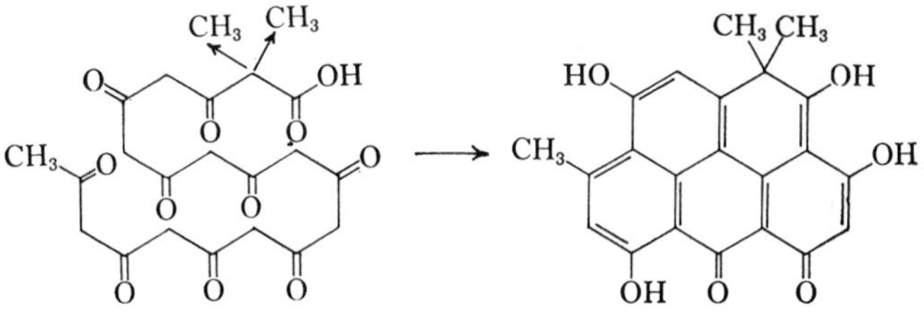

[234]

[235]

Resistomycin

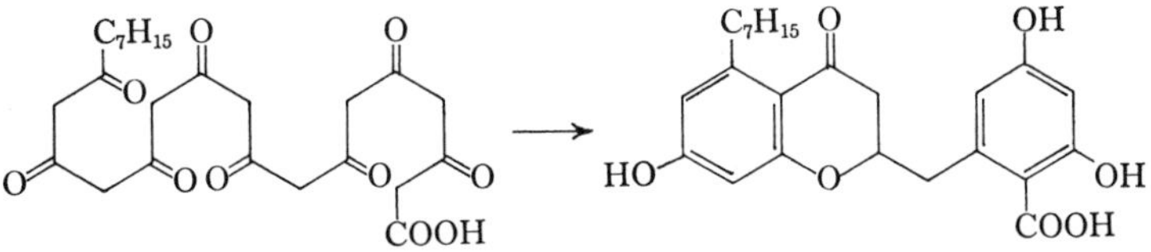

[236]

[237]

Siphulin

4–6 MISCELLANEOUS COMPOUNDS

Many natural products exist that are structurally too simple to afford meaningful inferences of biogenesis. Among these may be included the simple aromatics with no sidechains or single sidechains of one or two carbons, such as the various hydroxy benzoic acids, the cresols, and methyl ethers of these. In one case, ageratochromene [238], isoprenylation of a simple ether is evident, whereas in the structure of bergenin [239][101] the alkylation of a gallic acid by a hexose appears the simplest biogenetic explanation; in the latter case it is likely that cyclization occurs internally on a 2-gallate ester of the hexose. Such a cyclization on the enol gallate of HOOC—CH$_2$—CH(COOH)—CH$_2$—CO—COOH (from pyruvate intervention in the citric acid cycle?) could similarly produce chebulic acid,[102] but a biogenesis linked to brevifolin

101. J. E. Hay and L. J. Haynes, *J. Chem. Soc.*, **1958**, 2231.
102. O. T. Schmidt, Ref. 17, Chap. 8; E. Haslam, Chap. 7.

([240]–[244]) is probably more reasonable[103] in view of their isolation from similar tannin sources. The tannins include oxidative dimers of gallic acid, such as ellagic acid [240] and a number of others, the biosynthesis of which from shikimic acid seems clear.[102] Brevifolin carboxylic acid (and by decarboxylation, brevifolin) presumably arises

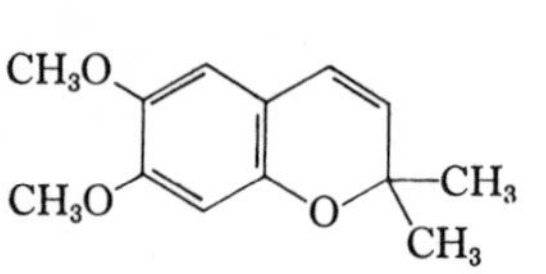

[238]
Ageratochromene

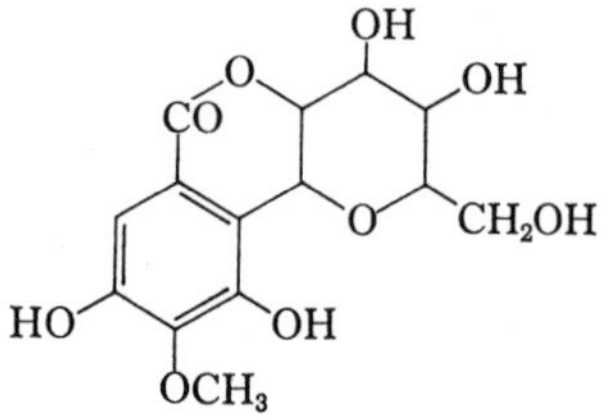

[239]
Bergenin

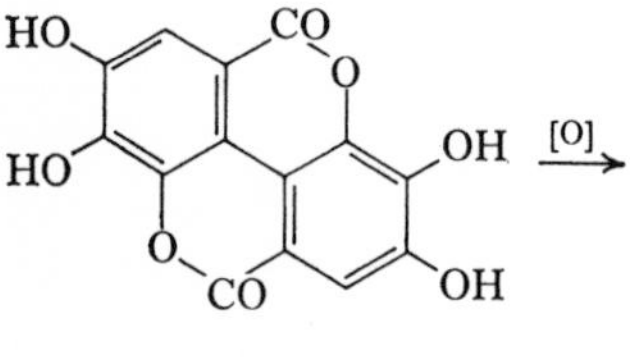

[240]
Ellagic Acid

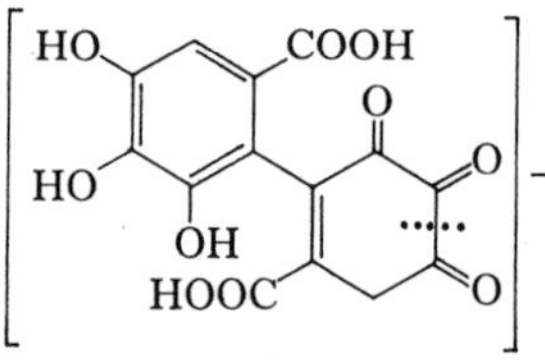

[241]

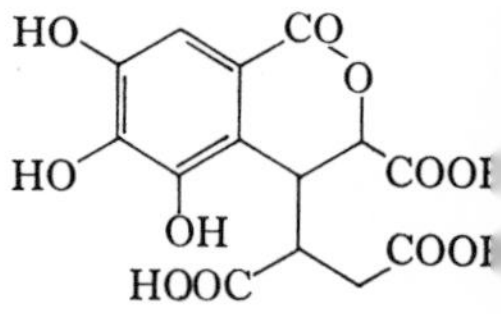

[242]
Chebulic Acid

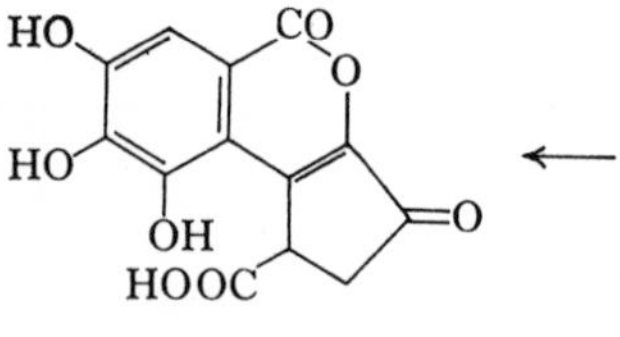

[244]
Brevifolin Carboxylic Acid

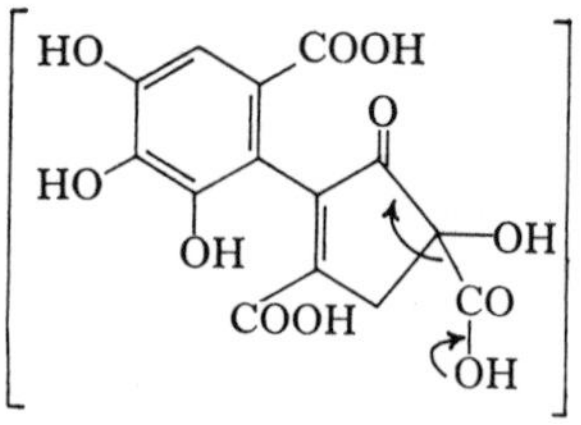

[243]

by a benzilic acid type of rearrangement ([241]–[243]) on ellagic acid. It has been suggested that chebulic acid [242] also arises from [241] by hydrolytic cleavage at the bond indicated ($\cdots$).[102]

103. H. R. V. Arnstein and R. Bentley, *Biochem. J.*, **54**, 493, 508 (1953); **62**, 403 (1956).

There are a number of simple furans and pyrans that are probably formed from sugars, such as kojic acid [103] and rubiginic acid [245], furfural or 5-hydroxymethyl-2-furoic acid.

The nonterpenoid cyclopentanes present an interesting group, since ordinary cyclization of a polyacetyl chain as described above must give an even-membered ring. Although it is by no means necessary to assume a common origin for all the cyclopentanes, some at least may derive by operation of the oxidative coupling variant on an open-chain polyacetic acid, as symbolized in [246] → [247]. The generalized product [247] could also be methylated, oxidized, or chlorinated at

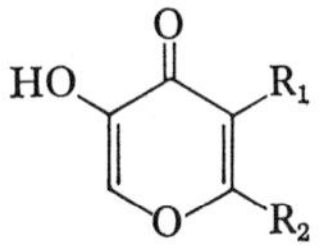

[245]
Kojic Acid (R_1 = H; R_2 = CH_2OH)
Rubiginic Acid (R_1 = OH, R_2 = COOH)

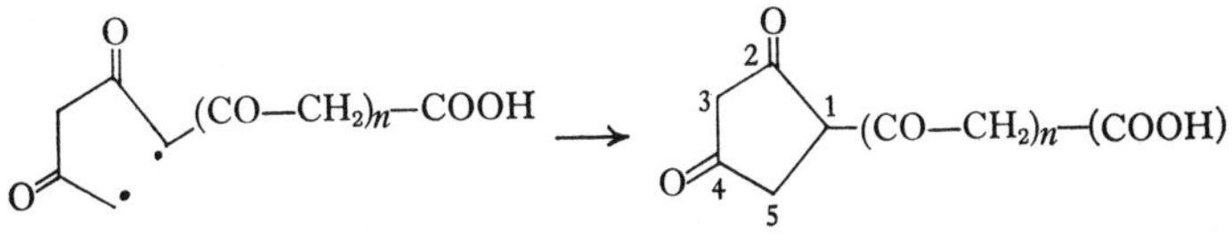

[246] → [247]

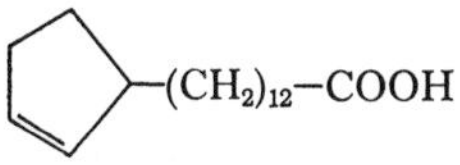

[248]
Chaulmoogric Acid

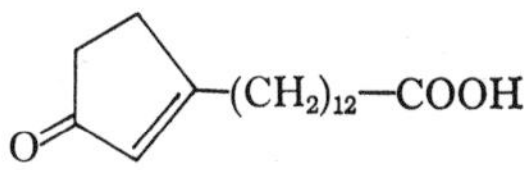

[249]
Ketochaulmoogric Acid

positions 1, 3, 5; this product suggests an odd-numbered sidechain for acids, which is characteristic of the nine acids of the chaulmoogric acid [248] family, two of which also have ring ketones, as in keto-chaulmoogric acid [249]. Caldariomycin [250] and 2,4,4-trimethyl-cyclopentanone are consistent chlorinated and methylated derivatives of the simplest cyclopentanones; cinerolone [251] also conforms but the related pyrethrolone [251] is less good.[104] Jasmone [252] and terrein [253] are by contrast more consistent with a cyclizing of keto rather than methylene carbons.

104. L. Crombie and S. H. Harper, *Chem. & Ind.* (*London*), **1958**, 1001.

A number of cyclopentanes not included here are considered terpenoid in origin after the pattern of asperuloside. Other compounds omitted on the same criterion include the C_{10} to C_{15} tropolones, such as thujaplicin and nootkatin, and furans, such as perilla-ketone and ngaione. Quassin was also omitted as a presumed terpene in origin although a coupling of two C_{10} phenols has been suggested.[105]

In quite a different vein is the biosynthesis ([254]–[257]) suggested for calythrone [257],[32] which is also applicable to the newly discovered

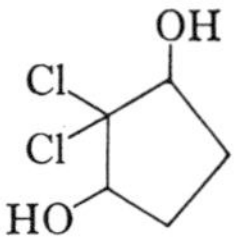

[250]

Caldariomycin

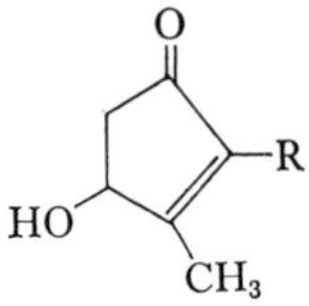

[251]

Cinerolone (R = /\\/\\/CH₃)

Pyrethrolone (R = /\\/\\/\\CH₂)

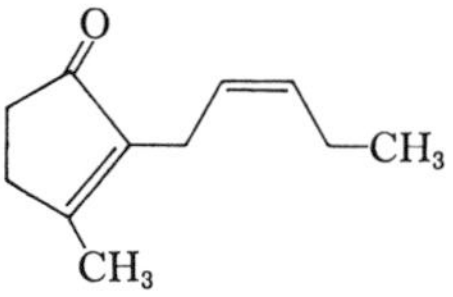

[252]

Jasmone

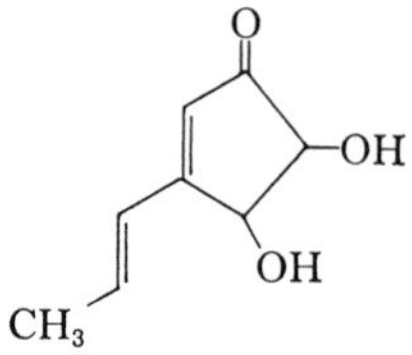

[253]

Terrein

cyclopentanone hop constituents such as hulupone [258][106]; the resemblance of these compounds to the acylphloroglucinols dictates their origin from such a ketone [254] by rearrangement. The recently announced structures of linderone [259] and methyl-linderone[107] are probably the flavonoid analogs of such a ring contraction.

The lichen di- and triacids[11] with long sidechains appear to arise by intervention of long-chain fatty acids in the citric acid cycle (cf.

105. Z. Valenta, S. Papadopoulos, and C. Podesva, *Tetrahedron*, **15**, 100 (1961).
106. R. Stevens and D. Wright, *Proc. Chem. Soc.*, **1960**, 417.
107. A. K. Kiang, H. H. Lee, and K. Y. Sim, *Proc. Chem. Soc.*, **1961**, 455.

norcaperatic acid **[260]**) and the lichen lactone-acids, such as protolichesterinic acid **[261]**, are probably simple congeners of these or variants of the tetronic acid route discussed in Section 5–4. The eight tetronic acids of *Penicillium* fungi (cf. examples **[262]**) also suggest acetate origin

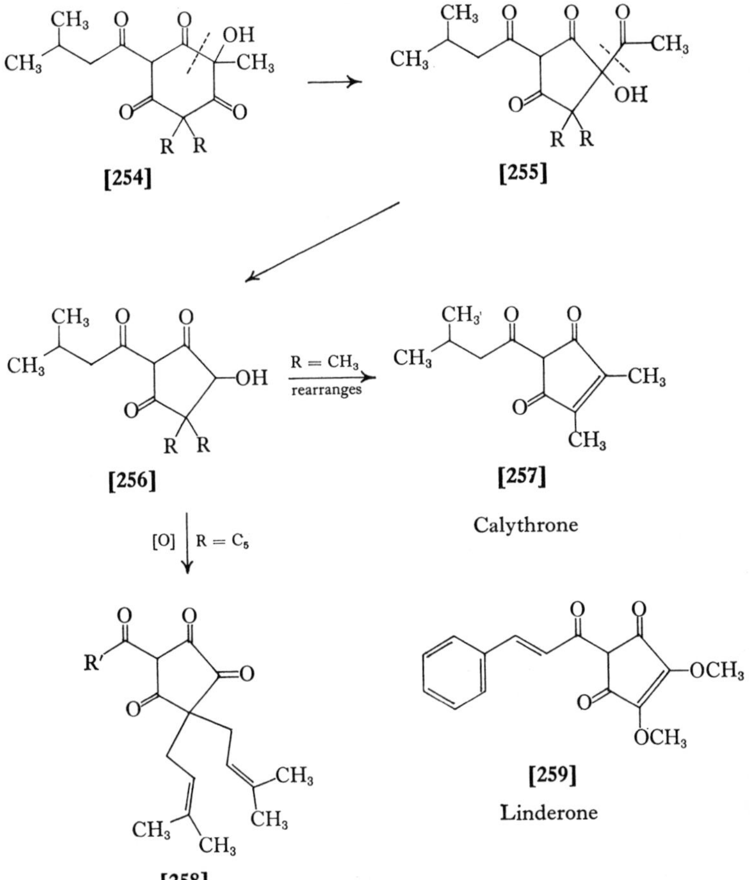

[254]

[255]

[256] R = CH₃ rearranges **[257]**

Calythrone

[O] R = C₅

[258]

Hulupone (R′ = isobutyl)
Adhulupone (R′ = sec-butyl)
Cohulupone (R′ = isopropyl)

[259]

Linderone

on casual inspection, and this has been partially confirmed by experiment (vide infra).

The miscellaneous group also includes three dicinnamoyl methanes (e.g., curcumin **[263]**), which are almost certainly of a simple ϕ-C₃ origin, and the nonterpene tropolones for which several biogenetic schemes have been suggested; direct evidence is now available on these tropolones, and their biosynthesis is outlined in Section 5–4.

The high correlation with the acetate hypothesis indicated by Table 4–6 suggests that a number of the miscellaneous, more complex structures may be merely more obscure acetogenins. The ring-oxygen pattern of brazilin [265], for example, suggests biogenesis from [264]. The resemblance of brazilin to the 4-aryl-coumarins (page 40) has prompted similar biogenetic proposals, i.e., through two

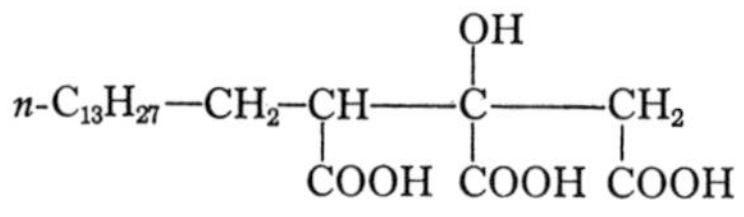

$$n\text{-}C_{13}H_{27}\text{---}CH_2\text{-}CH\overset{\overset{\displaystyle OH}{|}}{\text{---}}\overset{|}{C}\text{----}CH_2$$
$$\underset{COOH\ \ COOH\ \ COOH}{}$$

[260]

Norcaperatic Acid

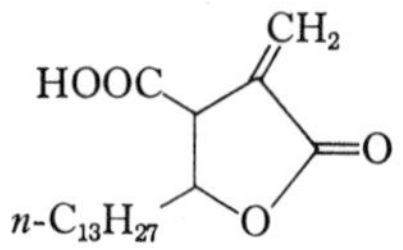

[261]

Protolichesterinic Acid

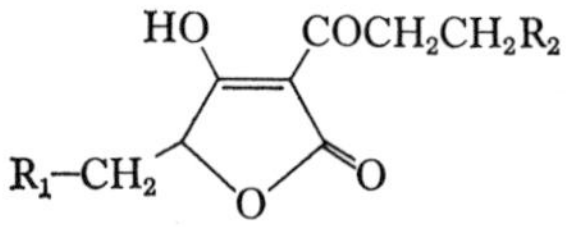

[262]

Tetronic Acids

Carolic Acid (R₁ = H; R₂ = CH₂OH)
Carolinic Acid (R₁ = H; R₂ = COOH)
Terrestric Acid (R₁ = H; R₂ = CH(OH)CH₂CH₃)
Carlosic Acid (R₁ = COOH; R₂ = CH₃)
Carlic Acid (R₁ = COOH; R₂ = CH₂OH)

successive migrations of phenyl (a variant from isoflavone [267] via [268] → [269] is shown below [108,109]) or by cyclization and methylenation of a resorcinol cinnamate [266]. All proposals suggest ring A is acetogenous and ring B is derived from shikimic acid.

Since those miscellaneous compounds isolated from fungi should be especially suspect of acetate derivation, the remarkable streptomyces derivative aureothin [270] [110] is probably an acetogenin but the structure

108. W. B. Whalley, *Chem. & Ind.* (*London*), **1956**, 1049; H. Grisebach, Ref. 17, Chap. 3.

109. O. A. Stamm, H. Schmid, and J. Büchi, *Helv. Chim. Acta*, **41**, 4006 (1958).

110. Y. Hirata, H. Nakata, and K. Yamada, *J. Chem. Soc.* (*Japan*), **79**, 1390 (1958).

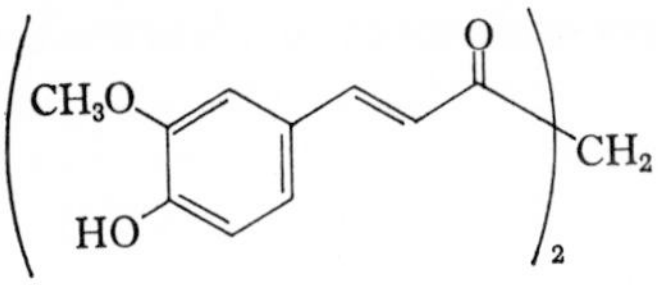

[263]

Curcumin

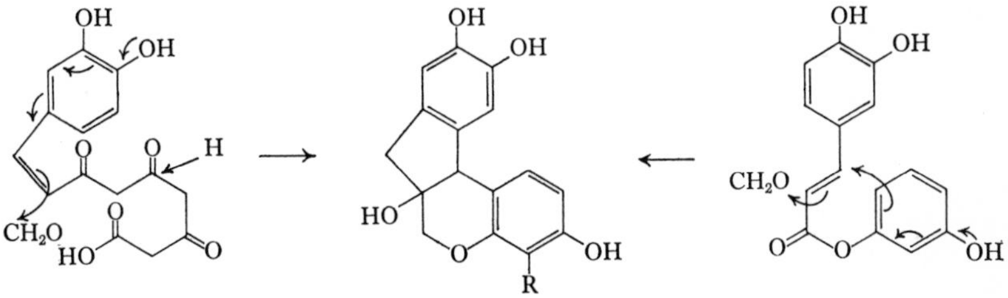

[264]   **[265]**   **[266]**

Hematoxylin (R = OH)
Brazilin (R = H)

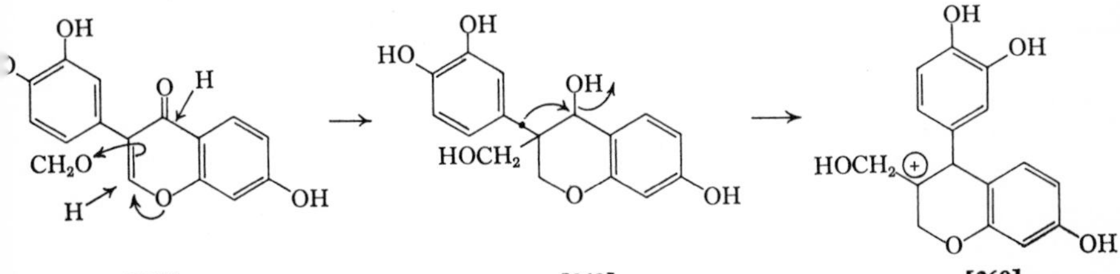

[267]   **[268]**   **[269]**

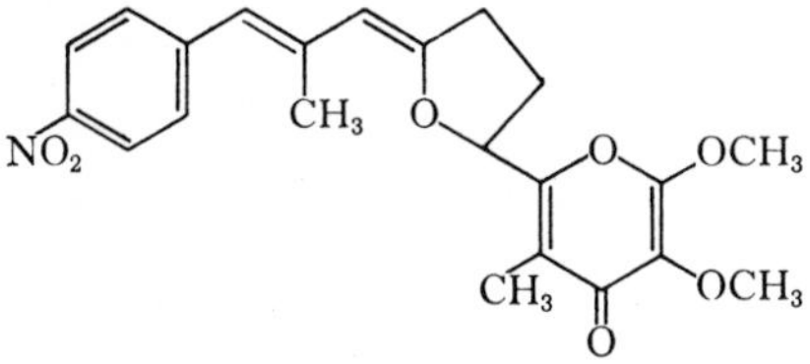

[270]   **[271]**

Aureothin   Miroestrol

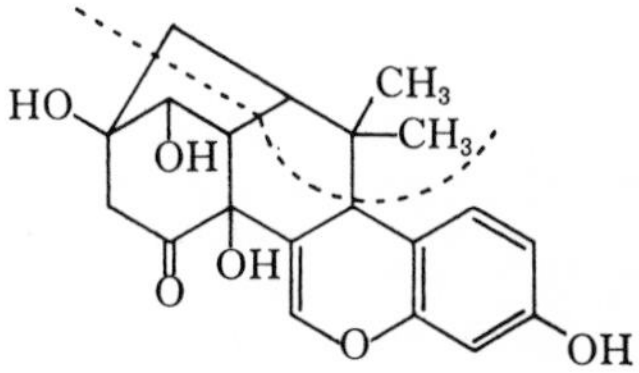

is not consonant with the discussion of Chapter 3.   A small number of other complex structures exist that do not yield to structural dissection in the foregoing manner, that is, miroestrol [271],[111] trachelogenin [272],[112] alternaric acid [273],[113] morellin [274],[114] and the closely related guttiferins,[115] chartreusin [275],[116] and egonol [276].[117]   A benzo-

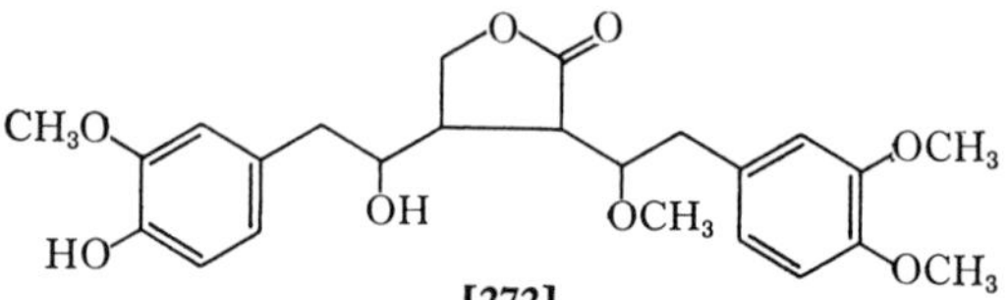

[272]

Trachelogenin

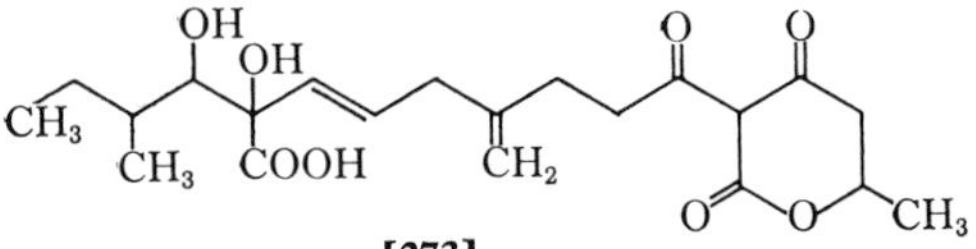

[273]

Alternaric Acid

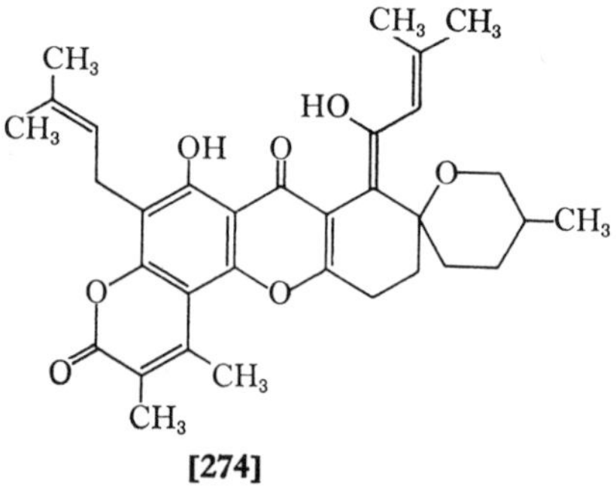

[274]

Morellin

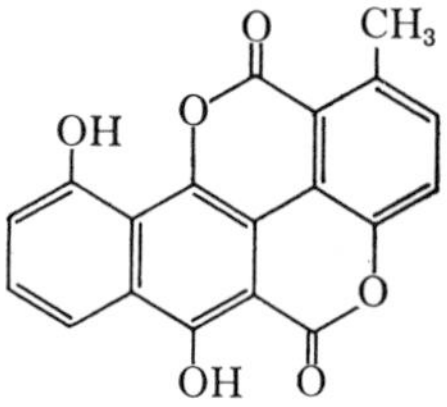

[275]

Chartreusin
Aglycone

111. D. G. Bounds and G. S. Pope, *J. Chem. Soc.*, **1960**, 3696.
112. T. Takano, *Yakagaku Zasshi*, **79**, 1449 (1959).
113. J. R. Bartels-Keith and J. F. Grove, *Proc. Chem. Soc.*, **1959**, 398.
114. D. V. K. Murthy and P. L. N. Rao, *Experientia*, **17**, 445 (1961).
115. K. V. N. Rao and P. L. N. Rao, *Experientia*, **17**, 213 (1961).
116. E. Simonitsch, W. Eisenhuth, O. A. Stamm, and H. Schmid, *Helv. Chim. Acta*, **43**, 58 (1960).
117. S. Kawai, T. Nakamura, and N. Sugiyama, *Ber.*, **72**, 1146 (1939).

furan **[278]** structurally related to egonol was recently isolated from yeast[118] and may be an acylphloroglucinol from a phenylacetic-terminal chain (2-hydroxyphenylacetic acid is in fact a natural compound) or, essentially equivalently, an isoflavonoid from which carbon 2 is lost, as it is in ononetin **[101]**. The suggestion[119] that it arises by an oxidative coupling between phenol and a tetrahydroxycinnamic acid (at the α-position) with subsequent decarboxylation seems less in accord with the precedents discussed this far. The structural relation of miroestrol **[271]** to an isoprenylated isoflavonoid has been pointed out.[120] The biogenesis of the *Chaetomium* diacid **[279]**[121] from phenylpyruvic and

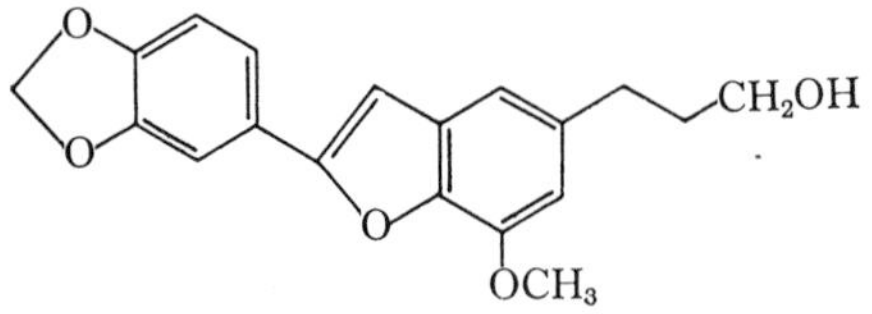

[276]
Egonol

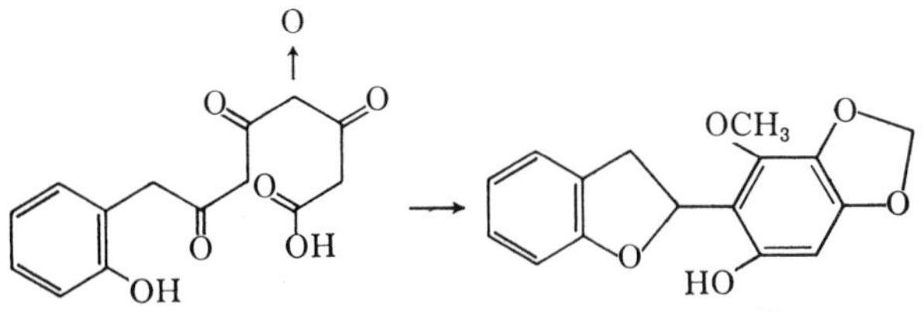

[277]   **[278]**

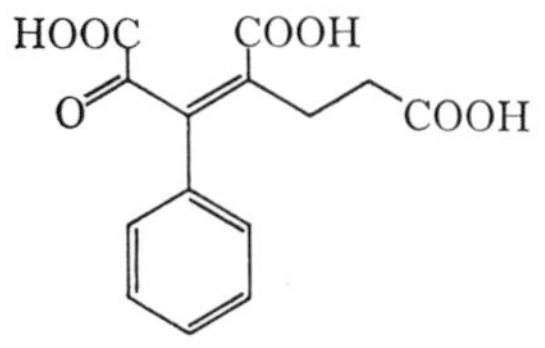

[279]

118. M. A. P. Meisinger, F. A. Kuehl, E. L. Rickes, N. G. Brink, K. Folkers, M. Forbes, F. Zilliken, and P. Gyorgy, *J. Am. Chem. Soc.*, **81**, 4979 (1959).
119. Ref. 2, Chap. 18b.
120. W. D. Ollis, Ref. 4, Chap. 12.
121. D. H. Johnson, A. Robertson, and W. B. Whalley, *J. Chem. Soc.*, **1953**, 2429.

α-ketoglutaric acids by an aldol reaction is likely, and, in view of the precedent for initial esterification followed by internal aldol cyclization which is implied by the monascin-type pigments and the 4-aryl-coumarins, the precursor may be the ketoadipyl enol ester of phenyl-pyruvic acid.

The actidione antibiotics ([280]–[283]) from *Streptomyces* appear to arise by an acetate route, and the nine known structures[2] should be capable of providing a clue; streptimidone [281] is the only non-carbocyclic member, and its origin from acetate may well be as indicated [280] with cyclization of the glutarimide in another internal aldol reminiscent of rotiorin [204]. All members of the group probably share a common biogenesis with only superficial variation.

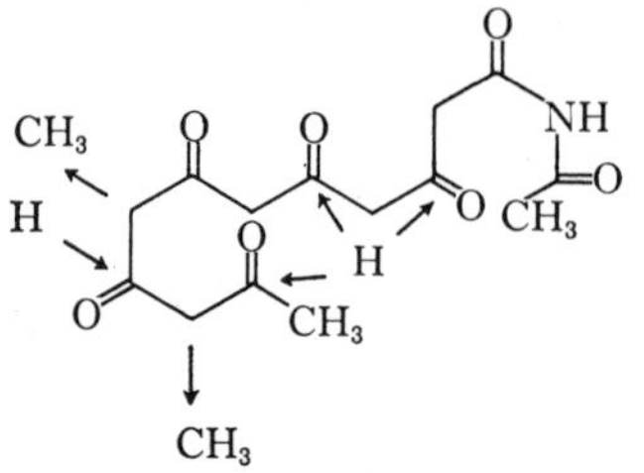

[280]

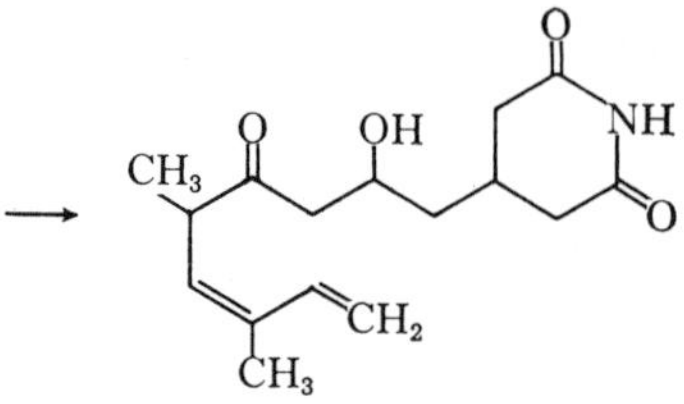

[281]
Streptimidone

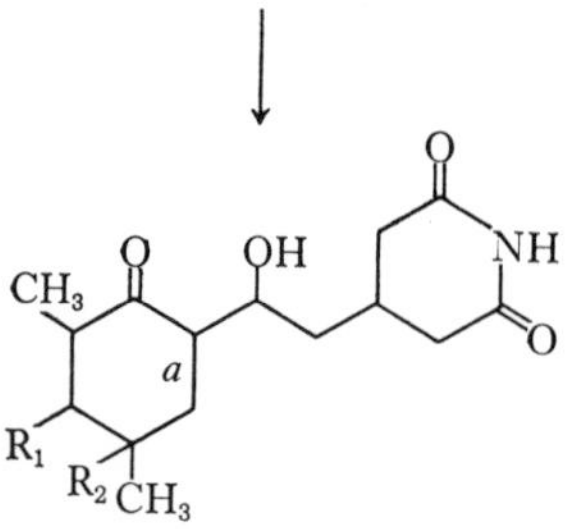

[282]
Actidione (R₁ = R₂ = H)
Acetoxy-actidione (R₁ = H; R₂ = OAc)
Streptovitacin A (R = H; R₂ = OH)
Streptovitacin B (R₁ = OH; R₂ = H)
Inactone (R₁ = R₂ = H; double bond at *a*)

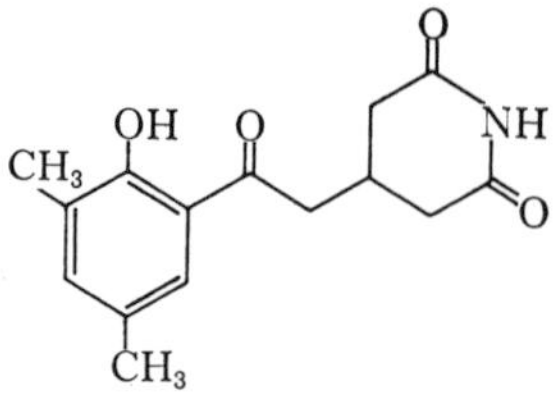

[283]
Actiphenol

4–7 CORRELATION AND COMMENTARY

In order to take a broad view of the acetate hypothesis, it will be valuable to enlist a summary of all natural products that are reasonable candidates for examination by the method of structure comparison.

In such a summary it is necessary to exclude molecules too small to have inferential utility as well as compounds of other biogenetic families, i.e., alkaloids and other nitrogenous natural products, carbohydrates, terpenoid skeletons, and the simple shikimic-derived acids (see footnotes to Table 4–6). Also, the fatty acids, musks, and long-chain linear acetylenes are excluded since, although they are all almost certainly acetogenins, their structures provide no oxygen-marked sites for deductive purposes.

With these exclusions made, the remaining families of compounds are presented in Table 4–6: the extent of the support their structures afford the acetate hypothesis may be seen in the correlation column, the data for which are discussed in the preceding sections. The breakdown of compounds is somewhat expanded from that of the preceding sections and follows structural lines more closely (the same breakdown is used in the survey list in the Appendix). The total figures are also separated into compounds found in microorganisms and those in higher biological forms, although these figures must be taken as slightly less reliable (since some compounds appear both in fungi and higher plants, the sum of the two columns will be greater than the single total of compounds). It should be observed that, although compounds are each taken as units in the correlation percentages, some compounds afford more correlative support than others, since they are larger molecules; it is generally true in fact that correlation with the hypothesis is higher among these more complex molecules, a fact that increases the value of the correlations as evidence for the validity of the acetate hypothesis.

In summary, it may be said that structure comparisons can provide a remarkably strong measure of support for the existence and the generality of the acetate biogenetic routes. The wide variety of structural types available through operation of this essentially simple hypothesis is quite remarkable, and it can often be observed in a single species that several modes of polyacetate cyclization occur together. Coto bark contains the phenylcoumalin paracotoin [6] as well as the benzophenone protocotoin [67], whereas *Pinus cembra* produces a methyl ether of the stilbene pinosylvin [154] as well as the flavone chrysin [77]. In both cases the same initial polyacetyl chain is utilized; other examples are common, many mentioned above.

Table 4–6 also points up some interesting differences in the operation of acetate and shikimic acid biogenetic routes between microorganisms and more complex biological systems (most examples of which here are higher plants). Thus the ϕ-C_3 units from shikimic acid (flavonoids, coumarins, stilbenes, etc.) are exceedingly rare among microbial metabolites, as are acylphloroglucinols and benzophenones of shikimic origin;

Table 4–6 *Correlation of*

Structural group	No. of examples	Consistency with acetate hypothesis	Consistency of ϕ-rings with shiki-mic origin (where applicable)	Isopr· group· fused
1. Macrolides	12	9(75)		
2. ϕ-C$_2$ compounds[a]	13		7(54)	
3. ϕ-C$_3$ compounds[b]	117		108(92)	
4. Coumarins[c]	85			6
5. Terphenyls and pulvic acids	16		12(75)	
6. Other ϕ-C$_n$ compounds[d]	41	36(88)	28/29(97)[d]	
7. Acetophenones and phloroglucinols[e]	66	58(88)		2
8. Benzophenones[f]	10	7(70)	7/8(88)[f]	
9. Xanthones[f,g]	24	22(92)[c]	3/11(27)[f]	
10. Flavonoids[h]	228	209(92)	215(94)	1
11. Isoflavonoids[h,i]	42	40(95)	23(55)	1
12. Rotenoids[h]	14	14(100)	0	1
13. Depsides and depsidones[j]	57	55(97)		
14. Other orcinol derivatives[k]; compounds of ⌬C—C	64	47(73) 47/51(92)[k]		1
15. Stilbenes and ϕ-C$_2$-ϕ	17	15(88)	15(88)	
16. Naphthalenes and naphthoquinones	50	26(52)		
17. Anthraquinones and bisanthraquinones	98	66(67)		
18. Other polycyclic aromatics[l]	24	24(100)	1/1(100)	
19. Cyclopentanes	26	0	2/2(100)	
20. Tetronic acids, tropolones, lichen polyacids and lactoneacids	32			
21. Miscellaneous[m]	27	3		
Total examples	1063			17
Acetate correlation[n]	800	631(79%)		
Acetate correlation corrected [n,o]	734	628(86%)		
Shikimic correlation [p]	498		421(85%)	

The numbers in parentheses are percentage correlations. Excluded from the table are benzenoid compounds and simple furans and pyrans of seven or less skeletal carbons as well as simple oxidative dimers of these, such as ellagic acid and phoenicin. However, all nonterpenoid cyclopentanes and tetronic acids are included (some are smaller than C$_7$). Where numbers are omitted, the matter is discussed in detail in the appropriate preceding section. Discussion of chlorine and isoprenoid substitution follows this table.

[a] Excludes acetophenones (group 7); includes tropic acid **[99]**.
[b] Includes lignanes as their separate ϕ-C$_3$ units (Section 4–2).
[c] Includes all 3- and 4-substituted coumarins except the isoflavonoids.
[d] Includes ageratochromene **[238]** and aureothin **[270]**.
[e] Includes 2-methylchromones, muellitol **[63]** and the compounds of Section 4–3 generally; excludes rottlerin **[83]** and isorottlerin (group 10).
[f] Several benzophenones and xanthones without shikimic-derived terminals, but acetate throughout (cf. lichexanthone), are included but excluded from the shikimic-origin correlation; see Section 4–3.

ine-ning unds	Microorganisms only			Higher plants and animals		
	No. of examples	Consistency with acetate hypothesis	Consistency of ϕ-rings with shikimic origin (where applicable)	No. of examples	Consistency with acetate hypothesis	Consistency of ϕ-rings with shikimic origin (where applicable)
	12	9(75)		0	0	0
	7		3(43)	8		5(62)
	2		2(100)	117		112(96)
	1			84		
	16		12(75)	0		
	3[d]	2(67)	2(67)	38	34(89)	26/26(100)
	10	10(100)		56	48(86)	
	3	1(33)		7	6(86)	7(100)
	13	11(85)		11	11(100)	3(27)
	0			228	209(92)	215(94)
	0			42	40(95)	23(55)
	0			14	14(100)	0
	57	55(97)		0		
	33	28(85)		35	23(66)	
		28/29(97)[k]			23/26(88)[k]	
	0			17	15(88)	15(88)
	14	5(36)		39	21(54)	
	48	46(96)		54	24(44)	
	23	23(100)		1	1(100)	1(100)
	3	0		23	0	
	32			0		
	15	3		12	0	
	291			786		
	234	193(82%)		577	446(77%)	
	212	190(90%)		533	446(84%)	
	28		19(68%)	471		407(86%)

[g] Includes quaternary coumaranones like the griseofulvins; the acetate consistency is taken for B rings only as in Section 4–3.

[h] See notes with Table 4–3.

[i] Includes angolensin [101] and ononetin [101].

[j] Includes picrolichenic acid and geodoxin [191] as well as the related benzfurans discussed with the depsidones (Chart III).

[k] Includes bergenin [239], chebulic acid [242], and the several tocopherols [142] and coenzymes Q [143]; a second acetate correlation is given excluding these.

[l] Includes the tetracyclines [232] as correlating consistently.

[m] Includes asterric acid [190], the only natural diphenylether.

[n] Excludes groups 2 through 5 and 20.

[o] Excludes groups 19 and 21 and includes only the second correlation of group 14 (note k).

[p] Excludes groups 1, 7, 13, 14, 16, 17, 20, and 21 and inapplicable compounds elsewhere as noted (cf. note f).

the benzophenones in fungi apparently arise entirely from acetate units without shikimic-derived terminals in the precursor chain. Most metabolites of the lower organisms appear to originate by path-B (orsellinic) cyclizations of simple polyacetyl chains without aromatic rings of shikimic origin or by the more complex cyclizations of these chains discussed in Section 4–5. It may conversely be observed that these routes are much less common among the higher plants. Over-all correlation of fungal products as acetogenins is higher than that of products from higher plants, but the difference is not striking except among the anthraquinones.

Further, more extensive oxidation at methylene sites is observed in fungal products than in the higher plants, and the occasional appearance of chlorine in the above compounds is limited exclusively to the lower organisms. In 20 of the 22 compounds containing chlorine the chlorines are always found at methylene sites of the initial polyacetyl chain, providing strong indirect evidence for their incorporation by oxidative rather than replacement reactions. Of the other two, one is caldariomycin [250], a cyclopentane, but even here the chlorines are flanked by two oxygen-bearing carbons; the other is mollisin [194], which has two vicinal chlorine atoms. It may also be noted that a high degree of oxidation is characteristic of the many benzoquinones found predominantly in fungi, including the fungal terphenyls [20], which are the major fungal ϕ-C_3 compounds.

Isoprenoid Substituents

Alkylation by isoprene groups is, by contrast, largely the province of the higher organisms, the only exceptions being flavoglaucin [144] and auroglaucin [144], mycophenolic acid [145], mycelianamide (Section 5–2), fuscin [159], atrovenetin [198], and the quinone coenzymes (vitamins K [305], coenzymes Q [143], etc., which are also widespread in higher organisms). Similarly, the isoprenoids are largely limited to the coumarins, acylphloroglucinols, and flavonoid-structure types. Alkylations by sugars (O- and C-glycosidation) are absent from the microorganisms.

The forms the isoprenoid group takes in various natural molecules are quite varied. Chart V provides a summary of almost all these natural forms codified for convenience into a biogenetic scheme, which, although essentially the simplest both in mechanism and economy, is certainly not the only reasonable scheme that may be envisioned. Under each form is given the number of times it appears in the compounds of Table 4–6 *; the uncyclized isoprenoid groups are all shown as attached at the carbon of the alkylated enol although most of the ether analogues

(O-alkylated) are known and are in fact included in the numbers shown for each form. The modes of interconversion involve a primary oxidation of the initial isopentenyl group, either as epoxidation (or hydroxylation) of the double bond or as the oxidation of the enol (or phenol) discussed in Section 3–2 to the intermediate (A), which is considered to cyclize or add water as shown. The subsequent reactions are either hydrations, dehydrations, or prototropic shifts of double bonds (annotated H$^+$); the forms to the right of the dotted dividing line are all at the next higher oxidation state, arising by a second application of the same oxidative mechanisms. Loss of acetone as indicated leads to the common unsubstituted furan ring. This over-all scheme

[284]

Khellin

[285]

Visnamminol

derives some measure of support not only from the mechanistically simple and reasonable reactions but also from the fact that all the involved forms are actually known in nature, often several in the same species; in some cases the hydroxyls of Chart V are either esterified or present as glycosides or methyl ethers in the natural compounds. Examples from the same species include rotenone **[106]**, elliptone **[107]**, and deguelin **[108]** from *Derris elliptica*, and five simple furanochromones, such as khellin **[284]**, coexistent with the more complex isoprenoids visnamminol **[285]**, visnadin **[286]**, samidin **[286]**, and dihydrosamidin **[286]** in *Ammi visnaga*. *Angelica glabra* and *Archangelica* contain osthenol **[287]**, glabra lactone **[288]**, angelicin **[289]**, xanthotoxol **[290]**, phellopterin **[291]**, byak-angelicol and byak-angelicin **[291]**, and isobyak-angelicolic acid **[292]**. Other umbelliferaceous plants,

---

* Examples of most of these forms are given in the subsequent discussion; samidin and its relatives (**[286]**) are taken as examples of the 1,2,3-trihydroxyisopentyl, closed in a ring. Examples of the other forms are found in previous sections, e.g., munetone **[97]**, euparin **[60]**, torquatone **[66]**, fuscin **[159]**, and icaritin **[78]**. There are two excellent reviews, with many examples cited, of the variations of isoprenoid attachment.[122,123]

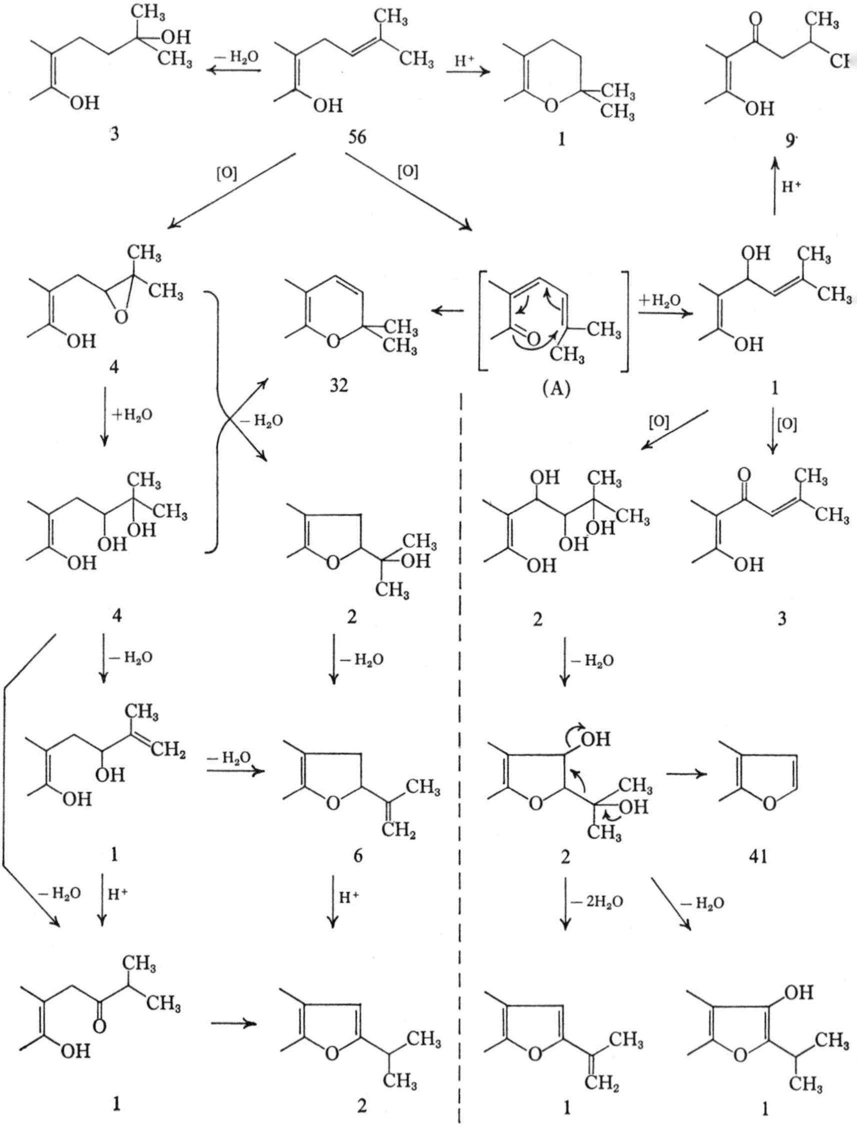

Chart V *Biogenetic codification of isoprenoid substituents*

the *Peucedanum* species, afford a variety in peucenin [293], isoimperatorin [294], oxypeucedanin [294] and ostruthol [294], osthruthin [295],
peucedanin [296], marmesin [297], and athamantin [298]. Close
examination of these and other co-occurrences [122,123] provides confidence
in the origin of the simple furans from isoprenoid substituents and in
the general interrelations of Chart V.

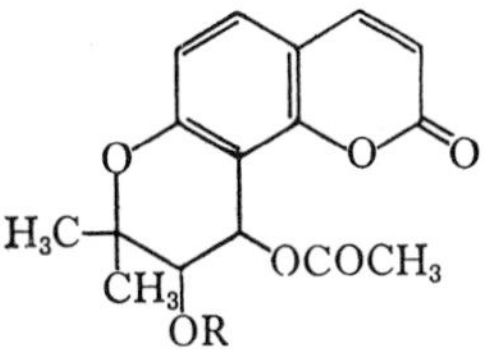

[286]

Samidin (R = $\begin{array}{c}O\\\parallel\end{array}$ CH₃, CH₃)

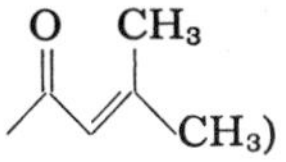

Dihydrosamidin (R = ... CH₃, CH₃)

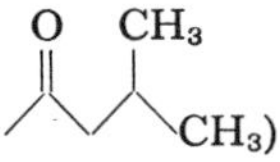

Visnadin (R = ... CH₃, CH₃)

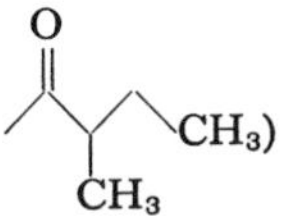

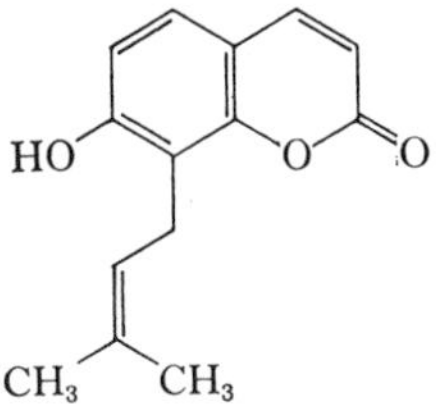

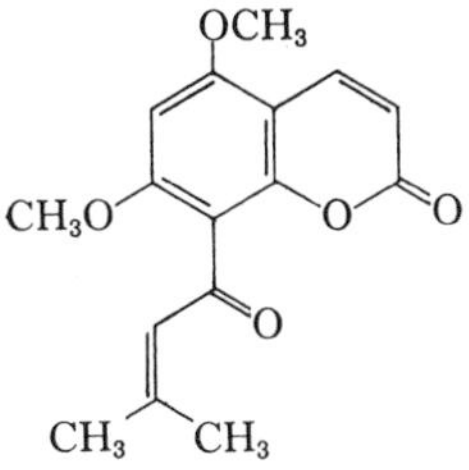

| [287] | [288] | [289] |
| Osthenol | Glabra Lactone | Angelicin |

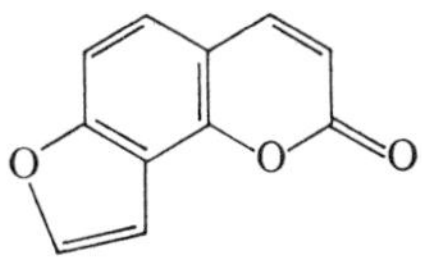

In the forms of Chart V it may be noted that the isoprenoid group is
always attached at the 1-position of that group as anticipated for
S_N2 alkylation by 3,3-dimethylallyl pyrophosphate, and that the simple

122. W. D. Ollis and I. O. Sutherland, Ref. 17, Chap. 5.
123. R. Aneja, S. K. Mukerjee, and T. R. Seshadri, *Tetrahedron*, **4**, 256
(1957).

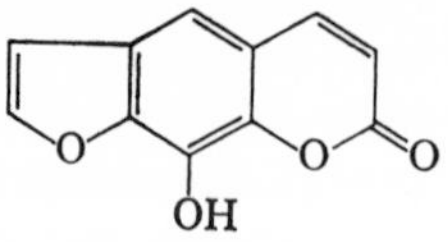

[290]

Xanthotoxol

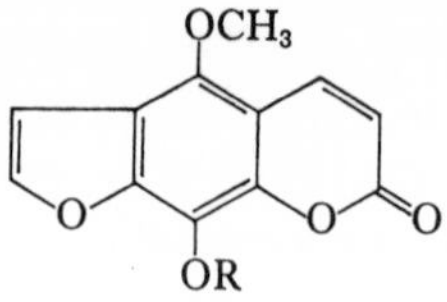

[291]

Phellopterin (R =)

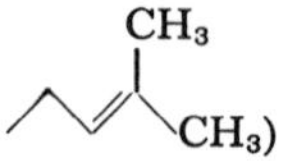

Byak-angelicol (R =)

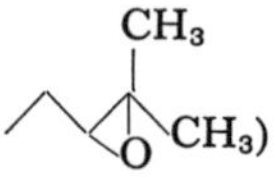

Byak-angelicin (R =)

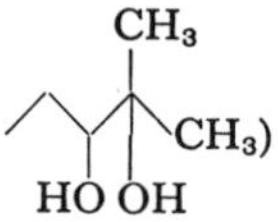

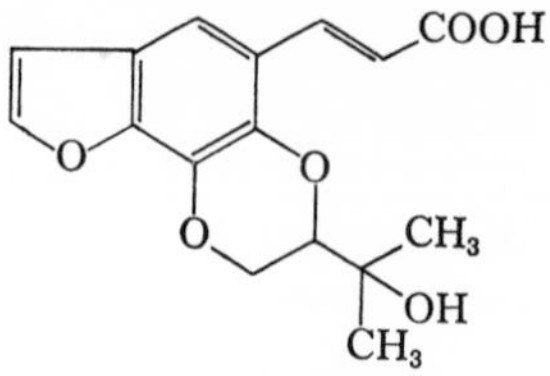

[292]

Isobyak-angelicolic
Acid

direct alkylation product is by far the most commonly occurring form. There are six attached isoprenoid forms in natural molecules that are not included in the chart.   Three of these correspond to simple allylic (S_N2') displacement on 3,3-dimethylallyl pyrophosphate, which is thus

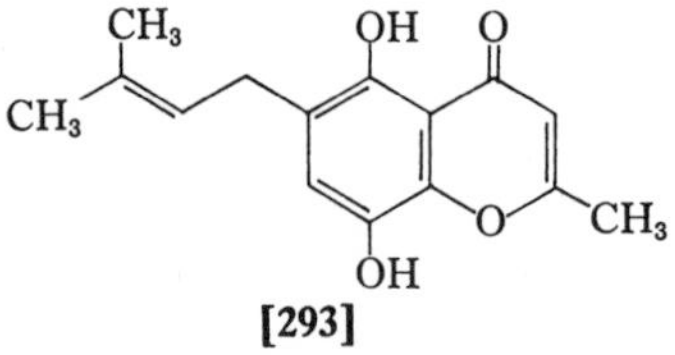

[293]

Peucenin

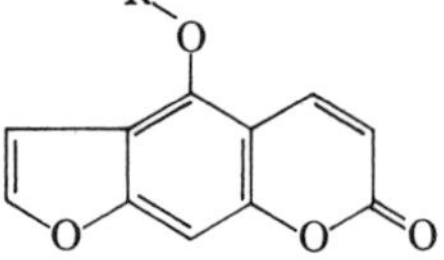

[294]

Isoimperatorin: R =

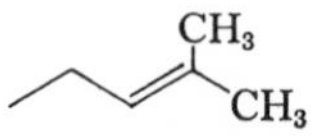

Oxypeucedanin: R =

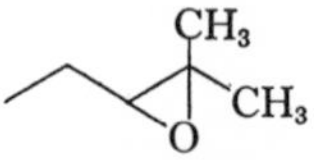

Ostruthol: R =

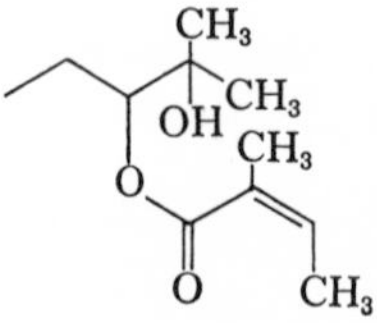

much less common an occurrence, as expected. The fungal indole echinulin [299] contains the simple isopentenyl attachment, but in dunnione [300] and atrovenetin [198] this appears cyclized to the hydroxyl. Primary attachment at oxygen and cyclization to carbon would

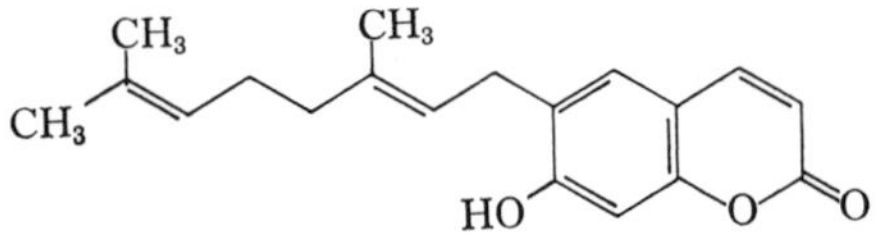

[295]

Ostruthin

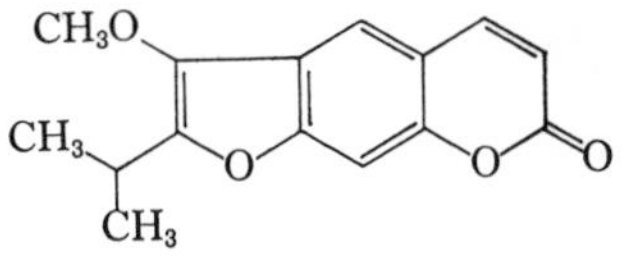

[296]

Peucedanin

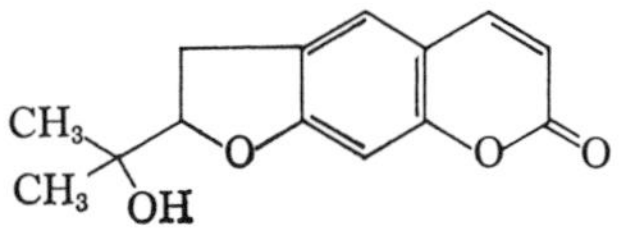

[297]

Marmesin

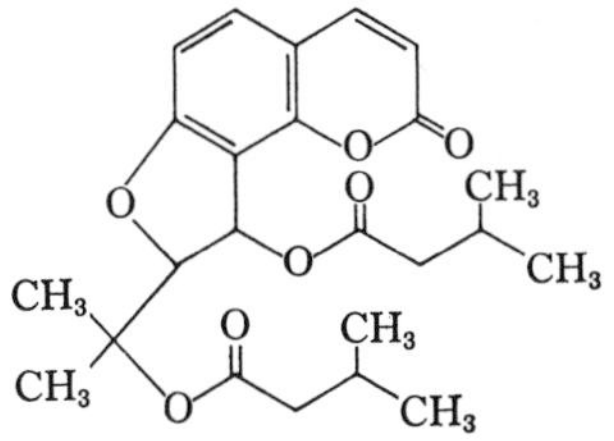

[298]

Athamantin

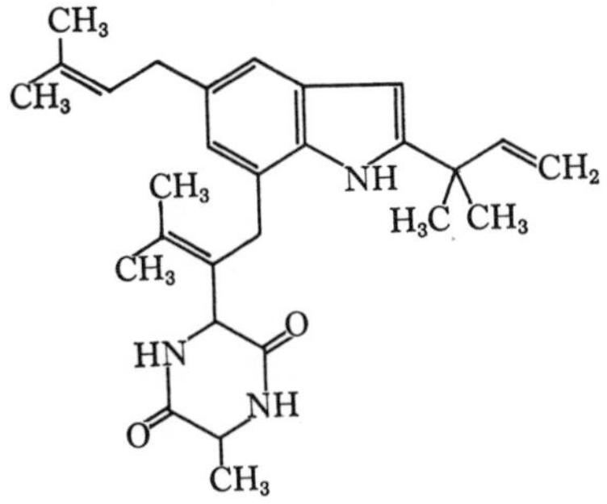

[299]

Echinulin

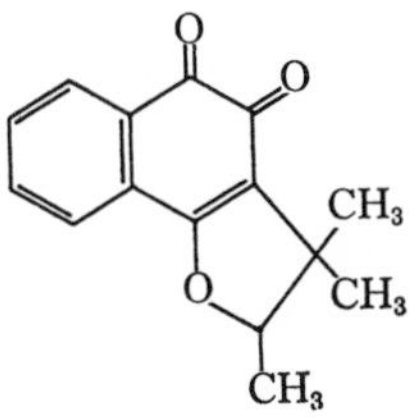

[300]

Dunnione

similarly account for the case of anisoxide [301], which may exist in the plant as the uncyclized precursor. These four cases are the only unambiguous instances of the allylic (S_N2') alkylation.

The other three forms are anomalous in being attached to the phenol by the branch carbon of the isoprene group as in ostruthol **[294]**, edultin **[302]**, and calophyllolide **[40]**; cyclization by conjugate addition is apparent in inophyllolide **[40]**, and reduction of the double bond appears in visnadin **[286]**.   The only other anomalous cases are the unique structures recently proposed for morellin **[274]**[114] and the guttiferins[115] on slight experimental evidence.

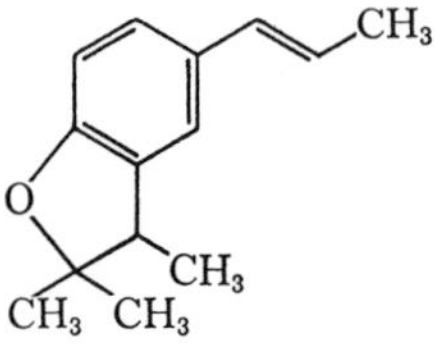

[301]

Anisoxide

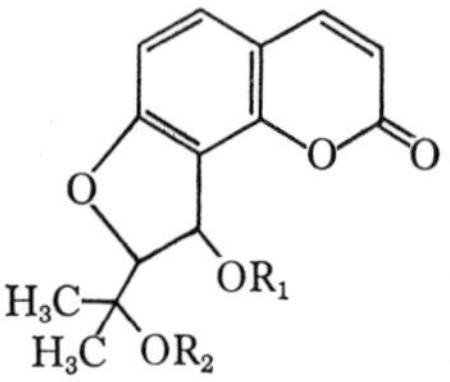

[302]

Edultin:

$R_1, R_2 = $ —COCH$_3$, —CO—C=CH
                              | |
                            CH$_3$ CH$_3$

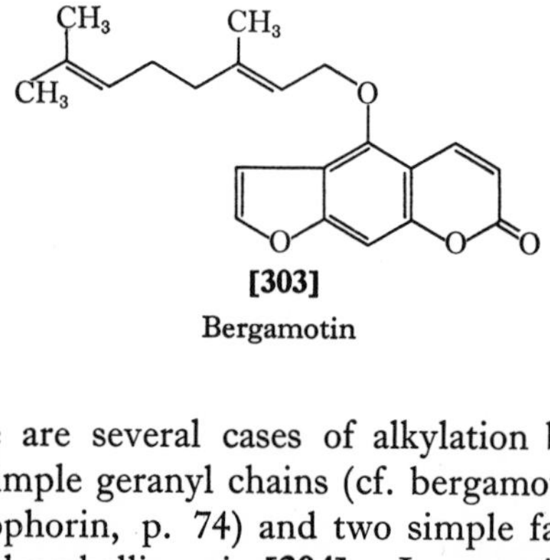

[303]

Bergamotin

Finally there are several cases of alkylation by polyisoprenoids, including seven simple geranyl chains (cf. bergamotin **[303]**, ostruthin **[295]**, and chlorophorin, p. 74) and two simple farnesyl chains (ammoresinol **[35]** and umbelliprenin **[304]**.   In marmin **[304]** the geranyl chains are hydrated and in mycophenolic acid **[145]** oxidative cleavage of the outermost double bond of a geranyl group has left it truncated; the *Cannabis* phenols (**[147]**–**[149]**) show cyclized geranyl sidechains, and a cyclized counterpart in the farnesyl series has recently been announced[124] in the structures of the farnesiferols **[304]**.   Longer poly-isoprene chains are found in the coenzymes Q **[143]**, the tocopherols **[142]**, and vitamins K **[305]**.

124. L. Caglioti, H. Naef, D. Arigoni, and O. Jeger, *Helv. Chim. Acta*, **41**, 2278 (1958); **42**, 2557 (1959).

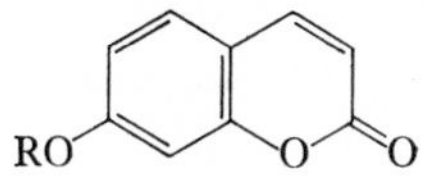

[304]

Marmin: R =

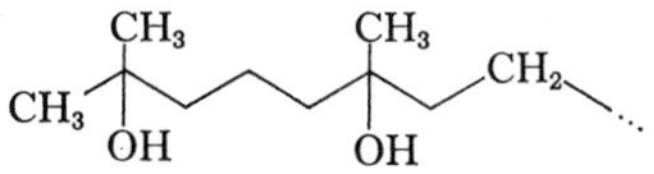

Umbelliprenin: R =

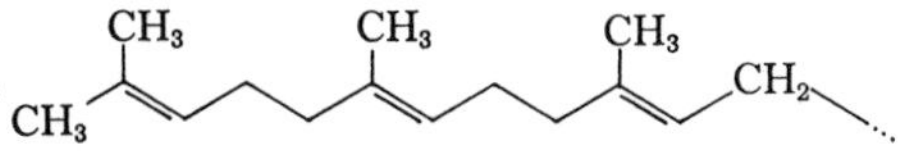

Farnesiferol-a: R =

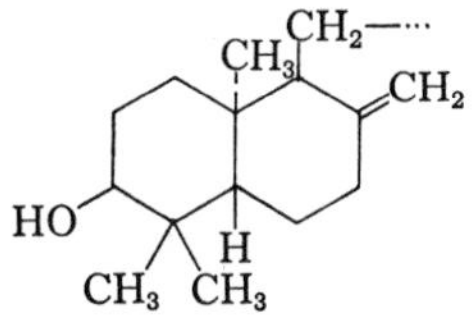

Farnesiferol-b: R =

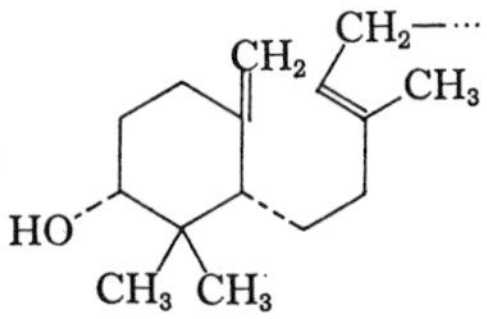

Farnesiferol-c: R =

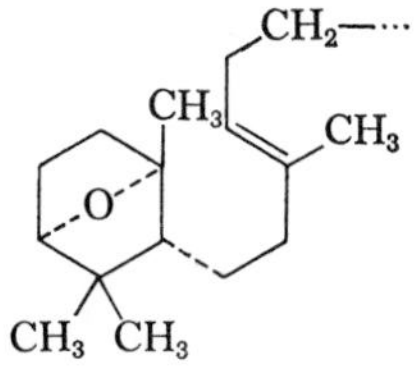

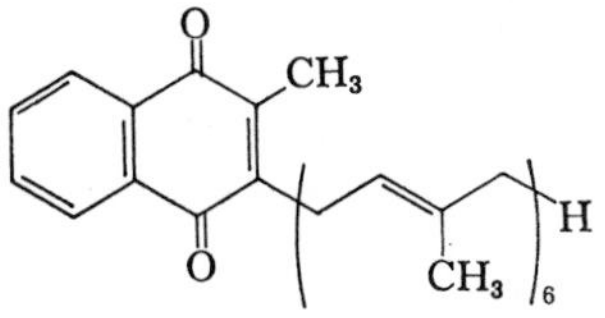

[305]

Vitamin K$_2$

4–8 ALKALOIDS

Until quite recently, the biogenesis of alkaloids had been believed to proceed almost exclusively from amino acid sources [125–127] and, with the exception of a few steroidal amines, to have been free of any involvement with the realm of acetate biosynthesis surveyed here.   In the last several years, however, preliminary reports in two important families of alkaloids have implicated acetate origins.   In contrast to the other acetogenins, studies with labeled acetate on the biosynthesis of these alkaloids are unfortunately in an embryonic state at this writing, so that it seems best to separate this discussion from that of the other acetogenins; such experimental evidence as is presently available is therefore incorporated in the following.

The alkaloids from the *Lycopodium* mosses (**[308]**–**[312]**) represent a structurally uniform family that has been satisfactorily postulated by Conroy [128] to arise wholly from cyclizations of polyacetyl chains.   In keeping with the correlations above it is of interest that the mosses are the lowest order of plants from which alkaloids have been obtained; they produce the only alkaloids thus far believed to arise solely from simple acetate chains.   The coupling of two tetraacetyl chains (**[306]**) to form the branched **[307]** provides a basis for all the known structures. The changes necessary to convert **[307]** to each of the known alkaloids are consonant with the standard variants observed so far in the other acetogenins; as Conroy has pointed out, although few of the original oxygen markers of the polyacetyl chains remain intact in the final structures **[308]**–**[312]**, each ketone group of **[307]** either remains or else serves a mechanistic function in the biogenesis of at least one of the several alkaloid molecules produced.

125. Sir Robert Robinson, *The Structural Relations of Natural Products,* Clarendon, Oxford, 1955.
126. E. Wenkert, *Experientia,* **15**, 165 (1959).
127. R. B. Woodward, *Angew. Chem.,* **68**, 13 (1956).
128. H. Conroy, *Tetrahedron Letters,* **1960**, 34.
129. D. B. MacLean and J. A. Harrison, *Chem. & Ind. (London),* **1960**, 261.
130. M. Curcumelli-Rodostamo and D. B. MacLean, *Can. J. Chem.,* **40**, 1068 (1962).
131. W. A. Ayer and G. G. Iverbach, *Tetrahedron Letters,* **1960**, 19; *Tetrahedron,* **18**, 567 (1962).
132. F. A. L. Anet and M. V. Rao, *Tetrahedron Letters,* **1960**, 9.
133. K. Wiesner, Z. Valenta, W. A. Ayer, L. R. Fowler, and J. E. Francis, *Tetrahedron,* **4**, 87 (1958).
134. W. N. French and D. B. MacLean, *Chem. & Ind. (London),* **1960**, 659.
135. F. A. L. Anet, *Tetrahedron Letters,* **1960**, 13.

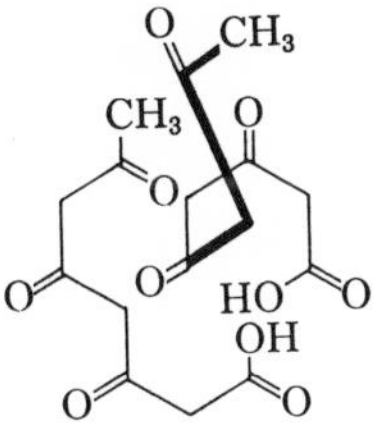

[306] 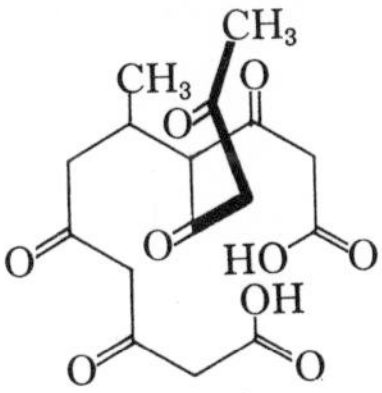 → [307] 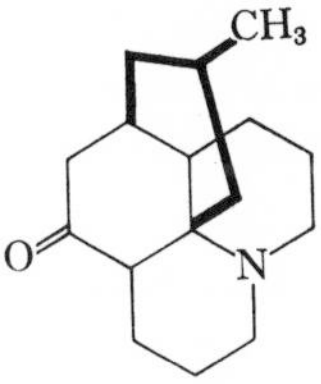 → [308]
Lycopodine[129] (R = H)
Flabelliformine[130] (R = OH)

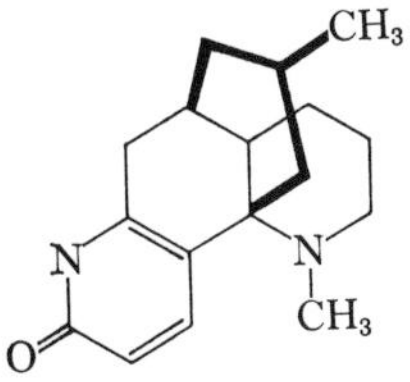

[309][131,132]

β-Obscurine
(α-Obscurine = dihydro)
Lycodine = corresponding
pyridine

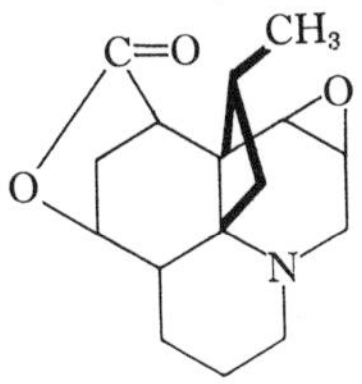

[310]

Annotinine[133]

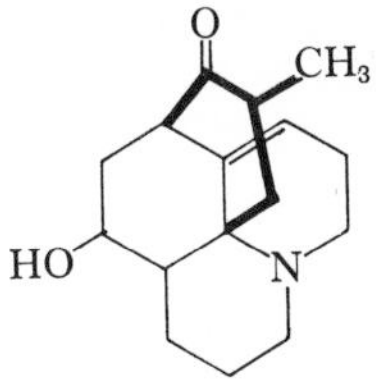

[311][134,135]

Acrifoline
(Annofoline = dihydro)

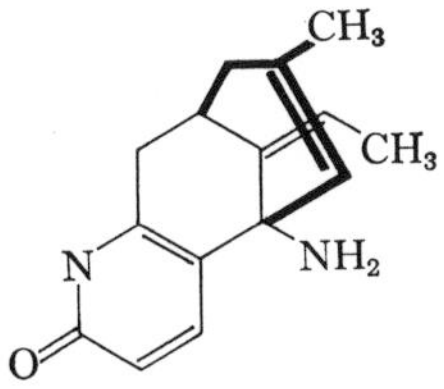

[312]

Selagine[136]

The indole alkaloids [137] represent a much larger and far more varied group of alkaloids, the indole portion of which is believed to arise from the amino acid tryptophan via tryptamine, which is then condensed

136. Z. Valenta, H. Yoshimura, E. F. Rogers, M. Ternbah, and K. Wiesner, *Tetrahedron Letters*, **1960**, 26.
137. J. E. Saxton in R. H. F Manske (ed.), *The Alkaloids, Vol. VII*, Academic, New York, 1960, Chap. 10.

with another fragment of 8 to 10 carbons, probably as an aldehyde in the classical Mannich reaction (which has so illustriously served to forge alkaloid skeletons in the extensive literature of biogenetic speculation).[125–127] Until recently, this second fragment was thought to arise from phenylalanine by conversion to a phenylacetaldehyde. A number of inadequacies in this postulation have, however, led to several ingenious hypotheses implicating instead shikimic acid[126] or monoterpenoid origins[138,139] for this fragment, and the search for a suitable source also led to consideration of a polyacetyl precursor.[140] The

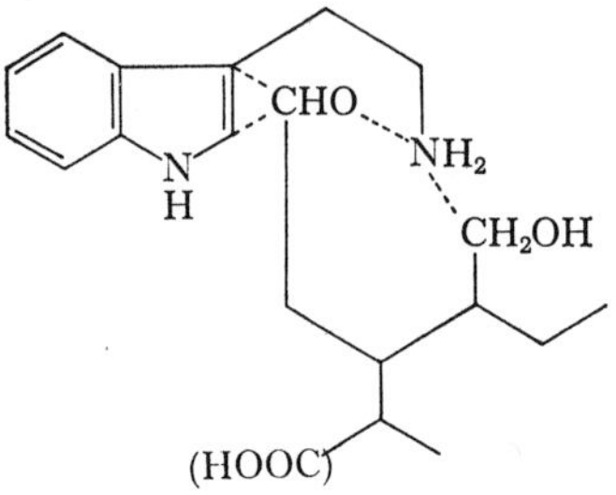

[313]

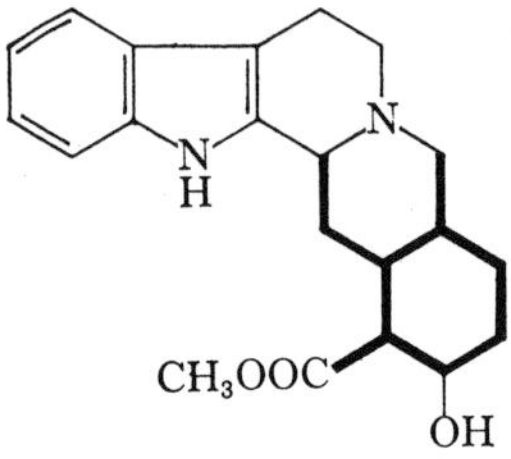

[314]
Yohimbine

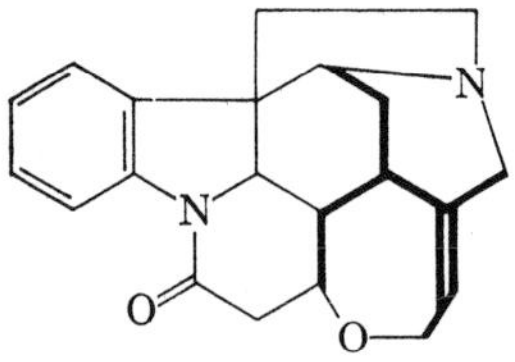

[315]
Strychnine

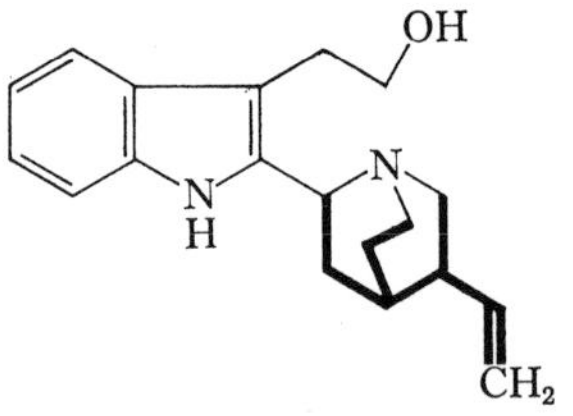

[316]
Cinchonamine

fragment in question may conveniently be formalized as in [313], showing the branched skeleton of an aldehyde suitable for an α- or β-condensation to tryptamine and containing the carboxyl that may later be lost in certain alkaloids; the fragment may be isolated in the formulas of representative alkaloids by the heavy lines shown here ([314]–[316]).

138. R. Thomas, *Tetrahedron Letters*, **1961**, 544.
139. E. Wenkert, *J. Am. Chem. Soc.*, **84**, 98 (1962).
140. E. Schlittler and W. I. Taylor, *Experientia*, **16**, 244 (1960).

At present the only clear evidence bearing on the controversy strongly supports an acetate origin for the umbrageous fragment. On feeding various labeled precursors to *Rauwolfia serpentina* and isolating the alkaloid ajmaline [317], Leete[141] found that it contained negligible activity after administration of radioactive tyrosine, alanine, or mevalonic acid. These findings militate seriously against the involvement of phenylalanine, a monoterpene or shikimic acid in the biogenesis. The latter was postulated[126] to condense with pyruvate in forming the requisite precursor and, as alanine is known to convert metabolically to pyruvate, this pathway is unlikely.

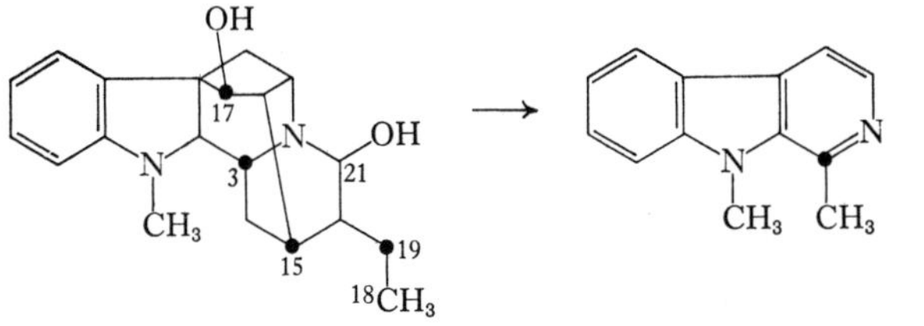

[317]	[318]
Ajmaline	N-(ind)-methylharman

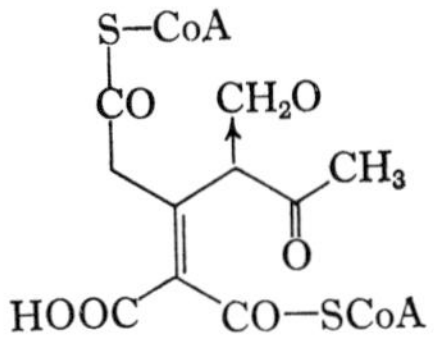

[319]

Administration of carboxyl-labeled acetate, by contrast, led to significant incorporation of radioactivity into ajmaline. Kuhn-Roth oxidation afforded acetic acid bearing one-fourth of the total alkaloid activity and that solely at the carboxyl carbon. Degradation of the alkaloid with soda lime yielded N-(ind)-methylharman [318] with another one-fourth of the total activity, this located at the marked carbon as determined by the Kuhn-Roth oxidation. Thus carbons 3 and 19 of ajmaline [317] share equally one-half of the total radioactivity arising

141. E. Leete, S. Ghosal, and P. N. Edwards, *J. Am. Chem. Soc.*, **84**, 1068 (1962).

from the labeled carboxyl of exogenous acetate.   Carbon 21 has been shown to arise from labeled formate, which serves as a source of one-carbon fragments for alkylation via a metabolic pool (cf. Section 5–2). This leads to the suggestion that the nine carbons of this biogenetic fragment in ajmaline originate in a branched tetraacetyl skeleton with

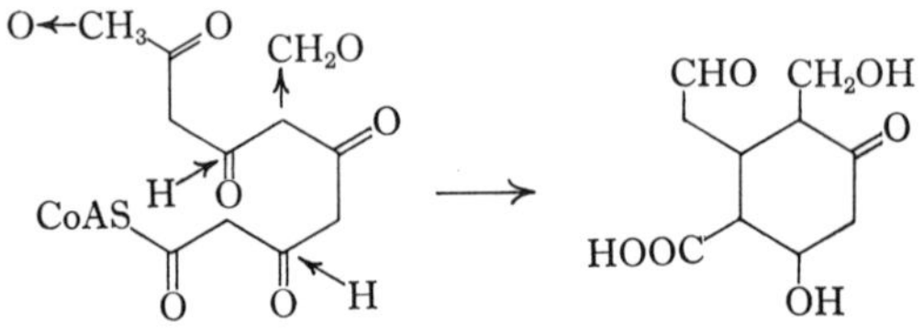

[320]   [321]

alkylation at methylene by a formaldehyde equivalent (the —CH$_2$OH of [313]).   In particular, Leete suggests [141] a linear triacetyl chain that condenses with malonyl-coenzyme A and a formaldehyde equivalent as represented in [319].   The resultant labeling pattern from 1-C^{14}-acetate, consistent with present evidence, would then be as shown in [317] (heavy dots) on the ajmaline skeleton; incidentally, this is inconsistent with the postulated monoterpenoid origin.

Several factors suggest that this hypothesis may be modified in detail: (1) the mechanism now emerging (Chapter 5) for the incorporation of malonyl-coenzyme A into fatty-acid biosynthesis requires concomitant decarboxylation; (2) chain-branching of the sort postulated is exceedingly uncommon in acetogenesis; and (3) the existence of the intact ring E in some indole alkaloids suggests origin from an intact ring in the precursor.   Thus, a biosynthesis as outlined in [320]–[321] satisfies these criteria.   The intermediate [321] so obtained is in fact identical with that devised by Wenkert [126] from a shikimic acid origin and shown by him to be highly suitable for elaboration of the various indole alkaloids!

| *chapter* *five* | # Acetogenins: Experimental Verification |

In the field of direct experimental examination of the pathways of biosynthesis of the fatty acids and acetogenins, enormous strides have been taken in the last several years with the result that a preliminary over-all view, involving well-substantiated detail, may now be taken with some confidence. The title of this chapter, experimental verification, is used advisedly, since virtually all the general tenets of the original acetate hypothesis have now been shown to be correct and are outlined here. The range and power of modern methods available for exploration of the subtle reactions of living systems are impressive, including the use of tracers (C^{14}, H^2, and H^3), the isolation and manipulation of operative enzymes, feeding-deprivation experiments, and kinetic studies on whole organisms and cell extracts from a wide spectrum of living matter.

5-1 FATTY ACIDS AND OTHER LINEAR CARBON SKELETONS

The earliest probes into fatty acid metabolism were made several decades ago by Knoop, who formulated the β-oxidation hypothesis for fatty acid degradation. In subsequent decades much detail was added to this hypothesis by tracer experiments and by the isolation and characterization of the several enzymes involved; the recognition that the involved acids occur as thiol-esters of coenzyme A also occurred. At present, the separate enzymes catalyzing each step of the degradation of fatty acids to acetic acid have been isolated from mammalian liver and have been carefully studied in vitro; the complete system can accordingly be refabricated by mixing the enzymes and their appropriate cofactors (acetyl coenzyme A, reduced nicotinamide adenine dinucleo-tide (NADH), reduced nicotinamide adenine dinucleotide phosphate (NADPH), etc.) and will degrade long-chain fatty acids to acetate. This *fatty acid cycle* has been well reviewed[1-4] and may be summarized as shown in Chart I.   It is important to observe that the reactions are all reversible, so that the cycle is, in principle, a path for the biosynthesis of long-chain fatty acids from acetic acid through acetyl coenzyme A. Since our primary interest here is in the genesis of compounds *from* acetate, the cycle is written as a synthetic one, and in fact the enzyme system can be reconstituted from its several components so as to accomplish this synthesis in vitro.

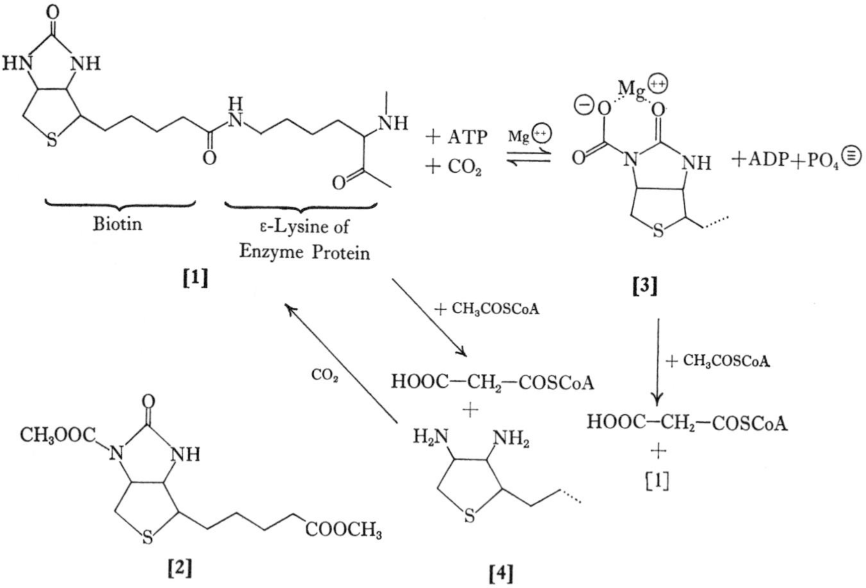

Fatty Acid Biosynthesis

The fatty acid cycle was believed for some time to be the main source of natural fatty acids, but events of recent years have led to the construction of another pathway now believed to be the prime biosyn-thetic route, although the fatty acid cycle may well be utilized in occasional organisms or as an alternative route (vide infra).   Several pieces of

1. C. Artom, *Ann. Rev. Biochem.*, **22**, 211 (1953).
2. F. Lynen, *Ann. Rev. Biochem.*, **24**, 653 (1955).
3. P. K. Stumpf, *Ann. Rev. Biochem.*, **29**, 261 (1960).
4. R. G. Langdon and A. H. Phillips, *Ann. Rev. Biochem.*, **30**, 189 (1961).

evidence first suggested that the reverse fatty acid cycle was not the major biosynthetic route. Theoretically, the equilibria in that cycle favored degradation, not synthesis, so that thermodynamically the postulation of removal of products from the system was required for the cycle to work synthetically. An early experimental clue was the discovery[5,6] that palmitic acid synthesis required CO_2 (or HCO_3^-), although the label from radioactive CO_2 was not incorporated in the final acid.[7,8] Wakil and Ganguly[9] postulated that the acetyl coenzyme

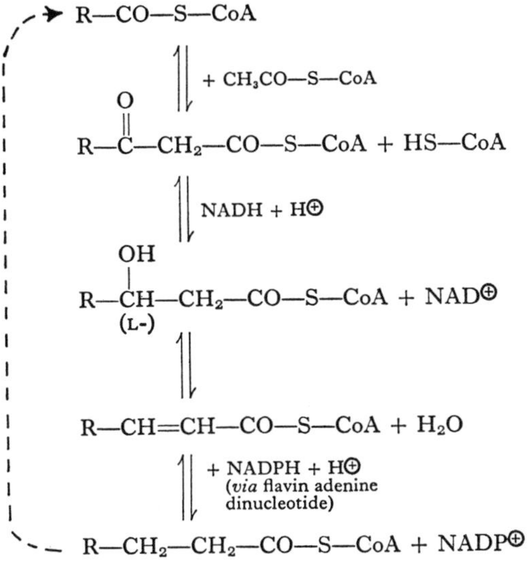

$$R\text{—}CO\text{—}S\text{—}CoA$$

$$+ CH_3CO\text{—}S\text{—}CoA$$

$$\underset{\substack{O \\ \parallel}}{R\text{—}C\text{—}CH_2\text{—}CO\text{—}S\text{—}CoA} + HS\text{—}CoA$$

$$NADH + H^\oplus$$

$$\underset{\substack{OH \\ | \\ (\text{L-})}}{R\text{—}CH\text{—}CH_2\text{—}CO\text{—}S\text{—}CoA} + NAD^\oplus$$

$$R\text{—}CH{=}CH\text{—}CO\text{—}S\text{—}CoA + H_2O$$

$$+ NADPH + H^\oplus \\ (via \text{ flavin adenine} \\ \text{dinucleotide})$$

$$R\text{—}CH_2\text{—}CH_2\text{—}CO\text{—}S\text{—}CoA + NADP^\oplus$$

$$(n + 1)\ CH_3COSCoA + n\text{NADPH} + n\text{NADH} + 2n\text{H}^\oplus \rightleftharpoons \\ CH_3(CH_2)_{2n}COSCoA + n\text{HSCoA} + n\text{NAD}^\oplus + n\text{NADP}^\oplus + n\text{H}_2O$$

Chart I *Fatty acid cycle*

A was carboxylated to form malonyl coenzyme A, which was then considered the active methylene agent for the Claisen condensation with acyl coenzyme A which adds the two carbons to the chain. With

5. H. P. Klein, *J. Bacteriol.*, **73**, 530 (1957).
6. R. O. Brady and S. Furin, *J. Biol. Chem.*, **217**, 757 (1955).
7. D. M. Gibson, E. B. Titchener, and S. J. Wakil, *J. Am. Chem. Soc.*, **80**, 2908 (1958); *Biochim. Biophys. Acta*, **30**, 376 (1958).
8. C. C. Squires, P. K. Stumpf, and C. Schmidt, *Plant Physiol.*, **33**, 365 (1958).
9. S. J. Wakil and J. Ganguly, *J. Am. Chem. Soc.*, **81**, 2597 (1959).

such a more reactive anionoid species initiating the condensation, the equilibrium will certainly be more favorable also.

The carboxylation of acetyl coenzyme A is now understood in some detail[10] and is known to require biotin [1], adenosine triphosphate, and magnesium ion stoichiometrically as cofactors. It has been suggested that the adenosine triphosphate adds first to the biotin nitrogen to activate that site for carboxylation.[10] Incubation of the enzyme with radioactive bicarbonate and the other cofactors followed by isolation, enzymatic peptide hydrolysis, and reaction with diazomethane led to the isolation of radioactive [2], identical with a synthetic sample.[11] These experiments confirmed the position of attachment of the donated carboxyl and suggested the carbamic acid [3] as the active enzymatic intermediate in transferring the carboxyl to acetyl coenzyme A:

$$[3] + CH_3COSCoA \rightarrow \text{biotin } [1] + \text{malonyl coenzyme A}$$

The intermediate [3] is shown here incorporating a chelated magnesium ion in such a way as to stabilize the carbamic acid as well as to assist mechanistically the nucleophilic attack on the carbamic carboxyl by acetyl coenzyme A.

Recently evidence has been advanced[12] that implicates instead the ureido-carbonyl of the biotin in the carboxylation reaction. Thus, although saponification of the active enzyme yielded biotin, saponification after stoichiometric conversion of radioactive acetyl coenzyme A to radioactive malonyl coenzyme A yielded "diaminobiotin" [4]. Furthermore, incorporation of $C^{14}O_2$ (as bicarbonate) into the enzyme followed by acid, basic, or enzymatic hydrolysis yielded free biotin containing over 80 per cent of the incorporated $C^{14}O_2$ radioactivity, all of it in the ureido-carbonyl. Unfortunately, it has not been shown that this ureido label is then transferred to the malonate. At present, therefore, it is not possible to decide which carbonyl is the direct source of the transferred carboxyl, although, if it is the ureido-carbonyl of the biotin as Wakil suggests, the carbamic acid [3] may well be an intermediate in the incorporation of labeled CO_2 into biotin.

10. O. Ochoa and Y. Kazior, *Federation Proc.*, **20**, 921 (1961); M. Waite and S. J. Wakil, *J. Biol. Chem.*, **237**, 2750 (1962).
11. F. Lynen, J. Knappe, E. Lorch, G. Jutting, and E. Ringelmann, *Angew. Chem.*, **71**, 481 (1959); J. Knappe, E. Ringelmann, and F. Lynen, *Biochem. Z.*, **335**, 168 (1961); J. Knappe, K. Biederbick, and W. Brummer, *ibid.*, **74**, 432 (1962).
12. M. Waite and S. J. Wakil, *J. Biol. Chem.*, **238**, 81 (1963).

Evidence for the over-all stoichiometry of fatty acid synthesis has been obtained from a variety of enzymatic studies on purified soluble systems from mammalian liver and is summarized below[9,13-17] for the synthesis of palmitic acid, the most common saturated fatty acid normally produced:

$$CH_3CO—S—CoA + 7\overset{\overset{\textstyle COOH}{\textstyle |}}{CH_2}—CO—S—CoA + 14NADPH + 14H^+ \rightarrow$$

$$CH_3(CH_2)_{14}CO—S—CoA + 7HS—CoA + 14NADP + 7H_2O + 7CO_2$$

Malonyl coenzyme A has been synthesized[18,19] and, when tritium-labeled at methylene, introduces seven tritium atoms into palmitic acid.[17] The system is dependent on acetyl coenzyme A but uses only one mole; tritium-labeled acetyl coenzyme A affords three tritium atoms per palmitate molecule, all on the terminal methyl.[17] Tritium-labeled reduced nicotinamide adenine dinucleotide phosphate shows direct tritium transfer to alternate carbons of the palmitic acid molecule.[15] Although the enzyme system requires acetyl coenzyme A to make palmitic acid, other small saturated fatty acids can also serve as chain initiators, being extended by malonyl units. Thus propionyl coenzyme A gave fatty acids with odd numbers of carbons; butyryl, hexanoyl, isobutyryl, and isovaleryl coenzyme A initiators also were incorporated,[20,21] although with more difficulty. The latter four yielded branched-chain fatty acids, but, surprisingly, the presumed intermediaries acetoacetyl, β-hydroxybutyryl, and crotonyl coenzyme A were virtually ineffective with this enzyme system in contrast to their activity with the enzymes of the fatty acid cycle.[9] This led

13. F. Lynen, T. Kessel, and H. Eggerer, *Bayerische Akademie, der Wissenschaften Sitzung*, March 4, 1960.
14. F. Lynen, *J. Cell Comp. Physiol.*, **54, Supp.** 1, 33 (1959).
15. R. O. Brady, R. M. Bradley, and E. G. Trams, *J. Biol. Chem.*, **235**, 3093, 3099 (1960).
16. D. R. Martin, M. G. Horning, and P. R. Vagelos, *J. Biol. Chem.*, **236**, 663 (1961).
17. R. Bressler and S. J. Wakil, *J. Biol. Chem.*, **236**, 1643 (1961).
18. E. G. Trams and R. O. Brady, *J. Am. Chem. Soc.*, **82**, 2972 (1960).
19. P. R. Vagelos, *J. Biol. Chem.*, **235**, 346 (1960).
20. D. B. Martin and P. R. Vagelos, *Biochem. Biophys. Res. Commun.*, **5**, 16 (1961).
21. M. G. Horning, D. B. Martin, A. Karmen, and P. R. Vagelos, *J. Biol. Chem.*, **236**, 669 (1961).

Wakil[9] to postulate a detailed scheme analogous to that of the fatty acid cycle (Chart I) but differing in the utilization of malonyl coenzyme A and in retention of the extra carboxyl from that source through the intermediate steps, with decarboxylation only occurring on the final, saturated alkylmalonyl coenzyme A. The retention of the carboxyl has been disputed and is now ruled out by the tritium labeling referred to above, since no malonate tritium would remain in the palmitate by this route, which involves the intermediate

$$\text{CH}_3\text{---CH}{=}\overset{\displaystyle \text{COOH}}{\overset{|}{\text{C}}}\text{---CO---S---CoA}$$

It is also interesting that in no natural products of the preceding chapter were there any that presented a linear acetogenin skeleton with residual carboxyl branches remaining.

In an important recent paper, Lynen[22] has offered impressive evidence that provides a satisfactory detailed picture of the biosynthesis. He found that the action of the new enzyme system, referred to as *fatty acid synthetase*, was virtually quenched by sulfhydryl-blocking agents (iodoacetamide, arsenite, etc.) but restored by additions of sulfhydryl-bearing scavengers for these agents (glutathione, cysteine, etc.). He postulated that the enzyme itself bore a sulfhydryl group to which the malonyl residue of malonyl coenzyme A was transferred so that subsequent reactions occurred on enzyme-bound thiolester rather than on coenzyme A thiolesters. The scheme is summarized in Chart II. This route takes advantage of decarboxylation at the first step to provide a forward driving force, but, since acetoacetyl, β-hydroxybutyryl, and crotonyl are not involved as their coenzyme A thiolesters as in the fatty acid cycle, the observed inactivity of these molecules constitutes no difficulty.

More recently, several groups have demonstrated the incorporation of β-hydroxybutyryl coenzyme A and crotonyl coenzyme A into fatty acid synthesis with isolated enzyme systems[23] and shown that enzyme-bound acetoacetate is in fact converted directly to long-chain fatty acids.[24]

Fatty acid synthetase was fractionated to a 200-fold increase in

22. F. Lynen, *Federation Proc.*, **20**, 941 (1961).
23. J. D. Robinson, R. M. Bradley, and R. O. Brady, *Biochemistry*, **2**, 191 (1963); *J. Biol. Chem.*, **238**, 528 (1963).
24. P. Goldman and P. R. Vagelos, *Biochem. Biophys. Res. Commun.*, **1**, 414 (1962).

activity and acted as a single component in the ultracentrifuge (molecular weight $\sim 2 \times 10^6$).[22] Incubated with stoichiometric amounts of acetyl coenzyme A, malonyl coenzyme A, and reduced nicotinamide

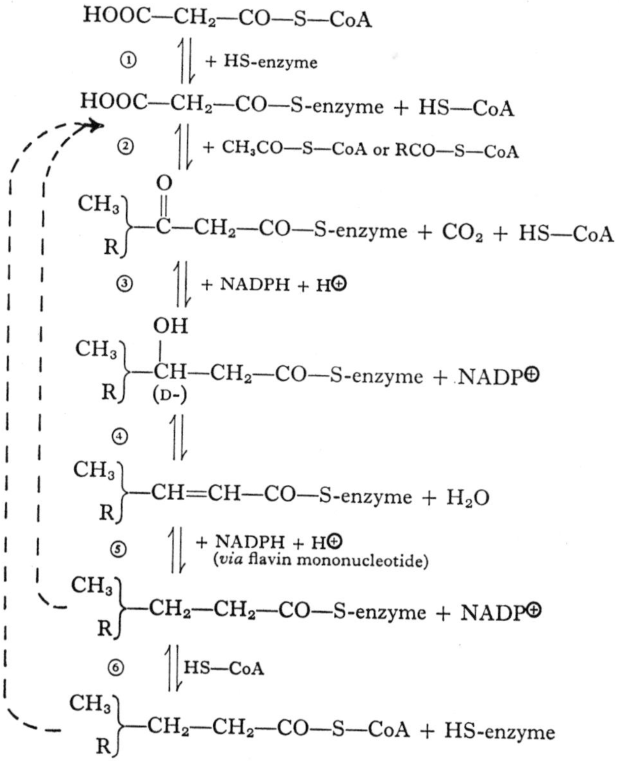

$$HOOC—CH_2—CO—S—CoA$$

① + HS-enzyme

$$HOOC—CH_2—CO—S\text{-enzyme} + HS—CoA$$

② + CH₃CO—S—CoA or RCO—S—CoA

$$\left.\begin{array}{c}CH_3 \\ R\end{array}\right\} \overset{O}{\underset{}{—C}}—CH_2—CO—S\text{-enzyme} + CO_2 + HS—CoA$$

③ + NADPH + H⊕

$$\left.\begin{array}{c}CH_3 \\ R\end{array}\right\} \overset{OH}{\underset{\text{(D-)}}{—CH}}—CH_2—CO—S\text{-enzyme} + NADP^\oplus$$

④

$$\left.\begin{array}{c}CH_3 \\ R\end{array}\right\} —CH{=}CH—CO—S\text{-enzyme} + H_2O$$

⑤ + NADPH + H⊕
(*via* flavin mononucleotide)

$$\left.\begin{array}{c}CH_3 \\ R\end{array}\right\} —CH_2—CH_2—CO—S\text{-enzyme} + NADP^\oplus$$

⑥ HS—CoA

$$\left.\begin{array}{c}CH_3 \\ R\end{array}\right\} —CH_2—CH_2—CO—S—CoA + HS\text{-enzyme}$$

1. $n\text{CH}_3\text{COSCoA} + n\text{CO}_2 + n\text{ATP} \rightleftharpoons n\text{HOOCCH}_2\text{COSCoA} + n\text{ADP} + n\text{℗}$

2. $\text{CH}_3\text{COSCoA} + n\text{HOOCCH}_2\text{COSCoA} + 2n\text{NADP} + 2n\text{H}^\oplus \rightleftharpoons$
$\text{CH}_3(\text{CH}_2)_{2n}\text{COSCoA} + n\text{CO}_2 + 2n\text{NADP}^\oplus + n\text{H}_2\text{O} + n\text{HSCoA}$

---

3. $(n + 1) \text{CH}_3\text{COSCoA} + 2n\text{NADPH} + 2n\text{H}^\oplus + n\text{ATP} \rightleftharpoons$
$\text{CH}_3(\text{CH}_2)_{2n}\text{COSCoA} + n\text{HSCoA} + 2n\text{NADP}^\oplus + n\text{H}_2\text{O} + n\text{ADP} + n\text{℗}$

Chart II *Fatty acid biosynthesis*

adenine dinucleotide phosphate (reduced nicotinamide adenine dinucleotide was only one-fourth as effective), the enzyme produced mostly palmitic but some stearic and lower (even-numbered) acids. The attachment of the intermediates directly to the enzyme was variously demonstrated, i.e., when 1-C^{14}-acetyl coenzyme A and malonyl coenzyme A were added without reduced nicotinamide adenine dinucleotide phosphate, and the protein then precipitated, it was radioactive, and labeled acetoacetate was cleaved off by mild base. In a similar experiment borohydride reduction of the precipitated protein followed by hydrolysis yielded labeled β-hydroxybutyric acid; in neither product acid was there activity in the carboxyl. Using 1-C^{14}-decanoyl coenzyme A as the initiating acyl group in the same way, they obtained an active β-ketododecanoyl-enzyme, which was hydrolyzed and decarboxylated to labeled nonyl methyl ketone.

Since the intermediate reactions are reversible, the incorporation of labeled CO_2 into malonyl coenzyme A by the β-ketoacyl-enzyme was

Pantothenic Acid

Adenylic Acid

[5]

Coenzyme A

[6]

N-Acetylcysteamine

studied and found to be dependent on the presence of acetyl or some acyl coenzyme A, as expected, and to proceed at about one-fifth the synthesis rate, so that the latter (the forward reaction) is favored. An important discovery allowed each step in the synthesis to be studied separately. Unlike the enzymes of the fatty acid cycle, synthetase accepted other thiolesters almost as well as coenzyme A esters, so that simple model thiolesters (usually N-acetylcysteamine **[6]**) could be used conveniently. Thus thiolesters of acetoacetic, β-hydroxybutyric, and crotonic acids, although incorporated more sluggishly by far, could be made to react in each of their respective synthetic steps regardless of the nature of the esterifying group. By contrast, the fatty-acid-cycle enzymes reacted rapidly with the appropriate coenzyme A esters but not at all with the model cysteamide esters, so that, in the case of synthetase, transfer of the acyl group to an —SH group on the enzyme is again implied. Using this technique, reaction 2 of Chart II was studied through the incorporation of label into malonylcysteamide using radioactive CO_2 and S-acetylcysteamide instead of acetyl coenzyme A; reaction 3 was studied by the dependence of reduced nicotinamide adenine dinucleotide phosphate oxidation rate on the concentration of added acetoacetyl thiolesters. Reactions 4 and 5 were followed by the growth or decay of the characteristic ultraviolet maximum of the unsaturated-thiolester system. Another difference from the fatty acid cycle was found in that the β-hydroxybutyrate formed and utilized in reactions 3 and 4, respectively, has the opposite stereochemistry from that used in the fatty acid cycle; the latter acid is inactive with synthetase.

Fatty acid synthetase has the yellow color characteristic of flavin mononucleotide; this material was separated from the colorless protein moiety and identified. The resultant protein retained most of its activity for all the synthetic steps except the olefin reduction (reaction 5), and this could be reactivated by addition of flavin mononucleotide to the colorless protein. Another point of difference from the fatty acid cycle is that the corresponding reduction in that cycle is accomplished by flavin adenine dinucleotide. It is of particular interest that the ratios of the rates of these various separate reactions catalyzed by synthetase remained constant through the fractionation and purification procedures that effected a 200-fold increase in activity and that, despite its diverse functions, the enzyme acted by all physical tests like a single protein. Hence Lynen has suggested that the enzyme combines on its surface prosthetic groups catalyzing each of the separate transformations and that the reacting molecule, while remaining bound to a single central sulfhydryl site on the enzyme, swings around to each of these catalytic centers in turn to effect the several reactions shown in Chart II. This is symbolized in Figure 1, which shows the bound acyl group as lying above a sexfoliate enzyme protein and bound to it by a central sulfhydryl group.

The biosynthesis of the fatty acids may then be summarized as follows: Acetate is first converted to acetyl coenzyme A, which in turn reacts with CO_2 in a reaction catalyzed by a biotin enzyme and energized by adenosine triphosphate to form malonyl coenzyme A. The malonyl residue is then transferred to the sulfhydryl group of synthetase where it condenses with a mole of acetyl coenzyme A or the coenzyme A thiolester of another chain-initiating acid with concomitant loss of CO_2 from the original malonyl moiety. The resultant β-ketoacyl residue, still attached to the sulfhydryl site, now moves around to enzymic centers that successively reduce, dehydrate, and reduce again until the acyl group is a saturated one with a skeletal chain two carbons longer than the initiating acid.　This may now transfer off the enzyme to coenzyme A (reaction 6) or be removed by condensation with another synthetase molecule bearing a reactive malonyl residue to continue the

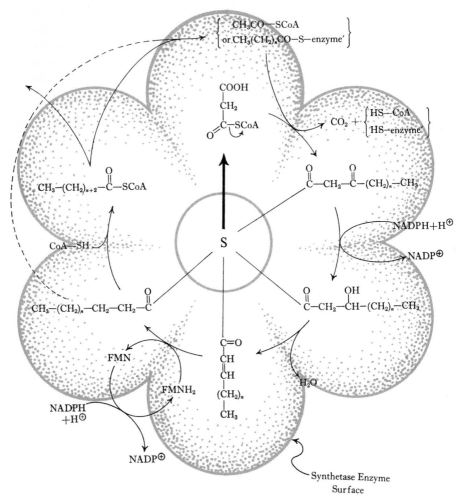

Figure 1　*Fatty acid synthetase*

chain-extension process.　That the latter alternative may be favored is suggested by the finding that intermediate-length fatty acids (as their thiolesters with coenzyme A) do not accumulate in the synthesis.[25,26]

25. S. J. Wakil, *Comp. Biochem. Physiol.*, **4**, 123 (1962).
26. R. Bressler and S. J. Wakil, *J. Biol. Chem.*, **237**, 1441 (1962).

Several ancillary points are relevant: the initial aldol condensation forming the new carbon-carbon bond should afford the intermediate [7], which is conformationally well suited for the internal decarboxylation indicated (M = H or metal); such a reaction would initially afford the enol form of the β-ketoacyl group and this form is indicated in Figure 1 as it is likely to be the tautomer on which the reduction occurs. The finding of one residual tritium per two-carbon unit[17] in palmitic acid produced from malonyl coenzyme A labeled at methylene is in accord with this mechanism and does not require a synchronous decarboxylation with condensation[27] as Wakil had previously concluded.[17]

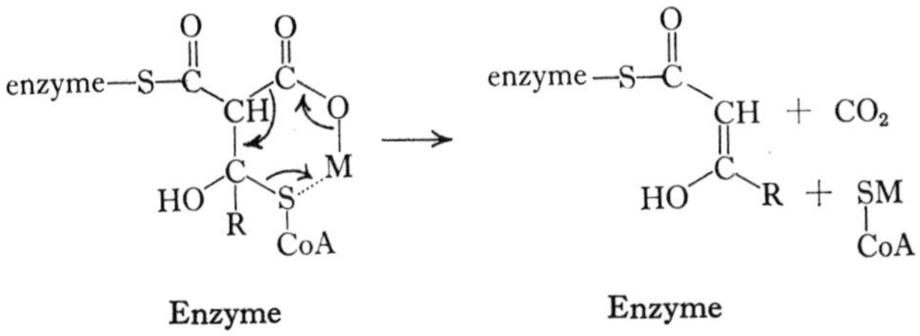

Enzyme   Enzyme

[7]   [8]

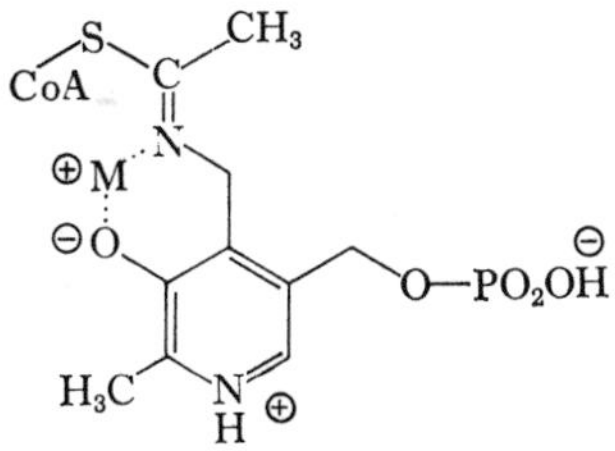

[9]

Lynen[22] has shown that the rate of transfer of the acyl group off the enzyme and back to coenzyme A (reaction 6, Chart II) reaches a maximum at the C_{16} acyl group, in accord with the observed predominance of palmitic acid as an end product of fatty acid biosynthesis. The synthetase route is considered the major route to fatty acids in living organisms, since it is apparently an enzyme of very widespread occurrence and because, thermodynamically, it favors synthesis, as the fatty acid cycle does not; this favorable equilibrium is attained at the cost of one mole of adenosine triphosphate per cycle. Nevertheless, the fatty

27. J. D. Bu'Lock, *Biochem. Biophys. Res. Commun.*, **8**, 48 (1962).

acid cycle may still account for synthesis in certain cases and this cycle or a variant is apparently the basis of a fatty acid, chain-lengthening process (cf. palmitic to stearic acids), which is particular to mitochondria according to recent studies of Wakil[25] and others. This system has been shown to be independent of $HC^{14}O_3^-$ but appears to be dependent on pyridoxal phosphate, which may serve to activate the acetyl coenzyme A for nucleophilic reactivity as an alternative to its activation by conversion to malonyl coenzyme A, discussed above. It has been suggested[25] that a complex such as [9] would serve this purpose.

Acetogenin Biosynthesis

It is appropriate at this stage to examine the implications of these studies for the biosynthesis of the polyacetyl chain postulated as the precursor of the acetogenins. It has often been remarked that no intermediates in the postulated biogenesis of acetogenins have been found; no more primitive polyacetyl compounds ($< C_8$) that might be precursors of orsellinic acid are ever isolated with that metabolite, for example. Similarly, the great instability of such β-polyketomethylene chains in vitro is well known, so that their existence as such may reasonably be doubted. Furthermore, the synthetase involved in their production must be incomplete in the sense of the enzyme described above, since, although reduction of an occasional ketone on the postulated polyacetyl precursor is implied in the structures considered above, complete reduction to methylene, as in fatty acid synthetase, is very uncommon. A modification of Lynen's enzyme may be constructed for a polyacetyl synthetase that incorporates these and other features satisfactorily, as illustrated in Chart III. The enzyme is viewed as a linear succession of sulfhydryl sites such that the adjacent enzyme surfaces afford room for only two or three of the six surrounding functions of the fatty acid synthetase. If these sites initially are all occupied by malonyl residues, reaction of the end malonyl group with an external chain-initiating acid (as its coenzyme A derivative), such as acetic or cinnamic, can cause successive aldol condensations to occur, yielding a polyacetyl chain. Furthermore, the sulfhydryl groups released in each condensation remain in place to bind the resultant ketone group by hydrogen bonding. Transfer of the sulfhydryl hydrogen to the ketone creates an enol, still hydrogen bound, and the enol may now react with oxidizing or alkylating agents ($X^\oplus$) as shown (modification of the hydrogen bond by metal ions allows O-alkylation). At certain sites, adjacent prosthetic groups could reduce certain of the ketones just as they do in fatty acid synthetase. Finally, a coiling of the entire coupled enzyme-polyacetyl complex could provide the requisite geometry for the internal acylation required in cyclizing the chain to an aromatic ring. Such a conception accounts for the evidence of the next section as well and may serve as a working hypothesis for the mechanism of acetogenin biosynthesis.

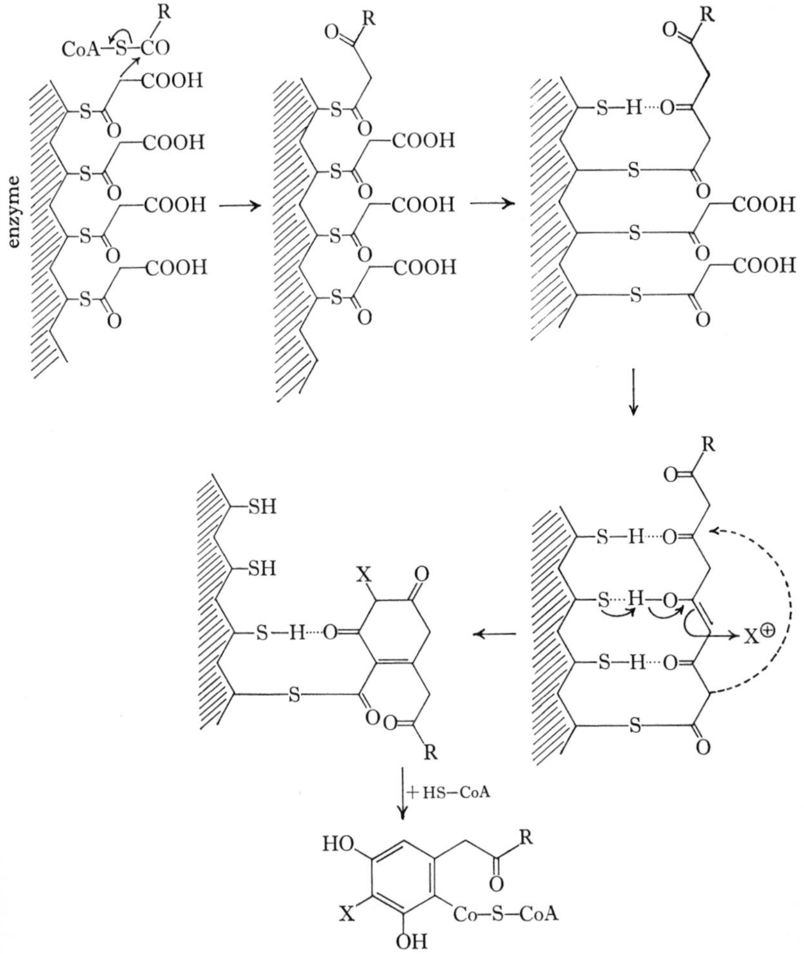

Chart III   *Enzyme model for acetogenin biosynthesis*

Unsaturated Fatty Acids

The unsaturated fatty acids found in nature have long posed an interesting and separate problem of biogenesis. The common unsaturated acids are listed in Table 5–1 and are to be found in a wide spectrum of living organisms. The outstanding characteristic features of the unsaturation in these acids are the prevalence of *cis* double bonds and the *divinylmethane rhythm* in which they repeat down a chain; both features are inconsistent with an origin in reduction and dehydration of the alternate ketones of a polyacetyl precursor. Furthermore, it is well established that the double bonds in these acids do not migrate or isomerize in vitro in most circumstances.

Table 5-1

	No. of carbons	Δ
Palmitoleic acid CH_3⌇⌇⌇COOH 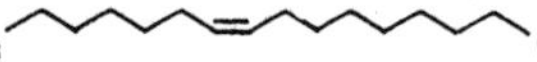	16	
Oleic acid CH_3⌇⌇⌇COOH 	18	
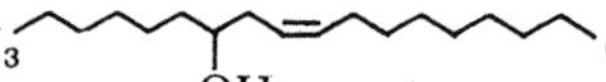 Ricinoleic acid CH_3⌇⌇ OH ⌇COOH	18	
Vaccenic acid CH_3⌇⌇COOH 	18	
Linoleic acid CH_3⌇⌇COOH 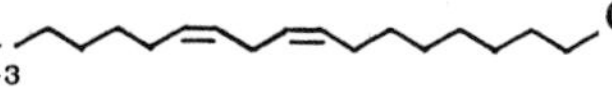	18	9,
γ-Linolenic acid CH_3⌇⌇COOH 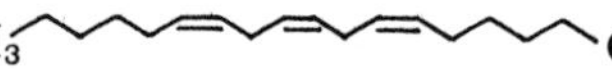	18	6, 9,
Linolenic acid CH_3⌇⌇COOH 	18	9, 12,
Arachidonic acid CH_3⌇⌇COOH 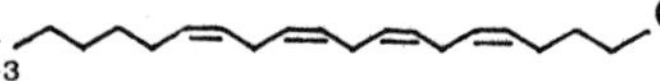	20	5, 8, 11,

Bloch and his colleagues[28] have found two routes that operate in the biosynthesis of the unsaturated acids. In the first a saturated fatty acid is converted to a monounsaturated one of the same length by an oxidation in which molecular oxygen is obligatory. The reaction is thus distinguished from the olefin formation in the fatty acid cycle (Chart I). Furthermore, the latter case introduces an α,β-double bond, whereas the oxidation involved in the present case introduces the olefin at the Δ^9 position and only there. The conversion of stearic to oleic

28. K. Bloch, P. Baronowsky, H. Goldfine, W. J. Lennarz, R. Light, A. T. Norris, and G. Scheverbrandt, *Federation Proc.*, **20**, 921 (1961).

acid was studied in cell-free extracts from yeast and found to require nicotinamide adenine dinucleotide phosphate and the coenzyme A derivative of the saturated acid as well as molecular oxygen.[29] In other respects it was also found to be similar to known hydroxylation reactions, so that intermediate production of 9- or 10-hydroxystearic acid seemed plausible. Both acids support the growth of deprived organisms, which would otherwise require exogenous oleic acid, but C^{14} labels in these acids are not appreciably incorporated into unsaturated acids either in vitro or in cell-free extracts, nor do coenzyme A thiolesters of the hydroxy acids produce oleic acid in cell-free extracts. Similarly, 1-C_{14}-oleic acid produces labeled linoleic acid in a reaction requiring oxygen, but ricinoleic acid does not appear to be an intermediate.

[10]   **[11]**

This unexpected behavior may tentatively be rationalized with the suggestion that O_2 reacts with the acyl coenzyme A by insertion of oxygen to form the species R—CO—O—O—S—CoA **[10]**, which may now undergo an intramolecular dehydrogenation to a *cis* olefin via a mechanism such as that shown (**[10]**–**[11]**) without ever introducing oxygen onto the carbon-chain of the molecule. Furthermore, it may be noted that ring A of the intermediate must be large enough to accommodate the fused ring B without strain; in order to oxidize at C_9, ring A is eleven-membered or just large enough to avoid the intra-annular hydrogen-compression strain that characterizes medium-sized rings (8 to 10 members). The reduced nicotinamide adenine dinucleotide phosphate requirement may be involved in reduction of the coenzyme A sulfenic acid produced.*

* Addition of O_2 to the acylcoenzyme A could also afford RCO—O—S—CoA and an oxidized species $^{\ominus}$O—X. The former, acting in the same cyclic mechanism as that proposed above except for the sulfur atom being now incorporated in ring B, would then give the unsaturated acid and coenzyme A as the direct products.

29. D. K. Bloomfield and K. Bloch, *J. Biol. Chem.*, **235**, 337 (1960).

A number of studies have cast light on the polyunsaturated acids. It now seems clear that these arise from monoolefins by addition of more double bonds in the divinylmethane rhythm toward the carboxyl end of the chain, as evidenced by the accompanying examples, which were demonstrated by tracer experiments and appropriate degradations.[30-34] It has been suggested that four families of unsaturated fats account for all known mammalian examples[32]; each family is

$$\text{Linoleic } (\Delta^{9,12}\text{-C}_{18}) \xrightarrow{-2H} \gamma\text{-Linolenic } (\Delta^{6,9,12}\text{-C}_{18}) \xrightarrow{+C_2} \Delta^{8,11,14}\text{-C}_{20}$$

$$\Big\downarrow +C_2 \qquad\qquad\qquad -2H \qquad\qquad \uparrow \quad \Big\downarrow -2H$$

$$\Delta^{11,14}\text{-C}_{20} \underline{\hspace{8cm}}$$

$$\text{Arachidonic } (\Delta^{5,8,11,14}\text{-C}_{20}) \tag{5-1}$$

$$\text{Linolenic } (\Delta^{9,12,15}\text{-C}_{18}) \xrightarrow{-2H} \Delta^{6,9,12,15}\text{-C}_{18} \xrightarrow{+C_2} \Delta^{8,11,14,17}\text{-C}_{20} \xrightarrow{-2H}$$

$$\Delta^{5,8,11,14,17}\text{-C}_{20} \xrightarrow{+C_2} \Delta^{7,10,13,16,19}\text{-C}_{22} \xrightarrow{-2H} \Delta^{4,7,10,13,16,19}\text{-C}_{22} \tag{5-2}$$

characterized by the distance from the methyl terminus to the first olefinic bond and the mono-unsaturated member of the family is presumed to be the first one formed in a series that generates the successive members by the above divinylmethane desaturations [Eqs. (5-1) and (5-2)] toward the carboxyl end and chain extensions at that end by malonyl units. Generalized as $CH_3(CH_2)_n CH{=}CH{-}\cdots{-}COOH$, the four families are $n = 1$ (linolenic), $n = 4$ (linoleic), $n = 5$ (palmitoleic), and $n = 7$ (oleic). Despite the general tendency for unsaturation to be introduced toward the carboxyl end, at least in mammalian tissue, an enzyme system from yeast with similar cofactor requirements apparently converts oleic to linoleic and perhaps linolenic,[35] so that it may prove that the primary Δ^9-desaturation (vide supra), which yields oleic and palmitoleic acids, may be the biosynthetic origin of all these unsaturated acids. The mechanism of olefinic introduction in the divinylmethane rhythm remains an unsolved and interesting problem.

30. E. Klenk and G. Kremer, *Z. Physiol. Chem.*, **320**, 111 (1960); E. Klenk and H. Mohrhaver, *ibid.*, **320**, 218 (1960).
31. J. F. Mead and D. B. Howton, *J. Biol. Chem.*, **205**, 683 (1953); **220**, 257 (1956); **229**, 575 (1957).
32. J. F. Mead, *Federation Proc.*, **20**, 952 (1961).
33. W. Stoffel, *Biochem. Biophys. Res. Commun.*, **6**, 270 (1961).
34. R. Reiser and N. L. Murty, *Biochem. Biophys. Res. Commun.*, **5**, 265 (1961).
35. C. Yuan and K. Bloch, *J. Biol. Chem.*, **236**, 1277 (1961).

Since molecular oxygen is obligatory for the desaturation of stearic and palmitic acids in mammalian tissue, yeast, and aerobic bacteria, the presence of unsaturated fatty acids in anaerobic bacteria implies a second mode of origin.[28,36,37] Anaerobes are characterized by the production primarily of vaccenic acid and by the nonoccurrence of polyolefinic acids. This second synthetic route does not require oxygen and has been shown to involve a normal fatty acid synthetic sequence that leaves behind a residual unreduced olefin in the chain as chain extension proceeds. Thus labeled $1\text{-}C^{14}$-octanoic acid produces $\Delta^9\text{-}C_{16}$ and $\Delta^{11}\text{-}C_{18}$ (vaccenic) acids with the label position correct as shown by olefin cleavage; labeled decanoic acid[22,31] similarly affords $\Delta^7\text{-}C_{16}$ and $\Delta^9\text{-}C_{18}$. Both these precursors also produce saturated fatty acids, whereas labeled C_{12}- and C_{14}-saturated-precursor acids give only saturated fatty acids with radioactivity. Similarly, shorter-chain unsaturated acids with the olefin the same distance from the methyl end replaced vaccenic acid as a growth factor.[36] These and other experiments[28,27] show that, in anaerobic (and some aerobic) systems, the normal chain of events in saturated fatty acid synthesis branches at a chain of C_8 or C_{10}, proceeding by one path to saturated acids, by another to leave a double bond in the chain before proceeding to the full normal C_{16} or C_{18} length. It may be observed that the position of the double bond produced in this way (cf. vaccenic acid) is such that it must be produced by $\beta\text{-}\gamma$ elimination of the intermediate β-hydroxyacyl group; this abnormal dehydration is the step at which the unsaturated acid route branches off, since the unconjugated double bond so produced is not reducible by the normal synthetase mechanism. (In fact in none of the natural unconjugated olefins is the bond reducible in vivo.) A fatty acid synthetase has now been isolated[38] that does afford both saturated and unsaturated fatty acids and catalyzes the requisite $\beta\text{-}\gamma$ elimination.

The highly unsaturated acids found in fungi have been studied with C^{14} tracers and found to derive as expected. A complete degradation of nemotinic acid from labeled acetate demonstrated the anticipated alternation of labeled carbon atoms down the chain.[39] Although it has an odd number of carbon atoms, nemotinic acid [12] does co-occur with odyssic acid, [12], and other like pairs are known in fungi.

36. K. Hofmann, W. M. O'Leary, C. W. Yoho, and T. Y. Liu, *J. Biol. Chem.*, **234**, 1672 (1959).
37. H. Goldfine and K. Bloch, *J. Biol. Chem.*, **236**, 2596 (1961).
38. W. J. Lennarz, R. J. Light, and K. Bloch, *Proc. Natl. Acad. Sci. (U.S.)*, **48**, 840 (1962).
39. J. D. Bu'Lock and H. Gregory, *Biochem. J.*, **72**, 322 (1959).

It now seems likely that they are all acetogenins and that methyl groups attached to terminal acetylenes are easily lost (perhaps by oxidation to $HO—CH_2—C{\equiv}C—R$ and loss of formaldehyde). In a similar study labeled matricaria ester [13] was produced from 1-C^{14}-acetic acid and showed one-fifth of its activity on the carboxyl carbon (*) as expected.[40] Furthermore, radioactivity from diethyl 2-C^{14}-malonate is incorporated specifically into the first eight carbons of dehydromatricarianal [14] but only negligibly into the CH_3—C terminus (isolated by Kuhn-Roth oxidation)[41] in accord with the fatty acid sequence above.

$$R—C{\equiv}C—C{\equiv}C—CH{=}C{=}CH—\underset{\underset{\textstyle OH}{|}}{CH}—CH_2—CH_2—COOH$$

[12]

Nemotinic Acid (R = H)
Odyssic Acid (R = CH_3)

$$CH_3—CH{=}CH—C{\equiv}C—C{\equiv}C—CH{=}CH—\overset{*}{C}OOCH_3$$

[13]

Matricaria Ester

$$CH_3—(C{\equiv}C)_3—CH{=}CH—CH_2OH$$

[14]

Matricarianol

The question of chain branching in acetogenins may well be raised by considering that carboxylation of other acids to alkylmalonic coenzyme A and use of these for chain extension would provide a route to alkyl-branched chains. It is known that such carboxylations occur,[10] and propionyl carboxylase has been crystallized and studied in detail; its incorporation into fatty acid biosynthesis would give rise to methyl groups on alternate carbons of the chain. Although few acetogenin structures show this feature, certain macrolides are clear possibilities for such a biogenesis. In the case of methymycin[42] it

40. J. D. Bu'Lock, D. C. Allport, and W. B. Turner, *J. Chem. Soc.*, **1961**, 1654.

41. J. D. Bu'Lock and H. M. Smalley, *J. Chem. Soc.*, **1962**, 4662.

42. A. J. Birch, E. Pride, R. W. Rickards, P. J. Thomson, J. D. Dutcher, D. Perlman, and C. Djerassi, *Chem. & Ind. (London)*, **1960**, 1245.

has been shown with labeled methionine that the pendent methyl groups do not derive by methylation as they do in a number of other acetogenins (Section 5–2); labeled 1-C^{14}-propionate was well incorporated. The specificity of its incorporation was shown by Kuhn-Roth oxidation, which produced acetic acid bearing no radioactivity. Labeled acetate was poorly incorporated but is likely, on the basis of the structure of methymycin, to provide at least one skeletal C_2 unit.

The structure of erythromycin bears methyl groups at every alternate carbon and has been shown to arise entirely and specifically

$$\text{structure [15]}$$

11 O, 12, 10, 9, 13, CH$_3$, 8, 7, CHO, 14, 6, O, 5, 15, 16, 4, O-sugars, 3, OCH$_3$, 18 CH$_3$, 17, O, 1, 2, OCOCH$_3$

[15]

Magnamycin

from propionate by various tracer experiments.[43] In both these macrolides as well as magnamycin,[44] although methionine did not label the lactone methyls, it was the source of methyl groups on the appended sugar moieties. Studies were made on erythromycin with both 1-C^{14}- and 2-C^{14}-propionate as well as with methyl-labeled methylmalonic acid, which provided labeled methyl groups in erythronolide, as shown by Kuhn-Roth oxidation.[43] In view of the more elaborate postulated biogenesis (page 28) for magnamycin [15] its examination by tracer techniques is of special interest. Carbon 10 and its attached methyl are derived from propionate (as is C_9) in consonance with the other macrolides.[45,46] The other atoms are all derived from acetate directly, except carbons 5 to 8, which show negligible radioactivity

43. T. Kaneda, J. C. Butte, S. B. Taubman, and J. W. Corcoran, *J. Biol. Chem.*, **237**, 322 (1962).
44. H. Grisebach, H. Achenbach, and W. Hofheinz, *Tetrahedron Letters*, **1961**, 234.
45. D. Gilner and P. R. Srinivasan, *Biochem. Biophys. Res. Commun.*, **8**, 299 (1962).
46. H. Grisebach and H. Achenbach, *Z. Naturforsch.*, **17b**, 6 (1962); *Tetrahedron Letters*, **1962**, 569.

after feeding 1-C^{14}- or 2-C^{14}-acetic acid and degrading the molecule
the first three atoms were shown by difference, but direct isolation of
the aldehyde carbon from degradation fragments showed it to be
inactive.[46]   On the other hand, random-labeled glucose afforded considerable activity in these four carbons; hence the origin of that part of
the molecule, which caused difficulty for deducing the biogenesis, appears
to lie in some other metabolite than acetate.   Several branched-chain
mycolic acids from mycobacteria[47] are formed by carboxylation of
long-chain fatty acids and synthetase-type coupling of two, as in corynomycolic acid [18], which was shown to arise specifically from labeled
palmitic acid as its structure suggests.[48]

$$CH_3-(CH_2)_{14}-CO-S-CoA \quad + \quad \begin{matrix} CO-S-CoA \\ | \\ CH-(CH_2)_{13}CH_3 \\ | \\ (COOH) \end{matrix} \quad \rightarrow$$

[16]   [17]

$$CH_3-(CH_2)_{14}-CH-\begin{matrix} COOH \\ | \\ CH \\ | \\ OH \end{matrix}-(CH_2)_{13}-CH_3$$

[18]

Corynomycolic Acid

Finally it may be noted that the biosynthesis of fatty acids and related compounds with linear skeletons has been studied not only in
mammalian tissue but also in plants,[49–51] yeasts,[28–29] bacteria,[28,36,48]
and fungi[22,52]; the same detailed biosynthetic mechanisms discussed
above appear to operate generally in all these diverse organisms.

5–2   AROMATIC COMPOUNDS

Following his original development of the acetate hypothesis on
the grounds of structure comparison, as elaborated in the previous
chapters, Birch and his colleagues have proceeded to examine at some

47. J. Asselineau and E. Lederer, *Ann. Rev. Biochem.*, **30**, 71 (1961).

48. M. Gastambide-Odier and E. Lederer, *Nature*, **184**, 1563 (1959).

49. E. S. Barron, C. Squires, and P. K. Stumpf, *J. Biol. Chem.*, **236**, 2610 (1961).

50. M. D. Hatch and P. K. Stumpf, *J. Biol. Chem.*, **236**, 2879 (1961).

51. J. B. Mudd and P. K. Stumpf, *J. Biol. Chem.*, **236**, 2602 (1961).

52. F. Lynen, *Federation Proc.*, **20**, 2441 (1961).

ength the results of feeding labeled acetate to microorganisms and
ave adduced, in this way, an impressive body of direct evidence
upporting the hypothesis.   In broad outline, the method used involves
eeding the microorganism on a medium containing C^{14}-labeled acetate,
isolating the natural product of interest, and determining the radio-
ctivity of it and a variety of degradation products chosen to isolate

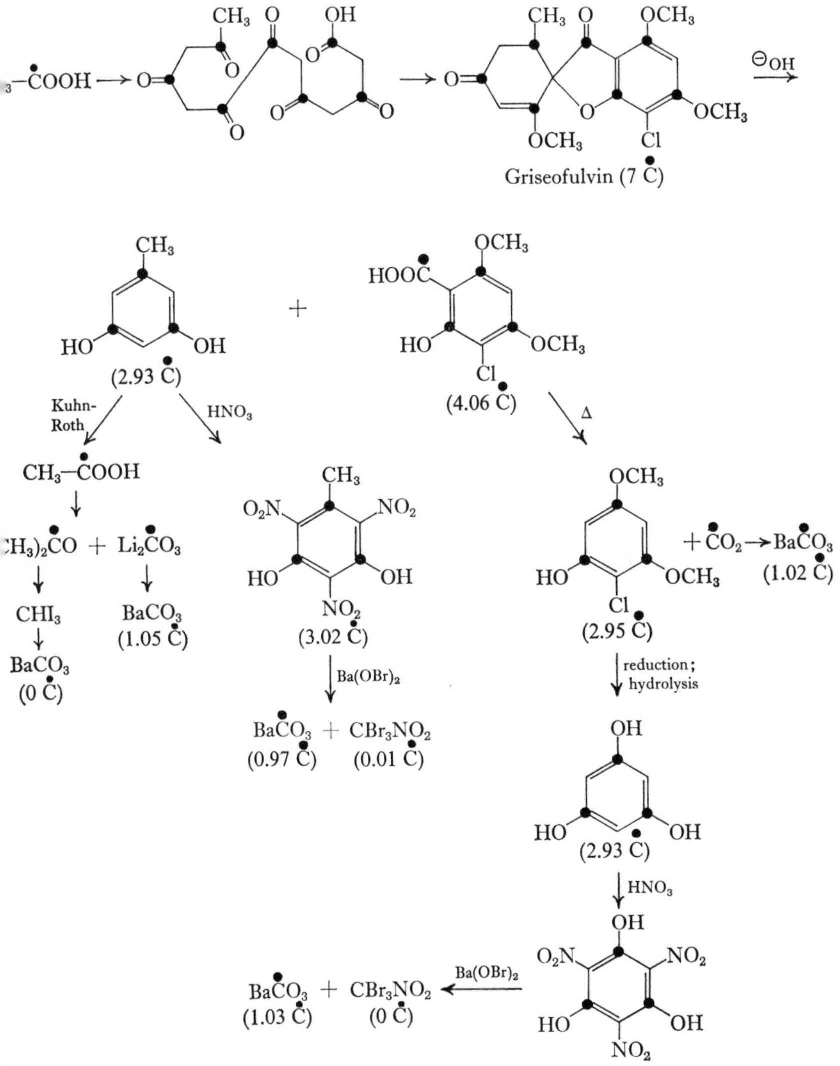

Chart IV *Degradation of radioactive griseofulvin*

separate skeletal carbons or groups of carbons, the relative radioactivity of which will be a direct indication of their origin. The general experience with labeled acetate (much of it in steroid studies, discussed in subsequent chapters) has been that, although carboxyl-labeled acetate yields products uniformly labeled at carboxyl-derived sites and quite unlabeled elsewhere, methyl-labeled acetate has a tendency to invest low levels of radioactivity uniformly in sites not derived from the acetate methyl. This result reflects the passage of some labeled acetate molecules through the tricarboxylic acid cycle prior to their incorporation into steroid or acetogenin molecules; such prior passage will be seen to regenerate only carboxyl-labeled acetate (and labeled carbon dioxide) from exogenous carboxyl-labeled acetate, but will scramble the labels of ingested methyl-labeled acetate to produce both methyl- and carboxyl-labeled acetate.

Several degradative reactions have been of special value in isolating the labels from the natural compounds. The Kuhn-Roth oxidation isolates the $C—CH_3$ groups of the molecule as acetic acid, the carbons of which may be further separated for radioactive counting by pyrolysis of the salt to a carbonate and acetone, which is further degraded by the iodoform reaction or by the Schmidt reaction to CO_2 and CH_3NH_2. The ubiquitous orcinol and phloroglucinol rings of acetogenins are degraded by nitration followed by bromination to bromopicrin, which contains the original "methylene" carbons of the phloroglucinol, and carbonate, representing the carbons bearing oxygen. A schematic representation of the detailed results from such a degradation on griseofulvin, presented in Chart IV, will illustrate the method and the results obtainable thereby.[53] The figures in parentheses represent the "relative molar activities" of radioactivity in each fragment, relative to the initial griseofulvin. The results dramatically support the acetate hypothesis and indicate clearly the incorporation of the carboxyl label (C^{14}) of the acetate used in feeding into the griseofulvin molecule at the sites marked with heavy dots.

Orsellinic and Related Aromatic Acids

The first acetogenin to be examined in this way was 6-methylsalicylic acid [20], produced by the same organism and found to arise from $1-C^{14}$-acetic acid with a labeling pattern similarly in strict conformity to the prediction of the acetate hypothesis.[54]   6-Methylsalicylic and

53. A. J. Birch, R. A. Massy-Westropp, R. W. Rickards, and H. Smith, *J. Chem. Soc.*, **1958**, 360.
54. A. J. Birch, R. A. Massy-Westropp, and C. J. Moye, *Australian J. Chem.*, **8**, 539 (1955).

orsellinic acids [20] are the primary examples of a fundamental mode of folding of the polyacetyl chain [19] and have since been studied in some detail. They should arise through extension of acetyl coenzyme A by successive reactions with three malonyl thioester molecules. When carboxyl-labeled acetate and unlabeled ethyl malonate were both fed to *Penicillium urticae* and the growth harvested in a short time (20 min to 3 hr), Birch[55] showed that C_6 was 12 to 15 per cent higher in incorporated activity than the carboxyl carbon; in ordinary labeled-acetate feeding they are of course the same. On the other hand, after feeding methylene-C^{14} ethyl malonate, Bu'Lock[56] degraded the 6-methylsalicylic acid produced by the Kuhn-Roth procedure and trapped the acetic acid and the CO_2 produced by the rest of the carbons as well. In this case the CO_2 contained all the malonate label, whereas when 1-C^{14}-acetic acid was fed the resultant CO_2 contained only 75 per cent and the acetic acid from the oxidation yielded the other 25 per cent, as

[19]   [20]

6-Methylsalicylic Acid (R = H)
Orsellinic Acid (R = OH)

predicted. Bassett and Tanenbaum[57] showed that labeled acetyl coenzyme A was converted directly to 6-methylsalicylic acid in *Penicillium patulum* without first reverting to free acetate. Lynen[52] has since shown that an enzyme extract from *Penicillium* catalyzed the reaction of one acetyl coenzyme A and three malonyl coenzyme A molecules to produce 6-methylsalicylic acid. In a different approach, the Swedish school[58] fed O^{18}-labeled acetate, isolated orsellinic acid,

55. A. J. Birch, A. Cassera, and R. W. Rickards, *Chem. & Ind. (London)*, **1961**, 792.
56. J. D. Bu'Lock, H. M. Smalley, and G. N. Smith, *Proc. Chem. Soc.*, **1961**, 209; *J. Biol. Chem.*, **237**, 1778 (1962).
57. E. W. Bassett and S. W. Tanenbaum, *Biochem. Biophys. Acta*, **40**, 535 (1960).
58. S. Gatenback and K. Mosbach, *Acta Chem. Scand.*, **13**, 1561 (1959).

and decarboxylated it. They were able to show that the excess O^1 per oxygen in the carboxyl group is half that in each phenolic hydroxyl which is the result expected if the O^{18} marker goes directly through the synthesis without random distribution, ending in orsellinic coenzyme A; the hydrolysis of the latter with unlabeled water dilutes the total carboxyl O^{18} per oxygen by half. Thus it is clear that the initial acetyl oxygens stay on a linear polyacetyl intermediate of four acetates in length and thereby are directly incorporated into the orsellinic acid.

Finally, it has been shown that appropriate labeled four-carbon precursors (butyrate, acetoacetate) are not converted intact into orsellinic acid but are degraded first to acetate.[59]

Among other simple, path-B acetogenins, the phthalic acid [21] related to orsellinic acid was isolated from *Penicillium islandicum* fed

[21]   [22]   [23] R = H or OH

Cyclopaldic Acid

1-C^{14}-acetate, and degraded by decarboxylation followed by bromo-picrin degradation of the ring.[60] Similarly, the orsellinic origin of cyclopaldic acid [22] was confirmed[61] by labeling with acetic acid-1-C^{14}. The C^{14} from the carboxyl of acetate was shown to exist at the marked sites (heavy dots) in these molecules. Hess[62] has shown that the dep-sides normally produced by lichens (symbiotic fungi + algae) are not produced by the fungus grown separately but that only an orsellinic moiety of the depside appears. In particular the fungus produced only orsellinic and haematommic (3-formyl-orsellinic) acids, whereas the whole lichen produced only depsides of these and not the parent acids; hence both partners are required for depside production.

In connection with the postulation of C-methylation of a polyacetyl chain (Section 3-2), the compound mycophenolic acid [24] is particu-

59. J. H. Birkinshaw and A. Gowlland, *Biochem. J.*, **84**, 342 (1962).
60. S. Gatenback, *Acta Chem. Scand.*, **12**, 1985 (1958).
61. A. J. Birch and M. Kocor, *J. Chem. Soc.*, **1960**, 866.
62. D. Hess, *Z. Naturforsch.*, **14b**, 345 (1959).

arly suited for study, for it possesses both C—CH$_3$ and O—CH$_3$
groups (marked Δ), which would be predicted to arise by the action
of a methylating agent.   When the fungus (*Penicillium brevi-compactum*)
was fed methyl-labeled methionine, a high incorporation of radioactivity was found[63]; the acid was degraded first by hydriodic acid to
remove the methyl from oxygen, and second by ozonolysis followed by
Kuhn-Roth on the resulting aromatic degradation product.   In this
way it was ascertained that the two methyl groups did in fact share
equally the entire radioactivity in mycophenolic acid which derived
from methionine, thus offering corroboration of the postulated operation
of C- as well as O-methylation in the acetate hypothesis.   The O-
methyl groups of griseofulvin were also shown to arise from the one-
carbon metabolic pool by labeling experiments feeding methyl-labeled

[24]	[25]	[26]
Mycophenolic Acid	Mevalonic Acid Lactone	Auroglaucin

choline.[64]   When the organism was fed carboxyl-labeled acetate and
degraded,[65] the orsellinic-type aromatic ring of mycophenolic acid
was found to possess the expected labeling pattern (asterisks).   Since
the mutilated terpenoid sidechain should arise by C-alkylation with
geranyl pyrophosphate, itself derived from mevalonic acid ([25], see
Section 4-4 and 6-4), the latter compound, labeled at C-2, was fed to the
organism, and the isolated mycophenolic acid was found to have only
one labeled carbon, and that in the levulinic acid obtained on ozonolysis,
thus supporting the C-alkylation hypothesis (the label is presumably

63. A. J. Birch, R. J. English, R. A. Massy-Westropp, M. Slaytor, and H.
    Smith, *J. Chem. Soc.*, **1958**, 365.
64. D. J. Hockenhull and W. F. Faulds, *Chem. & Ind. (London)*, **1955**,
    1390.
65. A. J. Birch, R. J. English, R. A. Massy-Westropp, and H. Smith,
    J. Chem. Soc., **1958**, 369.

at the circled carbon in [24]) and afforded the additional useful infor-
mation that mevalonic acid is not appreciably reconverted to acetate to
find its way into the aromatic nucleus.

More recent work [66] has established that $4\text{-}C^{14}$-mevalonic acid
lactone gives rise to specific equal labeling at the two anticipated positions, marked with a heavy dot. Furthermore, on steam distillation
after feeding $2\text{-}C^{14}$-mevalonic, the second isoprenoid label of the
geranyl precursor was isolated as acetone with activity equal to that
of the mycophenolic acid. This result implies that the oxidative
cleavage of the geranyl group occurs after its incorporation on the
mycophenolic aromatic nucleus. When labeled orsellinic acid was
fed to the organism, incorporation was poor, and the label turned up
in the corresponding position in mycophenolic acid only to an extent
of about one-fourth, indicating previous degradation in part to smaller
units.[66] Such a result may be due to problems of assimilation of the
orsellinic acid fed to the organism or it may suggest that the precursor
of mycophenolic acid is [23] (R = OH; cf. page 62) instead; the
compounds [23] accompany mycophenolic acid in *P. brevi-compactum*
and in growing experiments were found to reach a maximum concentration in early growth, which later decreased. The pentaacetyl [23]
(R = H) should be mechanistically easier to oxidize than orsellinic acid,
and hydrolytic cleavage of the extra acetyl would be unexceptional
(Section 3-2).

Alkylation with mevalonic acid was also demonstrated in the case
of auroglaucin,[68] in the biosynthesis of which the $2\text{-}C^{14}$ label of mevalonic acid appeared only on a methyl group of the isoprene fragment as
anticipated (ozonolysis yielded acetone, which contained all the activity).
The origin of the nucleus from $1\text{-}C^{14}$-acetate (heavy dots) was also shown
to follow the familiar path-B sequence with the feature of a terminal
carboxyl apparently reduced to the aldehyde state (cf. discussion of
citrinin, pages 75 and 147).

Mycelianamide [27] appears on inspection to be a $\phi\text{-}C_3$ fragment
with the sidechain oxidation state of phenylpyruvic acid and a terpenoid
ether grouping; feeding experiments with tracers demonstrated,[54]
as in mycophenolic acid, that mevalonic acid is an irreversible precursor
of the C_{10} sidechain; appropriately, the griseofulvin simultaneously
elaborated contains no labeled carbons from mevalonic acid. With

66. A. J. Birch, et al., quoted by R. W. Rickards in Ref. 67, Chap. 2.
67. W. D. Ollis (ed.), *The Chemistry of Natural Phenolic Compounds*,
   Pergamon, London, 1961.
68. A. J. Birch, J. Schofield, and H. Smith, *Chem. & Ind. (London)*, **1958**,
   1321.

ιoth labeled acetate and mevalonic acid, furthermore, there is only ιegligible incorporation of radioactivity into the ϕ-C_3 portion of ιιycelianamide, as would be anticipated from the presumed origins of ιhenylpyruvic acids from shikimic and pyruvic acids (Section 3–1).

[27]
Mycelianamide

Complex Polycyclic Metabolites

Tracer experiments were similarly used on the complex metabιlites citrinin **[28]**, citromycetin **[30]**, and sclerotiorin **[34]**, each of ιvhich was separately produced with labeled acetate and formate. Γhe labeling pattern of citrinin, examined in some detail,[69] corresponds ιo the prediction of Section 4–5 as shown ($\bullet$ = acetate carboxyl, ι = formate) and validates the possibility of reducing the terminal ιarboxyl of the polyacetyl chain to the aldehyde oxidation state it bears ιn citrinin. The alternative origin of the terminal aldehyde from ι one-carbon alkylation is ruled out, but reduction of the ketone in ι longer precursor chain, followed by retroaldol cleavage, remains a ιalid and attractive alternative (page 75). Citrinin biosynthesis was ιndependently studied by Schwenk,[70] who confirmed the acetate origin ιf the nucleus and showed that labeled methionine was a more efficient ιrecursor than formate of the two extra methyl groups and the carboxyl, ιvhereas radioactive bicarbonate and propionate were not utilized. It ιvas also observed that the two methyls and the carboxyl were incorιιorated at the same radioactivity level from the methionine, suggesting ιhat they are all first placed as methyl groups and that the carboxyl arises ιιy later oxidation.

Of interest in connection with methylation are some experiments ιn the origin of the methylenedioxy carbon in the alkaloid protopine,[71]

69. A. J. Birch, P. Fitton, E. Pride, A. J. Ryan, H. Smith, and W. B. Whalley, *J. Chem. Soc.*, **1958**, 4576.
70. E. Schwenk, G. J. Alexander, A. McGold, and D. F. Stevens, *J. Biol. Chem.*, **233**, 1211 (1958).
71. M. Scribney and S. Kirkwood, *Nature*, **171**, 931 (1953).

which appears with radioactivity equal to that in the N-CH$_3$ grou
when fed methyl-labeled methionine; since labeled formate is nc
incorporated, it appears that the catechol is first methylated, the
oxidized to methylenedioxy, rather than being methylenated from a one
carbon metabolic pool (as with an equivalent of formaldehyde).

The biosynthesis of citromycetin [30] was, however, found[6]

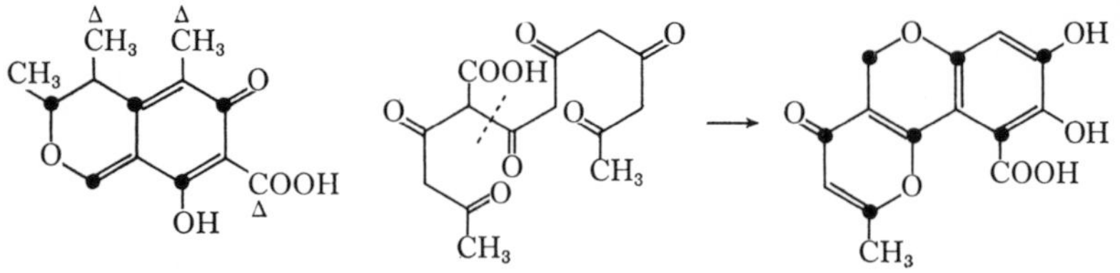

[28]   [29]   [30]
Citrinin   Citromycetin

to proceed entirely from seven acetate units without incorporation o
any one-carbon fragment (see Section 4–4); the seven equally labele
carbons incorporated from carboxyl-labeled acetate are as shown.   Thus
citromycetin may be an example of a biogenetic variant not hithert
touched on (and likely to be rare) in which a branched chain emerge
from condensations of acetate units, the branching indicated by th
dotted line in [29].   Such condensations are mechanistically analogou
to the acylation and aldol condensations of Section 3–2.   An alternate
more complex scheme, which equally explains the result, was offere

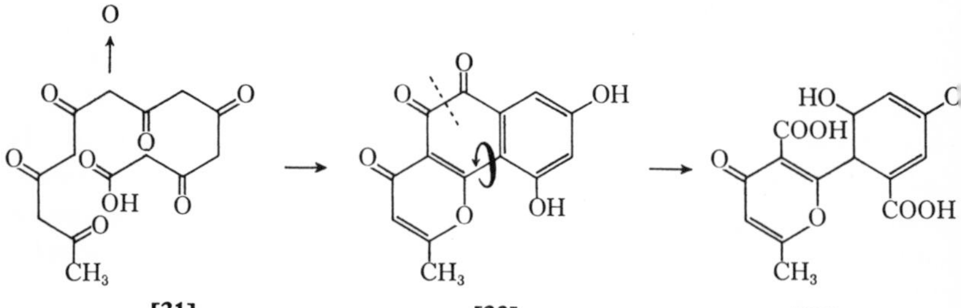

[31]   [32]   [33]

by Whalley[72] with the observation that a single long chain might under
go such an acylation internally, to be followed by a cleavage of the chai
(·······) as shown in [31] → [33].

72. W. B. Whalley, in Ref. 67, Chap. 3.

The complex condensation product sclerotiorin [34] exists with a number of similar compounds in *Penicillium* species, the structures of all of which imply the reduction of terminal carboxyl already established for auroglaucin [26] and citrinin [28]. Sclerotiorin biogenesis was examined with both 1-C^{14}- and 2-C^{14}-acetic acid as well as with C^{14}-formate.[69] The latter was incorporated solely into the added methyl groups as would be expected of a one-carbon metabolic pool that provided methylating agents when supplied with a number of C_1 precursors such as formate. No appreciable "crossing over" of labels from one source to another was observed, a fact that strengthens the validity of the tracer approach. The labeling pattern that conforms with the degradative results is shown in [34]. Entirely analogous results were

[34]   [35]
Sclerotiorin   Fuscin

source: ● = $CH_3\overset{\bullet}{C}OOH$
        * = $\overset{*}{C}H_3COOH$
        Δ = HCOOH

obtained with the closely related metabolites, rotiorin, monascin, and rubropunctatin (see Section 4–5).[73]

The complex acetogenins fuscin [35] and alternariol [36], both discussed in Section 4–5, have been subjected to similar tracer studies with the expected results. Thus, 1-C^{14}-acetic acid was incorporated into fuscin[66] as shown in [35], and 2-C^{14}-mevalonic acid lactone labeled only the methyls on the chromane ring. Analogously, degradation of alternariol[74] produced from carboxyl-labeled acetate showed radioactivity, as anticipated, specifically at the positions marked in [36]. The metabolite curvularin [37] may be compared to the macrolides, the large-ring lactone having here undergone an internal condensation of the characteristic acetogenin fashion to the orcinol ring. When

73. A. J. Birch, A. Cassera, P. Fitton, J. S. E. Holker, H. Smith, G. A. Thompson, and W. B. Whalley, *J. Chem. Soc.*, **1962**, 3583.
74. R. Thomas, *Proc. Chem. Soc.*, **1959**, 88.

fed carboxyl-labeled acetate,[75] the parent fungus produced radioactive curvularin yielding, upon Kuhn-Roth oxidation, acetic acid the carboxyl of which contained one-eighth of the molecular activity of the curvularin. A hydrobromic acid cleavage (at ········) yielded two C_8 fragments of equal activity. These results are in harmony with the prediction.

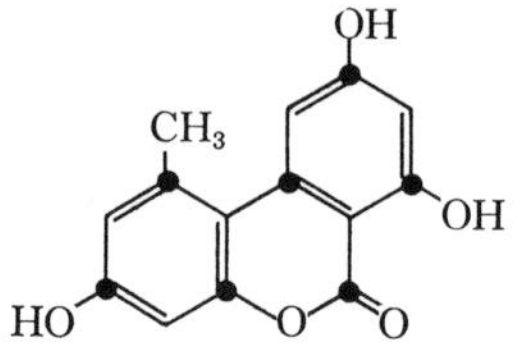

[36]   **[37]**

Alternariol   Curvularin

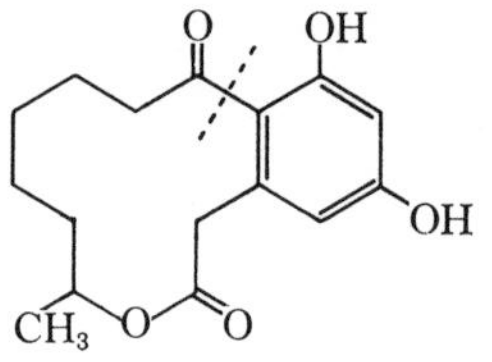

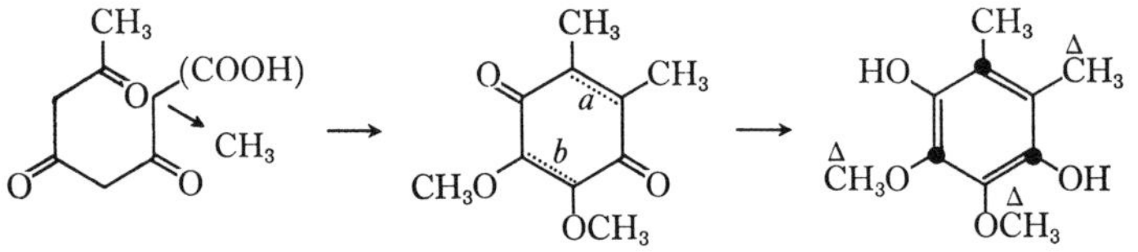

[38]   **[39]**   **[40]**

Aurantiogliocladin (bonds at *a* and *b*)
Rubriogliocladin (the quinhydrone)
Gliorosein (bond at *a* or *b*)

Quinones

A series of quinones bearing both C- and O-methylation (see aurantiogliocladin, rubriogliocladin, and gliorosein **[39]**) anticipated to arise as indicated **[38]** by an orsellinic route, are all produced by one fungus. This was examined[76] by feeding labeled acetate as well as labeled formate (in separate experiments), the latter assumed as before to participate freely in a one-carbon pool. The results from degradation of **[40]** were consistent with acetate-carboxyl labeling, as shown by heavy dots, and formate origin of the methyl groups, marked Δ. These compounds lend much support to the notion that, although considerable methylation and oxidation may occur in biogenesis to obscure the normal pattern, the compounds are often still acetogenins (see the

75. A. J. Birch, O. C. Musgrave, R. W. Rickards, and H. Smith, *J. Chem. Soc.*, **1959**, 3146.
76. A. J. Birch, R. I. Fryer, and H. Smith, *Proc. Chem. Soc.*, **1958**, 343.

discussion of gladiolic acid, flavipin, etc., in Section 4–4). Further evidence was afforded by a study of *p*-methoxytoluquinone bio-synthesis,[66] which showed that labeled 6-methylsalicylic acid was in fact a precursor but that labeled orsellinic acid was not; the latter piece of evidence is of value also in confirming the reduction and removal of polyacetyl oxygens only before aromatization (Chapter 3).   The same labeled acids behaved in a parallel fashion when used as precursors of aurantiogliocladin; the reason for nonincorporation of orsellinic acid here is less clear.   Orsellinic and 6-methylsaliccylic acids have been implicated in the synthesis of gentisic acid as well as patulin, pencillic acid, and the tropolones, all discussed in Section 5–4.

In studies on *Daldinia concentrica* Allport and Bu'Lock[77] showed the origin of the chromanone **[41]** (cf. page 79) to be acetate, the carboxyl labels of which were found specifically as anticipated (heavy dots). He also found that exogenous labeled orsellinic acid was not converted to **[41]**, so that the latter presumably arises from a pentaacetyl

chain **[42]** cyclized only *after* all four malonyl units have been added to the terminal acetyl.   The same fungus produced 1,8-dimethoxy-naphthalene **[43]** and **[44]**, which probably arise by methylation and oxidative coupling, respectively, on the 1,8-dihydroxynaphthalene pre-cursor; this precursor may in turn arise from the same pentaacetyl chain that cyclizes to the chromanone **[41]** by a slight variation in the mode of condensation (curved arrow in **[42]**).   Several strains of the fungus lacked the enzymes required to carry out certain steps in this scheme, as shown by the lack of certain of these metabolites in various cultures.[77]

The first anthraquinone to be examined in this way with 1-C^{14}-acetate was helminthosporin **[45]**; a Kuhn-Roth oxidation yielded

77. D. C. Allport and J. D. Bu'Lock, *J. Chem. Soc.*, **1958**, 4090; **1960**, 654.

acetic acid bearing one-seventh of the total activity of the isolated quinone, as expected from the predicted pattern (heavy dots) of carboxyl origin in the molecule.[78] Extensive investigations of the anthraquinone pigments of *Penicillium islandicum* have been carried out by Gatenbeck.[60,79] First, emodin ([46], obtained by reducing the dimeric skyrin [page 91] produced by the mold) was investigated with 1-C^{14}- and 2-C^{14}-acetic acid. In the former case, Kuhn-Roth oxidation produced acetic acid, which showed one-seventh of the emodin activity (heavy dot), whereas in the latter more extensive degradation ultimately involving the bromopicrin cleavage showed methyl labels at the sites in [46] marked with asterisks. A complete

[45]

Helminthosporin (R_1 = H; R_2 = OH)
Islandicin (R_1 = OH; R_2 = H)

[46]

Emodin

degradation of islandicin [45] from carboxyl-labeled acetate confirmed the labeling pattern shown (heavy dots). Doubly labeled acetic acid (CH_3—$C^{14}O_2^{18}H$) was then employed, and the isolated emodin and islandicin were found to contain roughly equal levels of C^{14} radioactivity. The prediction of oxygen labeling from examination of the formulas is that the emodin should have four and the islandicin three (ratio = 4/3 = 1.33) labeled oxygens per molecule; the ratio found for the two molecules was in fact 1.28, which provides strong support for the view that the initial acetate passes, through the polyacetyl chain, into the anthraquinone quite directly and without serious intermediate mixing or exchange. It was found, in fact, that uptake of radioactive acetate into the molds in these experiments was very rapid and that the ratio of C^{14} to O^{18} in the quinones in the double-label experiment was essentially the same as that in the given acetate. In another oxygen-labeling experiment, rubroskyrin (page 91) was isolated and the secondary hydroxyl removed by pyrolytic dehydration; this H_2O so obtained proved to have about one-half the O^{18} content of the islandicin from the

78. A. J. Birch, A. J. Ryan, and H. Smith, *J. Chem. Soc.*, **1958**, 4773.
79. S. Gatenbeck, *Acta. Chem. Scand.*, **14**, 102, 230, 296 (1960).

same culture (expected, approximately one-third). Plots of radioactivity vs. time on pigment production by these *Penicillia* imply that the various anthraquinones are not interconvertible but are formed from a common, presumably *prearomatic*, precursor; a search of mutants failed to produce any aromatic compound from pigment-free mutants. Rugulosin, another similar dimeric *Penicillium* anthraquinone, has been subjected to tracer studies with both labeled acetate and malonate separately[80] and found to arise in the predicted differential manner, acetate incorporating in the terminal C-methyl and malonate accounting for the other positions.

Partial investigation of three other anthraquinones has been

[47]
Cynodontin

[48]
Phomarizin

[49]
ε-Pyrromycinone

reported. Cynodontin [47] was fed both carboxyl- and methyl-labeled acetic acid and degraded by Kuhn-Roth oxidation.[81] In the latter case the isolated acetic acid possessed one-eighth of the total quinone activity; in the former the acetic acid produced showed one-seventh of the activity, this being as expected, since the biogenesis from eight acetates requires loss of the terminal carboxyl in producing cynodontin (Section 4–5).

Phomarizin [48] was similarly examined[81] with both labeled acetic acids and with formate, 75 per cent of the label of the latter residing on the methoxy CH_3. Methyl-labeled acetate provided labeled phomarizin, which, on Kuhn-Roth oxidation, produced CO_2 with one-eighth of the total activity on pyrolysis, and acetic acid with another eighth. A similar proportion of the label resided in the carboxyl of acetic acid from Kuhn-Roth oxidation after feeding carboxyl-labeled acetate. It was suggested, therefore, that a polyacetyl chain served as a linear forerunner of that part of the molecule above the dotted line and that glycine was the probable origin of the nitrogenous moiety below.

80. S. Shibata and T. Ikekawa, *Chem. & Ind.* (*London*), **1962**, 360.
81. A. J. Birch, R. I. Fryer, P. J. Thomson, and H. Smith, *Nature*, **190**, 441 (1961).

Similar tracer experiments[82] have shown that the ethyl group of ε-pyrromycinone ([49]; see page 153) originates in propionic acid, whereas acetic acid is incorporated into the remainder of the molecule. Hence this molecule provides an example of initiation of a polyacetyl chain by a molecule of propionic acid, followed by malonyl chain extension. Other examples of propionate incorporation were found in the macrolides (Section 5–1).

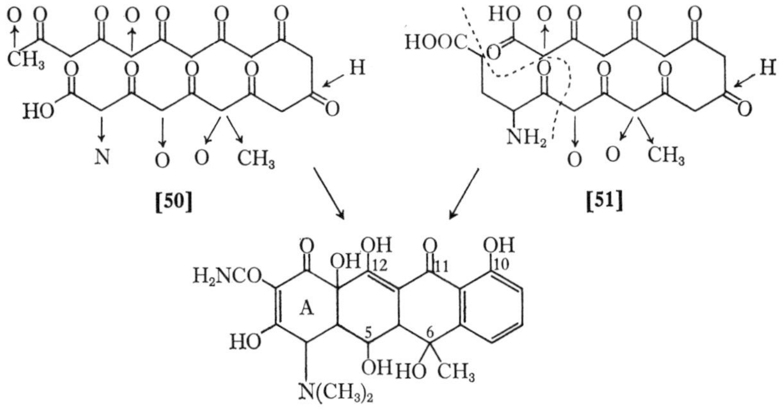

[50]

[51]

[52]

Terramycin

Two views of tetracycline biosynthesis have been advanced, in one of which, [50], ten acetates in a linear chain cyclize and add nitrogen as well as some normal hydroxyl and methyl at methylene sites. In the other, [51], the difficulties of losing the initial acetate methyl and of incorporating nitrogen are overcome by incorporation of a molecule of glutamic acid (below dotted line), reminiscent of the glycine suggestion in phomarizin [48]. Detailed degradation has shown that the region from C_5 to C_{12} derives in fact from acetate,[83] as anticipated by both schemes, and that labeled methionine provides the three methyl groups. Glutamic acid-2-C^{14} afforded a tetracycline labeled preferentially in ring A[84]; on the other hand, ring-A labeling, although apparently

82. W. D. Ollis, I. O. Sutherland, R. C. Codner, J. J. Gordon, and G. A. Miller, *Proc. Chem. Soc.*, **1960**, 347.
83. A. J. Birch, J. F. Snell, and P. L. Thompson, *J. Am. Chem. Soc.*, **82**, 2402 (1960); *J. Chem. Soc.*, **1962**, 425.
84. J. F. Snell, R. L. Wagner, and F. A. Hochstein, *Proc. Intern. Conf. Peaceful Uses At. Energy, Geneva*, **1955**, 431.

at a lower level than that in the other rings, arose from feeding labeled acetate.[83] Specific degradations of the A ring are difficult and the matter remains unresolved.

Finally it may be added that Birch[85] has made some investigations in vitro on the chemistry of poly-β-ketones as models for the polyacetyl chain. Collie's experiments (page 16) with diacetylacetone [53] were confirmed and some new products isolated, including [54] and [55], which may be compared with the natural naphthalene, chimaphilline [58]. Using the phenyl-terminated polyacetyl derivative [56], they were able to synthesize the natural dihydropinosylvin [57] by mild basic catalysis. Such experiments are of interest in confirming the capability of polyacetyl chains to undergo the postulated and often complex condensations of the acetate hypothesis.

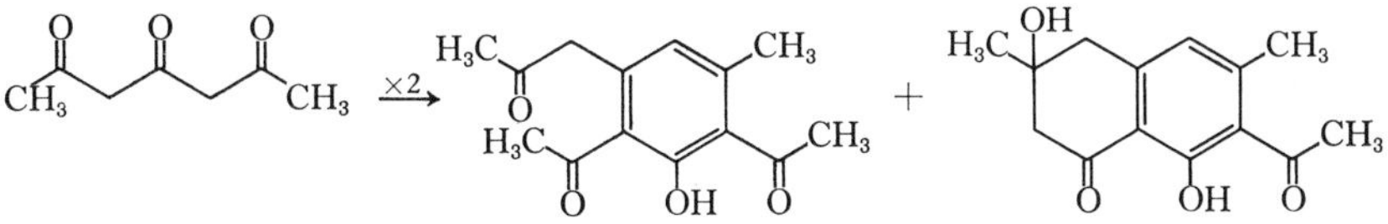

[53]   [54]   [55]

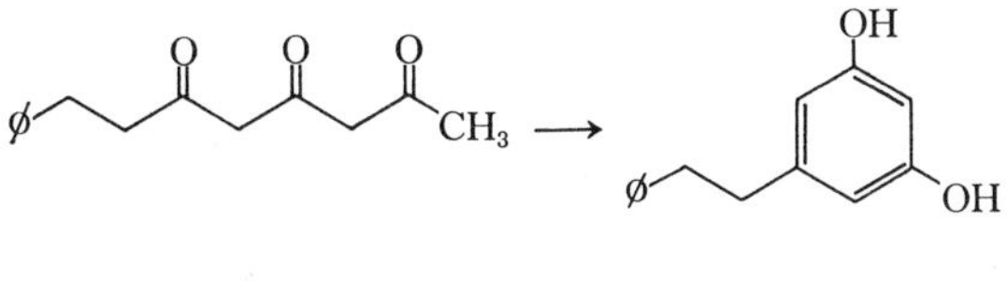

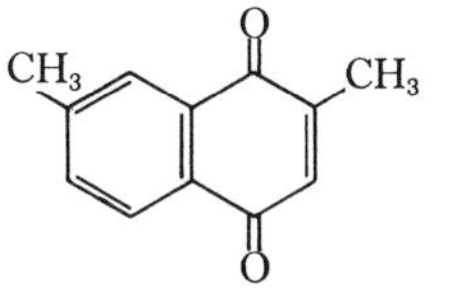

[56]   [57]   [58]

Dihydropinosylvin   Chimaphilline

5-3 PHENYLPROPANOID AND FLAVONOID COMPOUNDS

The question of acetate involvement in the biosynthesis of phenyl-propanoids has been examined in several cases, in each of which their origin via the shikimic-pyruvate pathway rather than by the benzoyl-acetate route is confirmed. In particular, in *Salvia* species Neish[86] found that generally labeled shikimic acid (biosynthetic from $C^{14}O_2$) was incorporated into caffeic acid (3,4-dihydroxycinnamic) only in

85. A. J. Birch, D. W. Cameron, and R. W. Rickards, *J. Chem. Soc.*, **1960**, 4395.
86. D. R. McCalla and A. C. Neish, *Can. J. Biochem. Physiol.*, **37**, 531, 537 (1959).

the aromatic ring and not in the sidechain, whereas Geissman[87] found that labeled phenylalanine but not acetate yielded active caffeic acid. In other studies[88] labeled acetate was not incorporated in the vanillin, syringaldehyde, or phenylpropanoid compounds that are isolated from lignins after feeding. A number of studies of the ϕ-C_3 portion of lignin have been made,[89–93] but in view of the complex nature of lignin, the results must be treated with greater reserve. Nevertheless, the results are consistent, shikimic acid, phenylalanine, and various cinnamic acid labels incorporating into the lignin (ϕ-C_3) aromatic ring and sidechain. 3,4-Dihydroxybenzoic acid and other

[60]   [61]

Volucrisporin

ϕ-C_1 compounds again were not precursors of the ϕ-C_3 unit.[90] In the fungal metabolite mycelianamide, the ϕ-C_3 portion was similarly free of acetate label (page 146). Similarly, the fungal terphenyl, volucrisporin [61], is labeled by exogenous phenylalanine, meta-tyrosine, or shikimic acid but not by acetate, the biogenesis presumably being from a phenylpyruvic acid [60] (see Section 4-2).[94]

It has been observed, however, that phenylpyruvic acids themselves have not been found in plants,[95] and recent evidence supports a route

87. T. A. Geissman and T. Swain, *Chem. & Ind.* (*London*), **1957**, 984.
88. S. A. Brown and A. C. Neish, *J. Am. Chem. Soc.*, **81**, 2419 (1959).
89. S. A. Brown and A. C. Neish, *Nature*, **175**, 688 (1955).
90. S. A. Brown and A. C. Neish, *Can. J. Biochem. Physiol.*, **33**, 948 (1955); **34**, 769 (1956).
91. G. Eberhardt and W. J. Schubert, *J. Am. Chem. Soc.*, **78**, 2835 (1956).
92. S. N. Acerbo, W. J. Schubert, and F. F. Nord, *J. Am. Chem. Soc.*, **80**, 1990 (1958).
93. H. Shimazono, W. J. Schubert, and F. F. Nord, *J. Am. Chem. Soc.*, **80**, 1992 (1958).
94. G. Read, L. C. Vining, and R. H. Haskins, *Can. J. Chem.*, **40**, 2357 (1962).
95. R. M. Krupka and G. H. N. Towers, *Botan. Rev.*, **25**, 108 (1959).

in which this key intermediate is most commonly converted first to phenylalanine, which in turn serves as the general precursor of phenylpropanoids via initial deamination to cinnamic acid. A phenylalanine deaminase has recently been isolated by Koukol and Conn [96] in a partially purified state from barley and other plants; this enzyme quantitatively and irreversibly converts phenylalanine directly to *trans*-cinnamic acid and ammonia. A comparable enzyme, named tyrase, similarly converts tyrosine to *p*-coumaric acid and ammonia in equimolar amounts.[97] In other tracer experiments Neish [86] found that *Salvia* species could convert the simpler to the more complex acids of the following series but not the reverse, hence the postulation of this biogenetic course: cinnamic → *p*-coumaric → caffeic-ferulic (3-O-methyl-caffeic) → sinapic [62]. Also, cinnamic acid and phenylalanine are generally found to be good labeling precursors of the hydroxylated ϕ-C_3 acids derived from shikimic acids. Isolation of various quinic acid esters has

[62]
Sinapic Acid

[63]
Quinic Acid Cinnamate

→ *p*-Coumaric Ester of Quinic Acid

↓

Chlorogenic Acid
(Caffeic Ester of Quinic Acid)

led to the view [98] that the hydroxylations of cinnamic acid occur on the quinic acid esters (cf. [63]).

Pungenin, a glucoside of 3,4-dihydroxyacetophenone, has been shown to have a shikimic origin as its hydroxylation pattern suggests (page 46); the best tracer precursors were phenylalanine and caffeic acid, whereas labeled cinnamic, *p*-coumaric, phenyl-lactic, and shikimic acids were also good, but C^{14}-acetic acid was very poorly incorporated.[99] Degradation of the sidechain showed specific labeling from the phenylpropanoid precursors as expected for origin through decarboxylation of a benzoylacetic acid arising from caffeic acid.

96. J. Koukol and E. E. Conn, *J. Biol. Chem.*, **236**, 2692 (1961).
97. A. C. Neish, *Phytochemistry*, **1**, 1 (1961).
98. C. C. Levy and M. Zucker, *J. Biol. Chem.*, **235**, 2418 (1960).
99. A. C. Neish, *Can. J. Botany*, **37**, 1085 (1959).

Coumarin [66] has been variously examined with tracers with the observations that labeled shikimic acid, phenylalanine, cinnamic, and o-coumaric acids were all incorporated well and with little randomization of label; however labeled acetate incorporation was very poor.[100] Labeled acetate was found not to be incorporated in coumarin biosynthesis in sweet clover, but the entire carbon skeleton of phenylalanine was incorporated.[101] Labeled coumarin was itself shown to yield dihydro-o-coumaric (melilotic acid).[102,103] Studies of the ortho-oxidation process have yielded a partially purified enzyme[104] (a β-glucosidase) from sweet clover, which cleaves cis-o-coumaryl β-glucoside but not trans, although genetic studies[105] point to coumarin biosynthesis from the action of β-glucosidase on the ortho-glucoside grouping, thus freeing the phenolic hydroxyl for spontaneous lactonization. Furthermore, C^{14}-tracer studies in sweet clover with labeled trans-

[64]   trans-[65]   cis-[65]   [66]

trans-Cinnamic Acid   Coumarin

cinnamic acid [64] show[103] its conversion to coumarin via the glucosides of trans-coumaric and cis-coumaric acids [65] successively. These studies tentatively suggest that the carboxyl of the cinnamic acid is not directly involved in the oxidation step producing the ortho-hydroxyl, in contravention of the several mechanistically reasonable proposals of Section 4-2.

The more complex coumarin, scopoletin [67], has been investigated[106] in tracer experiments on tobacco, which showed that, although phenylalanine is an excellent precursor, acetic and phenylacetic acids

100. S. A. Brown, G. H. N. Towers, and D. Wright, Can. J. Biochem. Physiol., 38, 143 (1960).
101. F. Weygand and H. Wendt, Z. Naturforsch., 14b, 421 (1959).
102. T. Kosuge and E. E. Conn, J. Biol. Chem., 234, 2133 (1959).
103. J. R. Stoker and D. M. Bellis, J. Biol. Chem., 237, 2303 (1962).
104. T. Kosuge and E. E. Conn, J. Biol. Chem., 236, 1617 (1961).
105. G. W. Schaeffer, F. A. Haskins, and H. J. Gorz, Biochem. Biophys. Res. Commun., 3, 268 (1960).
106. W. W. Reid, Chem. & Ind. (London), 1958, 1439.

are not. Scopoletin has also been shown to arise from labeled ferulic acid.[107] The interesting observation has also been made that, on paper chromatography with trace metal ions present (and not when absent), caffeic acid affords 6,7-dihydroxycoumarin ([67], R = H) with great facility by aerial oxidation.[108] The mechanism of coniferyl alcohol oxidation discussed in Section 4-2 for lignification is probably applicable here.

The fungal coumarin, novobiocin [68], was shown to arise from uniformyl labeled tyrosine, which is incorporated whole (all nine carbons) into the coumarin portion of novobiocin.[109] The 3-amino group is of course correctly placed to imply that even the amine of tyrosine has remained on the skeleton throughout. No 5,7-dioxy-coumarins have yet been examined (cf. page 38).

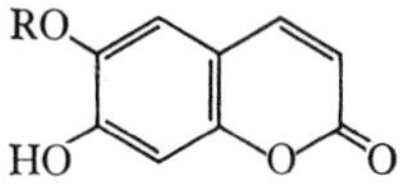

[67]

Scopoletin (R = CH₃)

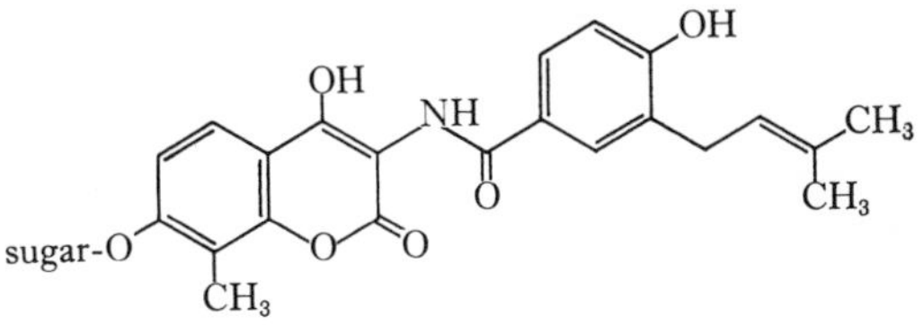

[68]

Novobiocin

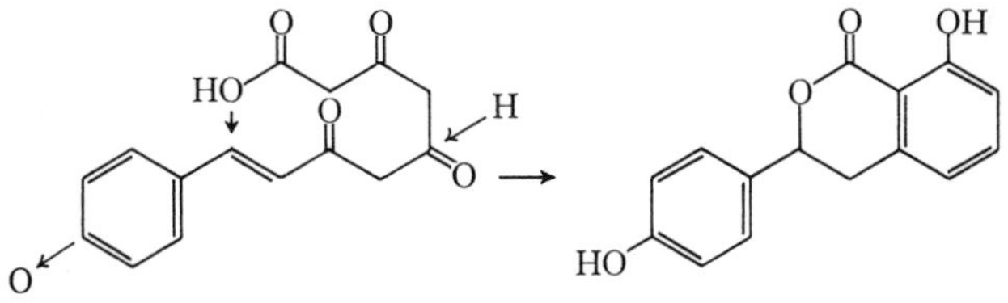

[69]

[70]
Hydrangeol

The cases referred to above go far to establish the universality of origin of the phenylpropanoid skeletons from the shikimic-pyruvic pathway; the subsequent cases, dealing with incorporation of the ϕ-C_3 unit into acetogenins, equally substantiate this mode of origin. For

107. H. Reznik and R. Urban, *Naturwissenschaften*, **44**, 13, 592 (1957).
108. N. L. Butler and H. W. Siegelman, *Nature*, **183**, 1813 (1959).
109. K. Chambers, G. W. Kenner, M. J. T. Robinson, and B. R. Webster, *Proc. Chem. Soc.*, **1960**, 291.

example, both labeled phenylalanine and acetate were found[110] to serve as good precursors (cf. [69]) of radioactive hydrangeol [70] in *Hydrangea macrophylla*, although degradations to ascertain position and specificity of labels were not reported. Such detailed degradations were done in recent studies[111] of the stilbene glucosides, piceid and rhapontin (only the parent phenols are shown in [71]). Labeled phenylalanines and acetate were fed and either *p*-hydroxybenzaldehyde or isovanillic acid isolated from the left-hand ring in [71] and α-resorcylic acid from the right-hand ring by oxidative degradation. In accordance with

[71]   [72]   [73]

Piceid (R = X = H)   Isovanillic Acid   α-Resorcylic Acid
Rhapontin (R = CH₃; X = OH)
Aglycones

prediction (page 73) the label from C^{14}-acetate and 1-C^{14}-phenylalanine or 2-C^{14}-phenylalanine showed up only in [73], whereas that from 3-C^{14}-phenylalanine appeared in *p*-hydroxybenzaldehyde and [72].

Flavones and Isoflavones

The flavonoids have been subjected to several investigations by radioactive tracers. Grisebach[112] fed red cabbage seedlings on labeled acetate, isolated the radioactive cyanidin [78], converted it to phloroglucinol (from ring A), and degraded this by the bromopicrin method. Both 1-C^{14}- and 2-C^{14}-acetic acids were used, yielding results that clearly support the biogenesis of ring A from acetic acid. In another series of experiments,[113] labeled inositol was shown not to be a precursor. Finally, phenylalanine (uniformly labeled) was incorporated and the cyanidin degraded to inactive phloroglucinol and to active 3,4-dihydroxybenzoic acid (from ring B), which was uniformly

110. R. K. Ibrahim and G. H. N. Towers, *Can. J. Biochem. Physiol.*, **38**, 627 (1960).
111. W. E. Hillis and M. Hasegawa, *Chem. & Ind. (London)*, **1962**, 1330.
112. H. Grisebach, *Z. Naturforsch.*, **12b**, 227, 597 (1957).
113. F. Weygand, W. Brucker, H. Grisebach, and E. Schulze, *Z. Naturforsch.*, **12b**, 221 (1957).

labeled.[114]   Thus it was found that phenylalanine was an effective ring-B precursor, whereas in an analogous experiment coniferyl alcohol although not a cyanidin precursor, was converted to a flavone.

Quercetin [74] biogenesis has been investigated in buckwheat[115] with a series of radioactive precursors and degraded by permethylation and alkaline hydrolysis to veratric acid [75] and [76].   Good precursors of ring B were shikimic acid, phenylalanine, cinnamic and p-hydroxy-cinnamic acids, but p-hydroxybenzoic, 3,4-dihydroxybenzoic, and caffeic acids were poor, as were methoxy acids.   Phenylpyruvic and phenyllactic acids were shown to be precursors, and p-hydroxycinnamic (p-coumaric) acid was shown to be formed irreversibly from the other

| [74] | [75] | [76] |
| Quercetin | Veratric Acid | |

phenylpropanoids and hence to be the most immediate precursor.[86,116] Labeled veratric acid was obtained from ring- or β-labeled cinnamic acid and contained seven-ninths of the activity of phenylalanine, whereas product [76] was labeled only when α- or carboxyl-labeled cinnamic acid was used and retained two-ninths of the uniform phenylalanine label.[115] In experiments on ring-A labeling, only labeled acetate yielded radio-active phloroglucinol and inactive 3,4-dihydroxybenzoic acid upon hydrolysis.   Other precursors gave low random or no labeling of quercetin (e.g., CO_2, sucrose, inositol).   Other studies have confirmed these results,[87] and cyanidin and quercetin were shown to arise by separate pathways, as they were not interconvertible.[117]   The chalcone glucoside [77], labeled as shown, was also converted into cyanidin [78] in red cabbage with the label located in the expected position.[118]

114. H. Grisebach, Z. Naturforsch., 13b, 335 (1958).
115. A. C. Neish, E. W. Underhill, and J. E. Watkin, Can. J. Biochem. Physiol., 35, 219, 229 (1957).
116. J. E. Watkin and A. C. Neish, Can. J. Biochem. Physiol., 38, 559 (1960).
117. H. Grisebach and M. Bopp, Z. Naturforsch., 14b, 485 (1959).
118. H. Grisebach, in Ref. 56, Chap. 4.

The flavone tricin **[79]** was provided in good activity yield from labeled ferulic acid in the same experiments,[107] producing scopoletin (**[67]** above). The dihydrochalcone glycoside, phloridzin **[80]**, was produced in tracer experiments on *Malus* leaves from labeled phenylalanine and less well from labeled tyrosine with incorporation of activity into the B ring (the phenylpropanoid unit, as in flavonoids), whereas acetate but not phloroglucinol yielded A-ring radioactivity.[119] Labeled cinnamic and *p*-hydroxycinnamic acids were also incorporated into phloridzin, but *p*-hydroxydihydrocinnamic acid surprisingly was not.[120]

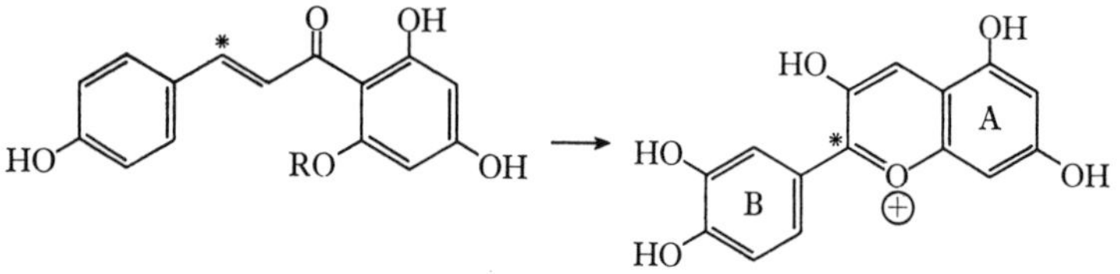

[77]

R = Glucosidyl

[78]

Cyanidin

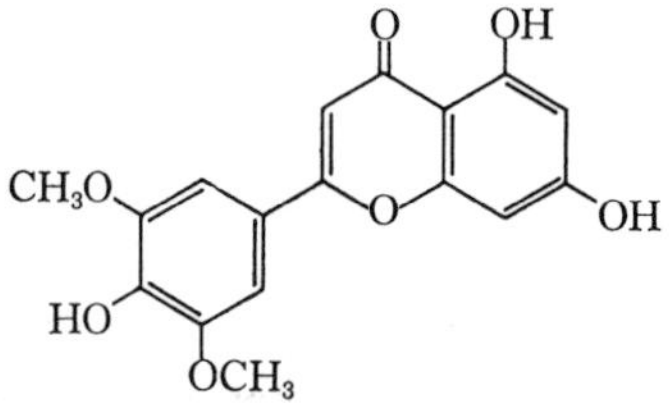

[79]

Tricin

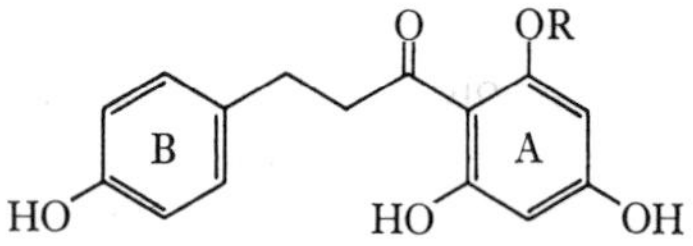

[80]

Phloretin (R = H)
Phloridzin (R = glucosidyl)

Some nontracer experiments on the flavonoids have also cast light on their biogenesis. Shimokoriyana,[121] observing that the occasional isolation of optically active flavanones in nature must imply enzyme-mediated biosynthesis, prepared three chalcone glycosides from the corresponding natural flavanone glycosides; he was able to obtain a crude enzyme extract from citrus peel ("flavanone synthease") that was

119. A. Hutchinson, C. D. Taper, and G. H. N. Towers, *Can. J. Biochem. Physiol.*, **37**, 902 (1959).
120. P. N. Avadhani and G. H. N. Towers, *Can. J. Biochem. Physiol.*, **39**, 1605 (1961).
121. M. Shimokoriyana, *J. Am. Chem. Soc.*, **79**, 4199 (1957).

capable of reconverting these to the optically active flavanone glycosides under solution conditions in which the chalcone glycosides were otherwise stable. Genetic experiments [122] also support the intermediacy of chalcones, for, in certain albino variants of *Antirrhinum* flowers, only cinnamic acids but no flavonoids are produced. Anthocyanins are always accompanied, when present, by 3-hydroxy-flavones, whereas in acyanic flowers only flavones, not flavonols, are found.

Finally, studies on the isoflavones [118] have now shown unmistakably their origin from aryl rearrangement of a flavonoid. Grisebach [123-125] has studied the biosynthesis of formononetin in red clover with three separately labeled phenylalanines with the results shown in Chart V;

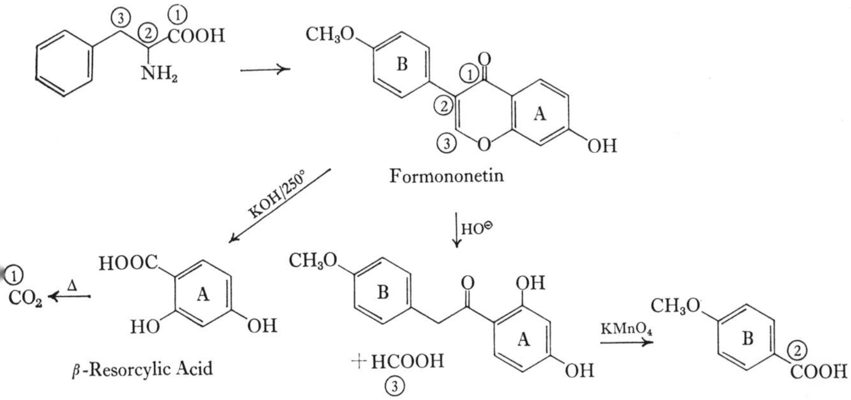

Chart V *Isoflavone biogenesis; tracer studies. Percentage of activity in product in each experiment:* ①, CO_2 = 93 *per cent;* ②, $CH_3O\phi COOH$ = 82 *per cent;* ③, HCOOH = 96 *per cent.*

the formononetin was degraded to β-resorcylic acid with alkali, and this was decarboxylated or, with milder base, cleaved to isolate formic acid, leaving a desoxybenzoin to be oxidized further to *p*-methoxybenzoic acid. This degradation scheme isolated the relevant atoms in each case and made clear the biosynthesis as a migration of the *p*-methoxyphenyl residue from a flavonoid skeleton precursor. Subsequently,[126] it was shown that 3-C^{14}-cinnamic acid yielded the radio-

122. T. A. Geissman, E. C. Jorgensen, and B. L. Johnson, *Arch. Biochem. Biophys.*, **49**, 368 (1959).
123. H. Grisebach, *Z. Naturforsch.*, **14b**, 802 (1959).
124. H. Grisebach and N. Doerr, *Z. Naturforsch*, **15b**, 284 (1960).
125. H. Grisebach and G. Brandner, *Z. Naturforsch.*, **16b**, 2 (1961).
126. H. Grisebach and G. Brandner, *Biochim. Biophys. Acta*, **60**, 51 (1962).

active chalcone **[81]**, labeled as shown (asterisk), which in turn was converted by cell-free enzyme extracts from the plant to formononetin, labeled at the position marked ③ in Chart V.

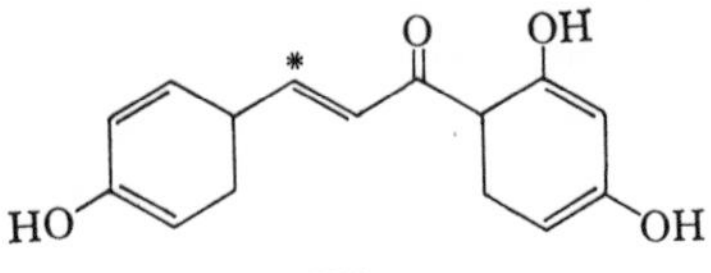

[81]

The results of the above experiments are implicit in the biogenetic charts previously presented in Sections 3-1 and 4-3.

5–4 MISCELLANEOUS COMPOUNDS

The mold metabolite palitantin **[82]**, although not aromatic, presents a structure that on other inferential grounds (oxygen positions, linear even-membered precursor chain) should be acetogenous; it shows a marked structural resemblance to auroglaucin **[26]** and flavoglaucin (vide supra).   When fed carboxyl-labeled acetate, the parent fungus in fact produced radioactive palitantin, which was degraded to show a labeling pattern consistent with prediction, as shown in **[82]**–**[84]** (heavy dots).[61]   The result is interesting in that it adds another example

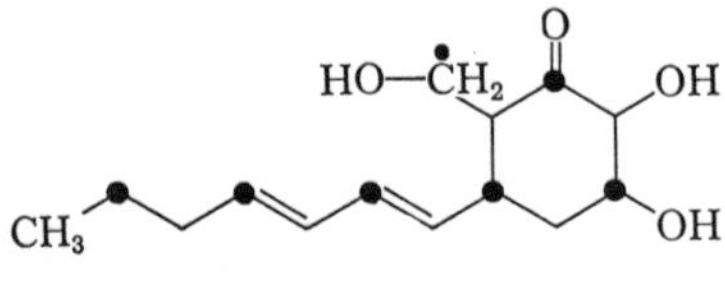

[82]
Palitantin

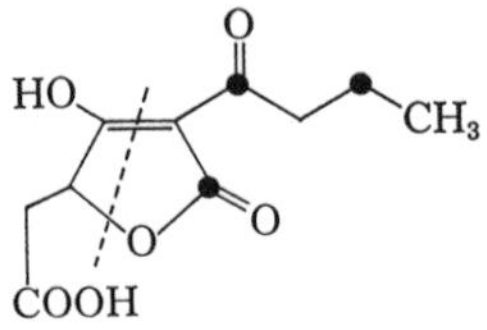

[83]
Carlosic Acid

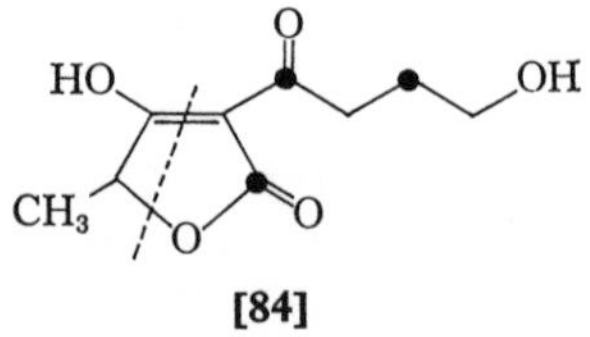

[84]
Carolic Acid

of reduced terminal carboxyl like those in citrinin, sclerotiorin, and the structurally related auroglaucin. Labeled mevalonate was not incorporated.

Initial work from Ehrensvärd's laboratory[127] has gone far toward clarifying the biogenesis of the tetronic acids. It was found that cultures of *Penicillium charlesii* produced much more carlosic [83] and carolic [84] acids and much less itaconic acid when fed supplemental acetate. When carboxyl-labeled acetate was fed and the former acids isolated and degraded, they were found to have incorporated radioactivity specifically at the carbons indicated by heavy dots in the formulae above; only negligible labeling was found in the carbons to the left of the dotted lines.

In a more recent study,[128] Bentley and others showed that the acetate-derived chain revealed the predicted differential labeling on feeding acetate and malonate separately and that labeled succinate (but not propionate) provided radioactivity to the left of the dotted line in [83]–[84].

The suggestion was made[127] that the acetogenin β-ketohexanoic acid, probably as the coenzyme-A thioester, intervenes in the citric acid cycle, esterifying malic acid and subsequently cyclizing in an aldol reaction, reminiscent of that invoked for rotiorin, to yield carlosic acid. Such a pathway accounts for the lowered production of itaconic acid from the citric acid cycle also. Utilization of other common metabolic hydroxy-acids in such a scheme, moreover, will account for the structures of the other tetronic acids (page 100). Thus lactic acid affords carolic acid, and isoleucine may well afford the nitrogenous analogue, tenuazonic acid [85]. Acetate incorporation into the latter has been shown[129] to follow the same pattern. This mode of biogenesis by intervention of other acids in the citric acid cycle was also suggested above (page 98) for the origin of the very similar lichen lactone-acids and poly-acids.

The unusual metabolite caldariomycin [89] has been shown[130] to arise by β-ketoadipic [86] and δ-chlorolevulinic acids [87], presumably by a pathway such as that outlined in [86] → [89]. It may be noted that, as above, the chlorines are introduced at methylene sites flanked by carbonyl groups. Labeled chloride ion (Cl^{36}) goes into organic

127. G. Ehrensvärd, *Chem. Soc. Spec. Publ.*, **12**, 13 (1958); S. Lybing and L. Reio, *Acta Chem. Scand.*, **12**, 1575 (1958).
128. R. Bentley, D. S. Bhate, and J. G. Keil, *J. Biol. Chem.*, **237**, 859 (1962).
129. C. E. Stickings and R. J. Townsend, *Proc. Biochem. Soc.*, **1960**, 36P.
130. P. D. Shaw, J. R. Beckwith, and L. P. Hager, *J. Biol. Chem.*, **234**, 2560 (1959).

material only in the presence of β-ketoadipic acid, and the extent of incorporation of the Cl^{36}-levulinic into labeled caldarionycin implies that no mixing with ionic chloride of the medium occurs in the last steps.

Initial inspection of the structure of penicillic acid **[90]** suggests intervention of an isoprene unit, but investigation of the biosynthesis with tracers showed only negligible incorporation of mevalonic acid.[131] Carboxyl-labeled acetate, however, was incorporated to an appreciable extent and in accord with the pattern shown above. More recent experiments in greater detail have been reported by Bentley,[132] who fed both methylene and carboxyl-labeled malonate to *Penicillium cyclopium* with high incorporation of radioactivity as shown in Chart VI;

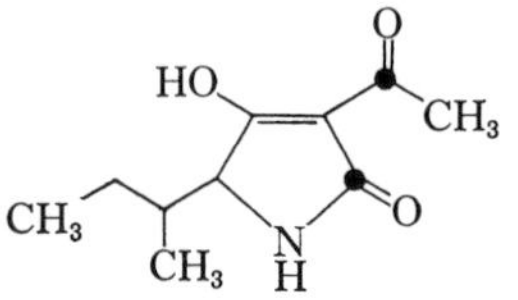

[85]
Tenuazonic Acid

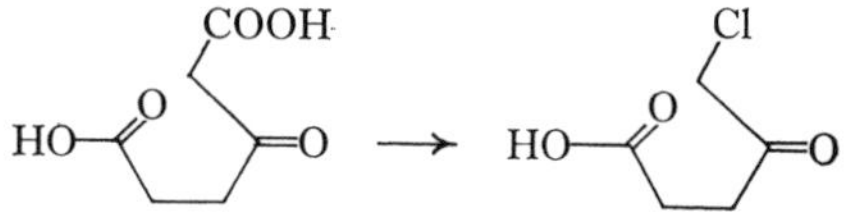

[86]
β-Ketoadipic Acid

[87]

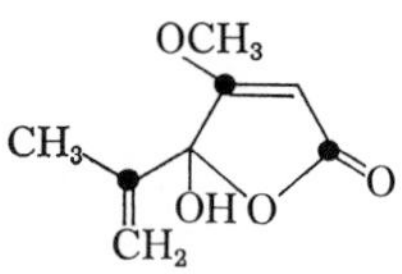

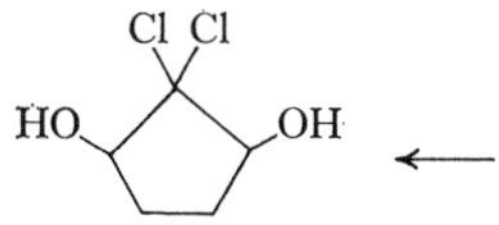

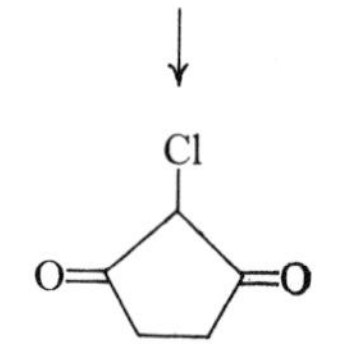

[90]
Penicillic Acid

[89]
Caldariomycin

[88]

methionine was the source of the methoxyl methyl group. Labeled-orsellinic acid has also been shown[133] to convert to labeled penicillic acid, so that a cleavage of orsellinic acid was postulated[132] as a biogenetic route to penicillic acid, shown in Chart VI. Either ring cleavage ($\cdots\cdots$) of orsellinic acid would afford a penicillic acid skeleton of the correct labeling pattern. Carbons ① and ② were not significantly labeled by either carbon of malonate, although they were labeled by acetate, which demonstrated again that malonate is not reconverted to acetate to any appreciable extent and so is valid as a separate tracer.

131. A. J. Birch, G. E. Blance, and H. Smith, *J. Chem. Soc.*, **1958**, 4582.
132. R. Bentley and J. G. Keil, *Proc. Chem. Soc.*, **1961**, 111; *J. Biol. Chem.*, **237**, 867 (1962).
133. K. Mosbach, *Acta Chem. Scand.*, **14**, 457 (1960).

A similar cleavage of the aromatic ring of 6-methylsalicylic acid has been established by Bassett and Tanenbaum[134,135] as the route to patulin in *Penicillium patulum*. This organism produces 6-methyl-salicylic acid (detailed labeling from acetate was verified), the aldehyde analog **[91]** and the acid **[21]** (shown elsewhere to be an acetogenin by tracers, page 144), as well as gentisyl alcohol, gentisaldehyde, gentisic acid,* and patulin. Furthermore, although the gentisic acid was

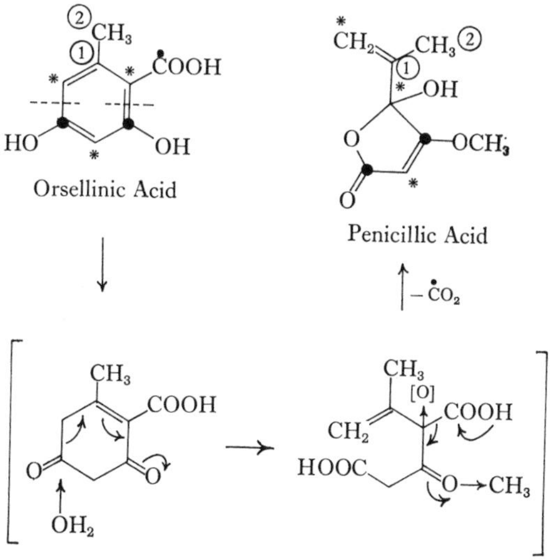

Orsellinic Acid

Penicillic Acid

Chart VI *Biosynthesis of penicillic acid.*

Labels: ● = $CH_2(\overset{\bullet}{C}OOH)_2$ (or $CH_3\overset{\bullet}{C}OOH$); * = $\overset{*}{C}H_2(COOH)_2$
(or $\overset{*}{C}H_3COOH$); ① = $CH_3\overset{①}{C}OOH$; ② = $\overset{②}{C}H_3COOH$.

shown not to be a precursor of patulin, the label from 2-C^{14}-acetic acid was incorporated at the sites indicated.[134,135] Biosynthetically labeled 6-methylsalicylic acid was also incorporated into the patulin in this way, but labeled mevalonate was virtually unincorporated. Subsequently, labeled acetyl coenzyme A was shown to produce patulin

* Gentisic acid has recently been shown to arise from labeled acetate, as shown here, by S. Gatenbeck and I. Lönnroth, *Acta Chem. Scand.*, **16**, 2298 (1962).
134. E. W. Bassett and S. W. Tanenbaum, *Experientia*, **14**, 38 (1958); *J. Biol. Chem.*, **234**, 1861 (1959).
135. E. W. Bassett and S. W. Tanenbaum, *Biochem. Biophys. Acta*, **28**, 21, 247 (1958).

in a cell-free extract without primary reversion to free acetate.[57] These various facts have been accommodated by the ring-cleavage biogenesis outlined in Chart VII.

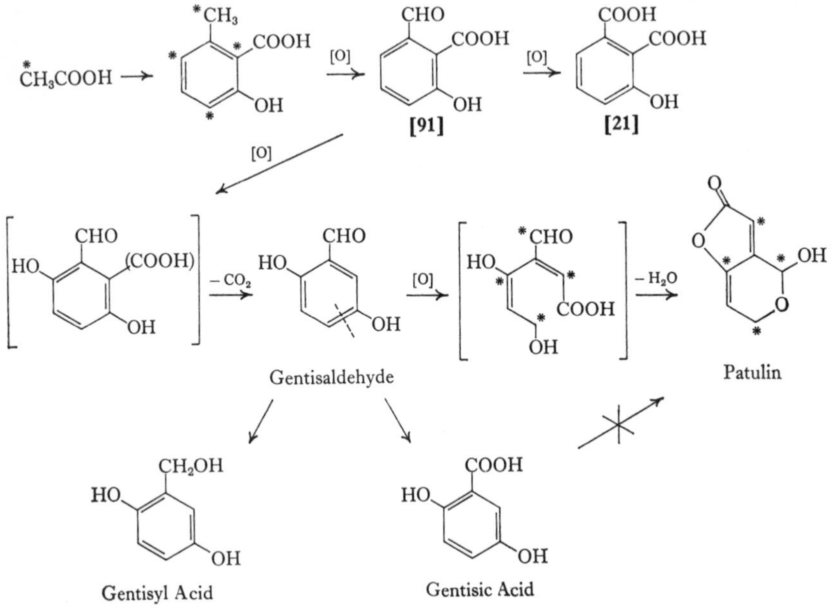

Chart VII *Biosynthesis of patulin*

The biogenesis of the tropolone acids has been a subject of specu-lation for many years, but tracer experiments now indicate that they arise by the same rather novel ring cleavage (Chart VIII) credited in the previous two examples. In feeding experiments with labeled acetate (1-C^{14} and 2-C^{14}), Richards [136,137] located seven of the carbons specifically labeled from acetate, as shown in puberulic and puberulonic acids; the extra carbon in the latter did not arise from acetate. Bentley [138,139] obtained similar results and showed that formate was the source of one ring carbon, whereas, curiously, in stipitatonic acid unlike puberulonic, the extra carboxyl derives from an acetate carboxyl.

136. J. H. Richards and L. D. Ferretti, *Biochem. Biophys. Res. Commun.*, **2**, 107 (1960).

137. L. D. Ferretti and J. H. Richards, *Proc. Natl. Acad. Sci. (U.S.)*, **46**, 1438 (1960).

138. R. Bentley, *Biochem. Biophys. Acta*, **29**, 266 (1958).

139. R. Bentley, *Biochem. Biophys. Res. Commun.*, **3**, 215 (1960).

This suggests an orsellinic-acid ring oxidation similar to patulin biogenesis but incorporating extra carbons from the one-carbon pool
analogous to the very similar case of cyclopaldic acid (page 144).
The path detailed below [137] incorporates an internal pinacol rearrangement, although a mechanistically equivalent scheme can be written
with an actual acyclic intermediate, as in patulin, followed by recyclization; discrimination among these similar routes is not possible

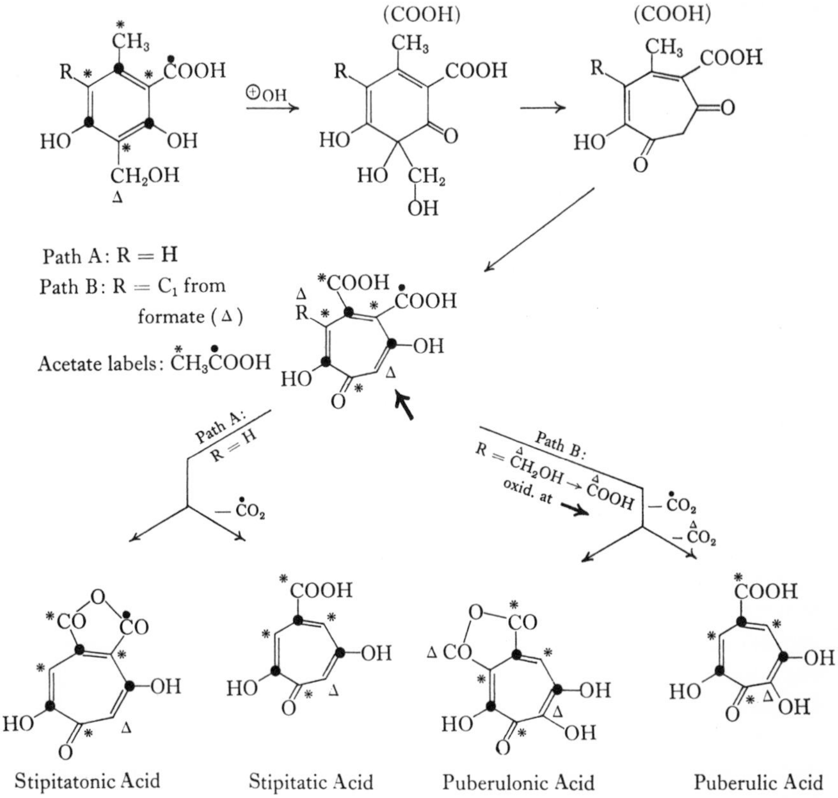

Path A: R = H
Path B: R = C₁ from
            formate (Δ)

Acetate labels: ĊH₃ĊOOH

Stipitatonic Acid   Stipitatic Acid   Puberulonic Acid   Puberulic Acid

Chart VIII   *The biosynthesis of tropolone acids*

on available evidence, nor is the timing of methyl oxidation, which is
left undecided below.   In connection with these studies on the simple
tropolone acids, it should be noted that the carbon atoms of the tropolone
ring in colchicine **[92]** have recently been shown *not* to arise from
labeled acetate.[140]

140. E. Leete and K. E. Nemeth, *J. Am. Chem. Soc.*, **83**, 2192 (1961).

5–5 ACETATE HYPOTHESIS: FINAL SUMMARY

The experimental evidence reported to date amply confirms the original tenets of the acetate hypothesis and provides considerable confidence in its future use. Furthermore, the operation of experiment and structural inference as complementary approaches may also be applied with assurance—the former to confirm the biosynthesis of particular examples, the latter to assert the generality of this biosynthetic mode over a wide range of examples and species. Conversely, the inferential results may profitably focus experimental attention on cases that are ambiguous, suggesting, for example, examination of the 5,7-dioxycoumarins, the 4-substituted coumarins, the naphthalenes and anthraquinones with unsubstituted A rings, and a number of miscellaneous misfits, as discussed in Chapter 4. Similarly, the detailed mechanisms of one-carbon alkylation (particularly for C_1 attachments more highly oxidized than methyl), of isoprenoid attachment and oxidation, and of chlorination are all areas of fruitful future study.

The basic operations of the acetate hypothesis, as originally postulated by Birch and detailed and summarized in Chapter 3, have been very little modified by experiment. It is likely that the polyacetyl chain only exists coupled to an enzyme surface as suggested in Section 5-1 and that many of the second-order variants, as enol alkylation, occur at that stage. The lack of interconvertibility observed in cooccurring flavonoids and anthraquinones also supports their common but separate origin from such a chain. There is also a clear indication in the compounds considered above that an upper size limit of about ten exists on the number of acetate units put together in this biosynthesis so that the size of acetogenin molecules is distinctly limited; this is also reasonable in terms of biosynthesis on an enzyme surface, for the number of enzymic sites must be limited as well as the effectiveness of the chain-linking function that may be competing with cyclization and removal of the substrate acetogenin.

In regard to the variants on the hypothesis, the details of fatty acid biosynthesis suggest that both intermediate- and full-length fatty acids, previously and separately synthesized from acetate, may serve as terminals for synthesis of the polyacetyl chain just as acetate does and as the *Campnospermum* cases (page 62) imply. The evidence from both structural interference and tracer experiments (Section 5-3) further implies that only the phenylpropanoid acids derived from shikimic acid, and not the benzoic acids, are the source of aromatic chain terminals in virtually all cases. A number of structures considered above* imply

---

* For example, monascorubin (page 77), the depsidones (page 67), the 4-substituted coumarins (page 40), carolic acid (page 100), bergenin (page 96), and the *Chaemotomium* di-acid (page 103).

that two fragments are first joined in an ester linkage that facilitates a further, perhaps often spontaneous, internal reaction between the two halves, such as an aldol reaction affording a chain branch. This may well turn out to be an important variant in the detailed modes of acetogenin biosynthesis and could be operative in more of the cases discussed above, as in the lignanes and fungal terphenyls (Section 4-2) and citromycetin [30]. There are, it may be noted, numerous cases of such esterifications (O-acylations) in the acetogenins (cf. depsides), but there appears to be only one clear case of C-acylation, that in the structure proposed[141] for fukugetin [93] and perhaps one more in citromycetin [30]. Another variant may be the interesting oxidative cleavage of an aromatic ring now demonstrated in several cases (Section 5-4) for conversions of orsellinic acid to patulin, penicillic acid, and the tropolone acids; it seems probable that this route will account for more cases in the future.

As to the future uses of the acetate hypothesis, the evident generality of its operation directs attention to those structures that are inconsistent; in the past the hypothesis has on several occasions (vide supra) served to correct wrong structures, whereas several other structures, originally formulated as exceptions to the tenets of the hypothesis, have been corrected in other ways and found to be in fact acetogenins; buddleoflavonol[142] was originally considered to be a 3-acetylflavone, sclerotiorin[143] to be a branched-chain skeleton, and telephoric acid [21], [93][144,145] a branched phenanthraquinone. Other structures presently in the literature may similarly be incorrect (cf. fukugetin, morellin, and guttiferin, page 102, and maesoquinone, page 64). The formula proposed[146] for muscarufin [95] is difficult to reconcile with the hypothesis and is based on evidence similar in kind to that recorded[144] by the same workers in support of the formula for thelephoric acid, which was recently discredited by synthesis[145] (see page 36). Furthermore, the reported reactions of muscarufin are not consonant with model studies,[147] so that the structure is highly suspect on various grounds. The high consistency of the depsides and depsidones with acetate biogenesis must also focus attention on the two inconsistent examples, e.g., gangaleoidin [135] and psoromic acid [134], for certainly either their

141. J. Shinoda and S. Ueda, *Yakagaku Zosshi*, **53**, 921 (1933); *C.A.*, **29**, 5433 (1935); cf. M. Marakami and T. Irie, *C.A.*, **29**, 1818 (1935).
142. W. Baker, R. Hemming, and W. D. Ollis, *J. Chem. Soc.*, **1951**, 691.
143. F. M. Dean, J. Staunton, and W. B. Whalley, *J. Chem. Soc.*, **1959**, 3004.
144. F. Kögl, H. Erxleben, and J. Jänecke, *Ann.*, **482**, 105 (1930).
145. J. Gripenberg, *Tetrahedron*, **10**, 135 (1960).
146. F. Kögl and H. Erxleben, *Ann.*, **479**, 11 (1930).
147. M. Nilsson, *Acta Chem. Scand.*, **14**, 2243 (1960) and preceding papers.

structures are incorrect or a detailed study of their biosynthesis will be interesting.

One future use of the acetate hypothesis to assist in structure determinations has already been demonstrated by Birch.[75] By feeding labeled acetate or formate to the organism it should be possible, for example, to count the total number of acetyl units in the chain after counting radioactive acetic acid formed in the Kuhn-Roth degradation. The structure of curvularin was determined in part concurrently with

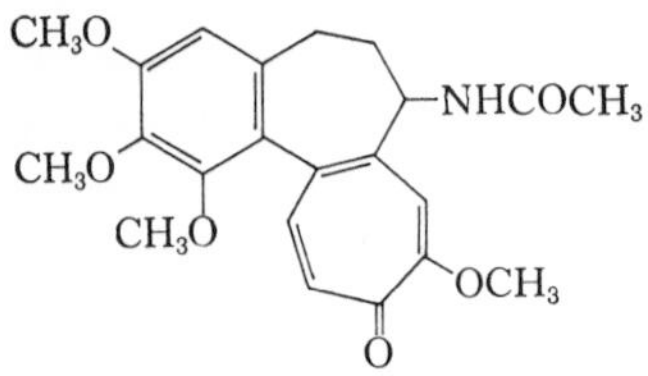

[92]

Colchicine

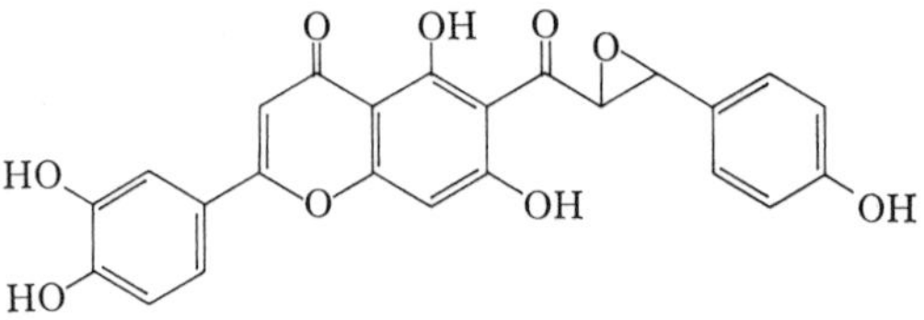

[93]

Fukugetin (?)

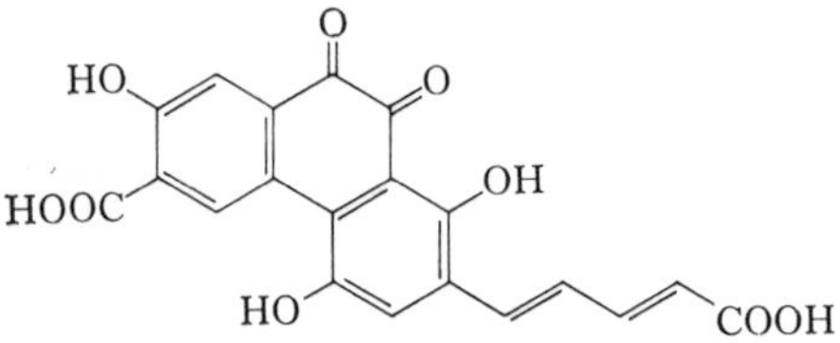

[94]

Thelephoric Acid (original incorrect formula)

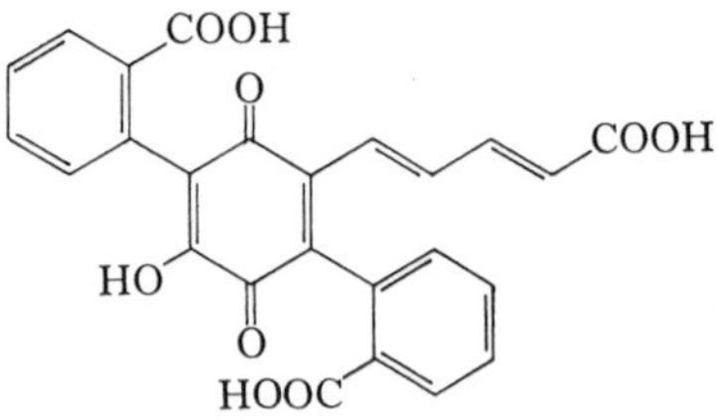

[95]

Muscarufin (?)

its biogenesis by such means.[75] Similar applications of tracers and determination of radioactivity in degradation products can, taken in conjunction with the acetate hypothesis, provide a valuable tool in determining structures of new compounds.

In view of the common antibiotic activity of the acetogenins, it may well be possible, when more is known of the detailed enzymes involved in their synthesis, to create unnatural acetogenins by feeding other terminal acids as substrates or altering in other ways the biosynthetic pathway and thereby to attempt to manufacture complex compounds with new antibiotic properties.

chapter six | The Isoprene Unit

The biogenesis of terpenes has a long and interesting background—which is largely a history of the "isoprene rule" discussed at various levels of sophistication. The earliest hint of the isoprene rule came from the dry distillation of rubber by Beale and Enderby[1] in London in the 1830s. However, Robinson,[2] in his presidential address to the British Association in 1955, pointed out that Daubeny, in an analogous address in 1836, referred to experiments of John Dalton on the distillation of caoutchouc. This distillation produced a volatile oil (doubtlessly crude isoprene), which Dalton named "double olefiant." The term *isoprene* was coined by Williams[3] in 1860, but it was not until 1897 that Ipatiev and Wittorf[4] conclusively proved isoprene to have the structure [1]. In subsequent years, isoprene was also obtained from turpentine oil by passage through a red-hot tube and also from other cyclic monoterpenes.[6] The reverse process, the dimerization of isoprene to dipentene [2] was observed by Bouchardat[7] in 1878. (This conversion is an early example of a Diels-Adler reaction and was first correctly described by Ipatiev and Wittorf.[4])

In spite of these observations, as late as 1921 it was still not unusual for possible terpene structures to be advanced that could not be dissected into isoprene units. However, with Ruzicka's entrance into

1. A. Bouchardat, *J. Pharm.*, **23**, 454 (1837).
2. R. Robinson, *Nature*, **176**, 433 (1955).
3. G. Williams, *Chem. News*, **2**, 206 (1860).
4. W. Ipatiev and N. Wittorf, *J. Prakt. Chem.*, **55**, 1 (1897).
5. H. Hiasiwetz and F. Hinterberger, *Z. Chem.*, **1868**, 180.
6. W. Tilden, *Trans. Chem. Soc.*, **1884**, 410.
7. G. Bouchardat, *Compt. Rend.*, **86**, 654 (1878).

the field of higher terpenes, the possible role of isoprene polymers (such as farnesol) in the generation of sesquiterpenes was acknowledged.[8] Such thoughts were of enormous value in the structural elucidation of many terpenoid substances. The basic biogenetic hypothesis was enlarged by Robinson in accounting for the structure of eremophilone (cf. page 235) and, later, by the promulgation of a "biogenetic isoprene rule" by the Zurich[9] school, which followed a suggestion of Woodward and Bloch[10] and of Dauben et al.[11] of the way in which squalene is biogenetically related to lanosterol and cholesterol.

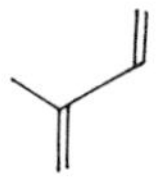

[1] 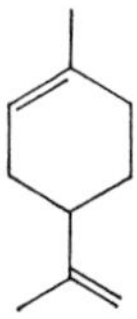   [2]

Though at first glance the structures of isoprenoid substances may appear to bear little relation to structures of polyacetate-derived compounds, the two types are, in biochemical fact, closely related.   Whereas

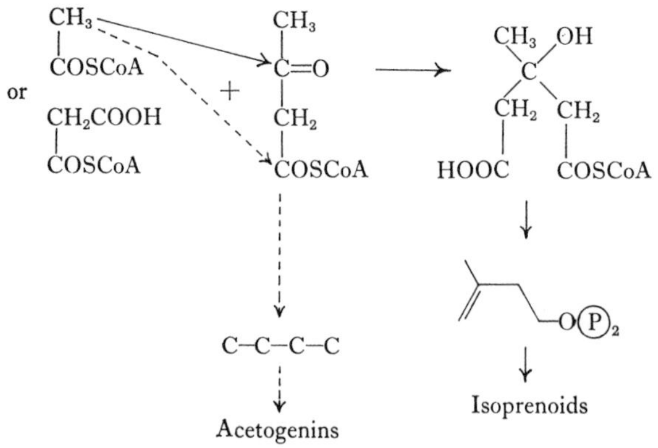

(6–1)

8. For a fuller historical discussion, cf. L. Ruzicka, *Proc. Chem. Soc.*, **1959**, 341.
9. L. Ruzicka and, in part, A. Eschenmoser, and H. Heusser, *Experientia*, **9**, 357 (1953).
10. R. B. Woodward and K. Bloch, *J. Am. Chem. Soc.*, **75**, 2023 (1953).
11. W. G. Dauben, S. Abraham, S. Hotta, I. L. Chaikoff, H. L. Bradlow, and A. H. Soloway, *J. Am. Chem. Soc.*, **75**, 3038 (1953).

polyacetyl substances are derived from a continuously linear linkage of acetate (or malonate) units, the branched isoprenoids result from a condensation to the central carbonyl group of acetoacetyl coenzyme A. This relationship is emphasized in Equation (6–1).

The biochemical reactions that lead from acetate to isoprenoid substances (in particular squalene) can be divided into four general areas; acetate → mevalonate; mevalonate → isopentenyl pyrophosphate; polymerization of isopentenyl pyrophosphate; and reductive dimerization of farnesyl pyrophosphate to squalene. The subsequent discussion will be subdivided under these headings.

6–1   ACETATE → MEVALONATE

The earliest steps in cholesterol and terpene biosynthesis were for a long while steeped in mystery, this area being greatly complicated by many confusing and apparently conflicting results, particularly with branched-chain acids. These results can now be understood in terms of the complex interconversion established among these substances.

Hydroxymethylglutaryl Coenzyme A Formation

The first step in the biosynthesis of terpenes from acetate is the formation of a four-carbon unit, acetoacetyl coenzyme A, from two molecules of acetyl coenzyme A via the reversal of the thiolase catalyzed cleavage of acetoacetyl coenzyme A.[12,13] From Chapter 5 on fatty acid synthesis from acetate, it will be recalled that malonyl coenzyme A was the active condensing species but that its condensation with acetyl coenzyme A apparently did not lead to a nonenzyme-bound four-carbon intermediate. Thus it might appear that terpene biosynthesis differs from acetogenin synthesis at the very outset, as Lynen has suggested.[14] However, Porter[15] has recently shown with an enzyme isolated from pigeon liver that malonyl coenzyme A can be incorporated into hydroxymethylglutaryl coenzyme A by a pathway that appears to be identical with the early steps in fatty acid biosynthesis. For a fuller discussion of the role of malonyl coenzyme A, see page 124.

12. H. Rudney, *J. Biol. Chem.*, **227**, 363 (1957).
13. J. D. Brodie and J. W. Porter, *Biochem. Biophys. Res. Commun.*, **3**, 173 (1960).
14. F. Lynen, *Colloq. Intern. Centre Nat. Rech. Sci. (Paris)*, **99**, 71 (1961).
15. J. D. Brodie, G. W. Wasson, and J. W. Porter, *Biochem. Biophys. Res. Commun.*, **8**, 76 (1962).

Acetoacetyl coenzyme A can proceed in two directions. By reduction of the carbonyl group, β-hydroxybutryl coenzyme A will be formed.[16] Alternatively, acquisition of another acetyl coenzyme A fragment at the carbonyl group will lead to β-hydroxy-β-methyl-glutaryl coenzyme A and free coenzyme A; the latter reaction (6–2) occurs under the influence of a hydroxymethylglutaryl-condensing enzyme.[17–21]

$$\tag{6-2}$$

Investigation of the intracellular localization of the principal enzymes involved in the formation and breakdown of hydroxymethyl-glutaryl coenzyme A in rat liver has shown[22] that hydroxymethyl-glutaryl coenzyme A condensing enzyme is preponderantly in the mitochondria (as is hydroxymethylglutaryl coenzyme A cleavage enzyme; cf. subsequent discussion).

A significant question in the condensation of acetoacetyl coenzyme A with acetyl coenzyme A yielding hydroxymethylglutaryl coenzyme A and free coenzyme A is which of the two thiolester groups is set free. Rudney and Ferguson[20] were able to show by a series of experiments with appropriately labeled substances that the free coenzyme A is liberated from the acetyl carboxyl group (cf. 6-2). It was not possible to demonstrate any reversal of this condensation reaction even under conditions in which this should have been favored.

By addition of a particle-free liver supernatant to a microsomal

16. F. Lynen, L. Wessely, O. Wieland, and L. Rueff, *Angew. Chem.*, **64**, 687 (1952).
17. J. J. Ferguson, Jr. and H. Rudney, *Federation Proc.*, **16**, 179 (1957).
18. J. J. Ferguson, Jr. and H. Rudney, *J. Biol. Chem.*, **234**, 1072 (1959).
19. F. Lynen, U. Henning, C. Bublitz, B. Sörbo, and L. K. Rueff, *Biochem. Z.*, **330**, 269 (1958).
20. H. Rudney and J. J. Ferguson, Jr., *J. Am. Chem. Soc.*, **79**, 5580 (1957).
21. H. Rudney and J. J. Ferguson, Jr., *J. Biol. Chem.*, **234**, 1076 (1959).
22. N. L. R. Bucher, P. Overath, and F. Lynen, *Biochim. Biophys. Acta*, **40**, 491 (1960).

preparation, Rudney[23] was able to shift acetate from incorporation into hydroxymethylglutaryl coenzyme A toward the synthesis of β-hydroxybutyryl coenzyme A. Porter and Tietz[24] also observed that the incorporation of acetoacetyl coenzyme A into hydroxymethylglutaryl coenzyme A by a pigeon-liver fraction was depressed by the addition of reduced nicotinamide adenine dinucleotide and that the acetyl coenzyme A was thereby directed toward β-hydroxybutyrate synthesis. There are undoubtedly many points along the biosynthetic pathway at which control can be exerted over the rate of steroid production. This diversion of acetate either to hydroxymethylglutaryl coenzyme A (which can lead in turn to terpenes and steroids) or to β-hydroxybutyryl coenzyme A may be just such a control point occurring at an early stage in terpene synthesis.

Leucine Metabolism

In addition to its synthesis by condensation of acetoacetyl coenzyme A and acetyl coenzyme A, there exists another, completely independent, pathway for hydroxymethylglutaryl coenzyme A synthesis that originates with the amino acid leucine and, in fact, is the course by which this amino acid is metabolized. As early as 1944, Bloch[25] concluded that isovaleric acid is an intermediate in the oxidative breakdown of leucine, a conclusion that has been fortified by the work of Coon.[26] By oxidation, isovaleryl coenzyme A will give rise to dimethylacrylyl coenzyme A (sometimes called β-methylcrotonyl coenzyme A), a substance whose position in the cholesterol biosynthetic pathway was extremely puzzling for some time. For example, addition of $3\text{-}C^{14}$-dimethylacrylic acid to biological systems led to cholesterol, which apparently was formed without any prior breakdown of the five-carbon precursor.[27] On the other hand, $1\text{-}C^{14}$-dimethylacrylic acid yielded cholesterol with a pattern of labeling suggestive of complete prior equilibration with two carbon units.[28] Although subsequent discussion will show how dimethylacrylyl coenzyme A eventually gives rise to terpenes, this differential incorporation of $3\text{-}C^{14}$- and $1\text{-}C^{14}$-dimethylacrylic acids is not readily understood.

Although earlier studies on leucine metabolism in crude heart extracts gave evidence that β-hydroxyisovaleryl coenzyme A can serve

23. H. Rudney, *J. Biol. Chem.*, **227**, 363 (1957).
24. J. W. Porter and A. Tietz, *Biochim. Biophys. Acta*, **25**, 41 (1957).
25. K. Bloch, *J. Biol. Chem.*, **155**, 255 (1944).
26. M. J. Coon, *J. Biol. Chem.*, **187**, 71 (1950).
27. K. Bloch, L. C. Clark, and I. Harary, *J. Biol. Chem.*, **211**, 687 (1954).
28. K. Bloch, *Vitamins Hormones*, **15**, 119 (1957).

as a substrate for a carboxylase enzyme yielding hydroxymethylglutaryl coenzyme A directly,[29] the evidence of Lynen,[30,31] working with an enzyme preparation from *Mycobacterium* spp., and of Coon,[32] with a 100-fold purified carboxylase system from chicken liver in which residual crotonase activity had been inhibited by *p*-chloromercuribenzoate, is overwhelming in that, at least in the last two systems, the true substrate for carboxylase action is dimethylacrylyl coenzyme A **[3]**. As Lynen[31] has pointed out, this is the more reasonable substrate, as the methyl group is vinylogously activated for carboxylation by the ester group of the molecule. The product of this carboxylation reaction is β-methylglutaconyl coenzyme A **[4]**. Under the influence of crotonase,

$$CO_2 + \quad \begin{array}{c} H_3C \\ \diagdown \\ \diagup \\ H_3C \end{array} C{=}CH{-}COSCoA \rightarrow \begin{array}{c} H_3C \\ \diagdown \\ \diagup \\ H_2C \\ | \\ HOOC \end{array} C{=}CH{-}COSCoA$$

[3]	**[4]**
Dimethylacrylyl Coenzyme A	β-Methylglutaconyl Coenzyme A

dimethylacrylyl coenzyme A can acquire the elements of water, yielding β-hydroxyisovaleryl coenzyme A **[5]**, a reaction that is reversible.[29]

$$\begin{array}{c} H_3C \\ \diagdown \\ \diagup \\ H_3C \end{array} C{=}CH{-}COSCoA + H_2O \rightleftharpoons \begin{array}{c} H_3C \\ \diagdown \\ \diagup \\ H_3C \end{array} C{-}CH_2COSCoA \\ | \\ OH$$

[5]
β-Hydroxyisovaleryl
Coenzyme A

This carboxylation reaction is worthy of special attention as it accounts for the requirement for biotin, which has been observed in the incorporation of dimethylacrylate into cholesterol[30] and a similar

29. B. K. Bachhawat, W. G. Robinson, and M. J. Coon, *J. Biol. Chem.*, **219**, 539 (1956).
30. J. Knappe and F. Lynen, *Proc. Intern. Congr. Biochem. 4th.*, Vienna, 1955, Abstr., 49, **1958**.
31. F. Lynen, *Proc. Intern. Symp. Enzyme Chem.*, Tokyo-Kyoto, **1957**, 57.
32. A. del Campillo-Campbell, E. E. Dekker, and M. J. Coon, *Biochim. Biophys. Acta*, **31**, 290 (1959).

requirement of biotin for the metabolism of either dimethylacrylate, methylvinyl acetate, or isovalerate to acetoacetate.[33,34] The mechanism of action of biotin has been discussed previously in Chapter 5, concerned with fatty acid synthesis.

Although biotin apparently plays an indispensable role in some biological carboxylation processes, its presence does not seem to be obligatory in enzymes that catalyze the reverse reaction—decarboxylation. Thus Hamilton and Westheimer[35] have purified a crystalline decarboxylase from *Clostridium acetobutylicum*, which does not contain biotin but which catalyzes the decarboxylation of acetoacetic acid. Oxaloacetate decarboxylase also does not contain biotin.[36]

Methylvinylacetyl coenzyme A can also enter this sequence by a nonreversible isomerization to dimethylcrotonyl coenzyme A[37] catalyzed by methylvinylacetyl isomerase, which has been partially purified from ox-liver extracts [see Equation (6–3)].[38] Although previous studies on the metabolism of dimethylacrylyl coenzyme A had not ruled out the possibility that isomerization to β-methylvinylacetyl coenzyme A might precede carboxylation, it was possible to show that dimethylacrylyl coenzyme A is carboxylated directly by using an isomerase-free carboxylase preparation from a hydrocarbon-utilizing *Pseudomonas*.

$$
\begin{array}{c}
H_3C \\
\diagdown \\
C\!-\!CH_2COSCoA \\
\diagup \\
H_2C
\end{array}
\xrightarrow[\text{bond}]{\sim\ \text{dbl.}}
\begin{array}{c}
H_3C \\
\diagdown \\
C\!=\!CH\!-\!COSCoA \\
\diagup \\
H_3C
\end{array}
\qquad (6\text{–}3)
$$

Methylvinylacetyl   Dimethylacrylyl
Coenzyme A   Coenzyme A

β-Methylglutaconyl coenzyme A can reversibly give rise to hydroxymethylglutaryl coenzyme A by acquisition of water (6–4) under the influence of a β-methylglutaconase, an enzyme that has been purified

33. J. E. Fischer, *Proc. Soc. Exptl. Biol. Med.*, **88**, 227 (1955).
34. G. W. E. Plaut, *Proc. Soc. Exptl. Biol. Med.*, **78**, 769 (1951).
35. G. A. Hamilton and F. H. Westheimer, *J. Am. Chem. Soc.*, **81**, 2277 (1959).
36. S. Ochoa, A. Mehler, M. L. Blanchard, T. H. Jukes, C. E. Hoffmann, and M. Regan, *J. Biol. Chem.*, **170**, 413 (1947).
37. M. J. Coon, *Abs. 135th Meeting, Am. Chem. Soc., Boston, April 5–10, 1959*, p. 39C; J. F. Woessner, Jr., B. K. Bachhawat, and M. J. Coon, *J. Biol. Chem.*, **233**, 520 (1958).
38. H. C. Rilling and M. J. Coon, *J. Biol. Chem.*, **235**, 3087 (1960).

50-fold from sheep-liver extract.[39]   There thus exists a pathway by which the amino acid leucine can enter a pool of interconvertible five- and six-carbon branched-chain acids, which include hydroxymethylglutaryl coenzyme A.

$$
\begin{array}{c}
H_3C \\
\quad\diagdown \\
\qquad C{=}CH{-}COSCoA + H_2O \rightleftharpoons \\
\quad\diagup \\
H_2C \\
| \\
HOOC
\end{array}
\qquad
\begin{array}{c}
H_3C \quad\; OH \\
\quad\diagdown\;/ \\
\qquad C \\
\quad\diagup\;\diagdown \\
H_2C \qquad CH_2 \\
| \qquad\quad | \\
HOOC \qquad COSCoA
\end{array}
\qquad (6\text{-}4)
$$

β-Hydroxy-β-methylglutaryl
Coenzyme A

The reaction sequences discussed above require that specifically labeled acetate will give rise to branched side chain acids with a discrete and predictable pattern of C^{14} distribution.   That this requirement is, indeed, satisfied has been proved for dimethylacrylate,[40] for β-hydroxyisovaleric acid,[41] and for hydroxymethylglutarate.[42]

Metabolism of Hydroxymethylglutaryl Coenzyme A

There are several possibilities open to hydroxymethylglutaryl coenzyme A.   This substance can be cleaved irreversibly to acetoacetate and acetyl coenzyme A by hydroxymethylglutaryl coenzyme A cleavage enzyme, which requires Mn^{2+} or Mg^{2+} in addition to a thiol. Hydroxymethylglutaryl coenzyme A is a specific substrate for this enzyme; other thiolesters are inert.[19,43]   The enzyme responsible for this cleavage is found largely in the mitochondria.[21]   Although it was once thought that the combination of reactions leading to hydroxymethylglutaryl coenzyme A followed by its cleavage was the mechanism for the formation of acetoacetic acid, in rat-liver extract it has been possible to demonstrate[44] acetoacetic acid synthesis after endogenous hydroxymethylglutaryl coenzyme A condensing and cleavage enzymes have been completely inactivated by treatment with iodoacetamide.

39. H. Hilz, J. Knappe, E. Ringelmann, and F. Lynen, *Biochem.* 2., **329**, 476 (1958).
40. H. Rudney, *J. Am. Chem. Soc.*, **77**, 1698 (1955).
41. J. L. Rabinowitz, *J. Am. Chem. Soc.*, **77**, 1295 (1955).
42. H. Rudney, *J. Am. Chem. Soc.*, **76**, 2595 (1954).
43. B. K. Bachhawat, W. G. Robinson, and M. J. Coon, *J. Biol. Chem.*, **216**, 727 (1955).
44. J. R. Stern and G. E. Miller, *Biochim. Biophys. Acta*, **35**, 576 (1959).

A more recent investigation[45] of this question, however, makes it appear that the pathway through hydroxymethylglutaryl coenzyme A accounts for most, if not all, of the acetoacetate formed by soluble extracts of beef liver when assayed by a system in which acetyl coenzyme A is formed from catalytic amounts of coenzyme A.

It is also possible for hydroxymethylglutaryl coenzyme A to suffer an irreversible hydrolysis to free hydroxymethylglutarate and free coenzyme A.[46] The appropriate deacylase enzyme has been found in several mammalian tissues and in bacteria. Studies[47] have shown that there are enzymes present in yeast that catalyze the release of free thiol from both diasteromers of hydroxymethylglutaryl coenzyme A. The evidence indicated the presence of two enzymes, each active toward one of the isomers of hydroxymethylglutaryl coenzyme A. That enzyme which catalyzed the deacylation of the natural isomer is inactivated by p-hydroxymercuriobenzoate resulting in a preparation active only toward the unnatural isomer. These deacylase enzymes were obtained free of any hydroxymethylglutaryl coenzyme A reductase activity [Equation (6–5)].

$$
\begin{array}{ccc}
\text{H}_3\text{C} \quad \text{OH} & & \text{CH}_3\text{COCH}_2\text{COOH} \\
\diagdown \diagup & \rightarrow & + \\
\text{C} & & \text{CH}_3\text{COSCoA} \\
\diagup \diagdown & & \\
\text{H}_2\text{C} \quad \text{CH}_2 & & \\
| \qquad | & & \\
\text{HOOC} \quad \text{COSCoA} & & \\
\end{array}
$$

$$\downarrow \text{H}_2\text{O}$$ (6–5)

$$
\begin{array}{cc}
\text{CH}_3 \quad \text{OH} & \\
\diagdown \diagup & \\
\text{C} & + \text{CoASH} \\
\diagup \diagdown & \\
\text{H}_2\text{C} \quad \text{CH}_2 & \\
| \qquad | & \\
\text{HOOC} \quad \text{COOH} & \\
\end{array}
$$

One of the most exciting and important developments in the biosynthesis of isoprenoid substances was the discovery[48] by a Merck group of a new acetate-replacing factor for *Lactobacillus acidophilus*.

45. I. C. Caldwell and G. I. Drummond, *J. Biol. Chem.*, **238**, 64 (1963).
46. E. E. Dekker, M. J. Schlesinger, and M. J. Coon, *J. Biol. Chem.*, **233**, 434 (1958).
47. M. E. Kirtley, H. Rudney, and I. F. Durr, *J. Biol. Chem.*, **237**, 1781 (1962).
48. H. R. Skeggs, L. D. Wright, E. L. Cresson, G. D. E. MacRae, C. H. Hoffman, D. E. Wolf, and K. Folkers, *J. Bacteriol.*, **72**, 519 (1956).

This discovery is a good example of scientific serendipity, as the investigation was in no way aimed at terpene biosynthesis but was rather directed toward an understanding of some concentrates from dried distillers' solubles that had been described as "vitamin B_{13}."[49] The active principle was soon shown[50] to be 3,5-dihydroxy-3-methylpentanoic acid (mevalonic acid), and its importance as a biosynthetic intermediate was quickly realized.

Mevalonic acid (mevalonate) is clearly related to hydroxymethylglutaryl coenzyme A by reduction of one of the carboxyl functions to a primary alcohol, probably by way of the aldehyde, mevaldic acid (mevaldehyde). That the over-all reduction of hydroxymethylglutaryl coenzyme A to mevalonate does actually occur was shown by Rudney.[51,52] Moreover, the incorporation of $1-C^{14}$ acetate into mevalonate by a preparation from rat liver consisting of microsomes and a soluble fraction that precipitates between 40 and 80 per cent of saturation with ammonium sulfate has been demonstrated.[53] It has also been shown[54] in a liver homogenate, which will not convert mevalonate to cholesterol, that the addition of mevaldehyde leads to an accumulation of mevalonate; this demonstrates that mevaldehyde can serve as a precursor for mevalonate. Further, Lynen[55] has demonstrated that mevalonate lies further along the pathway to cholesterol than mevaldehyde.

Durr and Rudney[56] have reported that the reduction of hydroxymethylglutaryl coenzyme A to mevalonate is apparently catalyzed by a single enzyme (hydroxymethylglutaryl coenzyme A reductase). The enzyme contains sulfhydryl groups essential for the catalytic activity as indicated by the severe inhibitory effect of p-hydroxymercuribenzoate, and the requirement of added thiols to maintain the activity of the

49. A. F. Novak and S. M. Hauge, *J. Biol. Chem.*, **174**, 647 (1948).
50. K. Folkers, C. H. Shunk, B. O. Linn, F. M. Robinson, P. E. Wittreich, J. W. Huff, J. L. Gilfillan, and H. R. Skeggs, in *Biosynthesis of Terpenes and Sterols*, Little, Brown, Boston, 1959, p. 20.
51. J. J. Ferguson, Jr., I. F. Durr, and H. Rudney, *Federation Proc.*, **17**, 219 (1958).
52. J. J. Ferguson, Jr., I. F. Durr, and H. Rudney, *Proc. Natl. Acad. Sci. (U.S.)*, **45**, 499 (1959).
53. H. J. Knauss, J. W. Porter, and G. Wasson, *J. Biol. Chem.*, **234**, 2835 (1959).
54. L. D. Wright, M. Cleland, B. N. Dutta, and J. S. Norton, *J. Am. Chem. Soc.*, **79**, 6572 (1957).
55. F. Lynen, in *Biosynthesis of Terpenes and Sterols*, Little, Brown, Boston, 1959, p. 95.
56. I. F. Durr and H. Rudney, *J. Biol. Chem.*, **235**, 2572 (1960).

purified enzyme.   For every mole of hydroxymethylglutaryl coenzyme A reduced, one mole of mevalonate is formed, two moles of reduced nicotinamide adenine dinucleotide phosphate are oxidized, and one mole of coenzyme A is released.

Fractionation of yeast has led to the isolation of two enzyme systems.   Found exclusively in the supernatant is mevalonate dehydrogenase, which catalyzes the reversible conversion of mevaldehyde to mevalonate, and concentrated mainly in the particulate fraction is mevaldic dehydrogenase, which effects the transformation of hydroxymethylglutaryl coenzyme A to mevaldehyde.   Both enzymes require reduced nicotinamide adenine dinucleotide phosphate, although there are reports that reduced nicotinamide adenine dinucleotide phosphate can be utilized less effectively.[57]   There has also been reported[58] the isolation and partial purification of an enzyme from liver which is called mevaldic reductase and which catalyzes the irreversible reduction of mevaldehyde to mevalonate by reduced nicotinamide adenine dinucleotide or reduced nicotinamide adenine dinucleotide phosphate.   As would seem most reasonable, it is the carboxyl group present in hydroxymethylglutaryl coenzyme A as the thiolester that is reduced in the above conversion.[52,59]

The reversibility of some of the above reactions can be demonstrated[55] only when the action of mevalonate dehydrogenase, mevaldehyde dehydrogenase, and hydroxymethylglutaryl coenzyme A cleavage enzyme are coupled.   In such a system the formation of radioactive acetone from 2-C^{14}-mevalonate can be observed.   That the reaction sequence can be forced in this direction only by the constant removal of hydroxymethylglutaryl coenzyme A by its practically irreversible cleavage to acetoacetic acid and acetyl coenzyme A, whereas hydroxymethylglutaryl coenzyme A can readily be transformed nearly quantitatively into mevalonate, implies that the equilibrium for the oxidation-reduction processes lies very much in favor of mevalonate; this supports the biologically important direction of the reactions leading from hydroxymethylglutaryl coenzyme A to mevalonate and then to the isoprenoids and steroids.   Such a situation is also of great importance in ensuring the clean tracer experiments that are observed when specifically labeled mevalonate is used as substrate.   As mentioned previously, the major

57. I. F. Durr, H. Rudney, and J. J. Ferguson, Jr., *Federation Proc.*, **18**, 219 (1959).

58. M. J. Schlesinger and M. J. Coon, *J. Biol. Chem.*, **236**, 2421 (1961).

59. I. F. Durr, H. Rudney, and J. J. Ferguson, Jr., *Federation Proc.*, **18**, 219 (1959).

intracellular site of hydroxymethylglutaryl coenzyme A condensing and cleavage enzyme in rat liver is the mitochondria. Hydroxymethylglutaryl coenzyme A reductase,[22] which leads to the pathway for cholesterol and terpene synthesis, is in the microsomes and is only one-twentieth as active as the cleavage enzyme that causes acetoacetate production. In spite of this unfavorable ratio, cholesterol synthesis does occur; possibly because a small amount of condensing enzyme and most or all of the reductase enzyme are in the microsomes that are low in cleavage enzyme.

The reversal of these processes, the degradation of mevalonate to acetoacetate has been reported in a bacterium.[60] The bacterial system specifically requires nicotinamide adenine dinucleotide rather than nicotinamide adenine dinucleotide phosphate.

The occurrence of free mevaldehyde as an obligatory intermediate in the above sequence is somewhat doubtful, as the addition of non-labeled mevaldehyde to a system that reduces C^{14}-hydroxymethylglutaryl coenzyme A to C^{14}-mevalonate [Eq. (6–6)] led to no incorporation of label into the reisolated mevaldehyde.[52,61] Also the addition of un-labeled mevaldehyde did not depress the incorporation of C^{14} into meva-lonate from C^{14}-hydroxymethylglutaryl coenzyme A. It would seem, therefore, that the mevaldehyde either remains bound to an enzyme surface or is present as a hemithioacetal with coenzyme A, which does not exchange rapidly with added mevaldehyde.

$$(6\text{--}6)$$

One of the great questions in cholesterol and terpene biogenesis concerns that step in the over-all process at which physiological control is exerted over the rate of cholesterol production. Although this control can undoubtedly be imposed at a number of points in the

60. M. A. Siddiqi and V. Rodwell, *Biochem. Biophys. Res. Commun.*, **8**, 110 (1962).
61. H. Rudney, I. F. Durr, and J. J. Ferguson, Jr., *Abstracts, 135th Meeting Am. Chem. Soc., Boston, April 5–10, 1959*, p. 40C.

multistage process, a beautiful series of experiments [62–65] utilizing cell-free preparations of livers from rats previously subjected to physiological trauma, e.g., treatment with Triton-WR 1339, X irradiation, fasting, or feeding of Δ^4-cholestenone or unnaturally large amounts of cholesterol, has indicated that a major point in the control of cholesterol production is a microsome-dependent step in that segment of the biosynthetic pathway preceding the utilization of mevalonate, quite possibly the sequence of reductions leading from hydroxymethylglutaryl coenzyme A to mevalonate. Further, it is observed that cholesterol can exert a negative-feedback control on its own production, a type of situation that is being found increasingly in microorganisms [66] and has been observed, among other places, in purine biosynthesis.[67]

Mevalonolactone [6] has been proved[68] to possess the (R)-(−) configuration by direct correlation of its antipode with quinic acid. It has also been possible to synthesize R(−)-mevalonolactone and S(+)-mevalonolactone from S(+)-linalool and R(−)-linalool, respectively.[69]

Thus, attainment of mevalonate constitutes, in a sense, passage through the gateway to isoprenoid biogenesis.

The complex sequence of interconversions between acetate, leucine and mevalonate is summarized in Chart I.

[6]
Mevalonolactone

62. N. L. R. Bucher, *Biosynthesis of Terpenes and Sterols*, Little, Brown, Boston, 1959, p. 46.

63. N. L. R. Bucher, P. Overrath, and F. Lynen, *Federation Proc.*, **18**, 20 (1959).

64. J. F. Scaife and B. B. Migicovsky, *Can. J. Biochem. Physiol.*, **35**, 615 (1957).

65. N. L. R. Bucher, K. McGarrahan, E. Gould, and A. V. Loud, *J. Biol. Chem.*, **234**, 262 (1959).

66. R. A. Yates and A. B. Pardee, *J. Biol. Chem.*, **221**, 757 (1956).

67. J. B. Wyngaarden and D. M. Ashton, *J. Biol. Chem.*, **234**, 1492 (1959).

68. M. Eberle and D. Arigoni, *Helv. Chim. Acta*, 43, 1508 (1960).

69. R. H. Cornforth, J. W. Cornforth, and G. Popják, *Tetrahedron*, **18**, 1351 (1962).

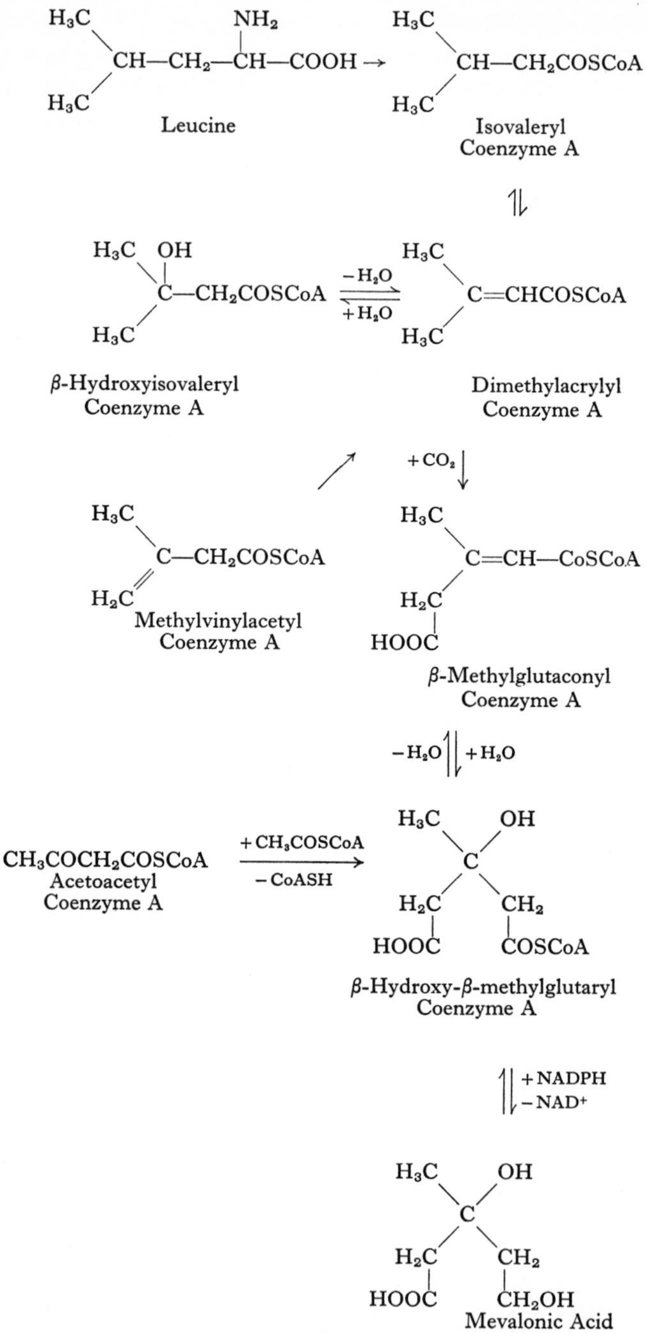

$$\underset{H_3C}{\overset{H_3C}{\diagdown}}CH-CH_2-\underset{}{\overset{NH_2}{\underset{|}{CH}}}-COOH \rightarrow \underset{H_3C}{\overset{H_3C}{\diagdown}}CH-CH_2COSCoA$$

Leucine   Isovaleryl
                                           Coenzyme A

$$\updownarrow$$

$$\underset{H_3C}{\overset{H_3C\quad OH}{\diagdown\underset{|}{C}}}-CH_2COSCoA \underset{+H_2O}{\overset{-H_2O}{\rightleftharpoons}} \underset{H_3C}{\overset{H_3C}{\diagdown}}C=CHCOSCoA$$

β-Hydroxyisovaleryl   Dimethylacrylyl
Coenzyme A   Coenzyme A

$$\nearrow \qquad +CO_2\downarrow$$

$$\underset{H_2C}{\overset{H_3C}{\diagdown}}C-CH_2COSCoA \qquad \underset{\underset{HOOC}{\overset{|}{H_2C}}}{\overset{H_3C}{\diagdown}}C=CH-CoSCoA$$

Methylvinylacetyl   β-Methylglutaconyl
Coenzyme A   Coenzyme A

$$-H_2O\updownarrow+H_2O$$

$$\underset{}{CH_3COCH_2COSCoA} \overset{+CH_3COSCoA}{\underset{-CoASH}{\longrightarrow}} \underset{HOOC}{\overset{H_3C\quad OH}{\underset{H_2C}{\diagdown\underset{|}{C}\diagup}}}\underset{COSCoA}{\overset{CH_2}{\diagup|}}$$

Acetoacetyl
Coenzyme A

β-Hydroxy-β-methylglutaryl
Coenzyme A

$$\updownarrow\begin{array}{l}+NADPH\\-NAD^+\end{array}$$

$$\underset{HOOC}{\overset{H_3C\quad OH}{\underset{H_2C}{\diagdown\underset{|}{C}\diagup}}}\underset{CH_2OH}{\overset{CH_2}{\diagup|}}$$

Mevalonic Acid

Chart I

The Role of Malonate

A pathway to mevalonate from malonyl coenzyme A and acetyl coenzyme A has recently been demonstrated in a purified pigeon liver enzyme system.[70,71]   In brief, this provides a route between these

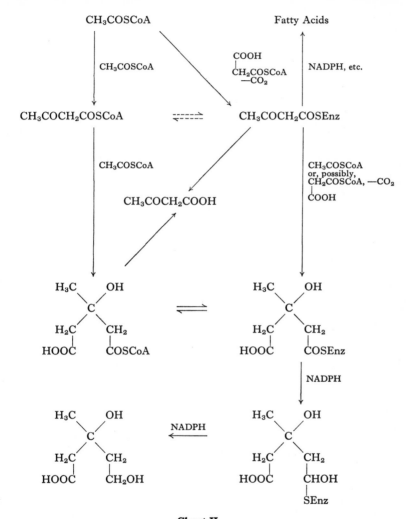

Chart II

70. J. D. Brodie, G. W. Wasson, and J. W. Porter, *J. Biol. Chem.*, **238**, 1294 (1963).
71. J. D. Brodie, G. W. Wasson, and J. W. Porter, *Biochem. Biophys. Res. Comm.*, **12**, 27 (1963).

two substrates and mevalonate that never involves the intermediacy of free acids or coenzyme A ester derivatives of any of the four- or six-carbon substances along the pathway. Instead, the intermediates are at all times bound to an enzyme until the final release of mevalonate. The importance of this pathway in the biosynthesis of sterols cannot be assessed at this time. However, its close similarity to that involving enzyme-bound intermediates in fatty acid synthesis is particularly striking. Moreover, if this is the major synthetic pathway, nature has cleanly separated the synthetic route to mevalonic and fatty acids from the degradative pathways which involve coenzyme A ester intermediates. The release of hydroxymethylglutaryl coenzyme A from the enzyme would then represent the first step in a degradative sequence.

As one might expect, when the enzyme system is deprived of reduced nicotinamide adenine dinucleotide phosphate, hydroxymethylglutaryl coenzyme A is released. The existence of a malonyl-enzyme complex was demonstrated. The attachment of the malonate to a sulfhydryl group on the enzyme was also shown: This site has a high sensitivity to N-ethyl maleimide and little sensitivity to iodoacetamide. Appropriate experiments also established that, in the presence of reduced nicotinamide adenine dinucleotide phosphate, neither acetoacetyl coenzyme A nor hydroxymethylglutaryl coenzyme A were intermediates in the pathway to mevalonate. Chart II summarizes this pathway and its possible relation to that discussed previously.

Utilization of Mevalonate

From the evidence presently at hand, it appears that the major biological role of mevalonate is to serve as a precursor for the biosynthesis of polyisoprenoid substances. For example, the intermediacy of mevalonate in the biosynthesis of rubber,[74] carotenoids,[75–77] the triterpene soyaspogenol A,[78] the diterpene rosenolactone,[79] the degenerate diterpene gibberelic acid,[79] the sesquiterpene trichothecin,[80]

74. R. B. Park and J. Bonner, *J. Biol. Chem.*, **233**, 340 (1958).
75. E. C. Grob, *Biosynthesis of Terpenes and Sterols*, Little, Brown, Boston, 1959, p. 267.
76. A. E. Purcell, G. A. Thompson, Jr., and J. Bonner, *J. Biol. Chem.*, **234**, 1081 (1959).
77. E. A. Shneour and I. Zabin, *J. Biol. Chem.*, **234**, 770 (1959).
78. D. Arigoni, *Biosynthesis of Terpenes and Sterols*, Little, Brown, Boston, 1959, p. 231.
79. A. J. Birch and H. Smith, *Biosynthesis of Terpenes and Sterols*, Little, Brown, Boston, 1959, p. 245.
80. J. Fishman, E. R. H. Jones, G. Lowe, and M. C. Whiting, *Proc. Chem. Soc.*, **1959**, 127.

the terpenoid sidechain of ubiquinone,[81] the alkaloid, lysergic acid[82-84] and other polyisoprenoid substances has been demonstrated.

Since much of the work on mevalonic acid and its role in terpene biosynthesis depends on experiments relating to cholesterol biosynthesis, it will be well to review these findings before moving on to a detailed consideration of the various biochemical steps involved.

The almost quantitative nature of the mevalonate → cholesterol conversion emphasizes the importance of mevalonate as a terpene precursor. If indeed the only metabolic fate of mevalonate is to produce cholesterol, feeding of $2-C^{14}$-[DL]-mevalonate should lead to the recovery of 50 per cent of the activity of mevalonate (the unnatural isomer), 41.7 per cent should be incorporated into cholesterol, and 8.3 per cent expired as carbon dioxide. That label which expired in carbon dioxide originates in the following way: Lanosterol biosynthesized from $2-C^{14}$-mevalonate will have one of the three methyl groups that are oxidized and lost in the lanosterol → cholesterol conversion derived from C-2 of the mevalonate precursor and this will give rise to $C^{14}O_2$ (for a detailed discussion of this point see the discussion in Chapter 12 on the conversion of lanosterol to cholesterol). As six mevalonate units are incorporated into each lanosterol molecule, this will represent one-sixth of the added natural isomer or one-twelfth (8.3 per cent) of the total [DL]-mevalonate expired as $C^{14}O_2$.

In the first experiment on mevalonate utilization[85] it was found that 43.4 per cent of added $2-C^{14}$-[DL]-mevalonate was converted to cholesterol. In experiments with intact mice, Gould and Popják[86] found that about 40 per cent of the $2-C^{14}$-[DL]-mevalonate was recovered as cholesterol, 10 per cent was found in respiratory CO_2 and about 50 per cent recovered in the urine. Oral administration of $2-C^{14}$-[DL]-mevalonate to humans resulted in recovery of 36 per cent of the activity in the urine, 10 per cent in respiratory carbon dioxide, and 24 per cent of the C^{14} not in the urine or expired as carbon dioxide was found

81. U. Gloor and O. Wiss, *Arch. Biochem. Biophys.*, **83**, 216 (1959).
82. A. J. Birch, J. McLoughlin, and H. Smith, *Tetrahedron Letters*, **No. 7**, 1 (1960).
83. K. Mothes, H. Simon, H. G. Floss, and F. Weygand, *Z. Naturstoffe.*, **156**, 141 (1960).
84. E. H. Taylor and E. Ramstad, *Nature*, **188**, 494 (1960).
85. P. A. Tavormina, H. M. Gibbs, and J. W. Huff, *J. Am. Chem. Soc.*, **78**, 4498 (1956).
86. R. G. Gould and G. Popják, *Biochem. J.*, **66**, 51P (1957).

in the blood and liver as cholesterol.[87] The remarkable agreement between theoretical and experimental figures shows that mevalonate → cholesterol conversion does, at least in some biological systems, occur almost quantitatively.

The differential incorporation of 2-C^{14}-mevalonolactone and potassium 2-C^{14}-mevalonate in rat brain has been investigated[88]; the potassium salt was incorporated more efficiently into unsaponifiable and digitonin-precipitable material by brain slices than was the lactone. This effect was not, however, observed in liver.

6-2 MEVALONATE → ISOPENTENYL PYROPHOSPHATE

As mevalonate possesses six carbons and squalene is a polymer of five-carbon units, it follows that one carbon of each mevalonate unit must be lost during its incorporation into any terpene such as squalene or derived substance such as cholesterol. This carbon that is lost in the conversion of mevalonate to terpenoid products has been shown[89] to be C-1, the carboxyl carbon of the mevalonate. Thus, 1-C^{14}-mevalonate gave rise to unlabeled cholesterol, whereas 2-C^{14}-mevalonate produced cholesterol with the expected level of activity. The distribution of label in cholesterol from 2-C^{14}-mevalonate has been examined,[90] and as anticipated, C-7, C-22, and C-26 or C-27 of cholesterol find their origin in C-2 of mevalonate. (The origin of other carbon atoms in the ring system of cholesterol was not determined.) Also, the distribution of C^{14} in squalene biosynthesized from 2-C^{14}-mevalonate has been established,[91-93] and, as indicated in Eq. (6–7), conforms to the expected pattern. Incidentally, the incorporation of the methyl and carboxyl carbons of acetate into squalene has also been determined[94] and the results shown in Eq. (6–8) are in exact agreement with expectations.

87. L. I. Gidez, H. A. Eder, and W. W. Shreeve, *Federation Proc.*, **17**, 228 (1958).
88. R. Fumagalli, E. Grossi, M. Poggi, P. Paoletti, and S. Garattini, *Arch. Biochem. Biophys.*, **99**, 529 (1962).
89. P. A. Tavormina and M. H. Gibbs, *J. Am. Chem. Soc.*, **78**, 6210 (1956).
90. O. Isler, R. Rüegg, J. Würsch, K. F. Gey, and A. Pletscher, *Helv. Chim. Acta*, **40**, 2369 (1957).
91. J. W. Cornforth, R. H. Cornforth, G. Popják, and I. Y. Gore, *Biochem. J.*, **66**, 10P (1957).
92. F. Dituri, S. Gurin, and J. L. Rabinowitz, *J. Am. Chem. Soc.*, **79**, 2650 (1957).
93. F. Dituri, J. L. Rabinowitz, R. P. Hullin, and S. Gurin, *J. Biol. Chem.*, **229**, 825 (1957).
94. J. W. Cornforth and G. Popják, *Biochem. J.*, **58**, 403 (1954).

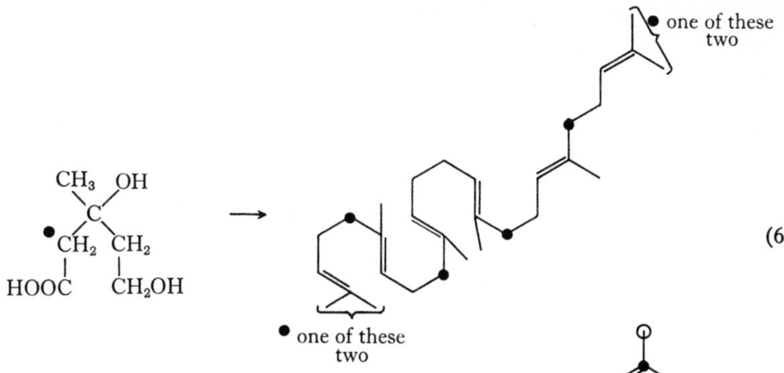

$$\begin{array}{c} \text{CH}_3 \quad \text{OH} \\ \bullet\text{C} \\ \bullet\text{CH}_2 \quad \text{CH}_2 \\ \text{HOOC} \quad \text{CH}_2\text{OH} \end{array} \quad \longrightarrow \qquad\qquad\qquad (6\text{-}7)$$

$$\overset{\circ}{\text{CH}_3}-\bullet\text{COOH} \quad \longrightarrow \qquad\qquad\qquad\qquad (6\text{-}8)$$

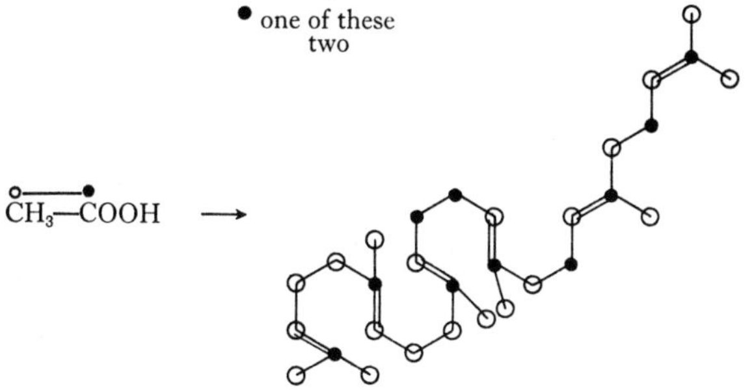

Antimetabolites

An interesting adjunct to a discussion of the utilization of mevalonate as a precursor of steroids is the recent report of experiments with potential antimetabolites of mevalonate.   Farnesinic acid, α,β-diphenylbutyric acid, β-hydroxy-β-methylglutaric acid, α-phenylbutyric acid, and β-methylcrotonic were found[95] to be effective as mevalonate antimetabolites in *L. acidophilus* in the order given.   Tamura[96] et al. tested β-ethyl-β-hydroxy-δ-valerolactone, 4-methyl mevalonate, 2-butyl mevalonate, 2,2-dimethyl mevalonate, 2-methyl mevalonate, and 2-ethyl mevalonate, and found that the last two inhibited the growth of *L. heterochii* in the presence of small amounts of mevalonate.   Also tested as antimetabolites[97] were 4-methyl mevalonate, 3-methyl-3,4-dihydroxyvaleric acid, 3-methyl-3,4-dihydroxybutyric acid, 2,3-dimethyl-3,4-dihydroxybutyric acid, and the corresponding amides, anilides, and hydrazides.   4-Methyl mevalonate was found to be the most effective inhibitor, although none of the compounds was highly active in suppressing ergosterol synthesis in yeast.

95. L. D. Wright, *Proc. Soc. Exptl. Biol. Med.*, **96**, 364 (1957).
96. S. Tamura, G. Tamura, M. Takai, S. Nakamura, and T. Shiro, *Agri. Chem. Soc. Japan Biol. Chem.* (*Tokyo*), **22**, 202 (1958).
97. J. M. Stewart and D. W. Wooley, *Federation Proc.*, **18**, 332 (1959).

Bacterial Metabolism of Mevalonate

Mevalonate, it will be recalled, was first discovered as an acetate replacement factor for *L. acidophilus*. This discussion so far has stressed the importance of mevalonate as a precursor of isoprenoids, especially sterols and terpenes. However bacteria do not appear[98] to contain sterols. What then is the biological function of mevalonate in lactobacilli? A recent series of papers[99] has been addressed to this question and, although the results do not provide a definitive and complete answer to this question, they do imply that mevalonate is not first metabolized to acetate; similarly, mevalonate is not incorporated into fatty acids for which acetate is a precursor but is found in un-saponifiable material of as yet unknown constitution. However, the metabolism of mevalonate back to acetoacetate by bacteria was pointed out earlier.[63]

Phosphorylation

There are several mechanisms possible on purely structural grounds by which mevalonate units might join together in the formation of terpenes such as squalene. The possible intermediacy of any mevalonate derivative in which C-5, the primary alcohol function, has become oxidized either to an aldehyde or carboxyl group was eliminated by Bloch,[100,101] who demonstrated by the use of $5\text{-diH}^3\text{-2-C}^{14}$-mevalonate and $5\text{-diH}^2\text{-2-C}^{14}$-mevalonate that no more than one or two of the original 12 atoms of hydrogen is lost from the C-5 carbons of the six mevalonate units that form one molecule of squalene. Lynen[55] has also shown that mevaldehyde is not an intermediate between mevalonate and squalene.

In addition to these experiments, which deal with the over-all conversion of mevalonate to squalene, it has been possible to define in some detail the nature of the intermediate steps in the process. These steps require adenosine triphosphate. The first reaction is the monophos-phorylation of mevalonate. Tchen[103] was able to separate an enzyme preparation of yeast into two fractions, one of which catalyzes the forma-tion of a monophosphate ester of mevalonate, which retains all six

98. A. Fiertel and H. P. Klein, *J. Bacteriol.*, **78**, 738 (1959).
99. K. J. I. Thorne and E. Kodicek, *Biochim. Biophys. Acta*, **59**, 273, 280, 295, 306 (1962).
100. B. H. Amdur, H. Rilling, and K. Bloch, *J. Am. Chem. Soc.*, **79**, 2646 (1957).
101. H. C. Rilling and K. Bloch, *J. Biol. Chem.*, **234**, 1424 (1959).
103. T. T. Tchen, *J. Am. Chem. Soc.*, **79**, 6344 (1957).

carbon atoms of mevalonate, since both $1\text{-}C^{14}\text{-}$ and $2\text{-}C^{14}$-mevalonate give rise to labeled ester.   The chemical characteristics of the ester led to its formulation as a phosphate ester of the primary hydroxyl group.   The enzyme involved in this transformation, mevalonic kinase, has been partially purified from a yeast extract,[104] from rabbit liver,[105] from higher plants (e.g., pumpkin seedlings, *Curcurbita pepo*),[106] from hog liver,[107] and from the latex of *Hevea brasiliensis*.[107b]   The product of this reaction, mevalonate-5-phosphate, has also been prepared synthetically.[108]

Further incubation [109,110] of mevalonate with this yeast or hog-liver extract leads to the formation of the corresponding pyrophosphate derivative of mevalonic acid.   The enzyme involved in this second phosphorylation, phosphomevalonic kinase, has been purified[111] by fractionation of yeast autolysates and also from hog liver.[112]   This enzyme catalyzes the phosphorylation of phosphomevalonic acid to mevalonic acid-5-pyrophosphate by adenosine triphosphate in the presence of a divalent metal ion.   Stoichiometric quantities of adenosine diphosphate are formed in the reaction.

Biological Isoprene Unit

From mevalonic acid-5-pyrosphosphate there originates the long-sought biological isoprene unit, which has been identified by Bloch's group [109,111] and by Lynen's group [114] as Δ^3-isopentyl pyrophosphate. Also, some of these intermediates have been isolated from rat-liver preparations by Witting and Porter.[115]   That the true intermediate should be so very similar to isoprene, which, since classical times, has been the hypothetical source of the terpenes, is but one of the many

104. T. T. Tchen, *J. Biol. Chem.*, **233**, 1100 (1958).
105. K. Markley and E. Smallman, *Biochim. Biophys. Acta*, **47**, 327 (1961).
106. W. D. Loomis and J. Battaile, *Biochim. Biophys. Acta*, **67**, 54 (1963).
107. H. R. Levy and G. Popják, *Biochem. J.*, **72**, 35P (1959).
107b. I. P. Williamson and R. G. O. Kerwick, *Biochem. J.*, **88**, 18P (1963).
108. H. Machleidt, E. Cohnen, and R. Tschesche, *Ann.*, **655**, 70 (1962).
109. S. Chaykin, J. Law, A. H. Phillips, T. T. Tchen, and K. Bloch, *Proc. Natl. Acad. Sci. U.S.*, **44**, 998 (1958).
110. A. H. Phillips, T. T. Tchen, and K. Bloch, *Federation Proc.*, **17**, 289 (1958).
111. K. Bloch, S. Chaykin, A. H. Phillips, and A. deWaard, *J. Biol. Chem.*, **234**, 2595 (1959).
112. H. Hellig and G. Popják, *J. Lipid Res.*, **2**, 235 (1961).
114. F. Lynen, H. Eggerer, U. Henning, and I Kessel, *Angew. Chem.*, **70**, 738 (1958).
115. L. A. Witting and J. W. Porter, *J. Biol. Chem.*, **234**, 2841 (1959).

surprises that have been met in the study of terpene biosynthesis. Bloch obtained the intermediate Δ^3-isopentenyl pyrophosphate by incubation of 5-phosphomevalonic acid with an enzyme fraction that had been separated by differential precipitation with ammonium sulfate from the supernatant of autolyzates of dried bakers' yeast. By a series of most elegant experiments using 1-C^{14}-mevalonate, 2-C^{14}-mevalonate and adenosine triphosphate, P^{32} alone and in combination, and by acid and snake-venom hydrolyses of the phosphate ester bonds, Bloch proved the chemical constitution of the intermediate. Lynen,[114] by blocking an enzyme preparation with iodoacetamide, was able to isolate the intermediate and, independently, to prove its structure as Δ^3-isopentenyl pyrophosphate. Moreover, he showed that 2-C^{14}-mevalonate gives rise to Δ^3-isopentenyl pyrophosphate with C^{14} activity only in the methylene group. Lynen[114] also synthesized Δ^3-isopentenyl pyrophosphate [Eq. (6–9)] and showed that this synthetic material

$$
\begin{array}{c}
H_3C \quad OH \\
\diagdown \diagup \\
C \\
\diagup \quad \diagdown \\
H_2C \quad\quad CH_2 \\
| \quad\quad\quad | \\
HOOC \quad CH_2OH
\end{array}
\rightarrow
\begin{array}{c}
H_3C \\
\diagdown \\
C-CH_2-CH_2O\textcircled{P}_2 \\
\diagup\diagup \\
H_2C
\end{array}
\qquad (6\text{--}9)
$$

gave rise to squalene in the presence of yeast extract, reduced nicotinamide adenine dinucleotide phosphate and Mg^{2+}; to cholesterol in the presence of a liver enzyme preparation; and to rubber when added to latex from *Taraxacum Kok saghyx*. Yuan and Bloch[116] have also reported similar results with synthetic Δ^3-isopentenyl pyrophosphate. Markley and Gurin[117] have isolated two enzyme systems, one of which requires adenosine triphosphate, Mn^{2+}, or Mg^{2+} but no reduced nicotinamide adenine dinucleotide, nicotinamide adenine dinucleotide phosphate, or free coenzyme A and which can decarboxylate mevalonate to an unidentified substance. This substance can then form squalene in the presence of the second enzyme fraction, which does require reduced nicotinamide adenine dinucleotide phosphate. It is worth noting that, before the discovery of Δ^3-isopentenyl pyrophosphate as the biological isoprene unit, Bloch[118] had earlier implicated either isoprene or a derivative of isopentenol as the true condensing fragment in polyisoprenoid biosynthesis.

116. C. Yuan and K. Bloch, *J. Biol. Chem.*, **234**, 2605 (1959).
117. K. Markley and S. Gurin, *Biochim. Biophys. Acta*, **31**, 287 (1959).
118. H. Rilling, T. T. Tchen, and K. Bloch, *Proc. Natl. Acad. Sci. U.S.*, **44**, 167 (1958).

Much light is thrown on the detailed mechanisms of the formation of Δ^3-isopentenyl pyrophosphate by the following considerations. The over-all conversion of six mevalonate units to one molecule of squalene is stoichiometrically a reductive process requiring two-electrons.

$$6C_6H_{12}O_4 + 2H^+ + 2e^- \rightarrow C_{30}H_{50} + 6CO_2 + 12H_2O$$

Bloch [118] allowed the formation of squalene from mevalonate to proceed in a medium of D_2O and found that only three to four atoms of deuterium had been acquired by each molecule of squalene [7]. These three or four atoms of deuterium are completely accounted for in the following way: Two are acquired in the formation of the two gem-dimethyl groups, one at each end of the squalene chain; and some are probably, though not necessarily, acquired as a result of the reduction. In addition to further disproving the occurrence of any oxidative

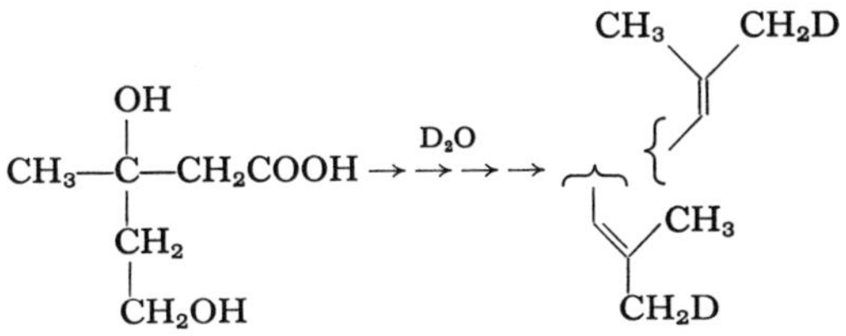

[7]
Squalene

processes between mevalonate and squalene, this result has other profound implications. It demands that elimination of C-1 as carbon dioxide from mevalonate be concerted with loss of the hydroxyl functions at C-3, as only in this way will no additional uptake of deuterium result. The conversion of mevalonic acid-5-pyrophosphate to Δ^3-isopentenyl pyrophosphate requires adenosine triphosphate [119] and it has been found [114] that carbon dioxide evolution and adenosine diphosphate production occur at identical rates during the irreversible transformation of mevalonic acid-5-pyrophosphate to Δ^3-isopentenyl pyrophosphate catalyzed by an enzyme system from yeast purified 100-fold. Moreover, [120] the enzymatic conversion of synthetic 3-O^{18}-

119. A. deWaard, A. H. Phillips, and K. Bloch, *J. Am. Chem. Soc.*, **81**, 2913 (1959).
120. M. Lindberg, C. Yuan, A. deWaard, and K. Bloch, *Biochemistry*, **1**, 182 (1962).

mevalonolactone to $3\text{-}O^{18}$-mevalonate-5-pyrophosphate followed by decarboxylation to isopentenyl pyrophosphate produces inorganic phosphate that contains O^{18}, showing that oxygen has been transferred from the tertiary hydroxyl group of mevalonate-5-pyrophosphate to a phosphorus atom that had been the terminal phosphate residue of adenosine triphosphate. This confirms that the 3-hydroxyl function is activated for expulsion as its phosphate ester.

When this conversion is allowed to take place in a medium containing tritium oxide, the Δ^3-isopentenyl pyrophosphate product is almost completely devoid of tritium, thus amplifying and confirming the previous results with deuterium. The mechanism of Eq. (6–10) can therefore be ascribed to the mevalonate $\rightarrow \Delta^3$-isopentenyl pyrophosphate conversion.

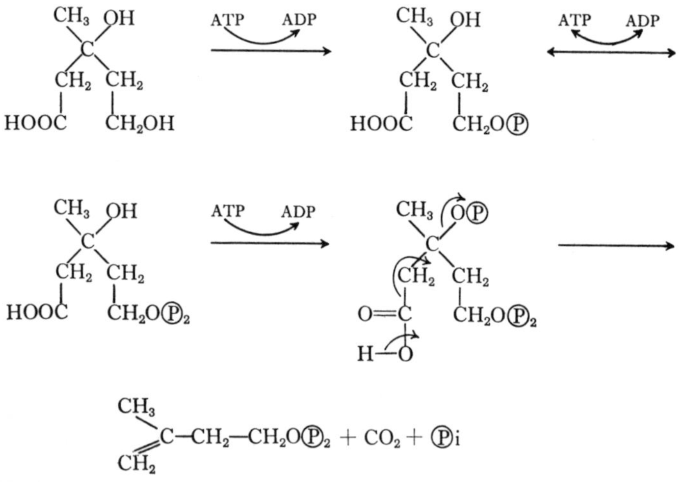

$$(6\text{--}10)$$

Tumor Cells

Tumor cells differ from many tissues in being unable to synthesize sterols from acetate.[121,122] Gore and Popják[123] have recently shown that the metabolic block involved in the interruption of this biosynthetic path lies beyond the acetyl coenzyme A stage of the synthesis. The nature of the controls operating against efficient sterol production

121. H. Busch, *Cancer Res.*, **13**, 789 (1953).
122. H. Busch and H. A. Baltrush, *Cancer Res.*, **14**, 448 (1954).
123. I. Y. Gore and G. Popják, *Biochem. J.*, **84**, 93 (1962).

was found to be due to three factors: (1) the pyrophosphatases deplete the available substrates for squalene synthesis by an irreversible hydrolysis of the allyl pyrophosphates to the inert free allylic alcohol,[124] (2) the amount of adenosine triphosphate available is insufficient for optimum formation of allyl pyrophosphates, and (3) a low concentration of endogenous reduced nicotinamide adenine dinucleotide phosphate does not meet the requirements for the steps of squalene and sterol formation.

Ergot Alkaloids

Before we proceed to a discussion of the polymerization of iso-pentyl pyrophosphate it will be interesting to cite one of many examples in which the isoprenoid unit is combined with another fragment from a quite different area of intermediate metabolism—in this case a derivative of the amino acid tryptophan—to produce the important

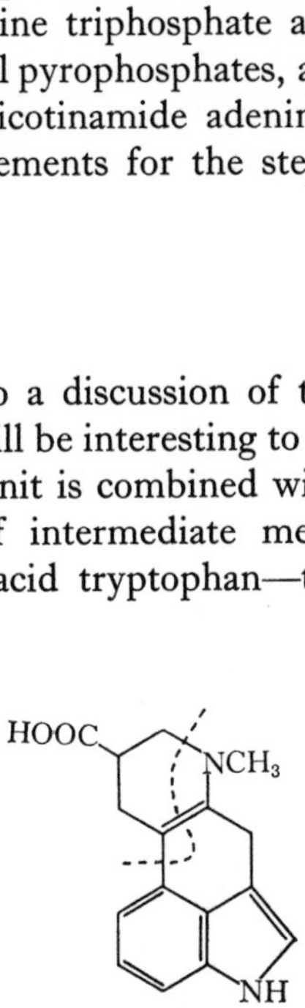

[8]

ergot alkaloids such as lysergic acid [8], whose dissection into a tryptamine and isoprenoid fragment is clear. The incorporation of mevalonate has been observed, C-2 of the mevalonate precursor appearing largely in that carbon of the ergoline skeleton which is the carboxyl carbon of lysergic acid.[85–87,125,126] There is also evidence that deuterated isopentenyl pyrophosphate is incorporated into the isoprenoid region of these substances,[127] and the biosynthetic interrelations between

124. J. Christophe and G. Popják, *J. Lipid Res.*, 2, 244 (1961).
125. B. M. Baxter, S. I. Kandel, and A. Okany, *Tetrahedron Letters*, **1961**, 596.
126. S. Bhattacharji, A. J. Birch, A. Brach, A. Hofmann, H. Kobel, D. C. C. Smith, H. Smith, and J. Winter, *J. Chem. Soc.*, **1962**, 421.
127. H. Plieninger, R. Fischer, G. Keilich, and H. D. Orth, *Ann.*, **642**, 214 (1961).

members of this group of alkaloids have received attention.[128,129] Another fungal alkaloid, echinulin, is known [130] to contain two isoprene units introduced onto an indole ring at positions 5 and 7.

6–3 POLYMERIZATION OF Δ³-ISOPENTENYL PYROPHOSPHATE

Dimethallyl Pyrophosphate

If Lynen[114] did not inhibit his enzyme preparation with iodoacetamide, another substance accumulated that was isolated by chromatography and shown to be farnesyl pyrophosphate. The conversion of Δ³-isopentenyl pyrophosphate to farnesyl pyrophosphate was found to require a sulfhydryl group, which, when poisoned by iodoacetamide, resulted in the accumulation of Δ³-isopentenyl pyrophosphate in the previous experiments. Also necessary for this conversion is Mg^{2+}, as its removal by complexing with ethylenediaminetetraacetic acid prevented the formation of squalene from Δ³-isopentenyl pyrophosphate. The addition of ethylenediaminetetraacetic acid had, however, no effect on the farnesyl pyrophosphate → squalene conversion.

The polymerization of Δ³-isopentenyl pyrophosphate to farnesyl pyrophosphate is postulated to proceed by an isomerization of Δ³-isopentenyl pyrophosphate to dimethallyl pyrophosphate[131] under the influence of an appropriate isomerase. Lynen and co-workers [132,133] have isolated a preparation from dried bakers' yeast which catalyzes this isomerization (isopentenyl pyrophosphate isomerase). This enzyme has been partially purified[128] and apparently contains a free sulfhydryl group as it is inhibited by $10^{-4} M$ p-chloromercuribenzoate or $10^{-3} M$ iodoacetamide (the only enzyme in the mevalonate-squalene conversion so poisoned). Lynen postulates a special role for the sulfhydryl group in the isomerization, such as the formation of an enzyme

128. S. Agurell and E. Ramstad, *Tetrahedron Letters*, **1961**, 501.
129. S. Agurell and E. Ramstad, *Arch. Biochem. Biophys.*, **98**, 457 (1962); K. Mothes and K. Winkler, *Tetrahedron Letters*, **1962**, 1243.
130. A. J. Birch, G. E. Blance, S. David, and H. Smith, *J. Chem. Soc.*, **1961**, 3128.
131. F. Lynen, B. W. Agranoff, H. Eggerer, U. Henning, and E. M. Möslein, *Angew. Chem.*, **71**, 657 (1959).
132. B. W. Agranoff, H. Eggerer, U. Henning, and F. Lynen, *J. Am. Chem. Soc.*, **81**, 1254 (1959).
133. B. W. Agranoff, H. Eggerer, U. Henning, and F. Lynen, *J. Biol. Chem.*, **235**, 326 (1960).

substrate complex.   The isomerization can be tentatively written as Eq. (6–11).   It is important to note that the occurrence of this isomeriza-

$$\begin{array}{c} H_3C \\ \diagdown \\ C—CH_2CH_2OP_2 + HS\text{-enzyme} \rightarrow \\ \diagup\diagup \\ H_2C \end{array} \quad \begin{array}{c} H_3C \\ \diagdown \\ C—CH_2CH_2OP_2 \rightarrow \\ \diagup \\ H_3C \;\; S\text{-enzyme} \end{array}$$

$$\begin{array}{c} H_3C \\ \diagdown \\ C{=}CH—CH_2OP_2 + HS\text{-enzyme} \\ \diagup \\ H_3C \end{array}$$

(6–11)

tion in a medium of D_2O will result in the incorporation of one atom of D unless there is an unlikely intramolecular hydrogen transfer.   If we bear in mind Bloch's results in D_2O it follows that the subsequent reactions of dimethallyl pyrophosphate must be much more rapid than the reversal of the isomerization, i.e., the isomerization reaction in the forward direction may well be the rate-determining step in the polymerization sequence.   Experimental support of this is found in the fact that considerably more synthetase activity[133] than isomerase activity is found in yeast extracts.   An interesting substance in light of the S-enzyme intermediate postulated by Lynen is felinine [9], a naturally occurring substance found in cats, which has been shown[134] to be derived either from mevalonic acid or from leucine.

$$\begin{array}{c} CH_3 \\ | \\ CH_3—C—CH_2CH_2OH \\ | \\ S—CH_2—CH—COOH \\ | \\ NH_2 \end{array}$$

[9]

Felinine

Another point of note is that the above isomerization does not result in a randomization of any label originally present in the methylene group of the Δ^3-isopentenyl pyrophosphate.   Thus, if one assumes that the reactions during the isomerization are all stereospecific, the methyl groups in the resulting dimethallyl pyrophosphate will retain their

134. P. V. Avizonis and J. C. Wriston, Jr., *Biochem. Biophys. Acta*, **34**, 279 (1959).

identity by being *cis* or *trans* in relation to the double bond.   Actually, results of studies of terpene biosynthesis indicate the methylene group becomes the *trans* methyl group [Eq. (6–12)].

$$(6\text{–}12)$$

Carbon-Carbon Bond Formation

The polymerization sequence of Eq. (6–13) is envisioned as proceeding by an ionization of the carbon-oxygen bond of the dimethallyl pyrophosphate to create a cationic center which then attacks a molecule of Δ^3-isopentenyl pyrophosphate.

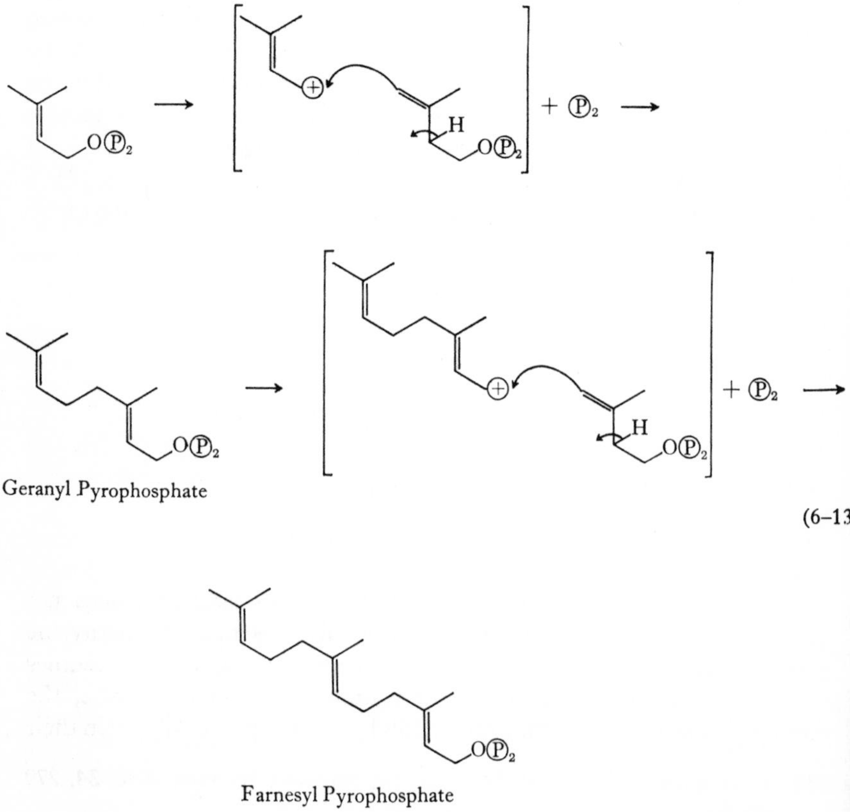

Geranyl Pyrophosphate

$$(6\text{–}13)$$

Farnesyl Pyrophosphate

It is to be emphasized that the cationic species in brackets is not, as such, postulated to be discrete intermediate, since it is probable that the ionization of the pyrophosphate fragment is concerted with the formation of the carbon–carbon bond. Rather it emphasizes that the ionization of the carbon–pyrophosphate bond is energetically favorable, owing to the stability of the resulting pyrophosphate anion and the allyl cation.

If one adds a large excess of dimethallyl pyrophosphate to the farnesyl pyrophosphate synthetic system, it is possible[131] to isolate the first condensation product, geranyl pyrophosphate, which by acquisition of another five-carbon fragment is converted to farnesyl pyrophosphate, the probable direct precursor of the sesquiterpenoids. A continuation of this process leads to the C_{20} geranyl-geranyl pyrophosphate, from which the diterpenes can be derived. Further acquisition of five-carbon units leads to the higher linear arrays that are found in the ubiquinones or gutta percha (the all-*trans* polyisoprene). A modification of the polymerization mechanism, which produces olefinic linkages with *cis* stereochemistry, accounts for natural rubber, the all-*cis* polyisoprene.

Squalene

This scheme omits intermediates of 30 to 40 carbons. These are produced by fundamentally different processes—dimerization of 15- or 20-carbon precursors. Squalene, the 30-carbon intermediate, is formed by a dimerization of farnesyl pyrophosphate. This process is a reducive coupling that requires the two electrons that were seen to be necessary for the over-all mevalonate-squalene conversion:

$$2C_{15}H_{25}O(P)_2 + 2e^- \rightarrow C_{30}H_{50} + 2(P)_i$$

In accord with this stoichiometric fact, Lynen has found[114] that this conversion requires reduced nicotinamide adenine dinucleotide phosphate.

Although various mechanisms have been postulated and some experimental work reported on the reductive dimerization of farnesyl pyrophosphate to squalene,[101,114,118,135,136] an English group has recently reported[137] a definitive set of experiments that give the following results:

135. G. Popják, *Tetrahedron Letters*, **No. 19**, 19 (1959).
136. J. W. Cornforth and G. Popják, *Tetrahedron Letters*, **No. 19**, 29 (1959).
137. G. Popják, D. S. Goodman, J. W. Cornforth, R. H. Cornforth, and R. Ryhage, *J. Biol. Chem.*, **236**, 1934 (1961).

(1) Squalene biosynthesized from $5\text{-}H^2$-mevalonate contains 11 atoms of deuterium, not the theoretically possible 12. Mass spectrometric analysis of the succinic acid (succinic anhydride and dimethyl succinate) derived from the center of the chain by ozonolysis of the deuterosqualene showed that the specimen consisted mostly of trideutero molecules. Consequently, the labeling in the center of the chain was asymmetrical:

$$-CHD-CD_2-$$

(2) $1\text{-}H_2{}^3\text{-}2C^{14}$-*trans-trans*-farnesyl pyrophosphate is converted to squalene by the standard synthetase system of liver microsomes and gives squalene with a H^3/C^{14} ratio of 0.76 when the same ratio in the farnesyl pyrophosphate is taken to be 1.00, indicating the loss of one labeled H atom from C-1 of one farnesyl pyrophosphate molecule during squalene synthesis.

(3) There is no incorporation of tritium from H^3HO into squalene during its synthesis from farnesyl pyrophosphate with liver microsomes.

(4) During squalene synthesis from farnesyl pyrophosphate with microsomes in the presence of tritium labeled reduced nicotinamide adenine dinucleotide phosphate, up to 0.8 μg-atom of labeled hydrogen per μg-mole of squalene was transferred to the hydrocarbon from the pyridine nucleotide. All the labeled hydrogen was attached to the central atoms of squalene.

(5) Rilling and Bloch[101] found that hydrogen from the water of the incubation medium was incorporated into the central position of squalene during its synthesis from mevalonate. However, when the squalene is synthesized by microsomes from its immediate precursor, farnesyl pyrophosphate, there is an almost complete lack of entry of hydrogen from water into the squalene.

The explanation of point (5) will be dealt with first. This result is almost surely a result of an exchange of hydrogen between nicotinamide adenine dinucleotide phosphate and the water of the incubation mixture through an oxidation reduction reaction, such as

$$NADPH + H^+ + X \rightleftharpoons XH_2 + NADP$$
$$XH_2 + D_2O \rightleftharpoons XHD + HDO \rightleftharpoons \text{etc.}$$

It seems probable that the enzyme or substrate (or both) that mediate this exchange reaction is present in one of the soluble preparations (F_{30}^{60}), i.e., that protein fraction precipitated between 30 and 60 per cent saturation with ammonium sulfate; support for this is found in the observation that the reaction[137] of farnesyl pyrophosphate in H^3HO

with reduced nicotinamide adenine dinucleotide phosphate in an enzyme system containing both microsomes and the soluble F_{30}^{60} proteins led to squalene, which contained tritium. In the absence of the F_{30}^{60}-protein fraction essentially no tritium is found in the squalene. The other results may be summarized by Eq. (6–14).

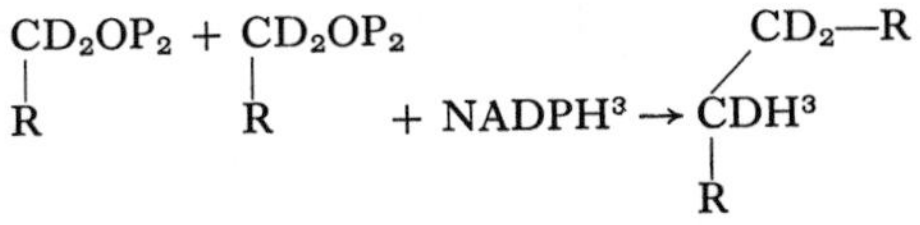

$$\begin{array}{cc} CD_2OP_2 + CD_2OP_2 \\ | \quad\quad\quad | \\ R \quad\quad\quad R \end{array} + NADPH^3 \rightarrow \begin{array}{c} CD_2{-}R \\ | \\ \dot{C}DH^3 \\ | \\ R \end{array}$$

$$(6\text{--}14)$$

Squalene

Although many mechanisms are possible to explain this conversion (cf. Ref. 137 for a discussion of alternate possibilities), one attractive possibility is given in Eq. (6–15).

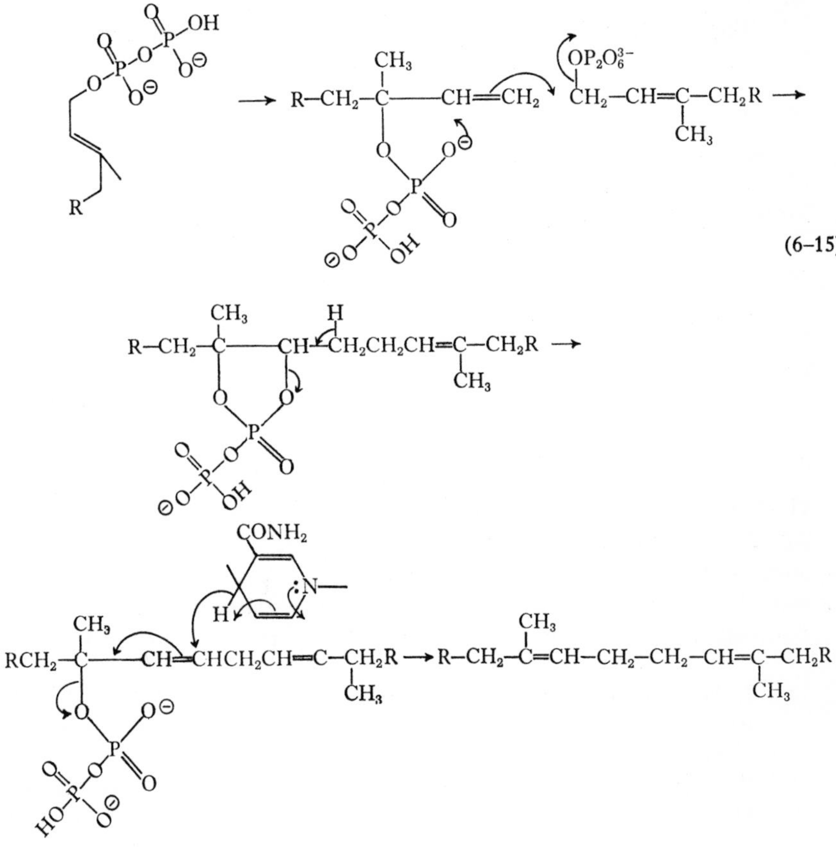

$$(6\text{--}15)$$

The four hydrogens attached to the central pair of carbons in squalene are not mutually equivalent. There are two pairs of identical hydrogens, but the two hydrogens in one pair are stereochemically dissimilar from the two hydrogens in the other pair. Two groups have demonstrated that the hydrogen transferred to the squalene from the

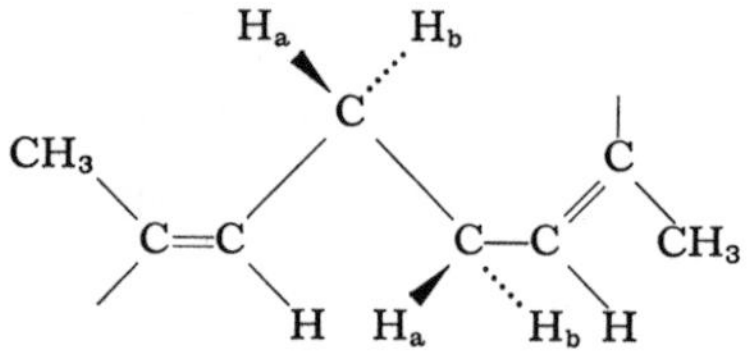

reduced nicotinamide adenine dinucleotide phosphate is transferred from the β side of the pyridine nucleotide to H_b in the above structure. The stereochemistry of the reduction process is thus that shown in Eq. (6–16).

The evidence for the location of the newly acquired hydrogen in

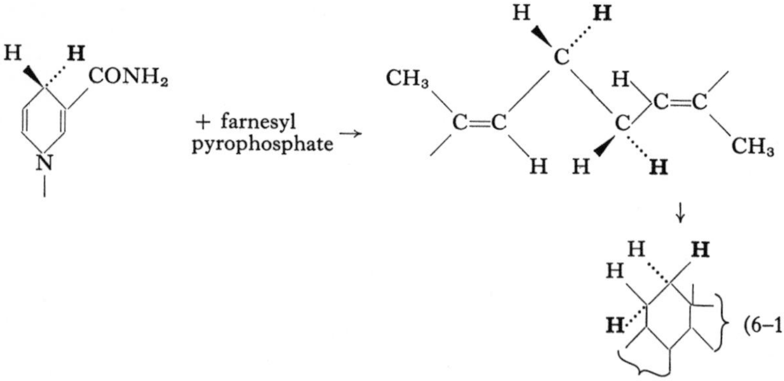

$$\text{(6–16)}$$

H_b site is of two kinds. Cornforth et al.[138] prepared monodeutero-squalene biosynthetically and, by ozonolysis, obtained monodeutero succinic acid from the central four carbon atoms. They then determined the absolute configuration of this deutero succinic acid. Samuelsson and Goodman[139] allowed the synthesis to proceed to the

138. J. W. Cornforth, R. H. Cornforth, G. Donninger, G. Popják, G. Ryback, and G. J. Schroepfer, Jr., *Biochem. Biophys. Res. Comm.*, **11**, 129 (1963).

139. B. Samuelsson and D. S. Goodman, *Biochem. Biophys. Res. Comm.*, **11**, 125 (1963).

cholesterol stage using tritium-labeled reduced pyridine nucleotide coenzyme. They then employed a 300-g bile fistula rat to convert cholesterol so obtained to cholic and chenodesoxycholic acids. They were able to show that the tritium was at 12β. Moreover, as the symmetry of squalene requires, there was an equal distribution of label between C-11 and C-12.

That the hydrogen transferred from reduced nicotinamide adenine dinucleotide phosphate comes from the β-position (that side utilized for

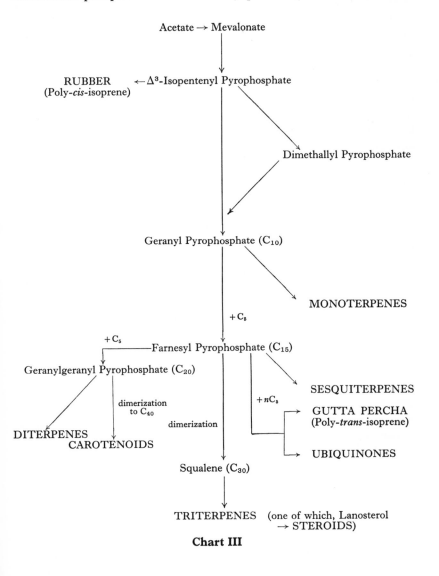

Chart III

example by glucose-6-phosphate dehydrogenase)[140] was shown by using reduced pyridine nucleotide with tritium in both the β- and α-position. Tritium was found in squalene only when the β-isomer was used.[141]

Summary

In summary, the pathways from acetate via mevalonate to iso-pentenyl pyrophosphate (the biological isoprene unit) are known in some detail, as are the mechanisms by which this monomer yields dimers, trimers, and higher polymers, and the ways in which the trimer (farnesyl pyrophosphate) can, in turn, be reductively dimerized to squalene. The dimerization of the C_{20} geranyl-geranyl pyrophosphate yields a 40-carbon intermediate, which is the precursor of the caro-tenoids, although the mechanism of this dimerization of C_{20} to C_{40} probably differs from that just discussed for the formation of squalene. Continuation of the polymerization sequence yields the C_{50} ubiquinones and the all *trans* gutta percha, whereas a process producing *cis* olefins accounts for the all *cis* natural rubber. See Chart III.

140. B. K. Stern and B. Vennesland, *J. Biol. Chem.*, **235**, 205 (1960). For a review, cf. H. R. Levy, P. Talalay, and B. Vennesland, *Prog. in Stereochem.*, **3**, 299 (1962).
141. G. Popják, G. Schroepfer, and J. W. Cornforth, *Biochem. Biophys. Res. Comm.*, **6**, 438 (1961/62).

chapter seven | Monoterpenes

The monoterpenes have challenged organic chemists since the earliest days of the science. Investigations of their structure led, for example, to the development of much of the theoretical knowledge of organic chemistry, such as Wagner-Meerwein rearrangements and non-classical cations. Biogenetically, these substances can for the most part be derived from geranyl pyrophosphate, whose synthesis by dimerization of isopentenyl pyrophosphate[1] has already been discussed.

7-1 ACYCLIC MONOTERPENES

Simple hydrolysis of the pyrophosphate leads to geraniol [1]* and appropriate reductions, dehydrations or allylic rearrangements account for citronellol [2], ocimene [3], and linalool [4] and most other acyclic monoterpenes.

Birch[2] has studied the biosynthesis of an acyclic monoterpene, citronellal [4a] in *Eucalyptus citriodora* (Hook) by following the incorporation of 2-C^{14}-acetate. Terminal branchlets were allowed to absorb, by transpiration, aqueous solutions containing the labeled precursor. Radioactive citronellal was isolated, and the expected pattern of labeling

---

* Unless otherwise specified, the structures herein cited are from J. L. Simonsen and L. N. Owen, *The Terpenes*, 2d ed., The University Press, Cambridge, Vols. I and II, 1953 and 1949, respectively.

1. F. Lynen, B. W. Agranoff, H. Eggerer, U. Henning, and E. M. Möslein, *Angew. Chem.*, **71**, 657 (1959).
2. A. J. Birch, D. Boulter, R. I. Fryer, P. J. Thomson, and J. L. Willis, *Tetrahedron Letters*, **No. 3**, 1 (**1959**).

was found—with the reservation that considerable randomization of the 2-C^{14}-acetate had occurred, giving rise to activity in positions derived from the carboxyl group of acetate.

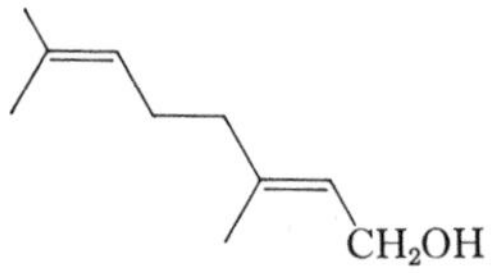

[1] 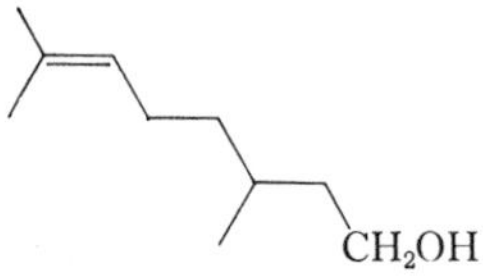   [2]

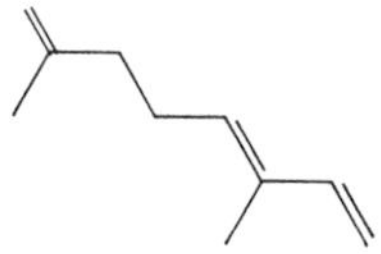

[3] 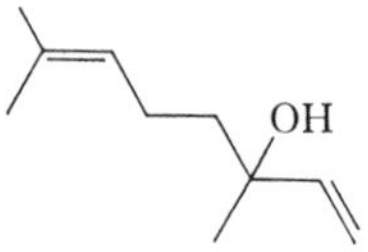   [4]

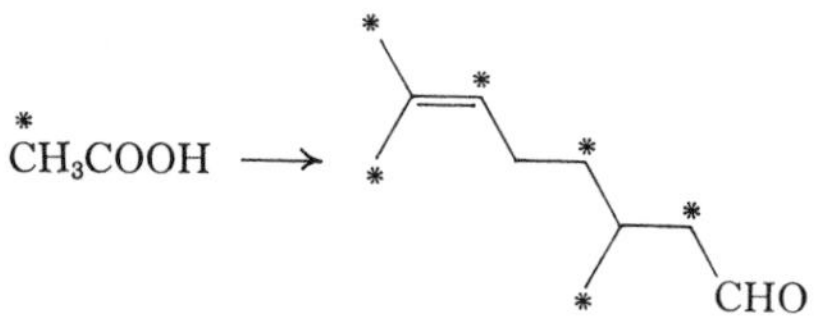

$\overset{*}{C}H_3\overset{}{C}OOH \longrightarrow$

[4a]

An interesting aspect of the acyclic monoterpenes is their occurrence as sidechains in various natural products, such as mycelianamide [5] [3,4] which has a C_{10} terpenoid chain readily isolated as 2,6-dimethyl-2,6-octadiene [6] by reduction of mycelianamide with sodium and liquid ammonia. Another instructive case is provided by mycophenolic acid[5] whose C_7 sidechain can be regarded as the remnant of an oxidized 10-carbon chain. In a study of the biogenesis of these two compounds, Birch[6] found that 1-C^{14}-acetate was incorporated in the expected manner into the terpenoid sidechain of the mycelianamide and throughout the mycophenolic acid skeleton. In the case of mycelianamide biogenesis from acetate it was particularly interesting to note that the

3. A. E. Oxford and H. Raistrick, *Biochem. J.*, **42**, 323 (1948).
4. A. J. Birch, R. A. Massy-Westropp, and R. W. Rickards, *J. Chem. Soc.*, **1956**, 3717.
5. J. H. Birkinshaw, H. Raistrick, and D. J. Ross, *Biochem. J.*, **50**, 630 (1952).
6. A. J. Birch, R. J. English, R. A. Massy-Westropp, and H. Smith, *J. Chem. Soc.*, **1958**, 369.

griseofulvin **[8]**, also produced by *Penicillium griseofulvum* (Dierckx), was also labeled.

Addition of 1-C^{14}-dimethylacrylic acid to the mold also gave rise to mycelianamide with the same pattern of labeling as obtained with 1-C^{14}-acetate. Moreover, the griseofulvin, a known acetogenin, was also labeled. Thus incorporation of the iso-five-carbon acid had been

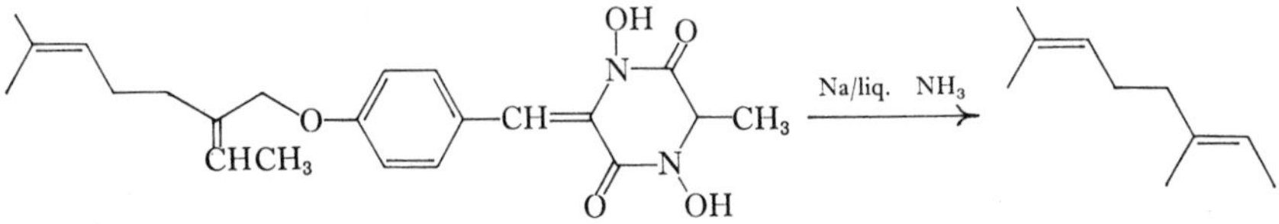

[5]   **[6]**

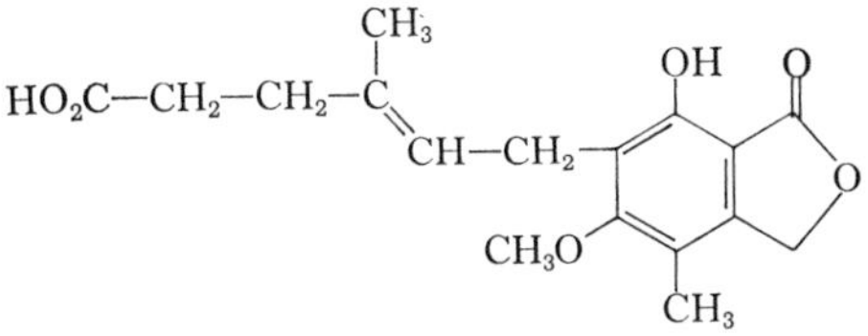

[7]

preceded by its equilibration with two carbon units. This result contrasts with the intact incorporation of dimethylacrylic acid into cholesterol in rats[7] and into pulegone in *Mentha pulegium* L.[8] to be discussed shortly. The study of 2-C^{14}-mevalonate as a precursor showed it to be an irreversible intermediate in terpene biogenesis. It was incorporated in the anticipated fashion into the C_{10} sidechain of mycelianamide, but the griseofulvin from the same culture was devoid of activity. The distribution of activity is that indicated in Eq. (7–1), and it is worth

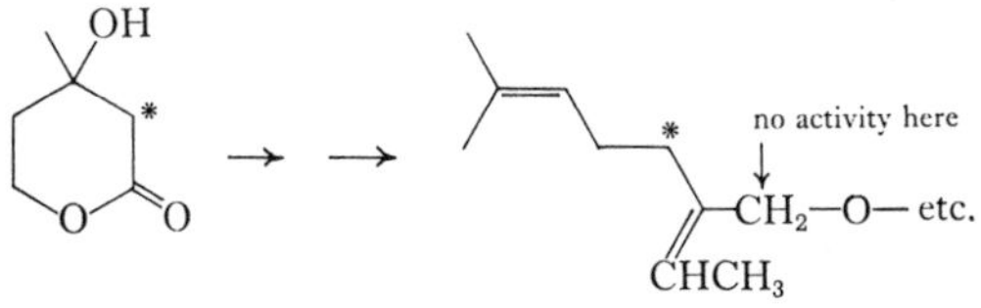

$$(7–1)$$

7. K. Bloch, L. C. Clarke, and I. Harary, *J. Am. Chem. Soc.*, **76**, 3859 (1954).
8. W. Sandermann and H. Stockman, *Naturwissenschaften*, **43**, 580 (1956).

noting that only one of the two methylene carbon atoms in the chain is labeled, a result that is expected on the basis of the mechanism of isopentenyl pyrophosphate polymerization discussed previously. The distinction between the two terminal methyl groups of the sidechain of mycelianamide was accomplished with the assistance of a rabbit which cooperatively oxidized 2,6-dimethyl-2,6-octadiene [6] to Hildebrandt's acid [8].[9] If, as seems reasonable, there is no geometric isomerization

[6]

[8]

Hildebrandt's Acid

of the olefin bonds within the rabbit, the carboxyl carbon will be derived from that methyl group which was originally *trans*. Further chemical degradation indicates that indeed most (80 per cent) of the activity is in this *trans*-methyl group. The degree of randomization observed is more likely a result of the degradative procedure than it is of nonspecificity during the biosynthesis.

In the case of mycophenolic acid it was possible to study a terpenoid fragment and an acetogenin fragment, both of which are part of the same molecule. Thus 1-C[14]-acetate is incorporated into both the degenerate terpenoid sidechain and the aromatic ring in the expected fashion. It is notable that the extent of incorporation into the sidechain and into the aromatic nucleus is exactly the same.

The results with 1-C[14]-dimethylacrylic acid essentially parallel those in the case of mycelianamide. Thus the five-carbon unit is apparently largely degraded to two-carbon units before incorporation. As there was a slightly higher incorporation into the sidechain than into the nucleus, there is the likelihood that some of the dimethylacrylic acid was utilized intact. In such cases the experimental results observed will clearly be dependent upon the rates of the competing routes open to dimethylacrylic acid, which will give rise to β-methyl-glutaryl coenzyme

9. A. J. Birch, M. Kocor, N. Sheppard, and J. Winter, *J. Chem. Soc.*, **1962**, 1502.

A, which can in turn be cleaved to acetate units or reduced to mevalonate. The feeding of 2-C^{14}-mevalonate yielded mycophenolic acid in which all the activity was located in the sidechain in the expected position, thus reinforcing the role of mevalonate as a precursor for the terpenoid portions of molecules and moreover as a precursor that does not suffer reversible conversion to smaller units such as acetate.

7–2 NON-HEAD-TO-TAIL MONOTERPENES

Artemisia ketone [9] is an unusual example of an acyclic mono-terpene, as the two isoprenoid units are here joined together in an interesting way, the tail of one being linked, not to the head, but to one of the central carbon atoms of the other. It is possible to envision such a

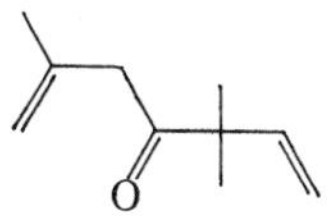

[9]

structure arising by the dimerization of two dimethallyl residues, as in Eq. (7–2).

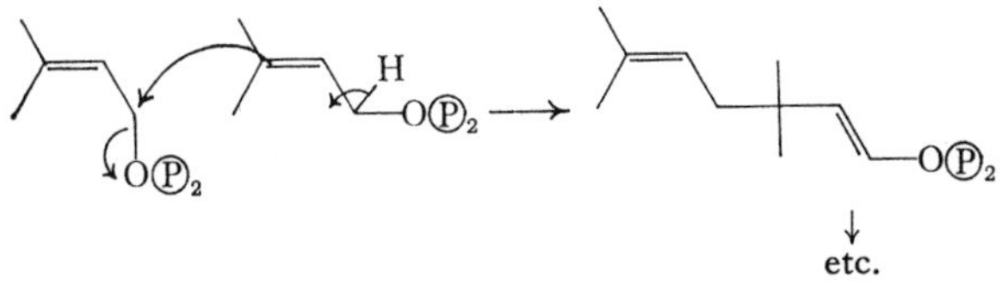

$$(7–2)$$

Chrysanthemum carboxylic acid [10] possesses an artemisia-like skeleton with the added feature of a cyclization producing a three-membered ring. The incorporation of 2-C^{14}-mevalonate into this substance has been reported,[10] the label being found in the indicated positions. The incorporation of mevalonate places these structures experimentally in the terpenoid category, and the location of the activity makes the type of dimerization mechanism presented above likely.

10. P. J. Godin and E. M. Thain, *Proc. Chem. Soc.*, **1961**, 452; M. P. Crowley, P. J. Godin, H. S. Inglis, M. Snarey, and E. M. Thain, *Biochim. Biophys. Acta*, **60**, 312 (1962).

A substance reminiscent of chrysanthemum carboxylic acid in its possession of a cyclopropane ring is the highly potent sex attractant of the female American cockroach, *Periplaneta americana* L., 2,2-dimethyl-3-isopropylidene cyclopropyl propionate [11].[11] This eight-carbon substance is clearly a degraded monoterpene, whose skeleton can be

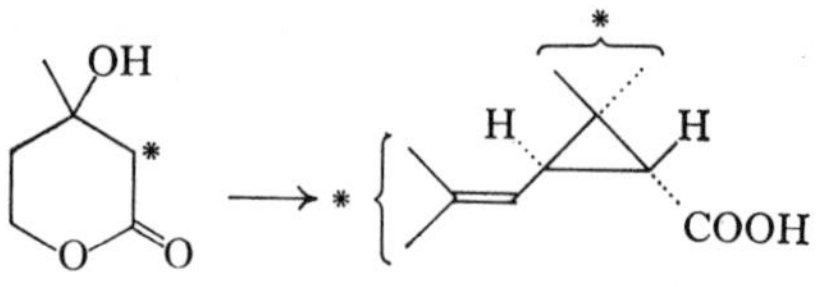

[10]

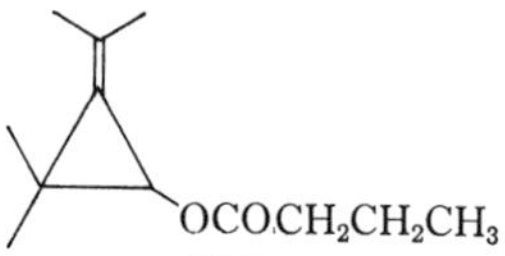

[11]

derived (7–3) from an artemisia-type intermediate.

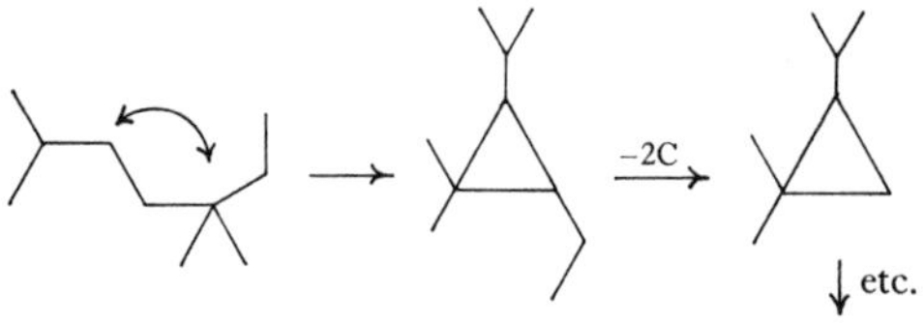

(7–3)

A still different joining of two isopropenoid units is encountered in lavandulal [12],[12] obtained from lavender. This joining can be accomplished as indicated, and such an intermediate could also serve as a

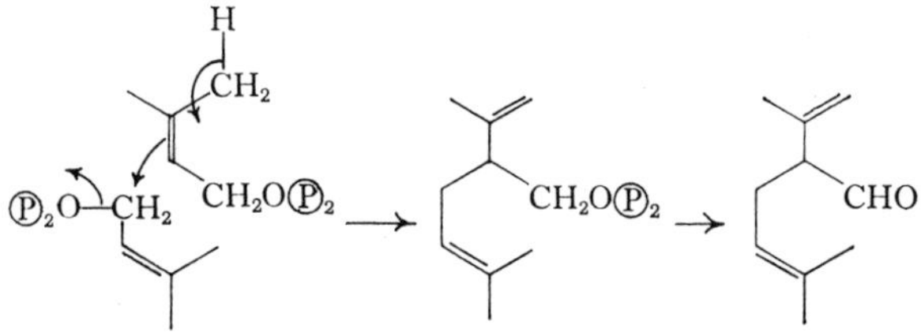

[12]

11. M. Jacobson, M. Beroza, and R. T. Yamamoto, *Science*, **139**, 48 (1963).
12. Y. R. Naves, *Bull. Soc. Chim. France*, **1960**, 1741.

precursor of the cockroach sex attractant. The rare occurrence of structures of these types is surely a commentary on the near universatility of the polymerization mechanism discussed in detail earlier.

7-3 MONOCYCLIC MONOTERPENES

The cyclic monoterpenes can be derived in most cases by appropriate cyclization processes beginning with geranyl pyrophosphate.[13,14] Thus the hypothetical cation [13] leads directly to such monocyclic substances as limonene [14], and via appropriate hydride migrations to α-phellandrene [15] and α-terpinene [16]. If the intermediate ion is considered in a nonclassical sense as [17], a 1,3-hydride shift will

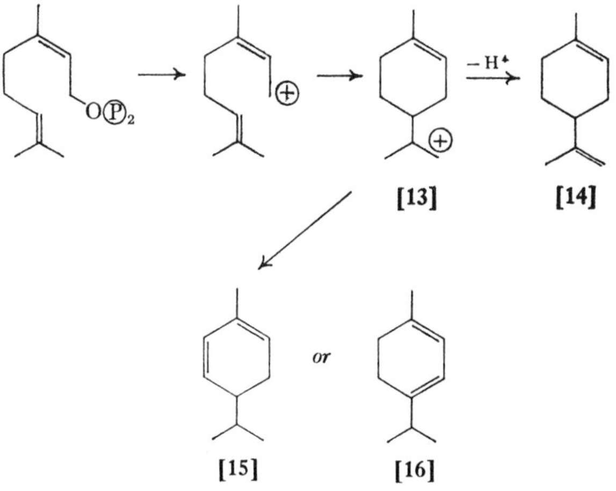

[13] [14]

[15] [16]

produce [18], from which sylvestrene [19] and the dicyclic monoterpene, Δ⁴-carene [20], are easily derived. Various saturated and/or oxygenated derivatives of such carbon skeletons are well known, e.g., menthol [21], pulegone [22], and ascaridole [23].

The biosynthesis of menthol in peppermint (*Mentha piperita* L. var. Mitcham) and pennyroyal (*Mentha pulegium* L.) was studied[15] using $C^{14}O_2$ as substrate. It was found that synthesis of monoterpenes occurs only in the young tissue in leaves that are still expanding. The de novo formation of the first terpenes in these young leaves is a rapid

13. L. Ruzicka, *Experientia*, **9**, 357 (1953).
14. R. Mayer, *Z. Chem.*, **1**, 161 (1961).
15. J. Battaile and W. D. Loomis, *Biochim. Biophys. Acta*, **51**, 545 (1961).

process, with several labeled terpenes being formed in less than one-half hour. The interconversion between various terpenes occurs in the older tissue. Although some terpenes became labeled rapidly, several days were required to label the saturated alcohol, menthol.

Attempts to demonstrate the incorporation of $2\text{-}C^{14}$-mevalonate into terpenes by these plants yielded only negative results, although activity was found in many compounds, including carotenoid pigments.

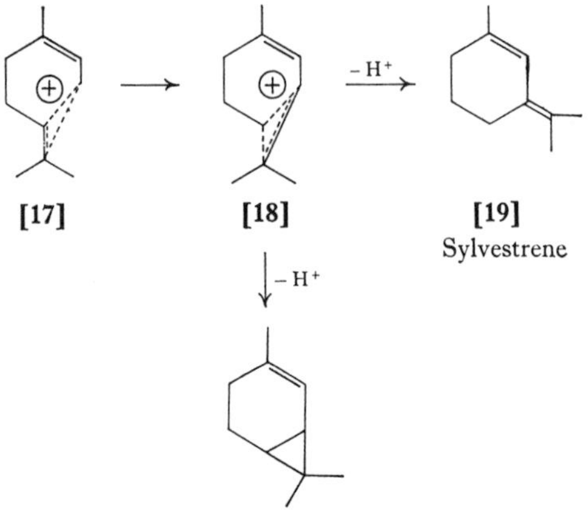

[17]   [18]   [19]
                            Sylvestrene

[20]
Δ^4-Carene

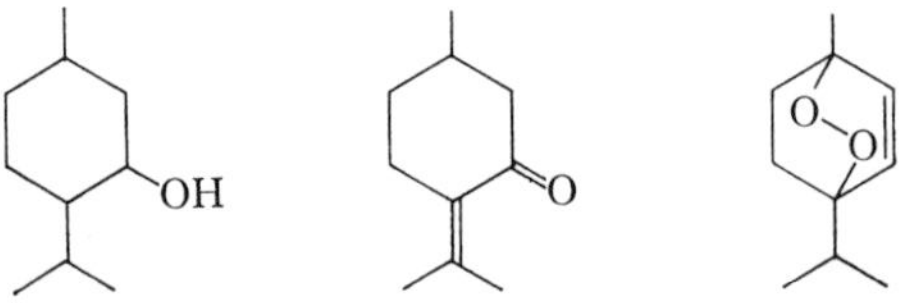

[21]   [22]   [23]

Labeled dimethylacrylic acid was also ineffectual as a terpene precursor in excised mint leaves. Labeling from $1\text{-}C^{14}$-acetate appeared slowly in terpenes and rapidly in respiratory CO_2, making it seem likely that $C^{14}O_2$ was the source of terpene labeling in these experiments. These negative results are probably due to the fact that these precursors have difficulty penetrating the oil gland, which is a modified epidermal hair covered externally by cuticle and connected to the blade of the leaf through a one-celled stem.

The results with $C^{14}O_2$ in these experiments led to the following suggestions [Eq. (7–4)] for interrelations between these monocyclic compounds, which had in part been suggested earlier on the basis of chromatographic evidence.[16,17]

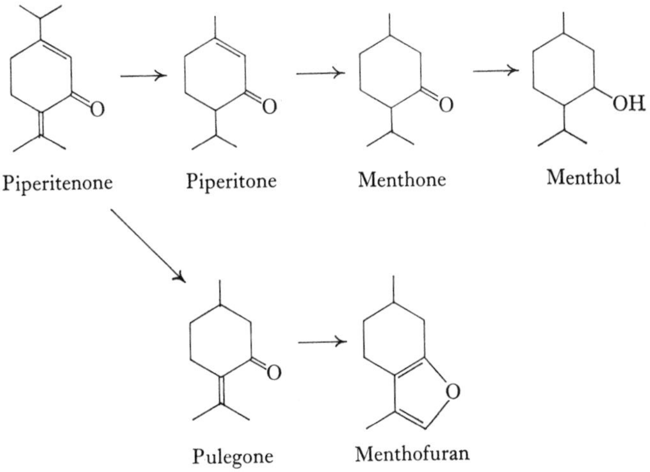

Piperitenone Piperitone Menthone Menthol

(7–4)

Pulegone Menthofuran

Another study of the biosynthesis of pulegone in *Mentha pulegium* has been reported[8] in which 1-C^{14}-dimethylacrylic acid was used as the labeled substrate. In contrast to Birch's results[6] with this substrate in fungal cultures, the German workers found that the five-carbon fragment was incorporated into pulegone without prior breakdown to two-carbon units.

Birch[2] has followed the incorporation of 2-C^{14}-mevalonic acid into cineole [24] in *Eucalyptus globulus* Lab. and found, as indicated, the expected pattern of labeling.

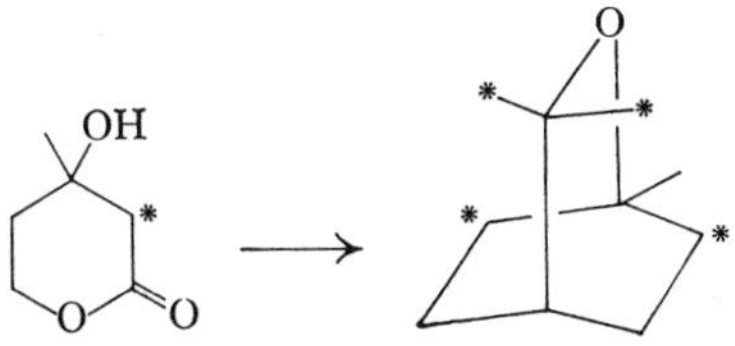

[24]
Cineole

16. R. H. Reitsema, *J. Pharm. Sci.*, **47**, 267 (1958).
17. R. H. Reitsema, F. J. Cramer, and W. E. Fass, *J. Agri. Food Chem.*, **5**, 779 (1957).

From the various monocyclic terpenes, it is possible[18] to derive the interesting group of terpenes, the thujaplicins which are found in the heartwood of *Thuja plicata*. Thus the caradiene skeleton can open in such a way as to produce the skeleton of thujic acid [Eq. (7–5)]. Ring enlargement reactions occurring on an appropriately oxygenated ter-

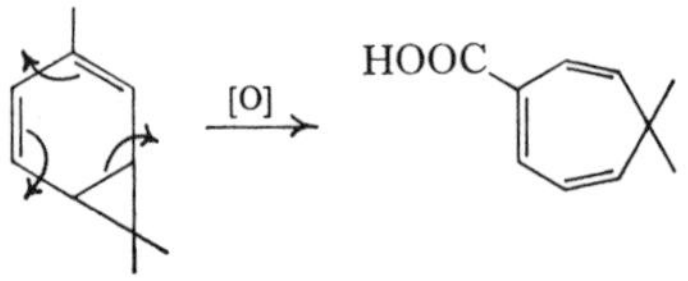

$$\text{(7–5)}$$

Thujic Acid

pinene skeleton can generate the various thujaplicins, as in Eq. (7–6). A discussion of a possible detailed mechanism by which such a ring

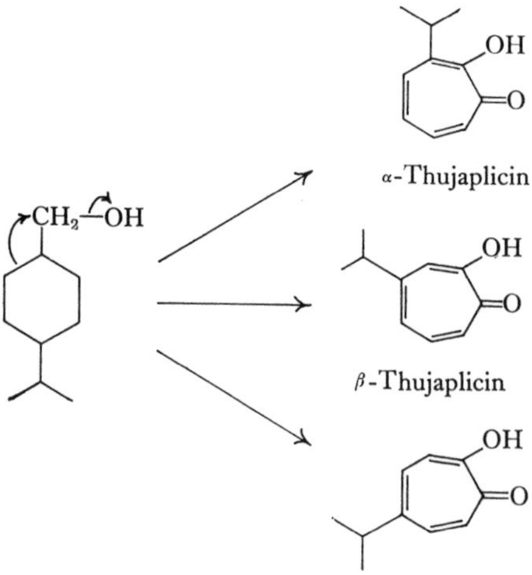

$$\text{(7–6)}$$

enlargement can produce a tropolone ring system, has been presented in the case of mold tropolone biogenesis (page 168). It is clear that, although the latter stages of the biogenesis of the thujaplicins may be analogous to the latter stages of mold tropolone production, the two

18. H. Erdtman, *Progr. Org. Chem.*, **1**, 22 (1952).

classes of compounds are of fundamentally different biogenetic origin, the former being terpenoid substances and the latter being corrupted acetogenins.

7–4 BICYCLIC MONOTERPENES

The host of bicyclic monoterpenes has long provided an arena in which workers in an advancing organic chemistry could perform increasingly subtle feats of intellectual gymnastics, and the many known in vitro rearrangements among the various skeletal types may well represent examples of the pathways by which the various substances are formed in nature. Thus if one restricts his thinking to ionic mechanisms, it is possible to envision a cation such as **[25]** (the one which by proton loss can hypothetically form limonene) undergoing a further cyclization to produce **[26]**, which can give rise to α-pinene or, by hydration, form borneol—a reduced form of camphor.

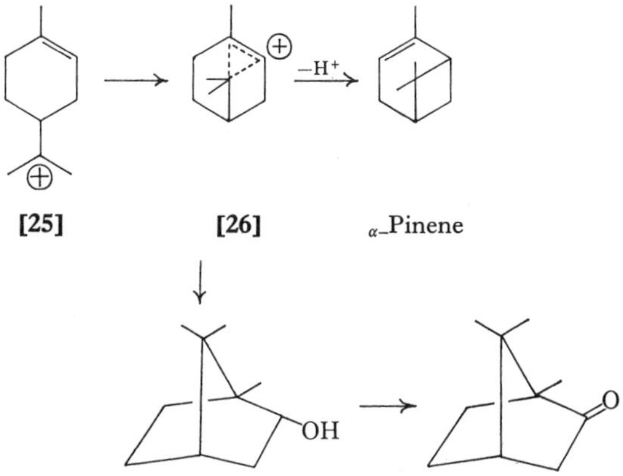

[25]   **[26]**   α–Pinene

Borneol   Camphor

The generation of α-pinene by such a mechanism is unusual, as it requires the formation of a four-membered ring in a cationic process, a situation not generally encountered. Indeed, the α-pinene structure if given any opportunity is exceedingly prone to rearrangements that convert the bicyclic (3,1,1) skeleton to a bicyclic (2,2,1) arrangement; the reverse process (2,2,1) to (3,1,1) has never been observed. Another possibility for the formation of the four-membered ring may be a cycloaddition reaction,[13] and the recent work [19] of Hammond

19. G. S. Hammond, N. J. Turro, and A. Fischer, *J. Am. Chem. Soc.*, **83**, 4674 (1961).

and co-workers on photosensitized reactions (7–7) such as the 2-acetonaphthone sensitized photodimerization of butadiene makes such a mechanism an attractive possibility for the genesis of a substance formed in green plants growing in ample sunlight. Recently, this very

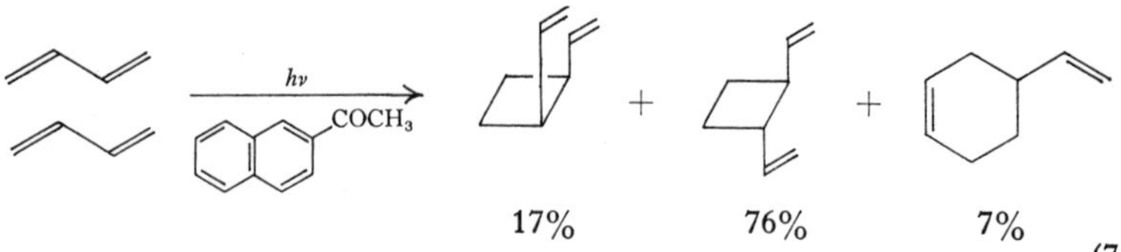

17%   76%   7%

(7–7)

process has been used to produce β-pinene in a yield of 9 per cent of total photoproducts by irradiation of a 1 per cent ethereal solution of myrcene[20] [(7–8)]. Still another hypothetical possibility, an internal Diels-Alder-type reaction, is shown in Eq. (7–9).

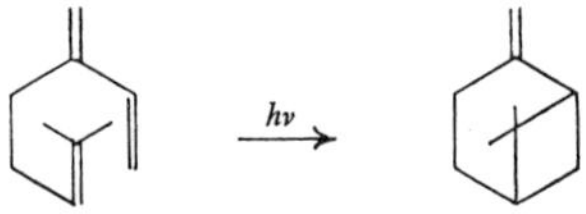

(7–8)

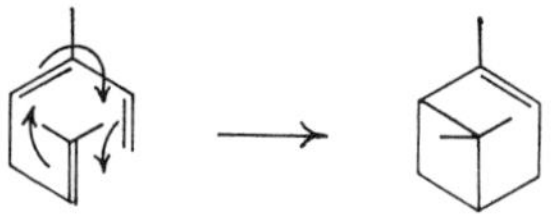

(7–9)

The biosynthesis of α-pinene in *Pinus attenuata* has been investigated[21] using $2\text{-}C^{14}$-acetate and $2\text{-}C^{14}$-mevalonic acid as substrate, and both these substrates were found to be incorporated into α-pinene, which was purified by vapor chromatography. A 2-hour incubation of slices of *P. attenuata* led to the incorporation of 0.5 per cent of the added $2\text{-}C^{14}$-mevalonic acid, and about 0.01 per cent of the added $2\text{-}C^{14}$-acetate was incorporated in the α-pinene fraction of whole shoot tips. The α-pinene obtained in these experiments was not degraded. Previous work had demonstrated the incorporation of atmospheric carbon dioxide into pine terpenes.[22]

20. K. J. Crowley, *Proc. Chem. Soc.*, **1962**, 245.
21. R. G. Stanley, *Nature*, **182**, 738 (1958).
22. G. V. Sukhov, *Intern. Conf. Radioisotopes in Sci. Res.*, Paris, September, 1957.

The most important experimental work [23] on the bicyclic terpenes has revealed that 2-C^{14}-mevalonate is incorporated into α-pinene by *Pinus nigra austriaca* in the manner of Eq. (7–10). This clearly

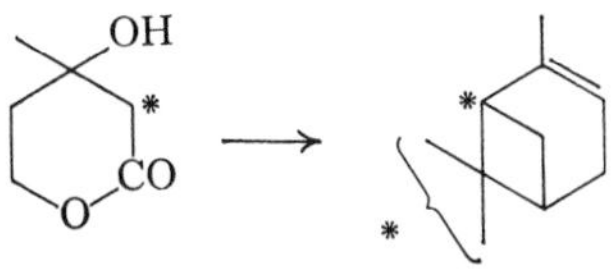

$$(7\text{--}10)$$

eliminates the simple Ruzicka proposal or the photochemical cyclo-addition and is in accord with the Diels-Alder cyclization or a process (7–11) in which the intermediate carbonium ion initiates an electrophilic attack on the allylic hydrogen.

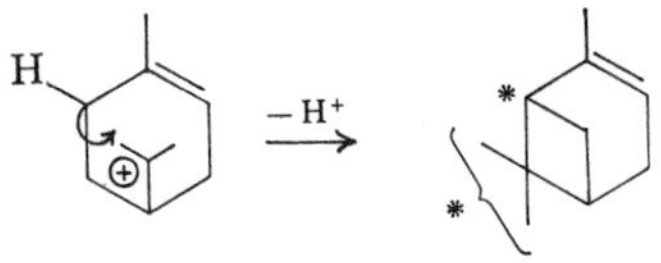

$$(7\text{--}11)$$

An analogous study on the biosynthesis of thujone by *Thuja occidentalis* [23] (7–12) has yielded similar results, which are also compatible with

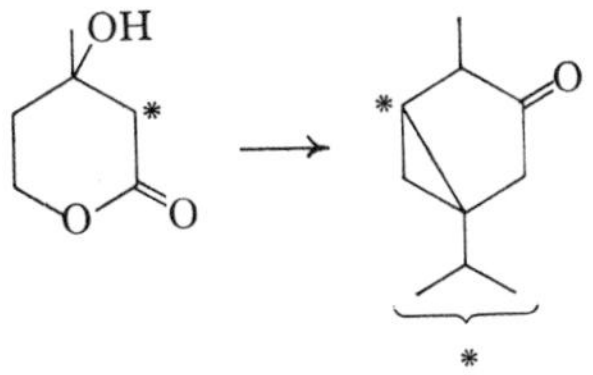

$$(7\text{--}12)$$

an electrophilic attack of an intermediate carbonium ion formed in the indicated manner upon the allylic hydrogen, yielding –(α)-thujene (of the indicated absolute configuration [24]), which will give rise to thujone on oxidation (7–13). Although some of these processes are without significant precedent, it is of the utmost importance not to turn the postulate

23. W. Sandermann and W. Schweers, *Tetrahedron Letters*, **1962**, 257.
24. T. Norin, *Acta Chem. Scand.*, **16**, 640 (1962).

that terpenes are derived by cationic mechanisms into a hypothetical Procrustean bed.   It may well be that many of the cyclizations proceed by radical mechanisms or represent processes whose mechanistic characteristics are just being elucidated.

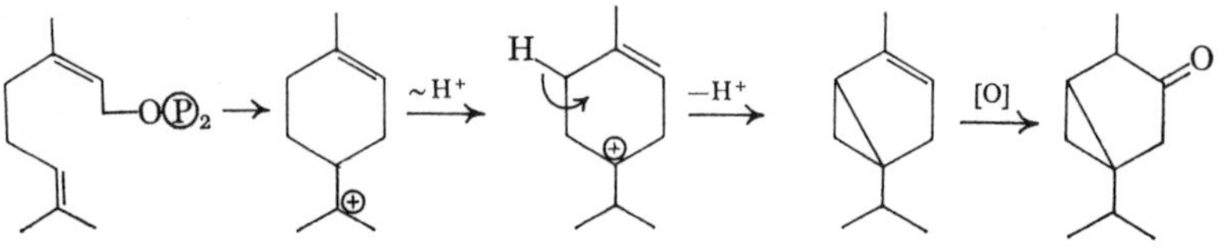

$$(7\text{--}13)$$

It is possible, by the indicated rearrangements, which are well authenticated in terpene chemistry, to proceed from the carbon skeletons of bicyclic monoterpenes such as α-pinene and borneol to the skeletal types such as fenchyl alcohol **[27]** or camphene **[28]**.

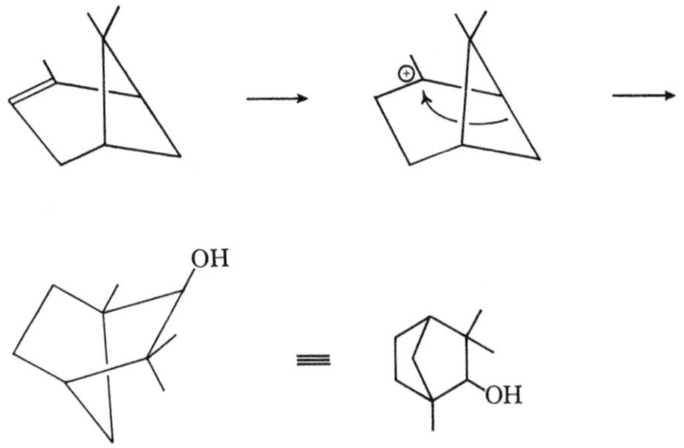

[27]
Fenchyl Alcohol

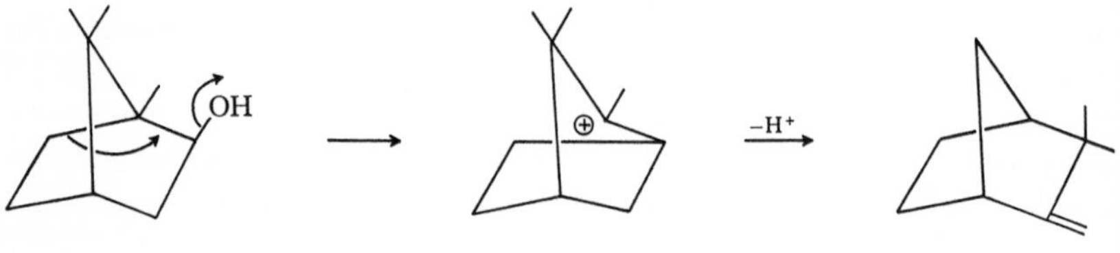

[28]
Camphene

7-5 CYCLOPENTANOID MONOTERPENES

In addition to the many acyclic monoterpenes and alicyclic compounds based on a cyclohexanoid skeleton, there are many substances with cyclopentanoid carbon skeletons that seem, in the main, to be cyclized derivatives of an oxidized geranyl skeleton. Examples of these substances are nepatalactone [29], the essence of the oil of catnip from *Nepeta cataria*,[25] iridomyremecin [30] from the Argentine ant, *Iridomyrmex humilis* (where it accounts for approximately 1 per cent of the

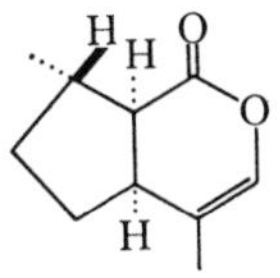

[29] 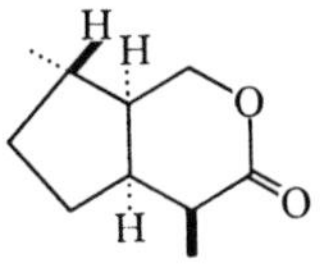   [30] 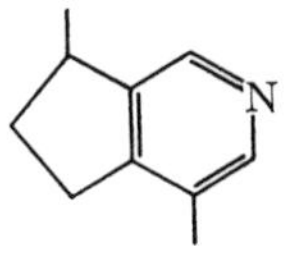   [31]

body weight), and even an alkaloid, actinidine [31] from *Actinidia polygama*. A form of these substances, anisomorphal, which lacks the heterocyclic ring, has been isolated from the southern walking-stick, *Anisomorpha buprestoides* (Stoll) and characterized[26] as the dialdehyde [32]. This substance is related to one isolated from crushed Australian

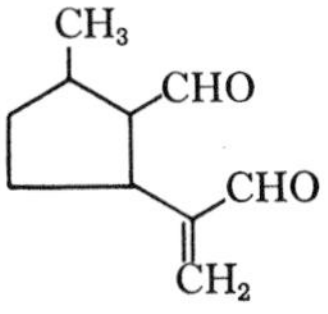

[32]

ants[27] (*Dolichoderus* and *Iridomyrmex*) and may be just a stereoisomer. In recent times attention has been focused on several highly oxygenated cyclopentanoid monoterpenes such as loganin [33],[28]

25. For a review of the chemistry of these three substances, cf. C. W. K. Cavill, *Rev. Pure Appl. Chem.*, **10**, 169 (1960).
26. J. Meinwald, M. S. Chadha, J. J. Hurst, and T. Eisner, *Tetrahedron Letters*, **1962**, 29.
27. G. W. K. Cavill and H. Hinterberger, *Australian J. Chem.*, **14**, 143 (1961).
28. K. Sheth, E. Ramstad, and J. Wolinsky, *Tetrahedron Letters*, **1961**, 394.

verbenalin [34],[29] genipin [35],[30] asperuloside [36],[31] and aucubin [37].[32] The essential structural feature of these compounds, the cyclopentane ring, can be derived by an internal Michael cyclization on an intermediate such as [38] (cf. page 207), which can be simply derived by

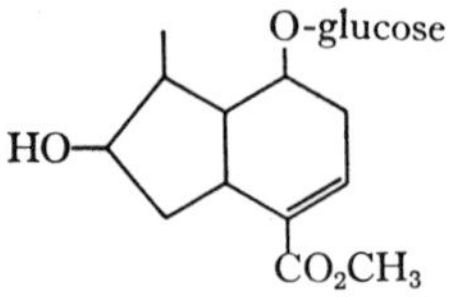

[33] 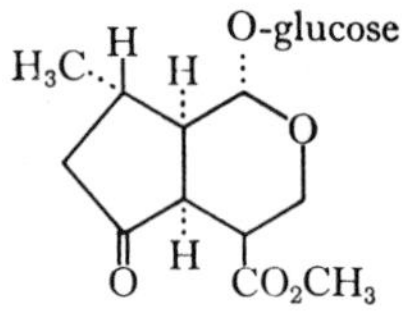   [34]

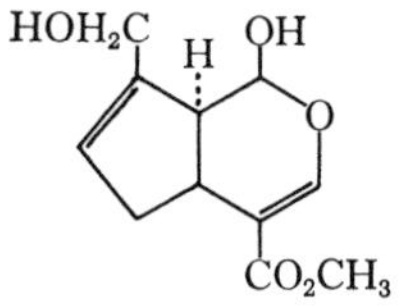

[35] 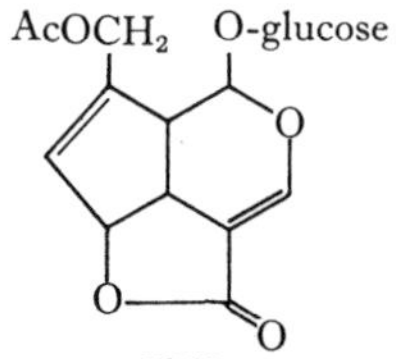   [36] 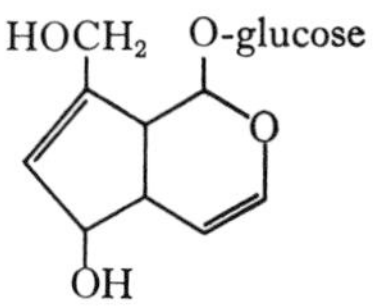   [37]

oxidation of one of the two methyl groups activated by the allylic double bond. Indeed both the oxidation and the cyclization have been

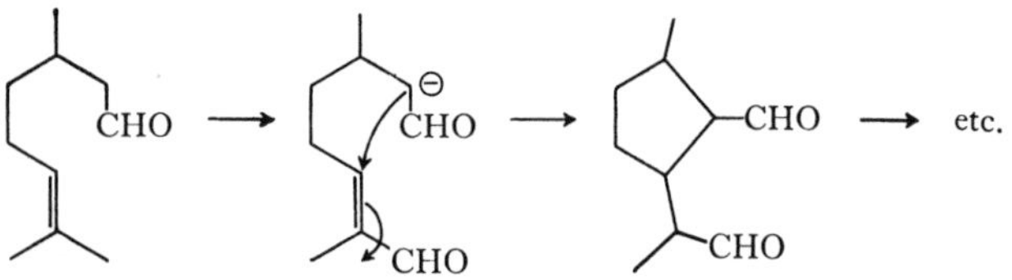

$$(7-14)$$

Citronellal   [38]

29. G. Büchi and R. E. Manning, *Tetrahedron Letters*, **No. 6**, 5 (1960).
30. C. Djerassi, T. Nakano, A. N. James, L. H. Zalkor, E. J. Eisenbraun, and J. N. Shoolery, *J. Org. Chem.*, **26**, 1192 (1961).
31. J. Grimshaw, *Chem. & Ind. (London)*, **1961**, 403.
    L. H. Briggs, B. F. Cain, P. W. Le Quesne, and J. N. Shoolery, *Tetrahedron Letters*, **1963**, 69.
32. S. Fujise, H. Obara, and H. Uda, *Chem. & Ind. (London)*, **1960**, 289.
    W. Haegele, F. Kaplan, and H. Schmid, *Tetrahedron Letters*, **1961**, 110.
    A. J. Birch, J. Grimshaw, and H. R. Juneja, *J. Chem. Soc.*, **1961**, 5194.

realized[33] in an in vitro synthesis of the dialdehyde from which iso-iridomyrmecin and related compounds were then prepared [Eq. (7–14)]. Cyclization to produce the heterocyclic six-membered rings presents no special problems.   In the case of the alkaloid actinidine, ammonia or a biological equivalent can be incorporated at an appropriate stage. Aucubin, though a C_9 compound, is clearly a member of this series differing only in the loss of an external carbon, which might well occur by a decarboxylation (7–15) from a β-carboxy aldehyde.   An opening

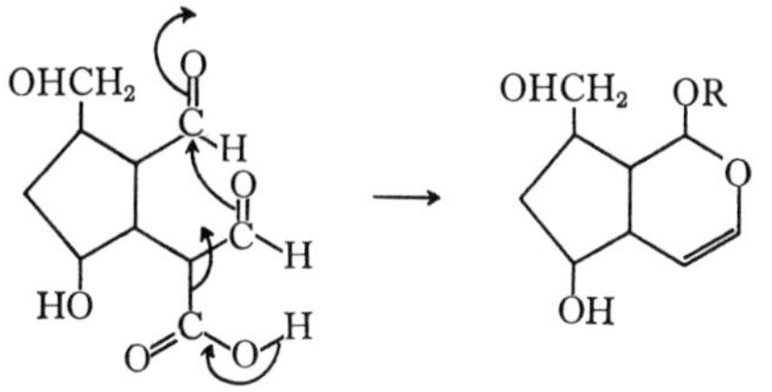

(7–15)

Acubin

[37]

of the cyclopentane ring can lead to such structures as swertiamarin [39],[34] and gentiopicrin [40][35] in which the original isoprenoid nature of the precursor is obscured.

A recent interesting biosynthetic theory[36,37] for certain indole alkaloids (e.g. yohimbine [41]) has centered on these oxygenated cyclo-pentanoids because the type of open chain intermediate envisioned above in the formation of swertiamarin or gentiopicrin can be successfully employed in deriving the structures of many of the indole alkaloids. More recent tracer evidence, however, is not compatible[38,39] with these suggestions (see Section 4-8).

33. K. J. Clark, G. I. Fray, R. H. Jaeger, and Sir Robert Robinson, *Tetra-hedron*, **6**, 217 (1959).
34. T. Kubota and Y. Tomita, *Tetrahedron Letters*, **1961**, 176.
35. L. Canonica, F. Pelizzoni, P. Manitto, and G. Jommi, *Tetrahedron Letters*, **No. 24**, 7 (1960).
36. R. Thomas, *Tetrahedron Letters*, **1961**, 544.
37. E. Wenkert, *J. Am. Chem. Soc.*, **84**, 98 (1962).
38. E. Leete, S. Ghosal, and P. N. Edwards, *J. Am. Chem. Soc.*, **84**, 1068 (1962).
39. D. Willner and J. H. Richards, unpublished results.

[39]

[40]

[41]

<table>
<tr><td>chapter
eight</td><td># Sesquiterpenes</td></tr>
</table>

chapter
eight | # Sesquiterpenes

8–1 ACYCLIC SESQUITERPENES

The sesquiterpenes (terpenes containing a 15-carbon skeleton) can be derived from farnesyl pyrophosphate. Ruzicka[1] has discussed in general terms the question of sesquiterpene biogenesis, and recently Hendrickson[2] has investigated the stereochemical aspects of this problem. In these treatments, it is assumed that the sesquiterpenes originate by appropriate cyclizations of farnesyl pyrophosphate [1],* with the further assumption that the central bond is *trans* (by analogy to squalene) and that the terminal double bond may be either *cis* or *trans*. This *cis-trans* isomerization may occur through an allylic isomeric intermediate with a nerolidol skeleton [2]. Such an allylic isomerization is clearly not possible for the hydrocarbon squalene.

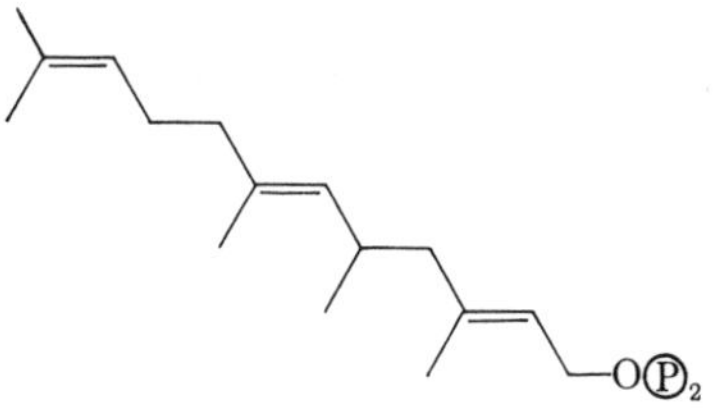

[1] 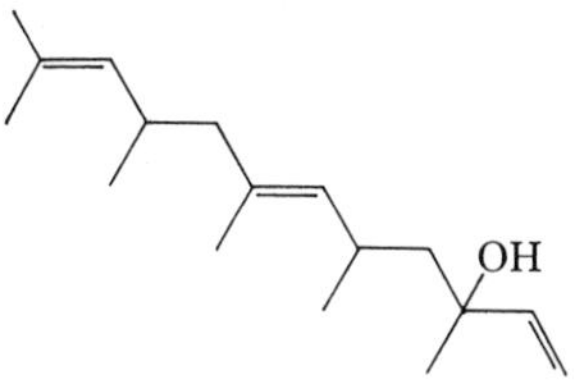   [2]

* Unless otherwise indicated, all structures in this chapter are taken from Sir John Simonsen, *The Terpenes*, 2nd ed., Vols. III and V, Cambridge University Press, Cambridge, 1952, 1957, and from Ref. 5.

1. L. Ruzicka, *Experientia*, **9**, 357 (1953).
2. J. B. Hendrickson, *Tetrahedron*, **7**, 82 (1959).

An interesting example of a sesquiterpene that can be derived from the farnesol chain without cyclization to carbocyclic rings is ipomeamarone [3] isolated from sweet potato root infected by the black rot fungus, *Cerotycystis timbriata.* This substance is easily seen to consist of three isoprenoid fragments linearly linked head to tail with the terminal unit becoming the carbon skeleton of a furan ring. Biosynthetic experiments[3] have demonstrated the incorporation of 2-C[14]-acetate and 2-C[14]-mevalonate into ipomeamarone.

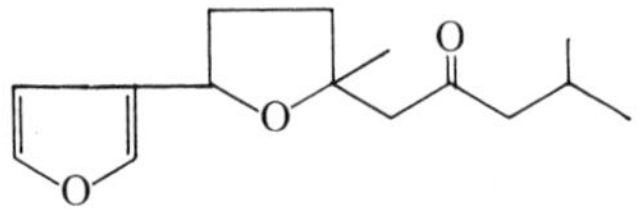

[3]

8-2   BISABOLENE

The lowest, most common oxidation state of sesquiterpenes is the same as that for farnesol, which suggests that the cyclizations proceed without concomitant oxidation as in the case of the usual cyclizations of squalene to triterpenes. The ionization of the allylic pyrophosphate,[4] may possibly be assisted by one of the isolated double bonds and, if this involves the central double bond of a farnesol with a *cis* stereochemistry for the terminal olefin, a cation such as [4] is formed. (The analogous cyclization to a seven-membered ring, i.e., [5] is disfavored by both steric and electronic factors.)   Loss of a proton from [4] leads directly to bisabolene [6].[5]   In general the monocyclic six-ring sesquiterpenes possess a pattern of oxidized sites similar to that of bisabolene.

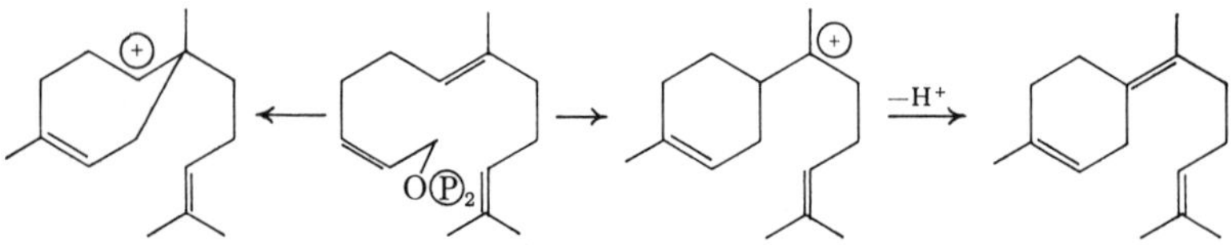

[5]   [4]   [6]

3. T. Akazawa, I. Uritani, and Y. Akazawa, *Arch. Biochem. Biophys.,* **99**, 52 (1962).
4. A. R. Todd, *Proc. Natl. Acad. Sci. U.S.,* **45**, 1389 (1959).
5. D. H. R. Barton and P. de Mayo, *Quart. Rev. (London),* **11**, 189 (1957).

8–3 β-SANTALENE AND CEDROL

Two other possibilities are open to the ion [4]. An attack of the positive center on the cyclic double bond, yielding [7], followed by a migration of the bridging methylene group and proton loss, produces β-santalene [8].[6] A 1,2-hydride migration to the ion [9] followed by

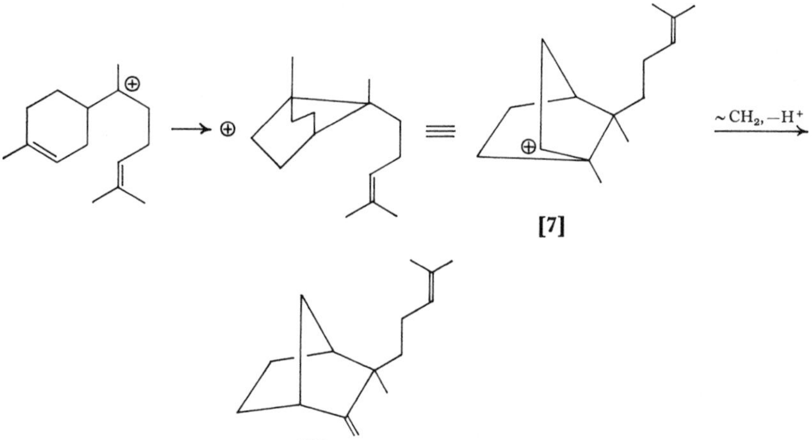

[7]

[8]

the indicated electronic shifts and acquisition of a nucleophile leads to cedrol [10].[7]

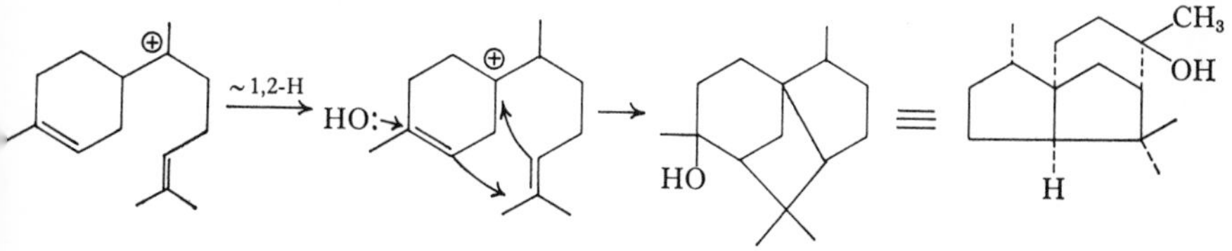

[9]   [10]

Cyclization of the allylic carbonium ion center onto the terminal double bond of the farnesol skeleton presents a greater variety of possibilities. Such attacks also have a stereochemical outcome controlled by a desire for a maximum overlap of π electrons and minimum steric interference. Thus cyclization to the *cis*-11-ring cation [11] is expected to be favored for steric reasons over the 10-ring analog [12].

6. L. Ruzicka and G. Thomann, *Helv. Chim. Acta.*, **18**, 355 (1935).
7. G. Stork and F. H. Clarke, Jr., *J. Am. Chem. Soc.*, **77**, 1072 (1955).

We shall first examine sesquiterpenes that can be derived from this *cis*-11-ring cation **[11]**. Models of this cation reveal two interesting features: (1) the double bonds are not very close to each other, thus discouraging internal cyclization, and (2) one of the hydrogens on C-1 is turned inside the ring, lying somewhat between C-6 and the cationic C-10, thus hindering attack of the C-10 cation of the C-6,7 double bond.

The *cis* cation **[11]** can be neutralized in a variety of ways. Simple proton loss produces humulene **[13]** whose double bonds have recently been shown [8,9] to be in the expected positions. Although their stereochemistry has not yet been determined, the theory[2] would anticipate that shown in **[13]**. A corresponding ketone is zerumbone **[14]** with a predictably similar stereochemistry.

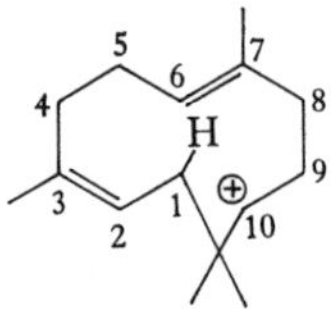

[11] 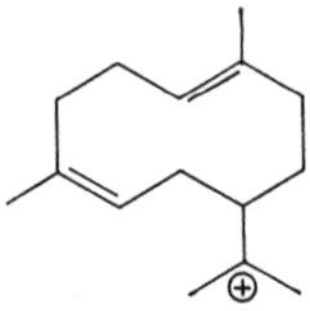   **[12]**

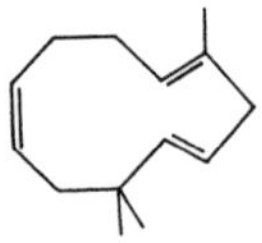

[13] 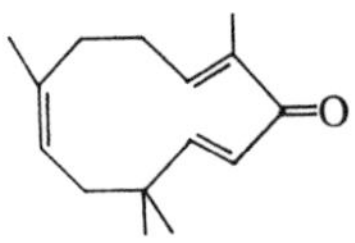   **[14]**

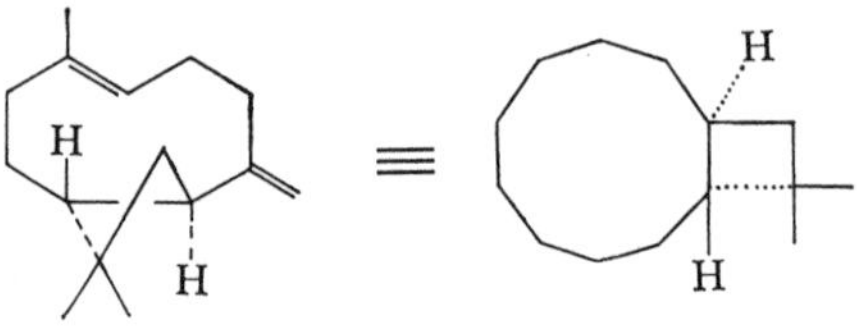

[15]

Although the inside hydrogen at C-1 prevents attack of C-10 on the Δ^{6-7} double bond, attack of C-10 on the Δ^{2-3} double bond is possible and will lead, after concerted proton loss from the C-3 methyl group, to caryophyllene **[15]**, with the correct stereochemistry.

8. R. P. Hildebrand, M. D. Sutherland, and O. J. Waters, *Chem. & Ind.* (*London*), **1959**, 489.
9. S. Dev, *Tetrahedron Letters*, **No. 7**, 12 (1959).

8–4 LONGIFOLENE

A further possibility is a 1,3-hydride migration of the inside hydrogen at C-6 to the cationic center at C-10 to produce the new ion **[16]**, the cationic center of which is so situated as to provide a facile

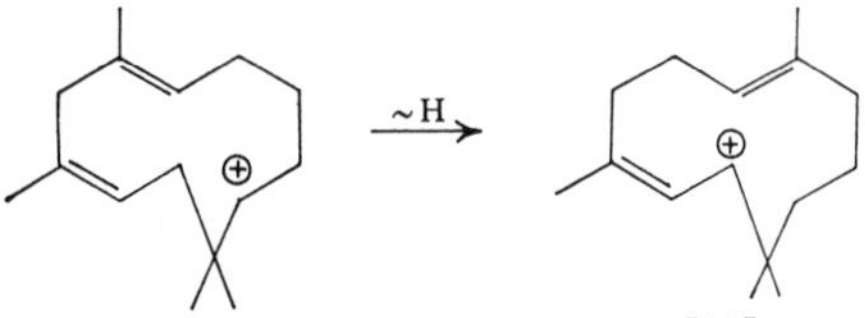

[11]   [16]

cyclization of the C-1 carbonium ion onto the Δ^{6-7} double bond with production of the ion **[17]**, which is in turn favorably oriented for formation of another new bond between C-7 and C-3 generating the ion **[18]**.   Although formation of the C-7, C-2 bond is, indeed, electronically favored, this would result in a highly strained four-membered ring in a polycyclic system.   Rearrangement of this ion **[18a,b]** by a 1,2-migration of the C-4 methylene bridge and proton loss produces longifolene **[19]**.

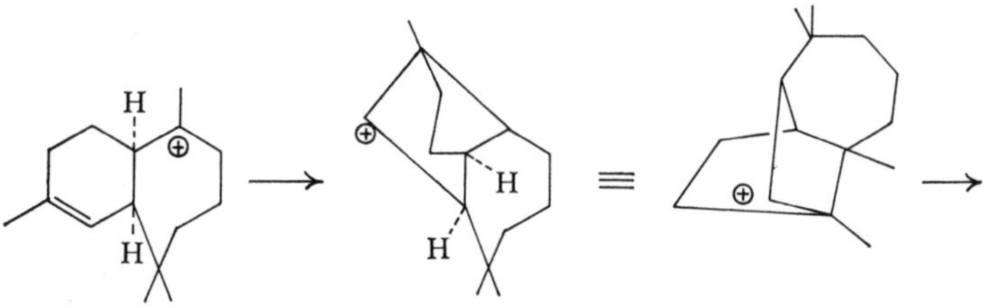

[17]   [18a]   [18b]

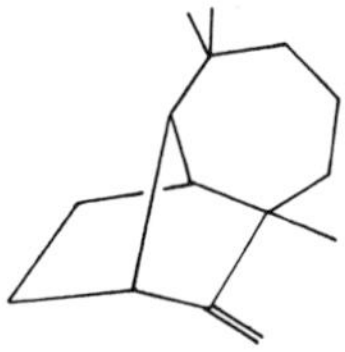

[19]

The biogenesis of longifolene has received brief experimental attention.[10]   The feeding of 1-C^{14}-acetate to *Pinus longifolia Roxb*. led to the incorporation of about 0.07 per cent of the added tracer into

10. W. Sandermann and K. Bruns, *Tetrahedron Letters*, **1962**, 261.

longifolene, the skeleton of which was essentially devoid of activity in the exocyclic methylene group. (The activity found in this position was only 1.6 per cent that anticipated if this carbon had been derived from the carboxyl group of acetate.) This result is entirely consonant with the hypothetical scheme just described.

An interesting botanical correlation exists in the co-occurrence of caryophyllene and humulene in *Eugenia caryophyllata*. Further, caryophyllene and longifolene are the only sesquiterpenes known to date in pines (*Pinus* spp.).

An examination of the detailed three dimensional conformation of the cation [11] shows that it can plausibly give rise to a *cis*-caryophyllene and also a perhydroazulene-type skeleton. That these particular skeletons have not yet appeared emphasizes that, however elegant an argument may be constructed on stereoelectronic grounds, enzymatic control is still absolutely necessary to account for the observed biological selection among the many chemically appealing processes. The impressive thing is not that some anticipated structures are not biosynthesized but that many of those anticipated on theoretical grounds have been and are being encountered.

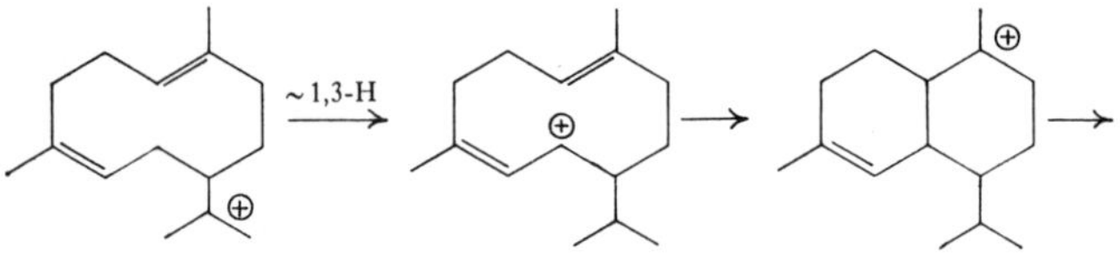

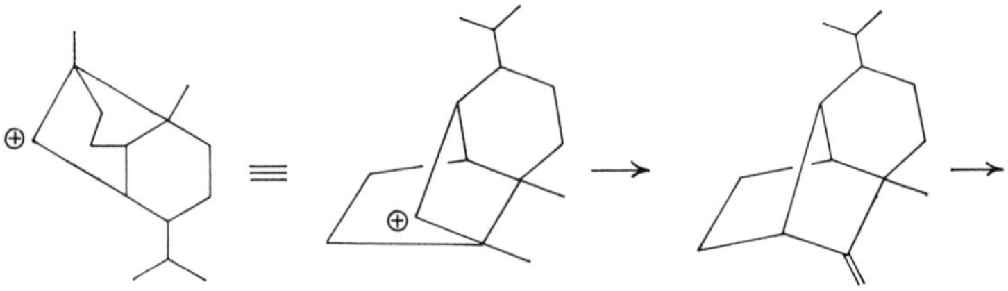

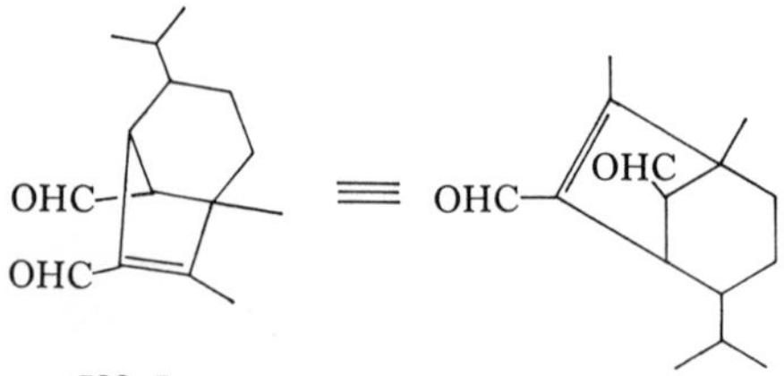

8–5 HELMINTHOSPORAL

The 10-ring cation [12] that can be formed from *cis*-farnesyl pyro-phosphate, although strained as pointed out earlier, appears to be the origin of fungal toxin, helminthosporal, which has been isolated from *Helminthosporium sativum* and shown to have the structure [20a,b].[11,12] The biosynthesis of this substance can parallel that for longifolene with the important difference that the starting point is the *cis*-10-ring cation. The oxidation of the carbon-carbon bond of the intermediate hydrocarbon [21] to produce the two dialdehyde functions has ample precedence in the monoterpene area.   If such a scheme is valid, 2-C^{14}-mevalonate should be incorporated as indicated and a degradation of helminthosporal biosynthesized from 2-C^{14}-mevalonate has shown [13] that the unsaturated aldehyde function contained about 38 per cent of the total activity in the molecule—in good agreement with the value expected if this carbon were one of the three derived from C-2 of mevalonate.

8–6 SANTONIN AND GUAIAZULENE SKELETONS

The cation [22] derived from an all-*trans* farnesol skeleton has its two internal double bonds close together and, unlike the *cis* cation [11], there is no "inside" hydrogen to interfere with their interaction. Simple hydration of the cationic center on the isopropyl group leads to an alcohol for which [23a,b; 24a,b] are entirely equivalent representations.

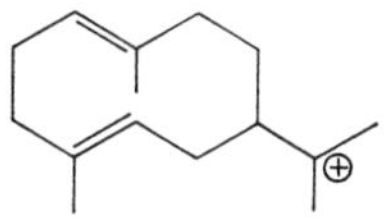

[22]

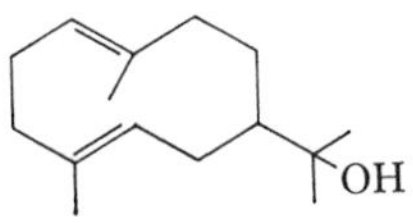

[23a] 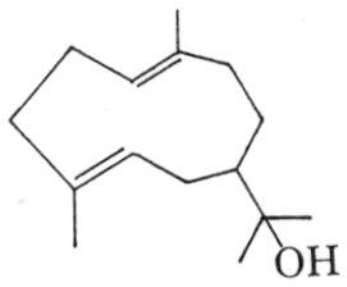   [24a]

11. P. de Mayo, E. Y. Spencer, and R. W. White, *Can. J. Chem.*, **39**, 1608 (1961).
12. P. de Mayo, E. Y. Spencer, and R. W. White, *J. Am. Chem. Soc.*, **84**, 494 (1962).
13. P. de Mayo, J. R. Robinson, E. Y. Spencer, and R. W. White, *Experientia*, **18**, 359 (1962).

It is immediately apparent that the double bonds in **[23]** or **[24]** are ideally situated for concerted cyclizations, with *trans* antiparallel additions to the double bonds to yield the products **[25a,b]** (from **[23a,b]**) and **[26a,b]** (from **[24a,b]**). The R group that initiates the cyclization can either be a proton, for a simple acid catalyzed cyclization, or "HO⊕" for oxidative cyclizations analogous to those leading from

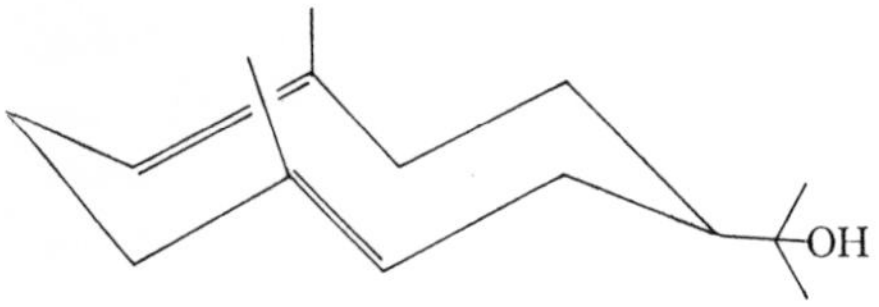

[23b] 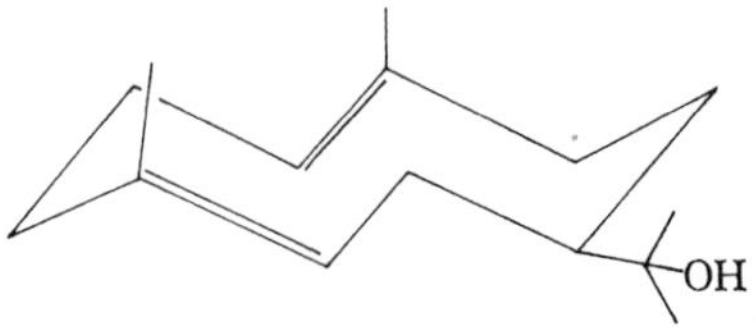   [24b]

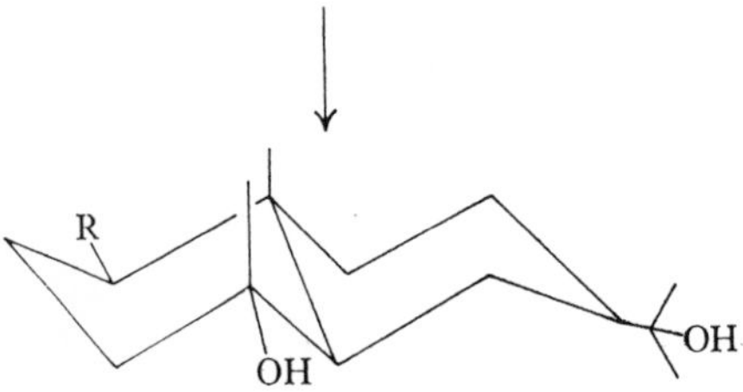

[25a] 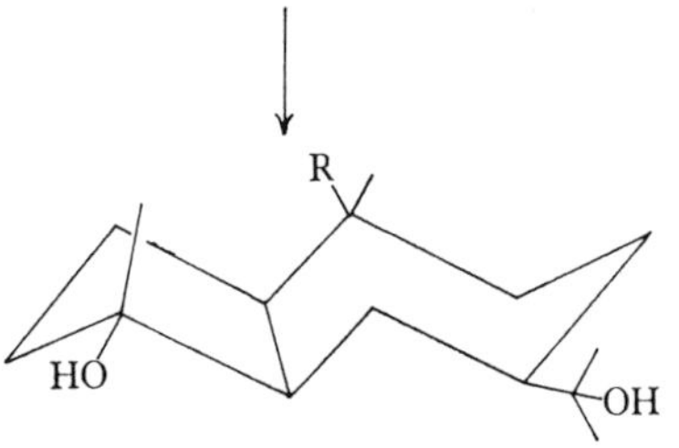   [26a]

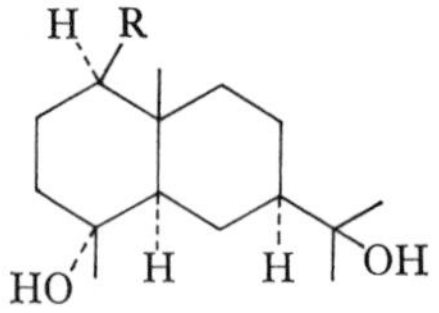

[25b] 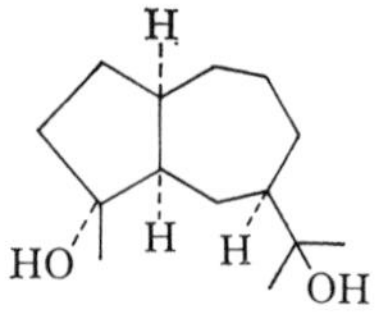   [26b]

squalene to the various triterpenes. As required by the geometry of such processes, all the newly formed bonds are parallel. The conversion of **[23b]** to **[25]** involves completely Markownikoff-oriented addition to both double bonds. The transformation of **[24b]** to **[26]** necessitates an initial anti-Markownikoff addition, which is allowable in this case, because the relative stereochemistry of the two double bonds compels this particular mode of interaction.

In addition to neutralization by nucleophile addition, the cyclization process can terminate by proton loss that from **[23b]** will lead to eudesmol **[27]** and similar substances such as santonin or cyperone. Recently a substance, cryptomeridiol, has been isolated from *Crypto-meria japonica D. Don* and characterized[13a] as **[27b]** (cf. **[25a,b]** R = H). This can be regarded as the biogenetic parent of this family.   Its structure represents the termination of the cyclization process by nucleophile acquisition.   Moreover, the equatorial location of this acquired nucleophile manifests the postulated stereoelectronic control.

   Product **[26]** is the precursor of the large body of sesquiterpenes with the guaiazulene skeleton such as geigerin **[28]**,[14] or, also, substances having an additional carbocyclic ring such as aromadendrene **[29]**.[15]

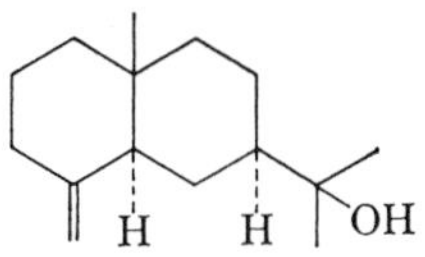

[27] 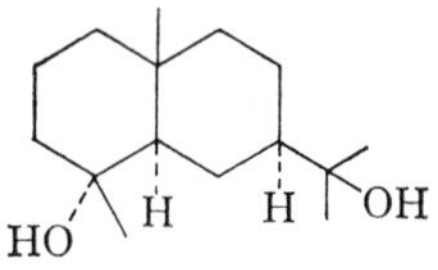   [27b]

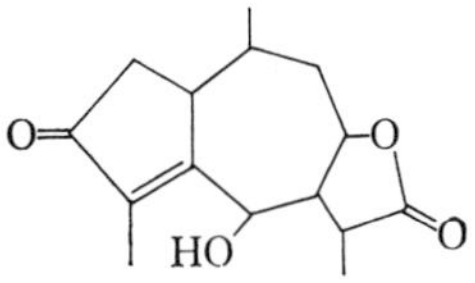

[28] 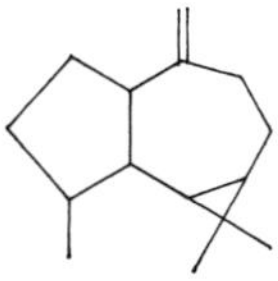   [29]

   A group of sesquiterpenes have recently come to light that possess a rearranged guaiazulene skeleton.   Tenulin **[30]** [16] is an example and its carbon skeleton can be derived by a simple 1,2-shift of the appropriate methyl group from a precursor of the guaiazulene type.

   Another sesquiterpene with a perturbed guaiazulene skeleton, this time an errant isopropyl group, is zierone **[31]**,[17] which may be derived

13a. M. Sumimoto, H. Ito, H. Hirai, and K. Wada, *Chem. & Ind. (London)*, **1963**, 780.
14. D. H. R. Barton and J. E. D. Levisalles, *J. Chem. Soc.*, **1958**, 4518.
15. A. J. Birch, J. Grimshaw, R. N. Speake, R. M. Gascoigne, and R. O. Hellyer, *Tetrahedron Letters*, **No. 3**, 15 (1959).
16. W. Herz, W. A. Rohde, K. Rabindran, P. Jayaraman, and N. Viswanathan, *J. Am. Chem. Soc.*, **84**, 3857 (1962); D. H. R. Barton and P. de Mayo, *J. Chem. Soc.*, **1956**, 142.
17. D. H. R. Barton and G. S. Gupta, *Proc. Chem. Soc.*, **1961**, 308.

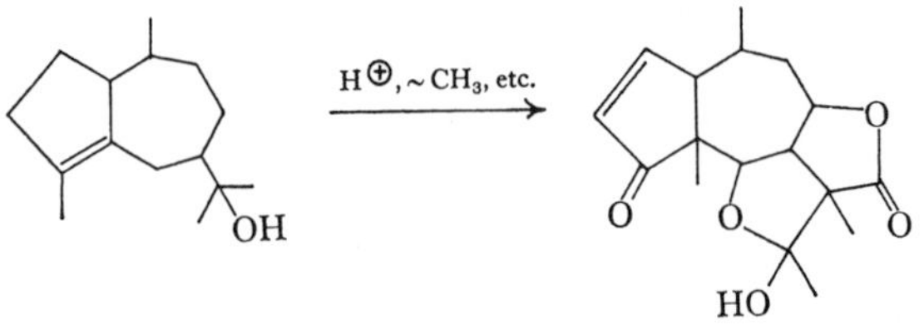

[30]

by the indicated migration or by oxidative opening of the cyclopropane ring [18] in an aromadendrene-type precursor.

From **[23a]** an electron migration analogous to the Cope rearrangement leads to elemol **[32]**.

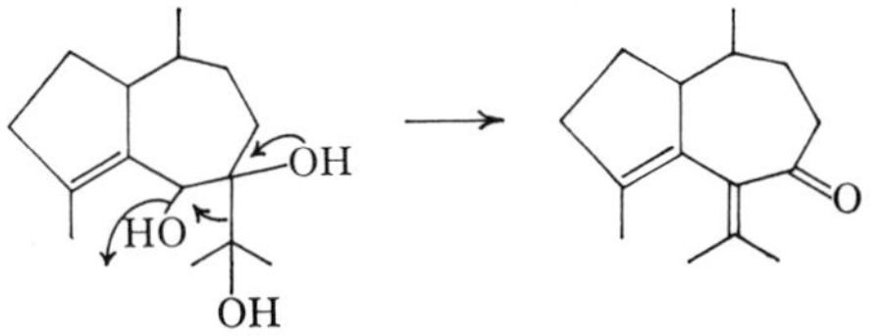

[31]

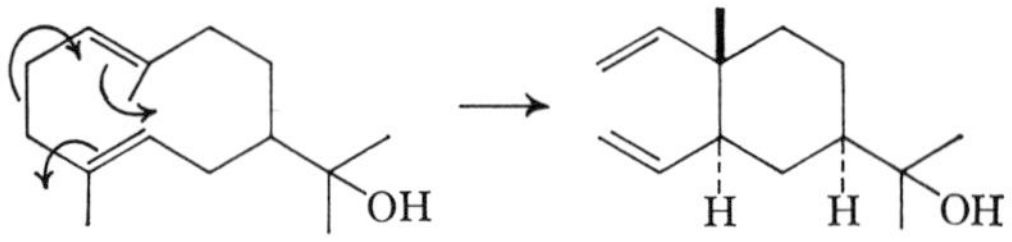

[23a]   **[32]**

Recently two sesquiterpenes, δ-elemene **[33]** and cogeijerene **[34]**, isolated as racemates, have been reported.[19]   If their lack of optical activity is an inherent characteristic of their synthesis by the plant and not an artifact of their isolation, their biogenesis may be the result of a nonenzymatic recyclization of electrons on the one hand and an acid-catalyzed cyclization on the other, from a symmetrical intermediate, as indicated.   Cogeijerene has also suffered amputation of the isopropyl sidechain.

18. A. J. Birch, D. J. Collins, A. R. Penfold, and J. P. Turnbull, *J. Chem. Soc.*, **1962**, 792.
19. J. Gough, V. Powell, and M. D. Sutherland, *Tetrahedron Letters*, **1961**, 763.

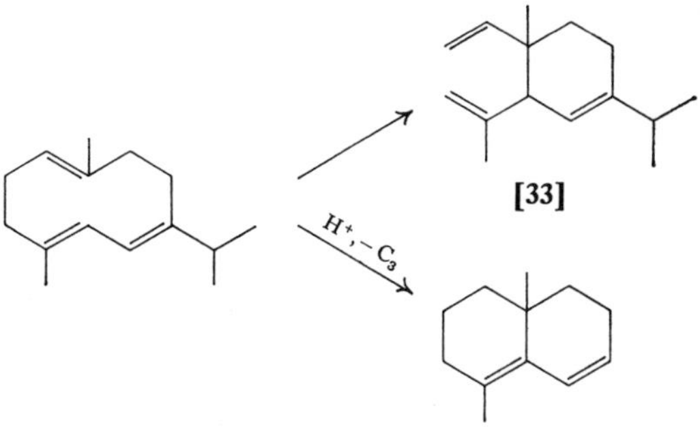

[33]

$H^+, -C_3$

[34]

8-7 VETIVAZULENES

An alternative pathway is available that begins with a simple double bond isomerization from **[23b]** to **[35]**, which can occur without steric complaint.   From this intermediate, cyclization can lead to **[36a,b]** and **[37a,b]**.   Thus **[37]** contains the essential stereochemical elements thought to be present in β-vetivone **[38]**.   The few other vetivazulene skeletons found in nature presumably also arise from **[37]**.

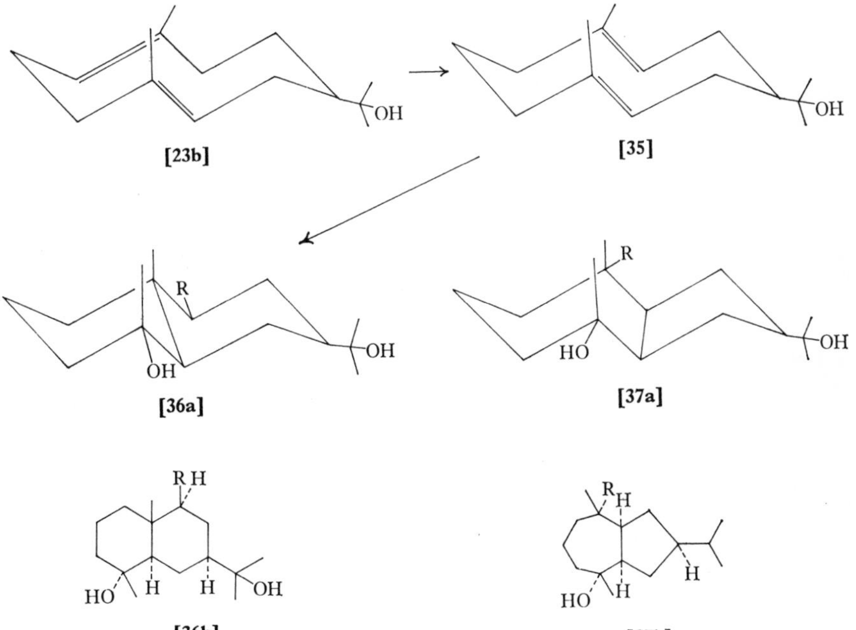

[23b]

[35]

[36a]

[37a]

[36b]

[37b]

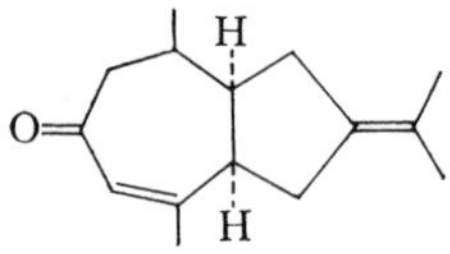

[38]

8–8 EREMOPHILONES

The eremophilones can be derived from [35]. If the cyclization is envisioned as oxidative, an intermediate [39] can be formed, that has appropriate groups so disposed (i.e., planar and *trans*) as to facilitate a series of 1,2-shifts leading to [40], which, if now allowed to undergo isomerization, side chain dehydration, and oxidation of either enol, yields eremophilone [41], hydroxyeremophilone [42], and hydroxydihydroeremophilone [43], all three of which co-exist in nature. The structures of eremophilone caused a bit of a sensation when first determined in 1937, because it is not directly derivable by polymerization of three isoprene units. However, the proposal of Robinson[20] of a migration of the type shown restored order. The requisite stereochemistry of such a migration is also afforded by the intermediate [26].

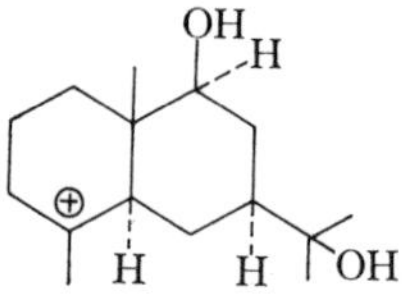

[39] 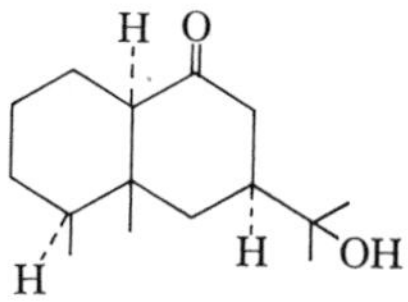   [40]

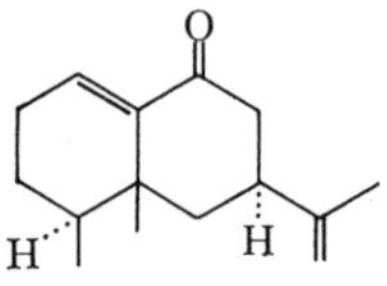

[41] 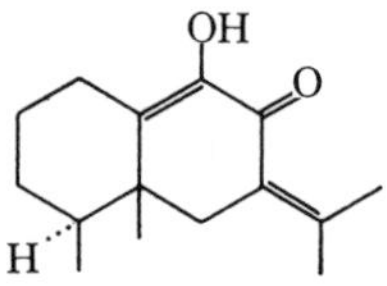   [42] 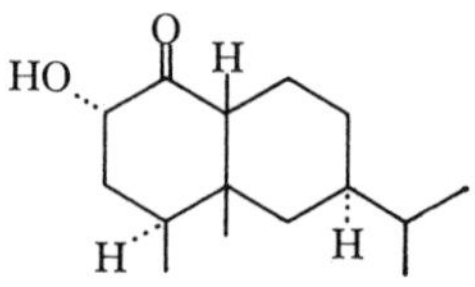   [43]

8–9 SESQUITERPENES WITH MEDIUM-SIZED RINGS

One might also expect, and does find, examples of monocyclic sesquiterpenes that undergo in vitro cyclizations analogous to those

20. R. Robinson, *The Structural Relations of Natural Products*, Clarendon, Oxford, 1955, p. 12; R. Robinson, cited in A. R. Penfold and J. L. Simonsen, *J. Chem. Soc.*, **1939**, 87.

postulated for terpene biosynthesis.   Thus pyrethrosin [44] [21] has been shown to cyclize under a variety of acidic conditions to give products such as [45].   Germacrone has been shown [22] to have structure [46], which readily accommodates the observation of Treibs [23] that germacrone yields [47] on treatment with acid, and selinane [48] when the alcohol corresponding to germacrone is hydrogenated under acidic conditions. An earlier formulation of germacrone was in fact first corrected [2] to [46] by application of this biosynthetic theory.   Other medium ring (nine, ten, or eleven membered) sesquiterpenes have been studied and a review of their chemistry has appeared.[24]

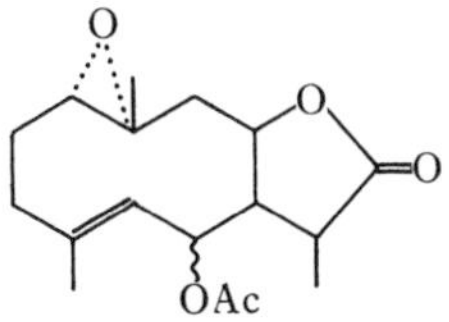

[44] 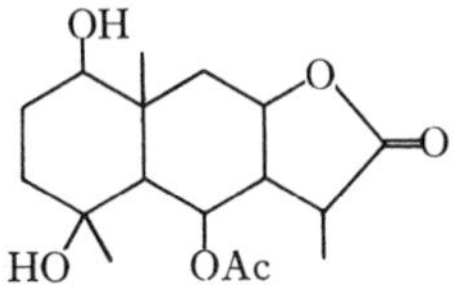   [45] 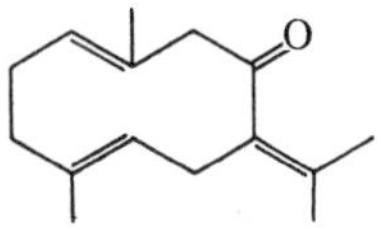   [46]

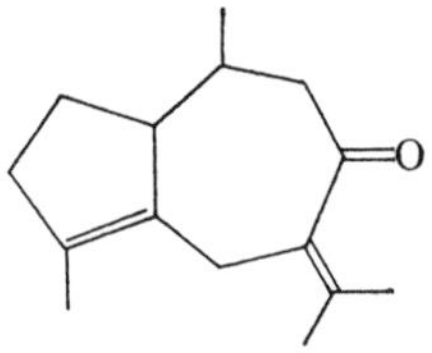

[47] 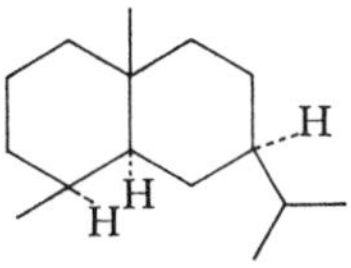   [48]

8-10   POLYGODIAL AND IRESIN

Although the majority of the sesquiterpenes are apparently derived by a cyclization process initiated by ionization of the allylic pyrophosphate ester of *cis*- or *trans*-farnesyl pyrophosphate, polygodial [49] [25] stands as one example of many that an electrophile-catalyzed cyclization, so typical of di- and triterpenes, is not totally absent from the sesquiterpene area.

21. D. H. R. Barton. O. C. Böckman, and P. de Mayo, *J. Chem. Soc.*, **1960**, 2263.
22. G. Ohloff and E. G. Hoffmann, *Z. Naturforsch.*, **16b**, 298 (1961); M. Suchý, V. Herout, and F. Šorm, *Collection Czech. Chem. Commun.*, **26**, 1358 (1961).
23. W. Treibs, *Ann.* **576**, 116 (1952).
24. T. G. Halsall and D. W. Theobald, *Quart. Rev. (London)*, **16**, 101 (1962).
25. C. S. Barnes and J. W. Loder, *Australian J. Chem.*, **15**, 322 (1962).

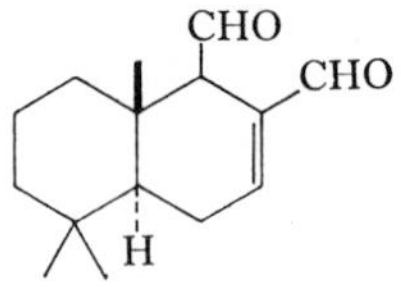

[49]

The first substance of this type which was discovered is iresin **[50]**.[26,27] It results from an oxidative cyclization and has the additional feature that its absolute configuration is antipodal to that normally encountered.

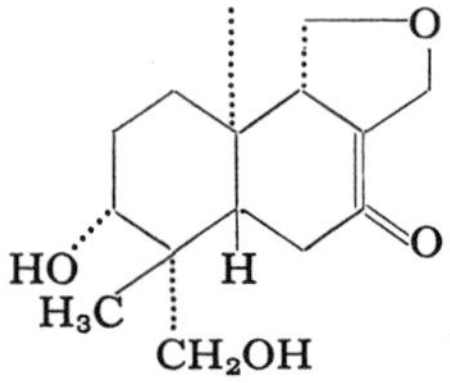

[50]

8–11 TRICHOTHECIN

In addition to the experimental results discussed previously, the biogenesis of the interesting sesquiterpene trichothecin **[51]**[28,29] has been investigated.[30] Although the C_{15} part of the molecule contains

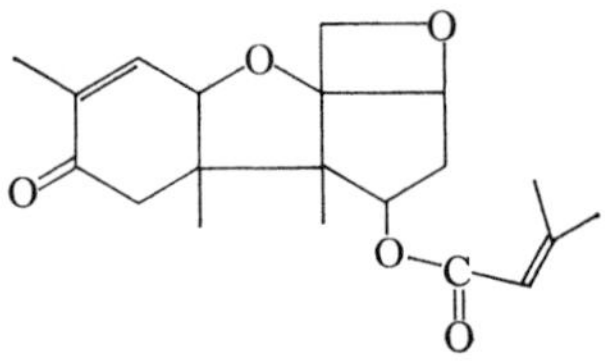

[51]

26. C. Djerassi and S. Burstein, *J. Am. Chem. Soc.*, **80**, 2593 (1958).
27. M. G. Rossmann and W. N. Lipscomb, *J. Am. Chem. Soc.*, **80**, 2592 (1958); *Tetrahedron*, **4**, 275 (1958).
28. G. G. Freeman, J. E. Gill, and W. S. Waring, *Soc.*, **1959**, *J. Chem.* 1105.
29. J. Fishman, E. R. H. Jones, G. Lowe, and M. C. Whiting, *J. Chem. Soc.*, **1960**, 3948.
30. E. R. H. Jones and G. Lowe, *J. Chem. Soc.*, **1960**, 3959.

the usual three methyl groups, its carbon skeleton does not manifest the regular head-to-tail arrangement of three isoprenoid units characteristic of farnesyl pyrophosphate.   An added interest in trichothecin is that it is a metabolite of *Trichothecium roseum* Link, a fungus that also produces rosennoolactone (cf. page 253), a degenerate diterpene.

It is possible, however, to derive the trichothecin carbon skeleton from a farnesyl backbone by allowing two 1,2-methyl shifts, i.e., [52] → [51].   From 2-C^{14}-mevalonate, one will anticipate labeling in the trichothecin, as indicated.   The experimental results confirm this expectation and moreover demonstrate the occurrence of the two postulated 1,2-methyl shifts and not a single, 1,3-shift.   It is also interesting to note the specificity with which the one of the methyl groups of the terminal gem-dimethyl group of the farnesyl pyrophosphate migrates, reinforcing observations in the diterpene and triterpene fields that the two methyl carbons of these terminal groups do not become randomized during the biosynthesis processes.

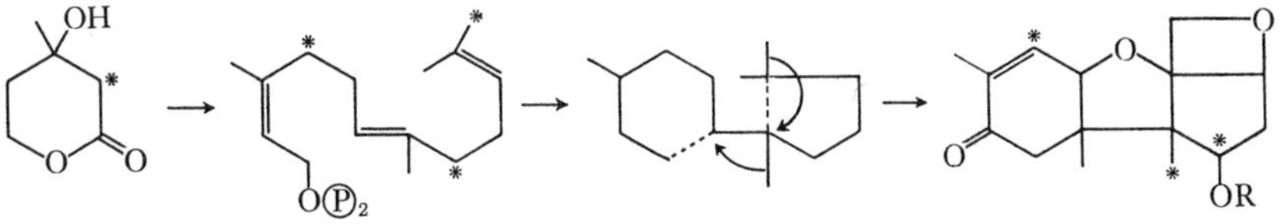

[52]

The labeling of the isocrotonyl ester function from 1-C^{14}-acetate was that expected, but with 2-C^{14}-mevalonate as substrate there was no activity found in this group.   This is yet another demonstration of the essentially irreversible steps in the formation of mevalonate from 3-hydroxy-3-methylglutaryl coenzyme A.

chapter nine | Diterpenes

The evolution of the isoprene rule as a generally accepted working hypothesis was in large measure due to the simultaneous investigation of the sesquiterpenes and the diterpene, abietic acid, a compound obtained from a mixture of isomers present in resin by treatment of the resin with boiling acetic acid. Abietic acid has been shown [1-4] to have the structure and relative and absolute stereochemistry shown in [1].

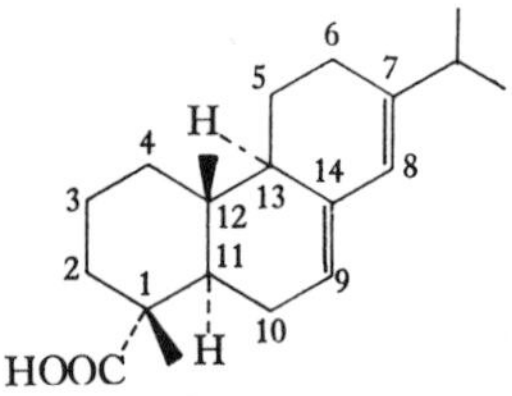

[1]

9–1 LINEAR DITERPENES

Abietic acid substance and all other diterpenes can hypothetically be derived from the C_{20} regular, head-to-tail polyisoprenoid, geranylgeranyl pyrophosphate [2], an allylic isomer of which (geranyllinaloöl [3]) has recently been isolated from jasmine oil.[5]

1. L. Ruzicka, H. Waldmann, P. J. Meier, and H. Hösli, *Helv. Chim. Acta,* **16,** 169 (1933).
2. L. Ruzicka and L. Sternbach, *Helv. Chim. Acta,* **25,** 1036 (1942).
3. D. H. R. Barton, *Quart. Rev. (London),* **3,** 36 (1949).
4. H. Heusser, E. Beriger, R. Anliker, O. Jeger, and L. Ruzicka, *Helv. Chim. Acta,* 36, 1918 (1953).
5. E. Lederer, *France Parfums,* **3** (14), 28 (1960); *C.A.,* **54,** 14579d (1960).

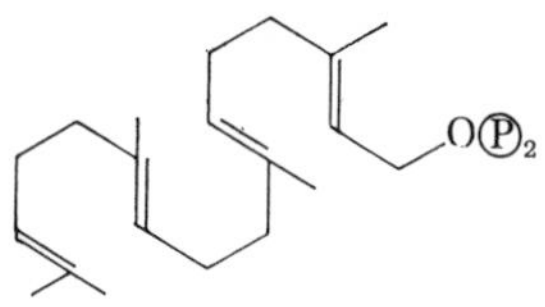

[2] 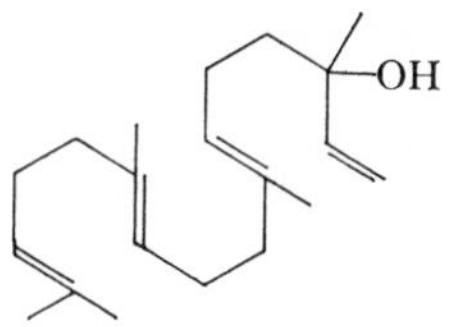   [3]

Another example of an uncyclized C_{20} polyisoprenoid has been long known in phytol [4], which is a hexahydro derivative of geranyl-

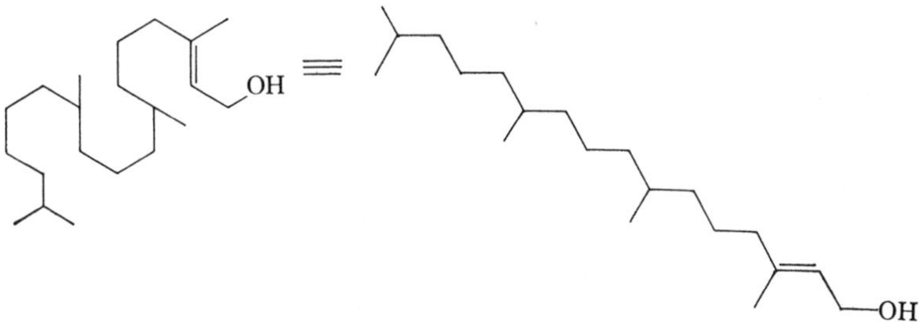

[4]

geraniol.[6]   Vitamin A [5] is clearly also a derivative of geranyl-geraniol in which the chain terminal has cyclized onto itself (a cyclization initiated by H^+), and additional unsaturation has been introduced into the chain.[7]

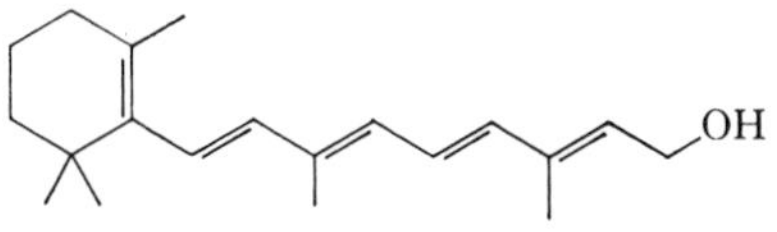

[5]

9–2 CATIVIC ACID, SCLAREOL, AND MANOÖL

If the cyclization of geranyl-geraniol proceeds through three isoprene units folded as two potential chair cyclohexane rings (cf. triterpene biosynthesis for a detailed discussion of the stereochemical

6. F. G. Fischer, *Ann.*, **464**, 69 (1928).
7. P. Karrer, R. Morf, and K. Schöpp, *Helv. Chim. Acta*, **14**, 1036, 1431 (1931).

implications of polyolefin cyclization), there results a molecule that by subsequent oxidation of two substituents, yields [8] cativic acid [8]; i.e., [6] → [7] → [8].

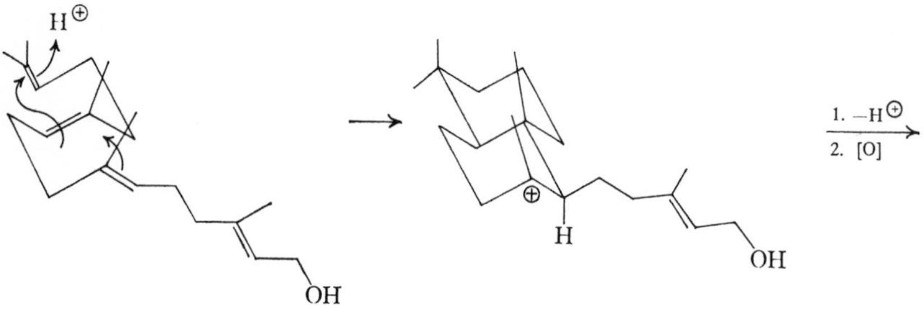

[6] [7]

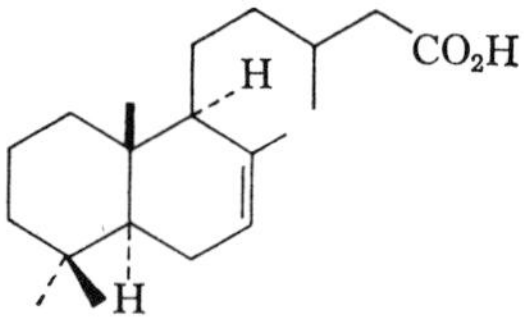

[8]

If a geranyllinaloöl-type skeleton cyclizes in a similar fashion and if the cationic intermediate analogous to [7] is hydrated, sclareol [9] is formed.[9-11] If the intermediate is stabilized not by hydration but by loss of a proton, manoöl [10] [12] is produced.

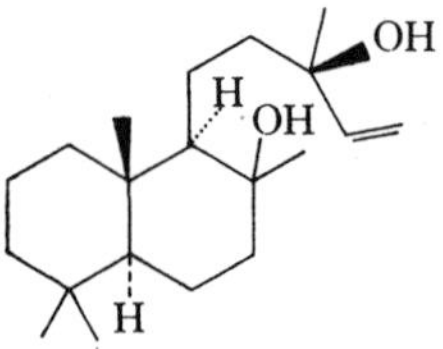

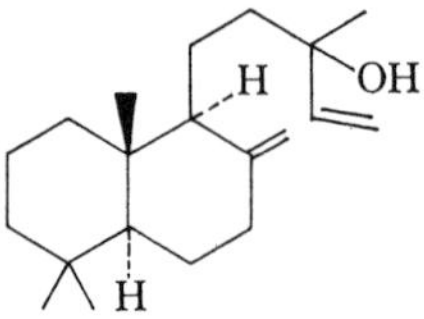

[9]   [10]

8. F. W. Grant, Jr., and H. H. Zeiss, *J. Am. Chem. Soc.*, **76**, 5001 (1954).
9. L. Ruzicka and M. M. Janot, *Helv. Chim. Acta*, **14**, 645 (1931).
10. L. Ruzicka, C. F. Seidel, and L. L. Engel, *Helv. Chim. Acta*, **25**, 621 (1942).
11. J. A. Barltrop and D. B. Bigley, *Chem. & Ind.* (*London*), **1959**, 1378.
12. J. R. Hosking and C. W. Brandt, *Ber.*, **68**, 1311 (1935).

9–3 PIMARANES AND ABIETANES

An ionization of the terminal nucleophile (e.g., —OH or —OP_2) similar to that postulated for the derivation of the cyclic sesquiterpenes, will lead from a manoöl skeleton to the pimarane skeleton of tricarbocyclic diterpenes such as pimaradiene **[13]**,[13,14] i.e., **[10]** → **[11]** → **[12]** → **[13]**.

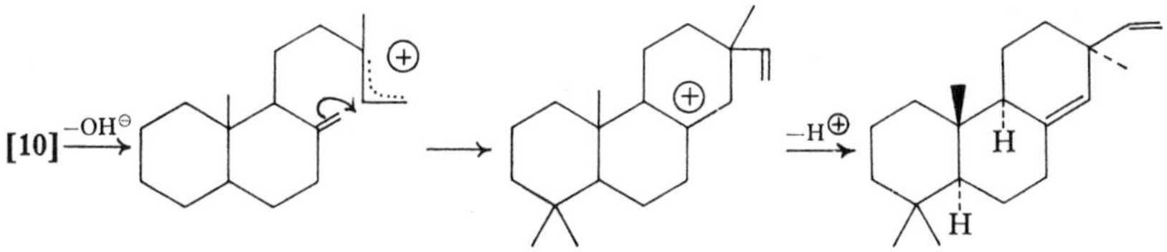

[11]   **[12]**   **[13]**

Ruzicka has pointed out[15] the potential biogenetic relationship between diterpenes with the pimarane skeleton (such as pimaradiene) and those with an abietane skeleton such as abietic acid. (**[13]** → **[14]** → etc.)

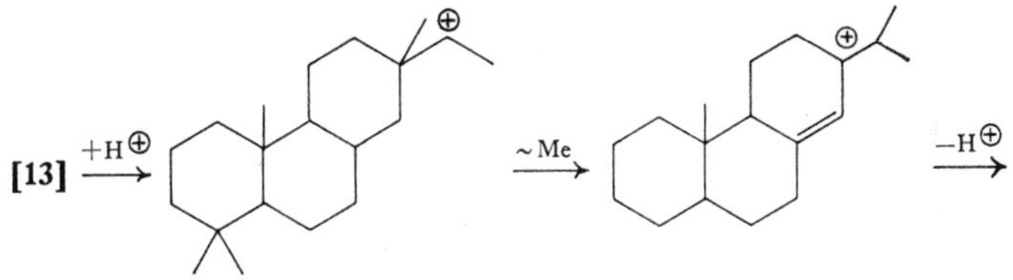

[14]   **[15]**

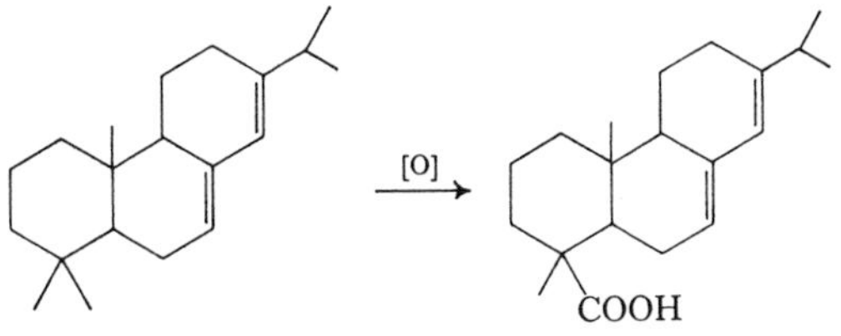

[16]

13. L. H. Briggs, B. F. Cain, and J. K. Wilmshurst, *Chem. & Ind. (London)*, **1958**, 599.
14. R. E. Ireland and P. W. Schiess, *Tetrahedron Letters*, **1960**, 37.
15. L. Ruzicka, *Experientia*, **9**, 357 (1953).

Recently an in vitro conversion of a pimaradiene into an abietadiene has been reported.[16]   Thus treatment of pimaric acid **[17]** with
sulfuric acid at 30° yields abietic acid.

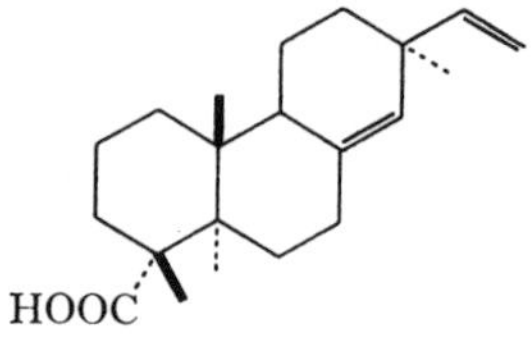

[17]

9–4   PHYLLOCLADENE-TYPE SKELETONS

Another type of rearrangement can lead from the pimaradiene type
of skeleton to the bicyclic structure found, for example, in phyllocladene
[18] [17,18] as has been pointed out by Wenkert.

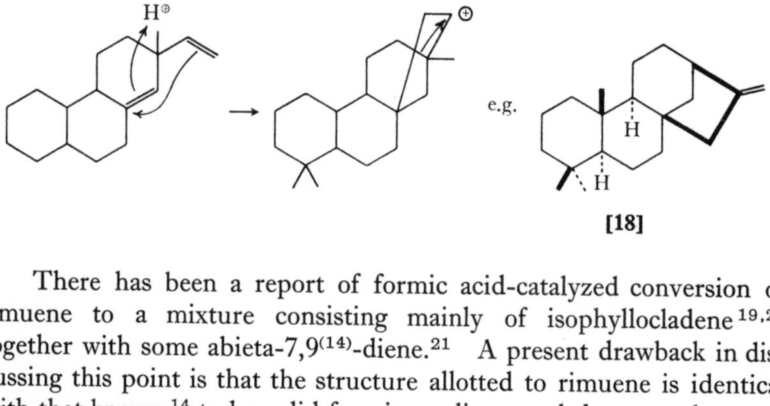

[18]

There has been a report of formic acid-catalyzed conversion of
rimuene to a mixture consisting mainly of isophyllocladene [19,20]
together with some abieta-7,9[(14)]-diene.[21]   A present drawback in dis-
cussing this point is that the structure allotted to rimuene is identical
with that known [14] to be valid for pimaradiene, and the two substances
are not identical.   Moreover, rimuene is not [22] a C-13 epimer of pimara-

16. E. Wenkert and J. W. Chamberlin, *J. Am. Chem. Soc.*, **81**, 688 (1959).
17. E. Wenkert, *Chem. & Ind.* (*London*), **1955**, 282.
18. L. H. Briggs, B. F. Cain, R. C. Cambie, and B. R. Davis, *J. Chem. Soc.*,
    1962, 1840.
19. L. H. Briggs, B. F. Cain, B. R. Davis, and J. K. Wilmshurst, *Tetrahedron
    Letters*, **1959**, 13.
20. P. K. Grant and R. Hodges, *Tetrahedron*, **8**, 261 (1960).
21. L. H. Briggs, B. F. Cain, and R. C. Cambie, *Tetrahedron Letters*, **1959**, 17.
22. R. F. Church and R. E. Ireland, *Tetrahedron Letters*, **No. 14**, 493 (1961).

diene, though such a structure was claimed.[23]   Although it is not possible, therefore, to discuss the details of this interesting in vitro isomerization, it is nevertheless clear that, from a single substance, which almost certainly has a structure similar to pimaradiene, reaction paths are open that can lead both to the abietadiene and phyllocladene skeletons [Eq. (9–1)].

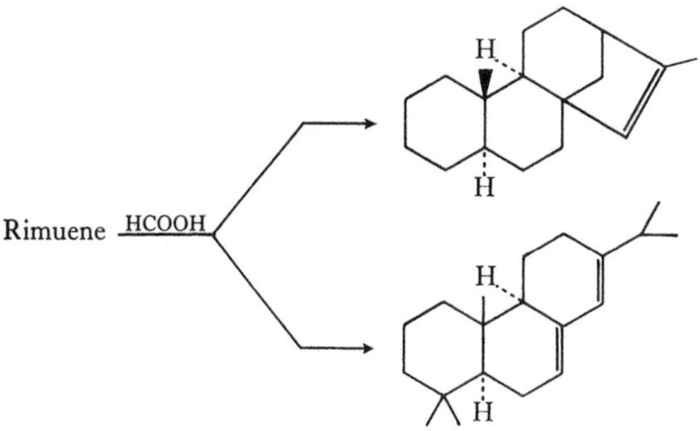

Rimuene —HCOOH→   (9–1)

9–5   STEREOCHEMISTRY

The homogeneous absolute stereochemistry that characterizes the triterpenes is not evidenced by the diterpenes, and there exist substances such as (−)kaurene **[19]**,[24–26] which have antipodal stereo-

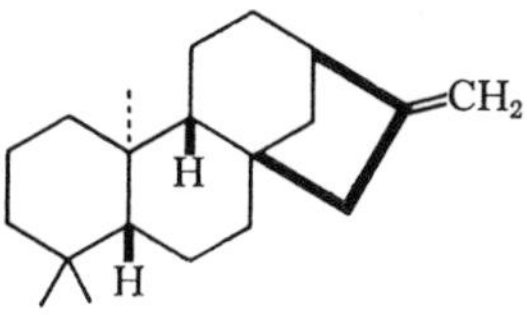

[19]

23. E. Wenkert and P. Beak, *J. Am. Chem. Soc.*, **83**, 998 (1961).
24. B. E. Cross, R. H. B. Galt, J. R. Hanson, and W. Klyne, *Tetrahedron Letters*, **No. 4**, 145 (1962).
25. R. A. Bell, R. E. Ireland, and R. A. Partyka, *J. Org. Chem.*, **27**, 3741 (1962).
26. B. E. Cross, J. R. Hanson, L. H. Briggs, R. C. Cambie, and P. S. Rutledge, *Proc. Chem. Soc.*, **1963**, 17.

chemistry at the A/B ring fusion. Andrographolide [20] [27,28,28b] also possesses such abnormal stereochemistry and is thus the diterpene analogue of the sesquiterpene, iresin (cf. 8–10).

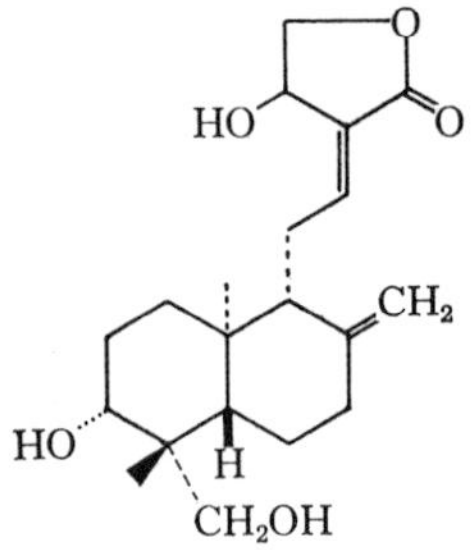

[20]

Another aspect of diterpene stereochemistry deserves comment. Although it has been felt for some time that the stereochemical integrity observed in the triterpene area (i.e., A/B/C-*trans-anti-trans*-stereochemistry) is violated in the diterpenes by examples of a 12,13-*syn* arrangement, more recent work seems to show that the supposed exceptions do, in fact, have a 12,13-*anti* configuration. Thus a recent investigation [29] by X-ray and optical dichroism techniques indicates that cafestol actually has structure [21], and possesses a 12,13-*anti* arrangement; earlier work had indicated a 12,13-*syn* configuration.

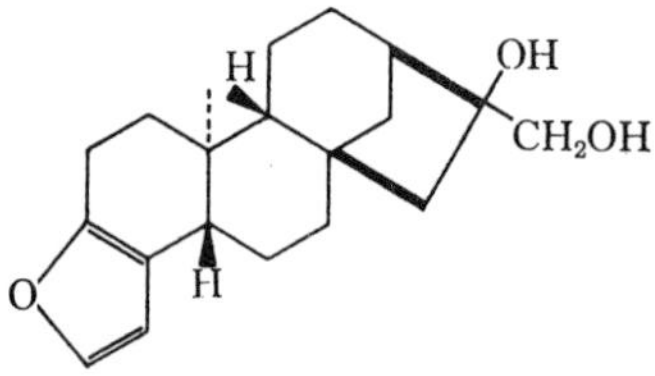

[21] 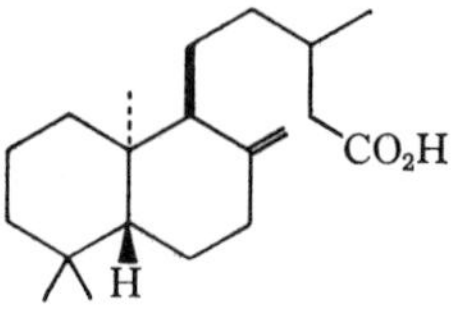   [22]

27. M. P. Cava, B. Weinstein, W. R. Chan, L. J. Haynes, and L. F. Johnson, *Chem. & Ind. (London)*, **1963**, 167.

28. M. P. Cava and B. Weinstein, *Chem. & Ind. (London)*, **1959**, 851.

28b. W. R. Chan, C. Willis, M. P. Cava, and R. P. Stein, *Chem. & Ind. (London)*, **1963**, 495.

29. A. I. Scott, G. A. Sim, G. Ferguson, D. W. Young, and F. McCapra, *J. Am. Chem. Soc.*, **84**, 3197 (1962).

As mentioned before, it appears that rimuene does not have a 12,13-*syn* configuration, although this had been proposed. Eperuic acid,[30,31] for which structure [22] has been proposed, stands as the sole remaining exception to the generalization that the diterpenes are based on an initial backbone of rings A and B in the *trans-anti* configuration; this also suggests that the presently accepted stereochemistry of this compound may be suspect. These substances also have a stereochemistry in the A/B region, which is antipodal to that normally encountered.

9-6 DITERPENES WITH REARRANGED SKELETONS

An interesting feature in the structure of cafestol [21] is the presence of a furan ring fused to ring A in place of the normal gem-dimethyl group. In principle this conversion can be accomplished by an appropriate rearrangement reaction,[32] e.g., Eq. (9–2). The apparent derivation [33] of menthofuran from pulegone in the monoterpene area

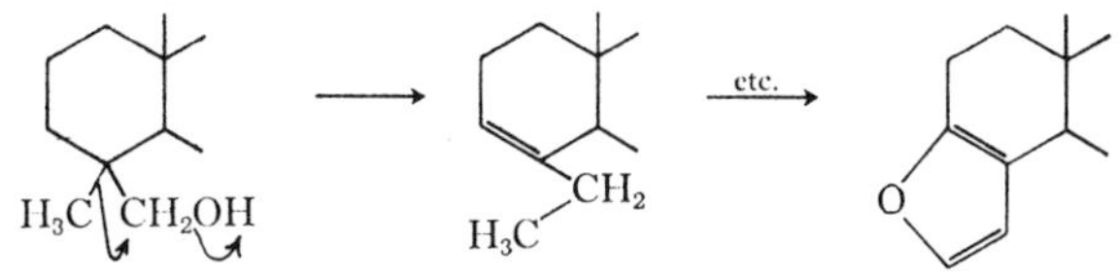

(9–2)

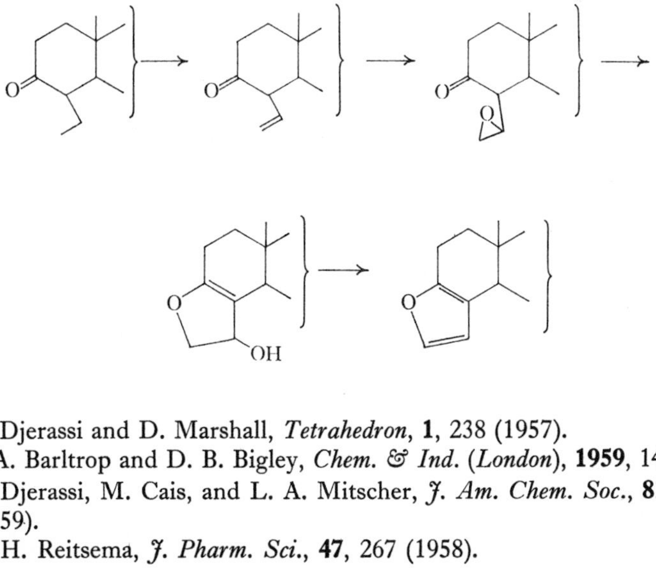

(9–3)

30. C. Djerassi and D. Marshall, *Tetrahedron*, **1**, 238 (1957).
31. J. A. Barltrop and D. B. Bigley, *Chem. & Ind. (London)*, **1959**, 1447.
32. C. Djerassi, M. Cais, and L. A. Mitscher, *J. Am. Chem. Soc.*, **81**, 2386 (1959).
33. R. H. Reitsema, *J. Pharm. Sci.*, **47**, 267 (1958).

(page 215) is an analogous situation. Wenkert[16] has suggested that the furan ring may be formed by an oxidation of an α,β unsaturated ketone, via an epoxide, as in Eq. (9–3).

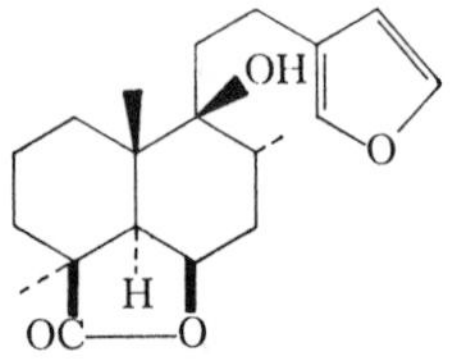

[23] 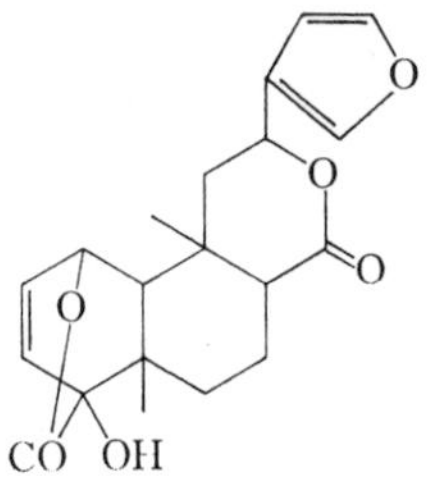   [24]

In some cases, the furan moiety is formed from the terminal isoprene fragment, e.g., marrubin [23].[35,36]

A furan ring is also an integral part of columbin [24],[37] one of the bitter principles of the Colombo root. This substance is even more

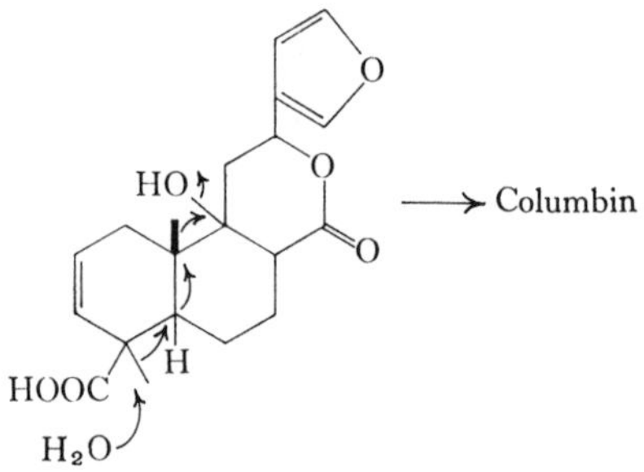

$\longrightarrow$ Columbin

[25]

striking as an example of a rearrangement of groups about the usual diterpene backbone and in this sense is biogenetically analogous to the triterpene friedelin (e.g., [25] $\rightarrow$ columbin).

35. W. Cocker, J. T. Edward, and T. F. Holley, *Chem. & Ind.* (*London*), **1954**, 1561.
36. D. Burn and W. Rigby, *Chem. & Ind.* (*London*), **1955**, 386.
37. D. H. R. Barton and D. Elad, *J. Chem. Soc.*, **1956**, 2085, 2090.

Another substance displaying an analogous type of skeletal re-arrangement is clerodin [26].[38,39] Such a biogenetic rearrangement will

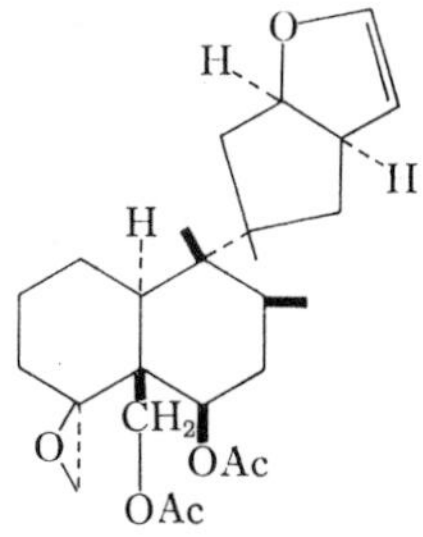

[26] 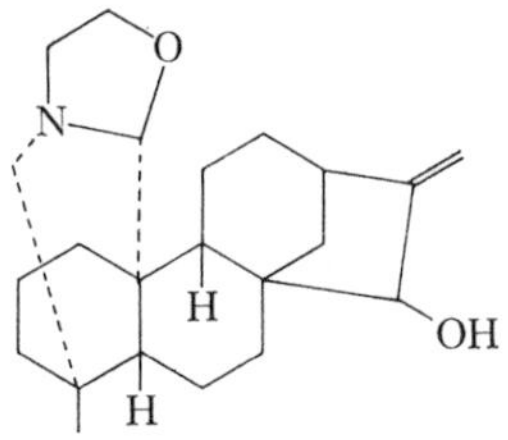   [27]

have the potential stereochemical result that the groups involved should be sequentially *trans*, a speculation that is confirmed by the stereochemistry of clerodin.

9–7 DITERPENE ALKALOIDS

The structure of certain alkaloids show clear diterpenoid biogenesis. Thus veatchine [27] [40,41] clearly contains the (−)-kaurene skeleton, and the atisine [28] skeleton [42,43] can be derived by a simple rearrange-ment involving a hydride shift.   Such relationships have been suggested by Wenkert.[17]   In this connection, the structure of mirene is an interest-ing bagatelle.   Mirene was suggested [17] to have structure [29] on the basis of its facile isomerization by mild acids to isophyllocladene.   On the other hand, a New Zealand group at one time [19,20,44] proposed a structure [30] for mirene but subsequently pointed out the difficulty of rationalizing the facile conversion by acid of mirene to isophyllo-cladene; they suggested instead [45] a structure [31] that isomerized to

38. G. A. Sim, T. A. Hamor, I. C. Paul, and J. M. Robertson, *Proc. Chem. Soc.*, **1961**, 75.
39. D. H. R. Barton, H. T. Cheung, A. D. Cross, L. M. Jackman, and M. M. Smith, *J. Chem. Soc.*, **1961**, 5061.
40. For a review, cf. K. Wiesner and Z. Valenta, *Fortschr. Chem. Org. Naturstoffe*, **16**, 26 (1958).
41. W. B. Whalley, *Tetrahedron*, **18**, 43 (1962).
42. J. W. Ap Simon and O. E. Edwards, *Can. J. Chem.*, **40**, 896 (1962).
43. H. Vorbrüggen and C. Djerassi, *Tetrahedron Letters*, **1961**, 119.
44. L. H. Briggs, B. F. Cain, B. R. Davis, and J. K. Wilmshurst, *Tetrahedron Letters*, **1959**, 8.
45. L. H. Briggs, B. F. Cain, R. C. Cambie, and B. R. Davis, *Tetrahedron Letters*, **1960**, 18.

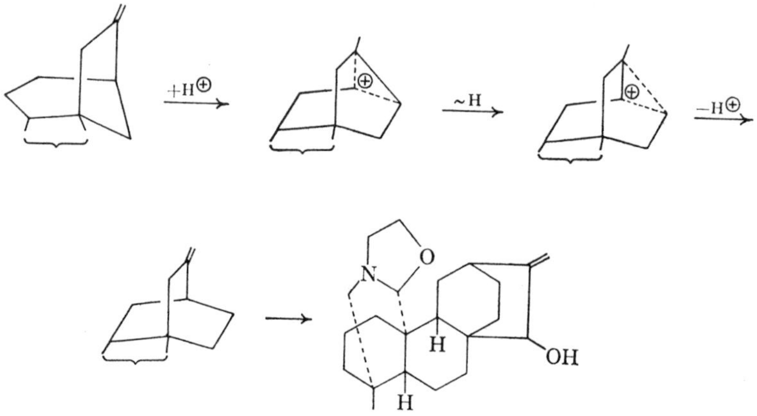

[28]

isophyllocladene by passage through the nonclassical carbonium ion **[32]**. Such an isomerization is, however, without precedent, and it is tempting to consider **[33]** the true structure for mirene.   This possesses an exomethylene group, which the chemical and spectroscopic evidence demands, and can easily give rise to isophyllocladene by an in vitro isomerization of the type just invoked in vivo to account for the alkaloids with skeletons like atisine.

The diterpene alkaloid deltaline **[34]** [46] contains clear evidence of a demethyl-atisine-like skeleton with an additional bond (C-9–C-17), which could easily be formed by **[35]** → **[36]**.

Such a bond is present also in the delphinium alkaloids such as delphinine **[37]**, [47-50] a molecule whose skeleton manifests an additional rearrangement that can be formalized as **[38]** → **[39]** [51,52] [cf. Eq. (9-4)].

46. M. Carmack, D. W. Mayo, and J. P. Ferris, *J. Am. Chem. Soc.*, **81**, 4110 (1959).

47. M. Przybylska and L. Marion, *Can. J. Chem.*, **37**, 1116, 1843 (1959).

48. K. Wiesner, M. Götz, D. L. Simmons, L. R. Fowler, F. W. Bachelor, R. F. C. Brown, and G. Büchi, *Tetrahedron Letters*, **1959**, 15.

49. K. Wiesner, D. L. Simmons, and L. R. Fowler, *Tetrahedron Letters*, **1959**, 1.

50. K. Wiesner, F. Bickelhaupt, D. R. Babin, and M. Götz, *Tetrahedron*, **9**, 254 (1960).

51. R. C. Cookson and M. E. Trevett, *J. Chem. Soc.*, **1956**, 3121.

52. Z. Valenta and K. Wiesner, *Chem. & Ind.* (*London*), **1956**, 354.

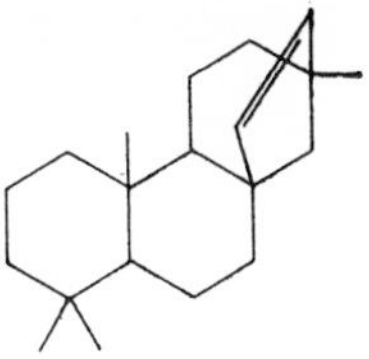

[29]

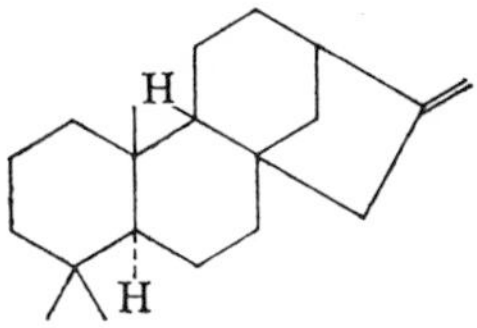

[30]

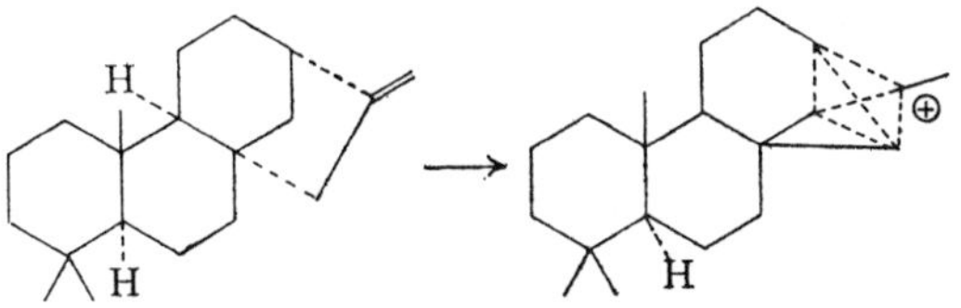

[31] $\longrightarrow$ [32] $\longrightarrow$ Isophyllocladene

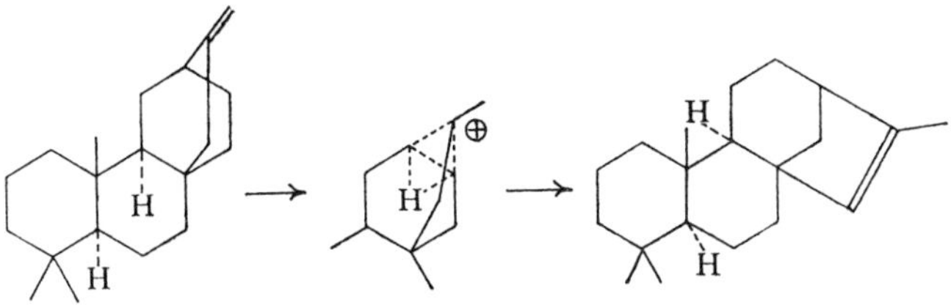

[33] $\longrightarrow$ $\longrightarrow$ Isophyllocladene

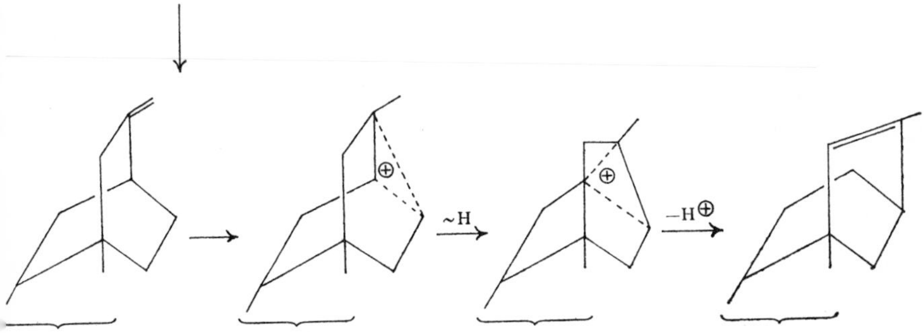

$\longrightarrow$ $\xrightarrow{\sim H}$ $\xrightarrow{-H^{\oplus}}$

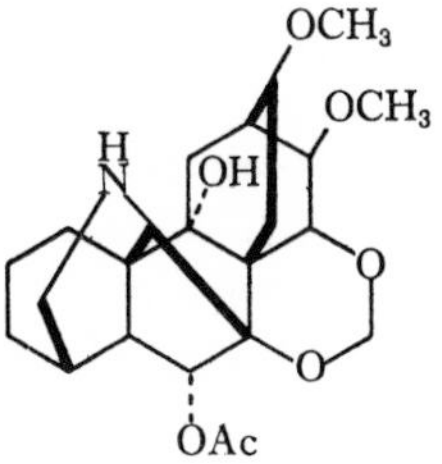

OCH₃

OCH₃

[34] 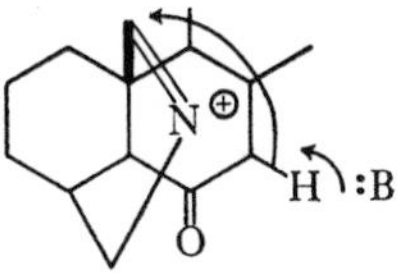   [35] 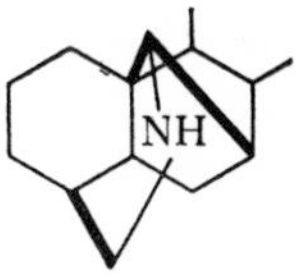   [36]

The absolute stereochemistry of the delphinium alkaloids [47] bears a resemblance to that of some of the diterpenes discussed earlier; all these substances share a common A/B stereochemistry that is enantiomorphic to that usually seen. A detailed discussion of various aspects of the stereochemistry and biogenesis of these alkaloids has been presented.[41]

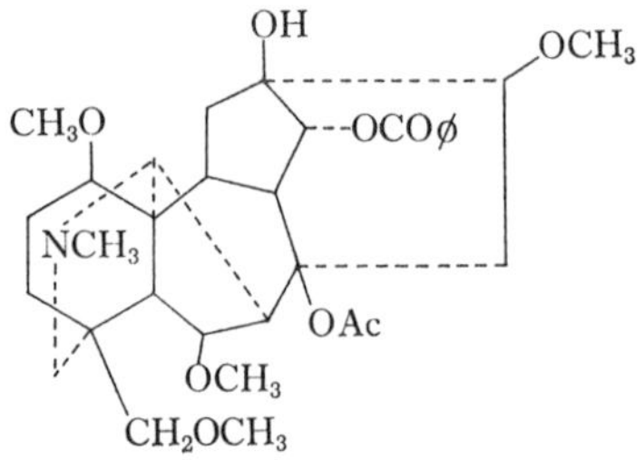

[37]

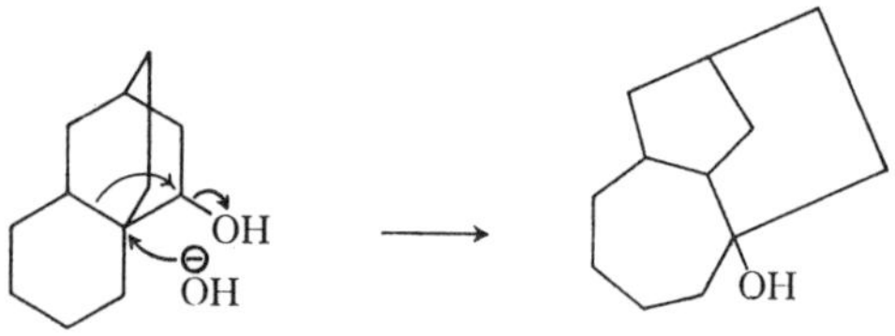

(9-4)

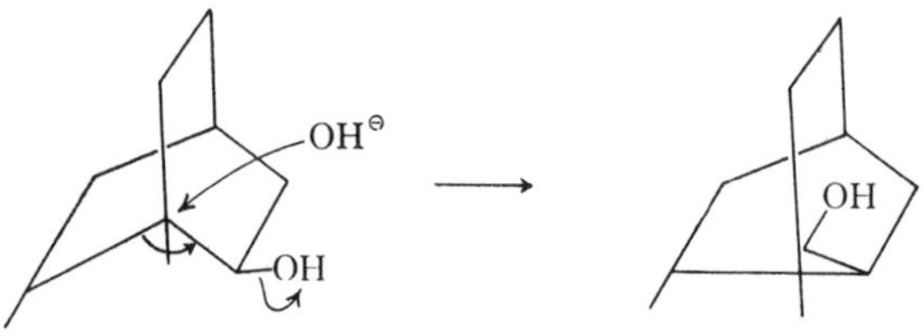

[38]   [39]

The feeding of 2-C^{14}-mevalonate to young plants of *Delphinium elatum* led[52b] to the isolation of labeled plant sterols. However the delphiline **[39b]** was devoid of activity and evidence of delphinine synthesis was provided in two ways: assays of the delphiline content of plants at the same stage of growth showed a marked increase with time and L-methionine labeled with C^{14} in the methyl group was incorporated into the delphiline, 88 per cent being located in the methoxyl group and 11 per cent in the N-ethyl group.

52b. E. J. Herbert and G. W. Kirby, *Tetrahedron Letters*, **1963**, 1505.

If one accepts that delphiline is, indeed, of isoprenoid origin, this negative result indicates that the added mevalonate is not in equilibrium with the mevalonate pool from which the delphiline is being synthesized, an interpretation which, though requiring caution, is by no means unprecedented.

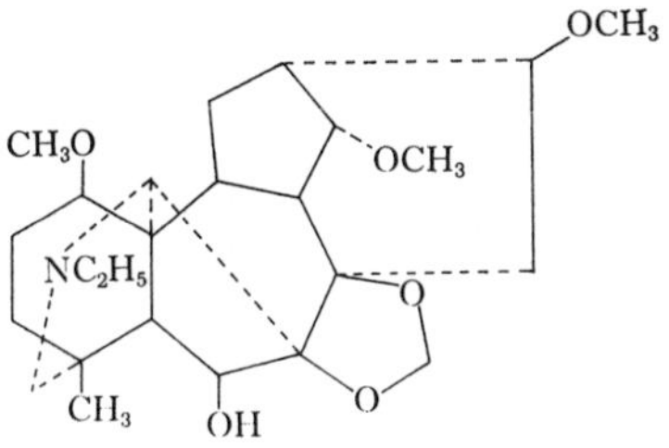

[39b]

These diterpenoid alkaloids thus provide an impressive example of the manifold variations which nature can produce on a single underlying theme.

9–8   EXPERIMENTAL BIOSYNTHETIC RESULTS

Rosenonolactone and Gibberellic Acid

The experimental justification for the previous discussion rests, in addition to strong analogy to triterpene biosynthesis, on experiments on the biosynthesis of the interesting diterpenes rosenonolactone [40] [53,54] and gibberellic acid [41]. [55–58]   Both possess modified diterpene backbones, rosenonolactone resulting from a rearrangement of the type encountered with columbin, and gibberellic acid having a contracted ring B with an appended carboxyl group.   Another noteworthy feature of gibberellic acid is the loss of one of the angular methyl groups

53. A. Harris, A. Robertson, and W. B. Whalley, *J. Chem. Soc.*, **1958**, 1799.
54. B. Green, A. Harris, W. B. Whalley, and H. Smith, *Chem. & Ind.* (*London*), **1958**, 1369.   A. J. Birch, R. W. Rickards, H. Smith, A. Harris, and W. B. Whalley, *Proc. Chem. Soc.*, **1958**, 223.
55. G. Stork and H. Newman, *J. Am. Chem. Soc.*, **81**, 5518 (1959).
56. B. E. Cross, J. F. Grove, P. McCloskey, and C. P. Mulholland, *Chem. & Ind.* (*London*), **1959**, 1345.
57. O. E. Edwards, A. Nicolson, J. W. Apsimon, and W. B. Whalley, *Chem. & Ind.* (*London*), **1960**, 624.
58. B. F. McCapra, A. I. Scott, G. A. Sim, and D. W. Young, *Proc. Chem. Soc.*, **1962**, 185.

(between rings A and B)—the result of a demethylation analogous to that which occurs in the conversion of lanosterol to cholesterol.

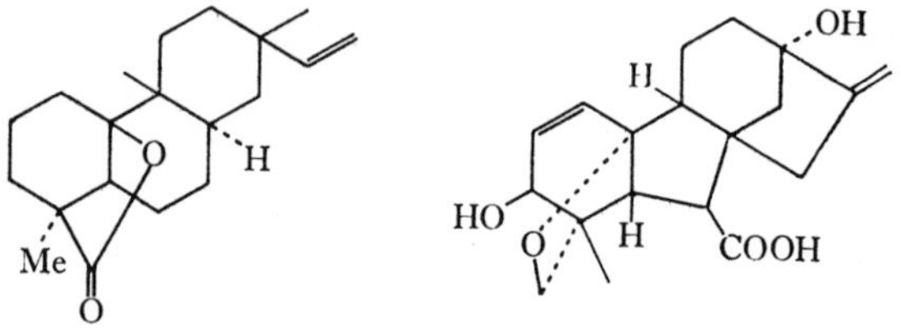

[40]   [41]

In independent studies of the biosynthesis of rosenonolactone by *Trichothecium roseum* Link, English[59] and Swiss[60] groups studied the incorporation of 1-C^{14}-acetate and 2-C^{14}-MVA, and in those positions examined found the pattern of labeling to be exactly that expected, i.e., [42].

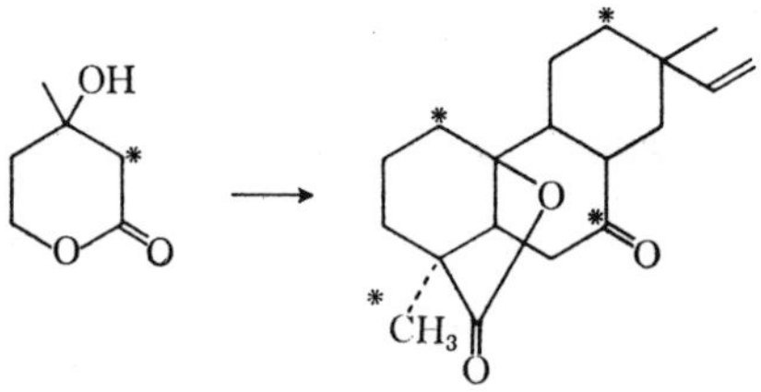

[42]

An item of especial interest is the observation that there has been no randomization of label among the two carbons that were at one time the gem-dimethyl group in the geranyl-geraniol chain, and now appear as the two substituents on ring A. An analogous result is encountered in soyasapogenol. In both cases the label from 2-C^{14}-mevalonate is found in the α, equatorial, nonoxidized substituent.

In the case of gibberellic acid, Birch[59,61] again studied the incorporation of 1-C^{14}-acetate and 2-C^{14}-mevalonate. With 1-C^{14}-acetate as substrate, the expected pattern of labeling was observed. With 2-C^{14}-mevalonate as substrate, the lactonic carboxyl of ring A

59. A. J. Birch, R. W. Rickards, H. Smith, A. Harris, and W. B. Whalley, *Tetrahedron*, **7**, 241 (1959).
60. J. J. Britt and D. Arigoni, *Proc. Chem. Soc.*, **1958**, 224.
61. A. J. Birch, R. W. Rickards, and H. Smith, *Proc. Chem. Soc.*, **1958**, 192.

was unlabeled—as in rosenonolactone and soyasapogenol—and the carboxyl group appended to ring B was labeled (cf. **[43]**).   The sites of labeling in rings C and D confirm the postulated biogenetic origin for this part of diterpenoids with skeletons of the phyllocladene type. Thus the experimental results presently at hand are in complete accord with the postulated mechanisms for diterpene biogenesis.

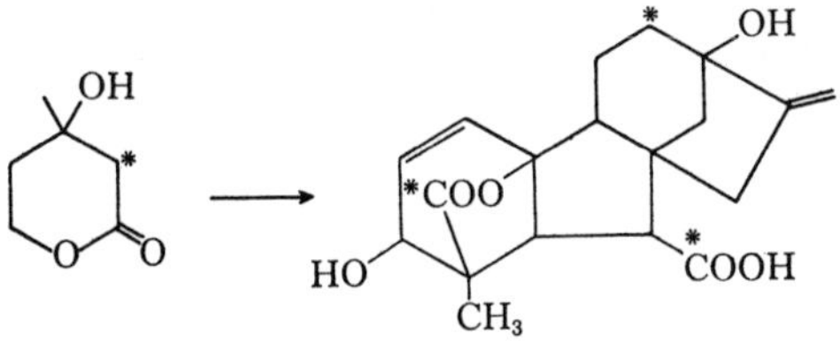

[43]

Pleuromutilin

An elegant case involving the use of tracer experiments, not just to study the biosynthesis of a natural product but even to aid in structural

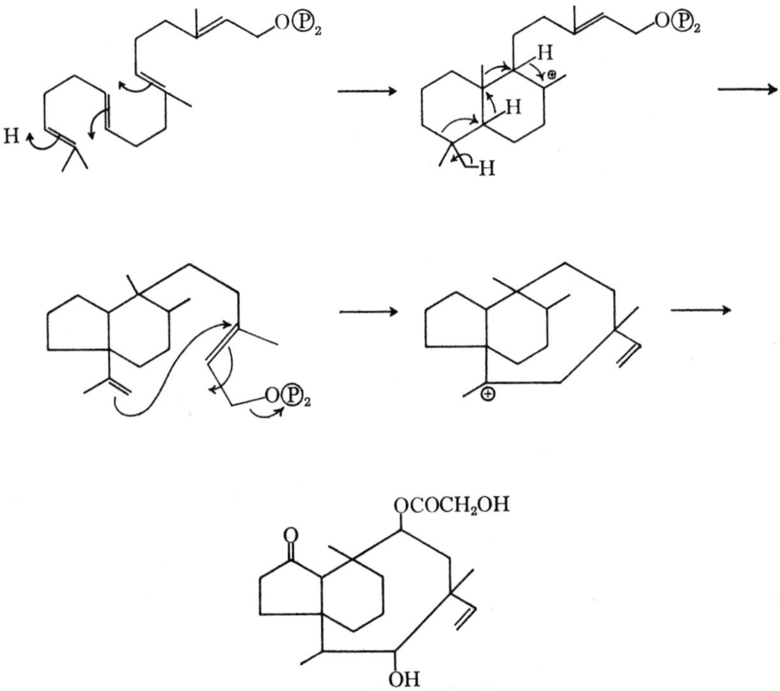

[44]

elucidation, is provided by investigations on pleuromutilin [44].[62-64] This substance was shown to have the indicated structure, and the experiments with labeled precursors were consonant with the hitherto completely unprecedented biosynthetic pathway to this most unusual diterpene.

62. A. J. Birch, *Proc. Chem. Soc.*, **1962**, 3.
63. D. Arigoni, *Gazz. Chim. Ital.*, **92**, 884 (1962).
64. A. J. Birch, D. W. Cameron, C. W. Holzapfel, and R. W. Rickards, *Chem. & Ind.* (*London*), **1963**, 374.

chapter ten | Triterpenes

10–1 PRINCIPLES OF REACTION MECHANISMS

Before we discuss in detail the various theoretical postulates that have been proposed for the genesis of cyclic triterpenes from acyclic precursors, it is well to review briefly the known chemistry of olefin cyclizations. First, it is well known that electrophilic addition to simple olefins proceeds so that the two newly attached groups are in the same plane and *trans* to one another [1]. In some cases, e.g., bromination, there is evidence for a symmetrical intermediate such as [2] in the reaction. This stereoelectronic control is thought to be a consequence of the maximum overlap of π-electrons, which is achieved by an intermediate such as [2]. The *trans* nature of the product is then controlled by the

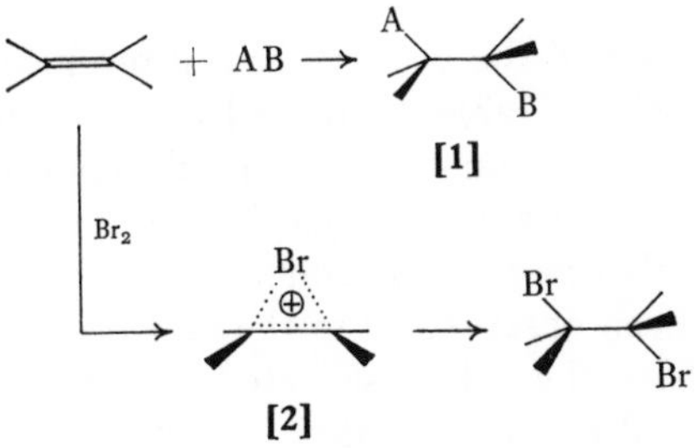

attack of the nucleophile from the opposite side of the molecule to that occupied by the electrophile. Such a *trans* attack results in a minimum of steric interference between the two groups, and the transition state is again one with a maximum overlap of π-electrons. These simple

257

stereoelectronic considerations are of the greatest importance to the following discussion.

If the nucleophile B is another double bond in the same molecule, these fundamental considerations will predict a specific stereochemistry for a cyclization.[1]   Thus a hexadiene will be folded in a potential chair [4] or boat [5] conformation to assure the planar *trans* arrangement of

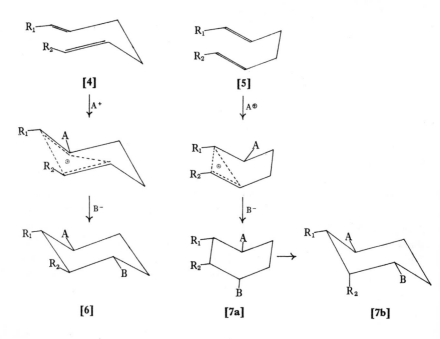

the reacting centers, and the cyclization will produce products such as [6] or [7a] (or [7b] derivable from [7a] by a simple conformational inversion of a boat to a chain cyclohexane) depending on the folding.

Such participation by an internal double bond may well manifest itself in an observable rate enhancement in appropriate systems; such participation has been observed[2,3] in the case of 2-(Δ^3-cyclopentenyl)-ethyl tosylate, where the solvolysis rate[3] of the olefin relative to its saturated analogue 2-cyclopentylethyl tosylate is 1900 in 98 per cent

1. For a more detailed discussion of these points, cf. L. Ruzicka, in Sir A. Todd (ed.), *Perspectives in Organic Chemistry*, Interscience, New York, 1956, p. 265.
2. R. G. Lawton, *J. Am. Chem. Soc.*, **83**, 2399 (1961).
3. P. D. Bartlett and S. Bank, *J. Am. Chem. Soc.*, **83**, 2591 (1961).

formic acid at 60°. This case is slightly special in that the participation gives rise to the norbornyl carbonium ion, and the product is a mixture of the resulting alcohol and its ester [Eq. (10–1)].

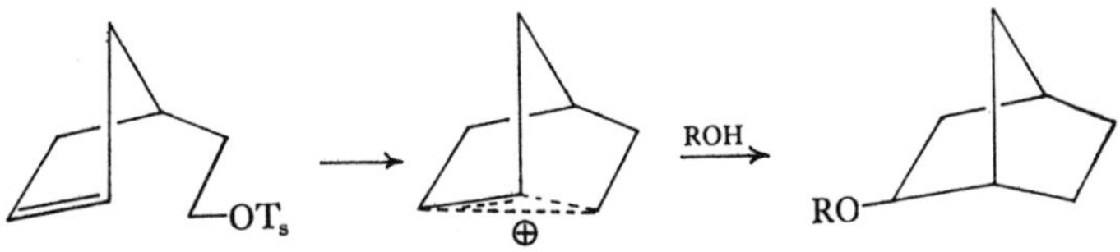

$$(10–1)$$

Moreover, one expects the Wagner-Meerwein-type migrations and other similar rearrangement processes to occur with stereoelectronic control. Thus a process in which a bridged carbonium ion of the type [8] rearranges, so that one of the groups originally attached to the olefin is now bridging, will be expected to proceed stereospecifically, e.g., [8] → [9]. Last, in any concerted series of migrations, one will expect

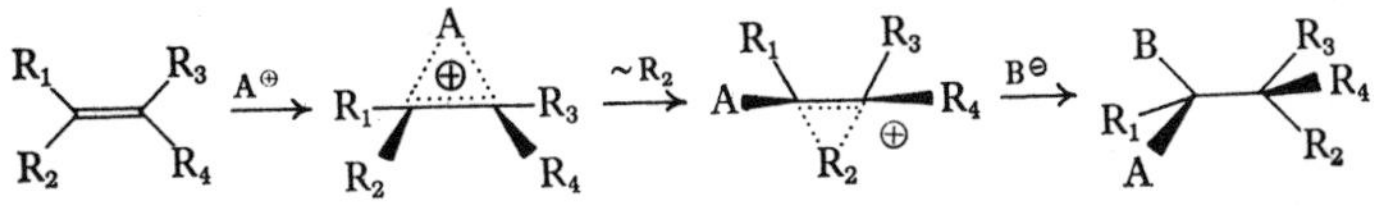

the migrating groups to be coplanar and sequentially *trans*, e.g., [10] → [11].

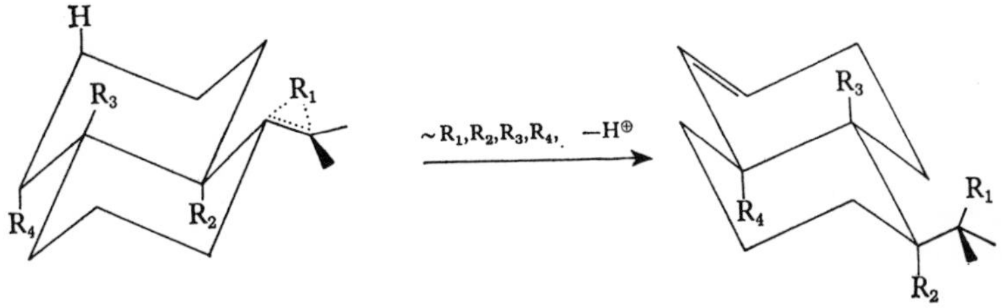

10-2 OLEFIN CYCLIZATIONS

Although by no means all attempts to reproduce such highly stereospecific cyclizations under purely chemical conditions in high yields have been successful,[4] the cyclizations [5,6] of the two stereoisomeric *cis*- and *trans*-apogeranic acids [12] and [13] lead to the expected products [14] and [15], respectively.   It is important to note in this case

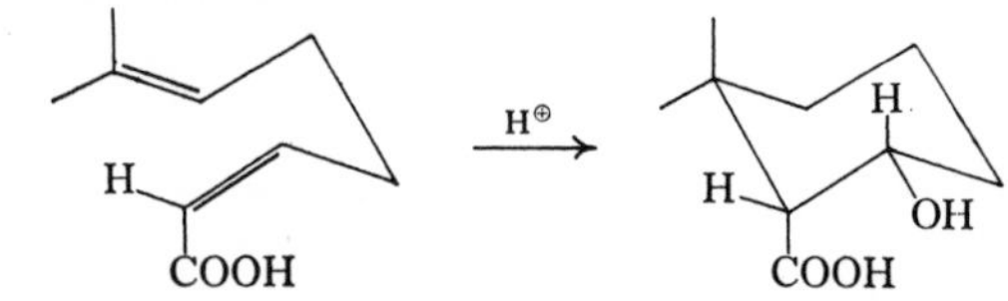

[12]   H⊕ →   [14]

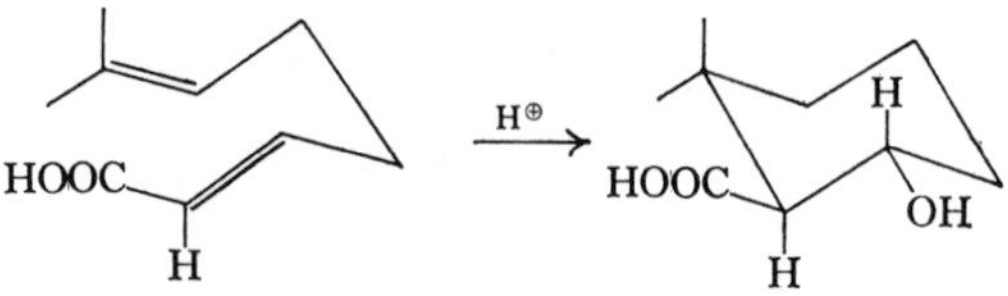

[13]   H⊕ →   [15]

that the only steric control demanded by this system is a classical *trans* addition to the final double bond.

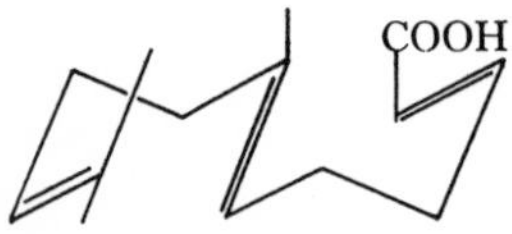

[16] 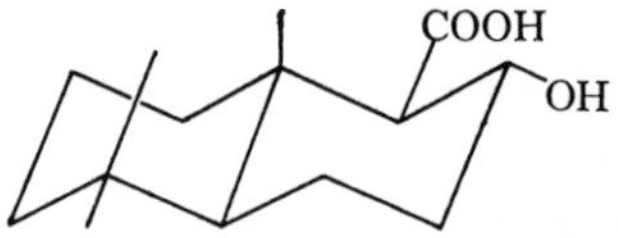   [17]

$$H_2SO_4, \quad HCOOH$$

[18] 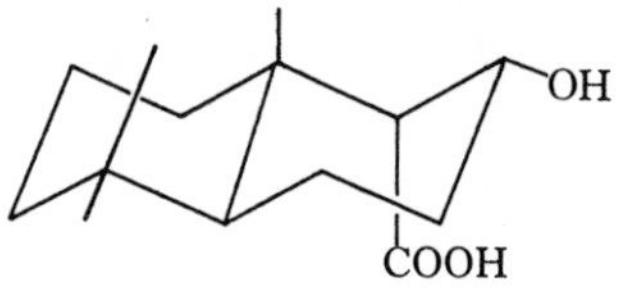   [19]

4. G. Stork and A. W. Burgstahler, *J. Am. Chem. Soc.*, **77**, 5068 (1955).
5. G. Gamboni, H. Schinz, and A. Eschenmoser, *Helv. Chim. Acta*, **37**, 964 (1954).
6. R. Helg and H. Schinz, *Helv. Chim. Acta*, **35**, 2406 (1952).

Another case [7] in which the steric result is that theoretically expected is the cyclization of *nor*farnesenic esters with *cis* and *trans* terminal double bonds ([16] → [17], [18] → [19]). The stereochemical consequences pertinent to the geometry of the central double bond have also been examined by studying the cyclization of the isomers, [20], and [21].

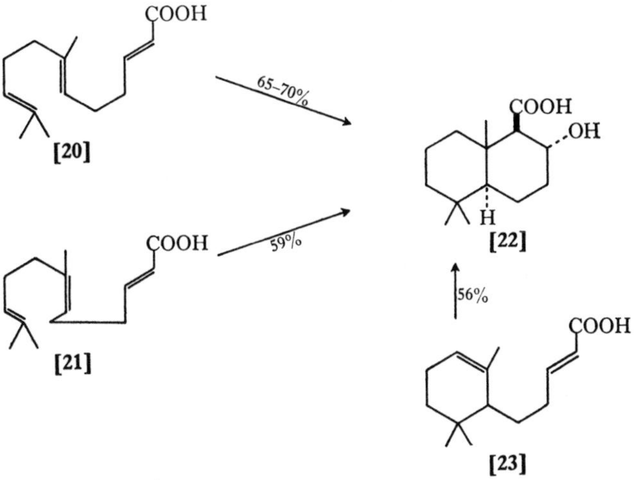

In this case the same product [22] was obtained in nearly equal yield from either isomer; moreover the same product resulted from the monocyclic diolefin [23] as well.[8] In all cases the reaction conditions were identical. These results thus demand the existence of intermediates that can undergo conformational changes leading to the formation of the thermodynamically stable *trans*-decalin ring system.

A recent study [9] on the acid-catalyzed cyclization of *trans,trans*-2,6-octadiene [24] and *cis,cis*-2,6-octadiene [25] in mixtures of deuterated formic and sulfuric acids has defined the stereochemistry at all four of the carbons that change from sp^2 to sp^3 hybridization during the cyclization reaction. The cyclization of the *trans,trans*-olefin leads to a single homogeneous cyclohexyl product [26] (less than 0.1 per cent impurity), whose stereochemistry is at all centers that expected for a

7. P. A. Stadler, A. Nechvatal, A. J. Frey, and A. Eschenmoser, *Helv. Chim. Acta*, **40**, 1373 (1957).
8. A. Eschenmoser in *The Biosynthesis of Terpenes and Sterols*, Little, Brown, Boston, 1900, p. 217.
9. H. Ulery, Thesis, California Institute of Technology, 1963.

sterically controlled process.   The *cis,cis*-olefin yields a cyclohexyl product whose main component **[27]** exhibits steric control at three of the four centers; this suggests interaction of the electrophile and the two double bonds leading to a carbonium ion **[29]**, which lives long enough to undergo inversion and acquisition of a nucleophile from the

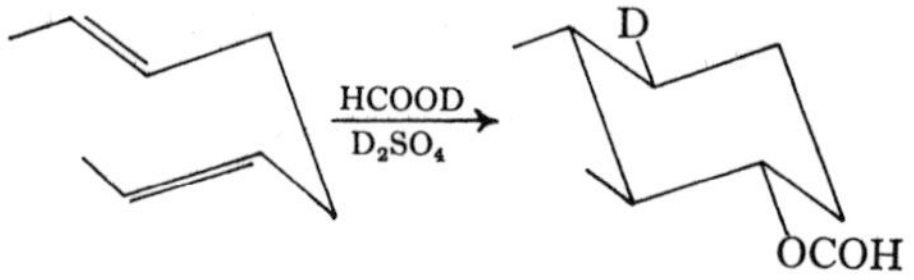

[24]

[26]

37–40%

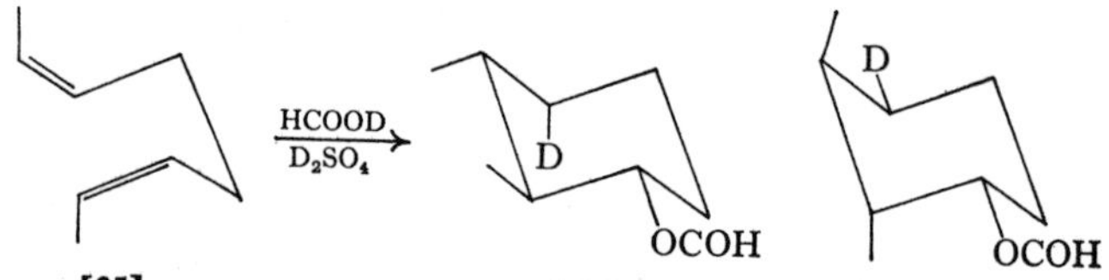

[25]

[27]

10%

[28]

1%

preferred equatorial direction.   That product formed in small yield **[28]** (1 per cent) arises from interception of this cation before conformational inversion can occur and is the result of a process that manifests steric control at all four rehybridized centers.[9]

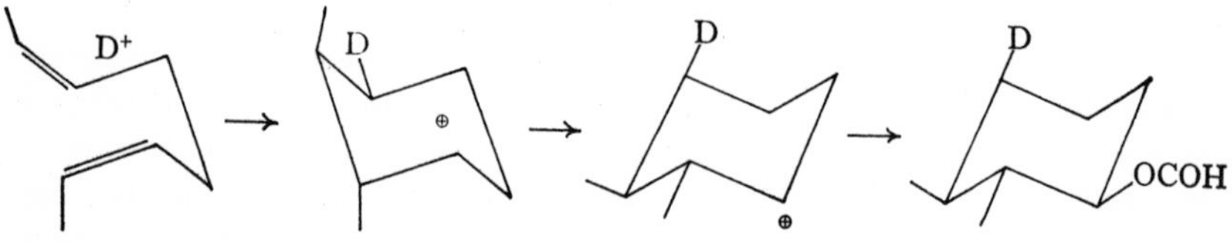

[29]

[27]

Johnson has reported some interesting work on model cyclizations that are initiated by ionization of a *p*-nitrobenzenesulfonate ester to produce a carbonium ion which, in turn, may initiate the cyclization of polyolefins.[9b]

9b. W. S. Johnson, *Pure Appl. Chem.*, **7**, 317 (1963).

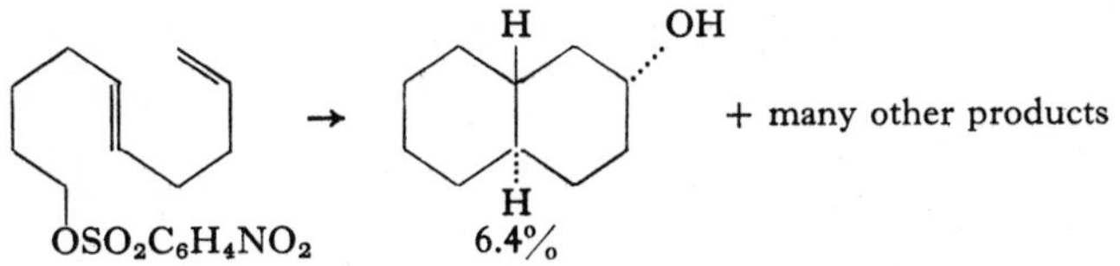

$OSO_2C_6H_4NO_2$ 6.4%   + many other products

These results of model cyclizations of polyolefins show, in a few selected cases, a type of steric control expected on the basis of *trans-*, planar, concerted additions to interacting olefinic linkages. Products that are the result of such control are, however, formed in very much less than quantitative yield—particularly when the products do not possess the thermodynamically stable configuration. These reactions thus exhibit a caprice quite unlike the controlled specificity found in biochemical processes, which fact serves to emphasize anew the crucial role the cyclizing enzyme plays in orienting the polyolefin chain in just that requisite configuration appropriate to the production of the particular terpene desired by the biological system in question.

10-3 TRITERPENE REARRANGEMENTS

The conversion [10,11] of euphenol **[30]** into *iso*euphenol **[31]** and a similar rearrangement [12-14] of Δ^3-friedelin **[32]** to $\Delta^{13(18)}$-oleanene **[33]** provide two particularly germane examples of Wagner-Meerwein rearrangement about the backbone of the triterpene molecule.

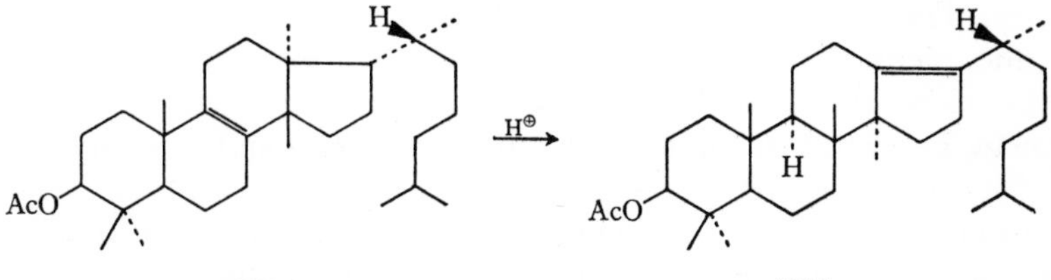

[30]   **[31]**

10. D. Arigoni, R. Viterbo, M. Dünnenberger, O. Jeger, and L. Ruzicka, *Helv. Chim. Acta*, **37**, 2306 (1954).
11. D. H. R. Barton, J. F. McGhie, M. K. Pradhan, and S. A. Knight, *Chem. & Ind. (London)*, **1954**, 1325.
12. G. Brownlie, F. S. Spring, R. Stevenson, and W. S. Strachan, *Chem. & Ind. (London)*, **1955**, 686, 1156.
13. E. J. Corey and J. J. Ursprung, *J. Am. Chem. Soc.*, **77**, 3667 (1955).
14. H. Dutler, O. Jeger, and L. Ruzicka, *Helv. Chim. Acta*, **38**, 1268 (1955).

[32]   [33]

10–4 THEORETICAL POSTULATES

The clear demonstration that squalene is a precursor of lanosterol which gives rise to cholesterol is a tempting basis for the assumption that all triterpenes are similarly derived from this acyclic precursor. A brilliant theoretical model of triterpene biogenesis, which rests on the assumption that triterpenes are derived from all-*trans* squalene by a series of concerted cyclization and rearrangement reactions, has been constructed by the Zürich school.[1,15,16]

The following rules, based on the theoretical arguments just presented, are prescribed for these processes:

1. The cyclizations proceed from an all *trans*-squalene.

2. For each cyclization, the squalene chain is specifically oriented by being folded into a series of potential chair or boat cyclohexane rings. This specific folding is assumed to be caused by the cyclization enzyme system (e.g., squalene oxidocyclase for lanosterol synthesis).

3. The cyclizations proceed by a sequence of planar *trans* additions to the olefin bonds. Wagner-Meerwein rearrangements and 1,2-eliminations are allowed only under optimal stereoelectronic circumstances, i.e., when the appropriate groups are *trans* and co-planar.

4. All transformations between squalene and the final product occur in a nonstop sequence, i.e., without the intervention of any stabilized intermediate formed by proton loss or nucleophile addition.

Aside from the aesthetic appeal of these rules, there is a modest amount of experimental evidence available that is compatible with these rules but does not demand them. Thus squalene of biological origin is known to have an all-*trans* stereochemistry; *trans*-squalene is an efficient and apparently obligatory precursor of lanosterol; lanosterol formed from

15. L. Ruzicka, *Experientia*, **9**, 357 (1953).
16. A. Eschenmoser, L. Ruzicka, O. Jeger, and D. Arigoni, *Helv. Chim. Acta*, **38**, 1890 (1955).

squalene in a medium of deuterium oxide has incorporated no deuterium; the rearrangement of methyl groups in the squalene to lanosterol cyclization occurs by two successive 1,2-migrations; so far no intermediate between squalene and lanosterol has been isolated. Therefore, as a working hypothesis, these simple rules have much in their favor, although it is entirely possible that the future will show biochemical reality not to be subject to such facile intellectual regimentation. Certain possible minor perturbations on this simplest hypothesis are discussed in connection with the cyclization of squalene to lanosterol.

The various modes of cyclization and examples of the derived natural products can be summarized as follows (the terms refer to the folding of the five segments of the squalene chain into nascent boat or chair rings):

A. Chair–chair–unfolded–unfolded–chair
   e.g., ambrein [16]
B. Chair–chair–unfolded–chair–chair
   e.g., onocerin
C. Chair–chair–chair–boat–unfolded
   e.g., dammarendiol, euphol, tirucallol
D. Chair–chair–chair–boat–boat
   e.g., lupeol, taraxasterol, α-amyrin,[17] germanicol, β-amyrin, taraxerol, glutenone,[18–21] friedelin[22–24]
E. Chair–boat–chair–boat–unfolded
   lanosterol, cycloartenol [25]
F. Chair–chair–chair–chair–chair
   hydroxyhopenone [26–30], davallic acid [30b]

17. E. J. Corey and E. W. Cantrall, *J. Am. Chem. Soc.*, **80**, 499 (1958).
18. S. Chapon and S. David, *Bull. Soc. Chim. France*, **1953**, 333; *Compt. Rend.*, **238**, 1600 (1954).
19. J. M. Beaton, F. S. Spring, and R. Stevenson, *J. Chem. Soc.*, **1955**, 2616.
20. F. S. Spring, J. M. Beaton, R. Stevenson, and J. L. Stewart, *Chem. & Ind. (London)*, **1956**, 1054.
21. J. M. Beaton, F. S. Spring, R. Stevenson, and J. L. Stewart, *Tetrahedron*, 2, 246 (1958).
22. E. J. Corey and J. J. Ursprung, *J. Am. Chem. Soc.*, **78**, 5041 (1956).
23. T. Takahashi and G. Ourisson, *Bull. Soc. Chim. France*, **1956**, 353.
24. G. Brownlie, F. S. Spring, R. Stevenson, and W. S. Strachan, *J. Chem. Soc.*, **1956**, 2419.
25. D. S. Irvine, J. A. Henry, and F. S. Spring, *J. Chem. Soc.*, **1955**, 1316.
26. J. S. Mills and A. E. A. Werner, *J. Chem. Soc.*, **1955**, 3132.
27. O. Jeger, H. Fazakerley, T. G. Halsall, and E. R. H. Jones, *Proc. Chem. Soc.*, **1957**, 353.

10–5 AMBREIN (CHAIR–CHAIR–UNFOLDED–UNFOLDED–CHAIR)

An interesting aspect of ambrein [34] is that the cyclization is apparently initiated by proton attack and is not oxidative as are the other cyclizations of squalene to be discussed. It is also significant, and

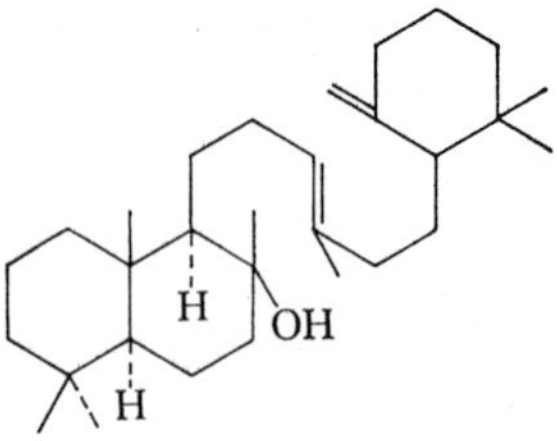

[34]

unusual, that the cyclization begins from both ends of the squalene chain, leaving the potential rings in the central part of the molecule unclosed.

10–6 ONOCERIN (CHAIR–CHAIR–UNFOLDED–CHAIR–CHAIR)

Onocerin [35] presents a case very like ambrein in that cyclization proceeds from both ends of the squalene chain to produce a substance whose two halves are superimposable. In this case the cyclization is initiated by an oxidizing species.

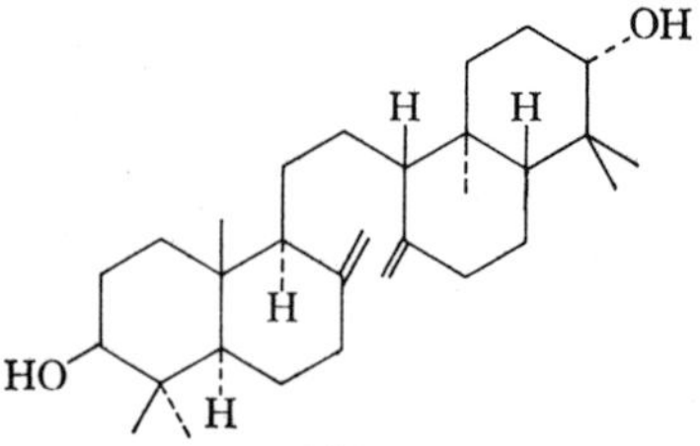

[35]

28. H. Fazakerley, T. G. Halsall, and E. R. H. Jones, *J. Chem. Soc.*, **1959**, 1877.
29. K. Schaffner, E. Gaglioti, D. Arigoni, and O. Jeger, *Helv. Chim. Acta*, **41**, 152 (1958).
30. G. V. Baddeley, T. G. Halsall, and E. R. H. Jones, *J. Chem. Soc.*, **1960**, 1715.
30b. K. Nakanishi, Y. Lin, H. Kakisawa, H. Hsü, and H. C. Hsiu, *Tetrahedron Letters*, **1963**, 1451.

10–7 TETRACYCLIC TRITERPENES
(CHAIR–CHAIR–CHAIR–BOAT–UNFOLDED)

Cyclization of a squalene chain oriented chair–chair–chair–boat–unfolded [36] will lead to an intermediate [37] that can directly acquire a nucleophile and produce a dammarenediol [38]. On the other hand, the intermediate [37] can rearrange by hydride migration to another intermediate [39] or by migration of the C-16 methylene carbon to still another intermediate [40]. The path from [39] can lead by an appropriate series of Wagner-Meerwein rearrangements, followed by proton loss, to euphol [41]. If the other intermediate [40] undergoes a hydride migration to [42], followed by a series of rearrangements, tirucallol [43] results. It is readily seen that all these rearrangements involve groups moving sequentially *trans* to one another. A point of particular interest is that the sequence [36] → [40] → [42] has as its objective the production of a stereochemistry at C-21 in tirucallol, which is epimeric to that at C-21 in euphol. Loss of the nucleophile from dammarenediol concerted with the appropriate subsequent rearrangements would also serve as an acceptable biogenetic mechanism for tirucallol except for the simplifying (but not necessarily true) assumption that all transformations from squalene to the final products shall occur in a nonstop fashion.

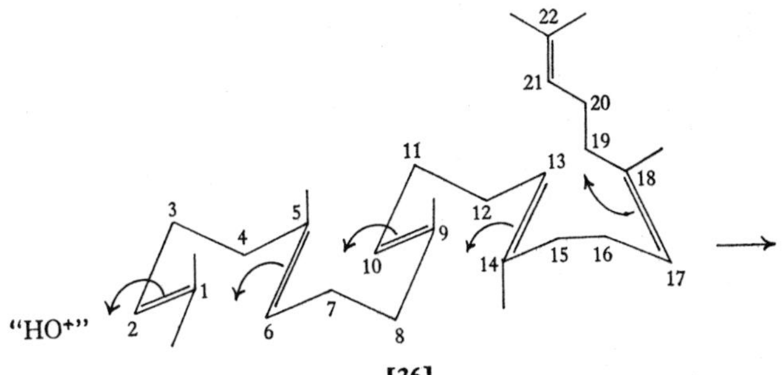

[36]

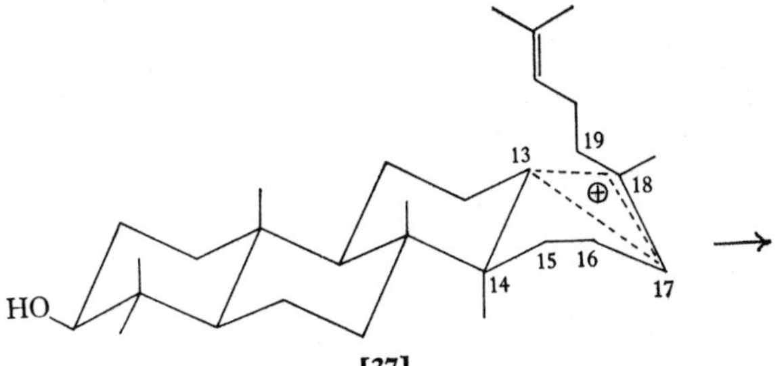

[37]

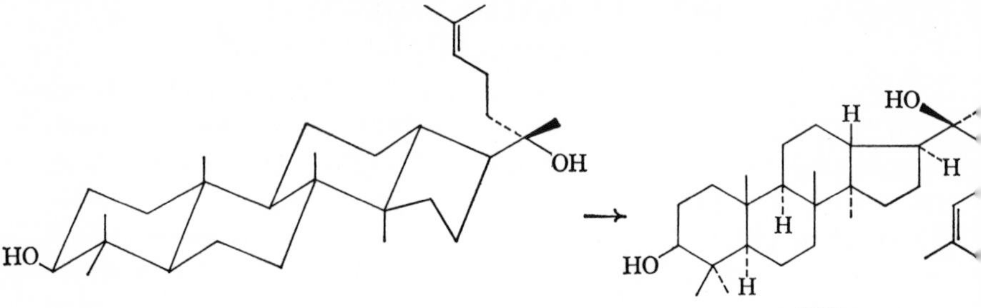

[38]

Dammarenediol

10–8 PENTACYCLIC TRITERPENES
(CHAIR–CHAIR–CHAIR–BOAT–CHAIR)

The entry into the pentacyclic triterpene area is achieved not by an uninterrupted cyclization sequence but by a process that proceeds from **[36]** to the intermediate **[37]**.   This intermediate pauses for reorganization by migration of the C-16 methylene group to **[40]** (as above), and then continues along the pathway to pentacyclic products by further cyclization.   The migrations during the pause at the tetracyclic stage result in a rearrangement of the carbon backbone of squalene such that C-16 is now joined to C-18 and not to C-17 in the pentacyclic triterpenes. (Hydroxyhopenone is an exception to this generalization.) This skeletal rearrangement is demonstrated in two dimensions by Eq. (10–1).

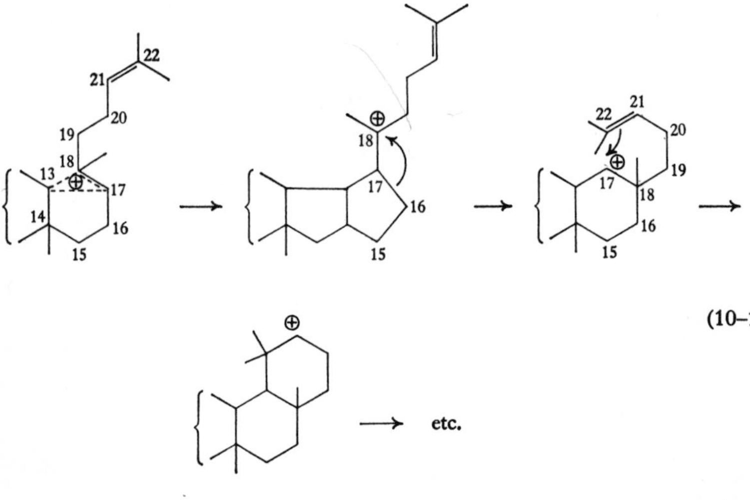

(10–1)

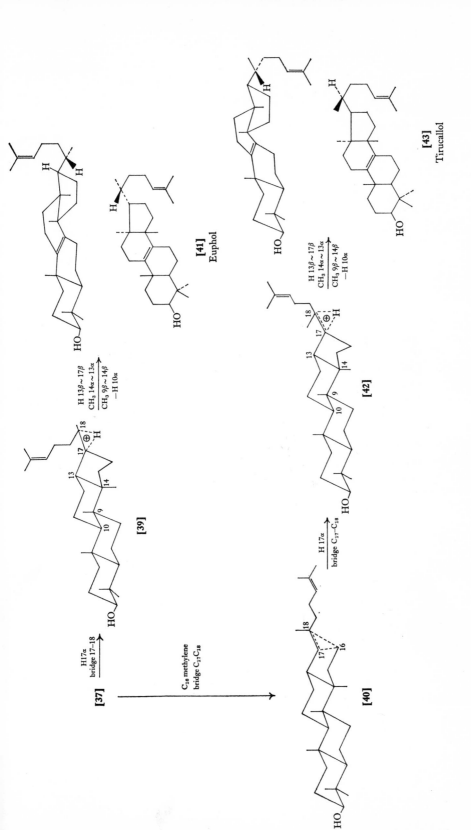

[41]
Euphol

[43]
Tirucallol

H 13β∼17β
CH₃ 14α∼13α
───────────→
CH₃ 9β∼14β
−H 10α

[42]

H 13β∼17β
CH₃ 14α∼13α
───────────→
CH₃ 9β∼14β
−H 10α

[39]

H 17α
───────→
bridge C₁₇–C₁₈

[40]

H 17α
───────→
bridge 17–18

[37]

C₁₈ methylene
bridge C₁₇C₁₈

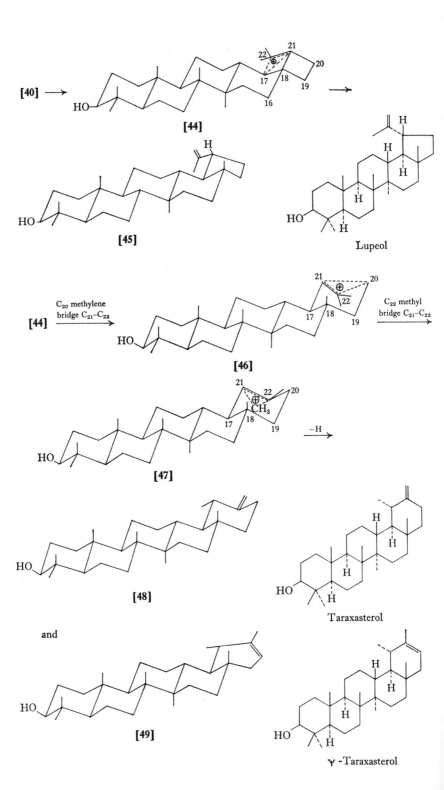

[40] →

[44]

[45]

Lupeol

[44] —C₂₀ methylene bridge C₂₁–C₂₂→ [46] —C₂₂ methyl bridge C₂₁–C₂₂→

[47] —H→

[48]

and

[49]

Taraxasterol

γ-Taraxasterol

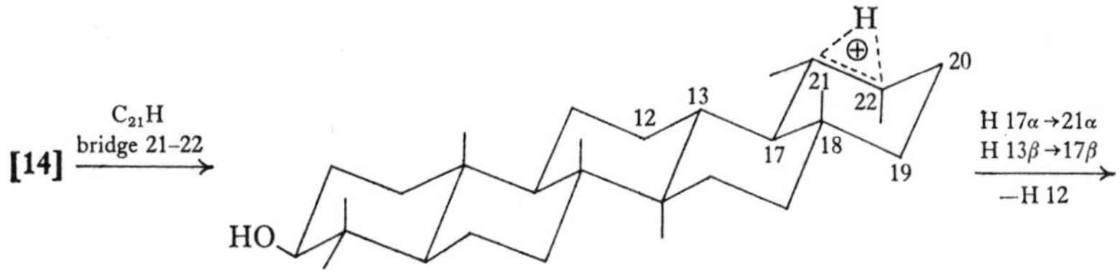

$[14]$ $\xrightarrow{\text{C}_{21}\text{H}\text{ bridge 21–22}}$ [50] $\xrightarrow[\text{$-$H 12}]{\substack{\text{H }17\alpha\to21\alpha\\ \text{H }13\beta\to17\beta}}$

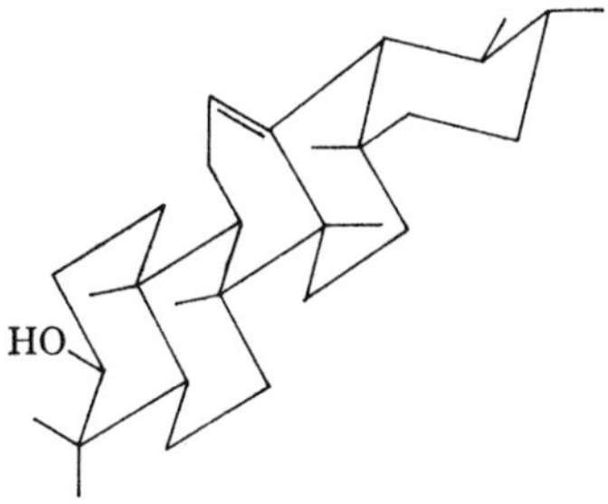

[51] 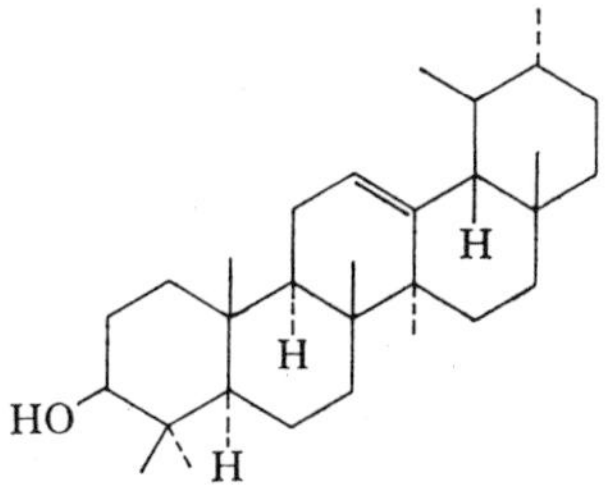   α-Amyrin

If the terminal isoprene unit is folded as a boat, its cyclization onto the tetracyclic nucleus already formed produces an intermediate [44]. Loss of a proton from a methyl group of [44] leads directly to lupeol [45]. On the other hand, a carbon skeleton rearrangement (C-20 methylene migration from C-21 to C-22) will produce a new intermediate [46] (again with a rearrangement of the squalene backbone). From intermediate [46] it is possible to derive all the pentacyclic triterpenes of the reduced picene type.

Thus a methyl group migration from C-22 to C-21 to the intermediate [47] followed by proton loss yields taraxasterol [48] or ψ-taraxasterol [49]. If this migration is followed by a hydride migration (from C-21 to C-22) to yield the intermediate [50] and there then occurs the indicated series of 1,2-shifts, α-amyrin [51] will arise.

The intermediate [46] can serve as the origin for a variety of 1,2-shifts and proton losses. There are examples of natural products that represent stops at many of the possible stations along this path, which leads in the end to friedelin. Thus, from this sequence it is possible to obtain germanicol [52] by a simple proton loss. Migration of hydride and a methyl group gives β-amyrin [53]. A subsequent movement of an additional methyl group yields taraxerol [54]; by a further migration of methyl groups and hydrides glutinone [55] is produced. The final stages of rearrangement are reached with the attainment of friedelin [56]. (The C-3 hydroxyl of a hypothetical precursor of glutinone has apparently been oxidized as an ancillary operation.)

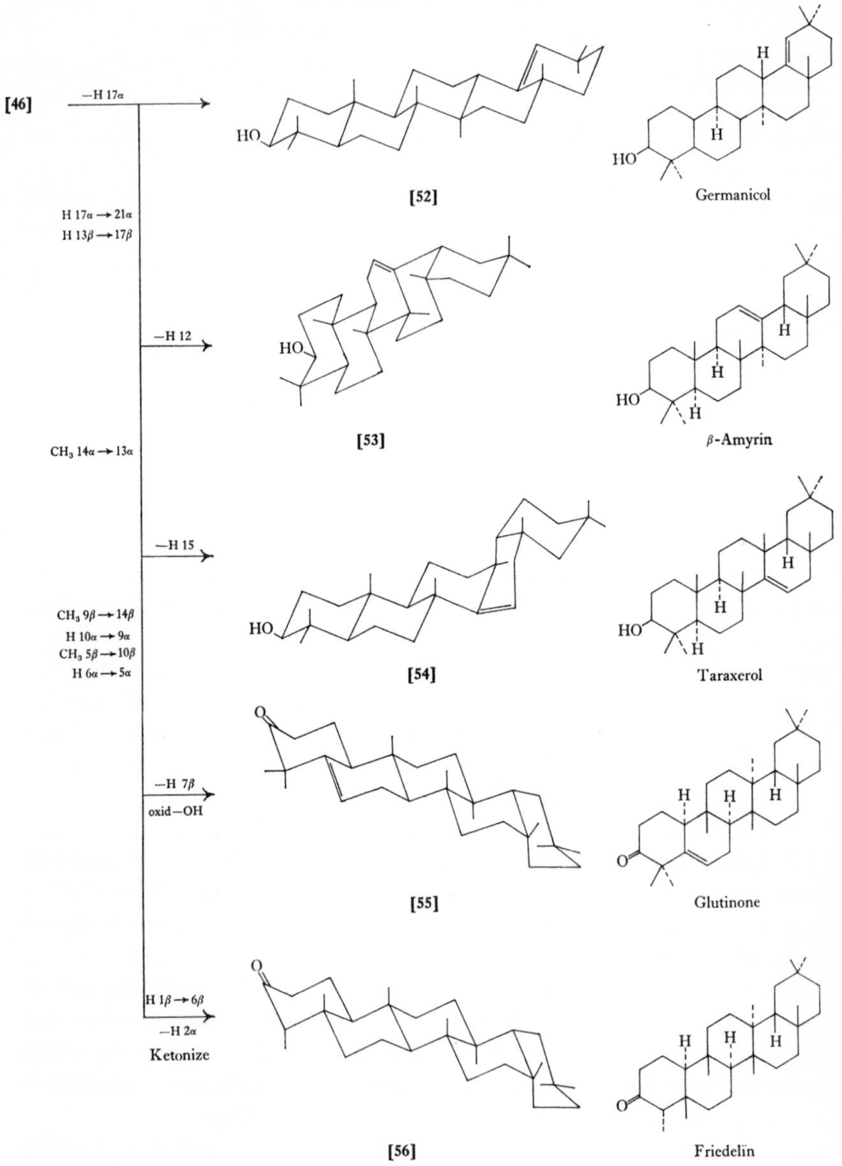

[46]   ---H 17α

[52]   Germanicol

H 17α → 21α
H 13β → 17β

    ---H 12

[53]   β-Amyrin

CH₃ 14α → 13α

    ---H 15

CH₃ 9β → 14β
H 10α → 9α
CH₃ 5β → 10β
H 6α → 5α

[54]   Taraxerol

    ---H 7β
    oxid—OH

[55]   Glutinone

H 1β → 6β
    ---H 2α
    Ketonize

[56]   Friedelin

10-9 LANOSTEROL
(CHAIR–BOAT–CHAIR–BOAT–UNFOLDED)

The cyclization of squalene to lanosterol is of particular interest because of the intermediacy of the latter in the pathway of steroid biogenesis. More than 30 years ago it was suggested,[31] simply on the basis of structural similarities, that squalene is biogenetically related to the steroids. The first evidence that this speculation might, indeed represent biochemical fact came when Channon showed[32] that the feeding of squalene increased the amounts of steroids in rat liver.

Robinson was the first to propose a detailed statement of the relationship between squalene and steroids when he suggested[33] that squalene could produce cholesterol by the type of cyclization shown in Eq. (10–2), with loss of three superfluous methyl groups.

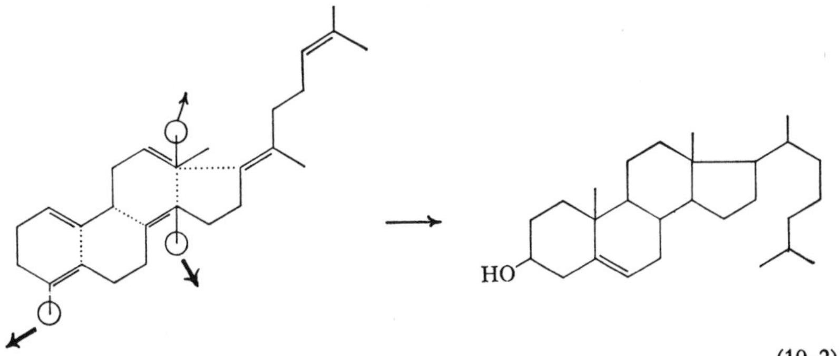

(10–2)

The structural elucidation of lanosterol gave rise to an alternate proposal by Woodward and Bloch[34] and also by Dauben and colleagues[35] that at once rationalized the biogenetic origin of both lanosterol and cholesterol and, further, implicated lanosterol as an intermediate in cholesterol synthesis. The mode of cyclization proposed was that of Eq. (10–3). It will be seen that the two modes of cyclization predict different origins for C-7, C-12, and C-13 of cholesterol from either the carboxyl or methyl carbon of acetate. The distribution of acetate carbons

31. I. M. Heilbron, E. D. Kamm, and W. M. Owens, *J. Chem. Soc.*, **1926**, 1630.
32. H. J. Channon, *Biochem. J.*, **20**, 400 (1926).
33. R. Robinson, *J. Soc. Chem. Ind.*, **53**, 1062 (1934).
34. R. B. Woodward and K. Bloch, *J. Am. Chem. Soc.*, **75**, 2023 (1953).
35. W. G. Dauben, S. Abraham, S. Hotta, I. L. Charkoff, H. L. Bradlow, and A. H. Soloway, *J. Am. Chem. Soc.*, **75**, 3038 (1953).

in the cholesterol skeleton, which is discussed in detail on page 305, is clearly in accord only with the more recent cyclization proposal.   Moreover, the conversions of squalene to lanosterol [36] and of lanosterol to cholesterol [37] have been demonstrated.

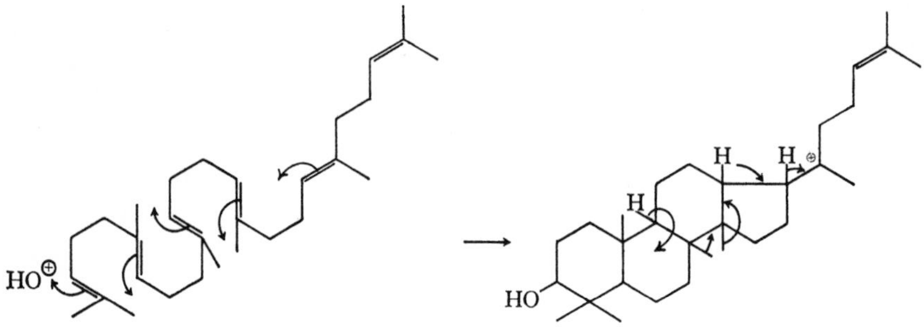

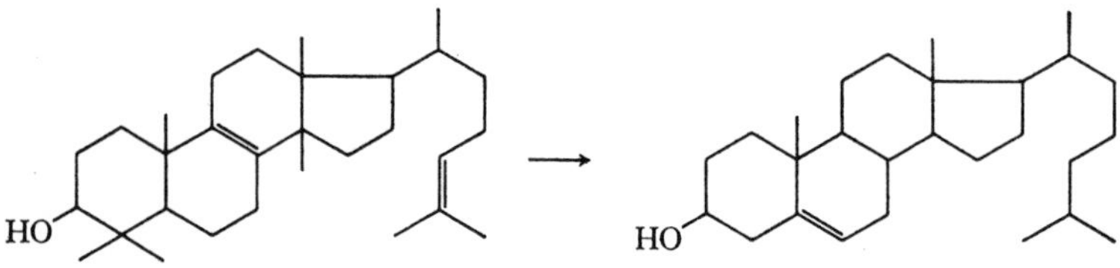

Lanosterol

The production of lanosterol has another significant requirement, that the squalene chain be folded in a different manner from any of those previously discussed; chair–boat–chair–boat.   Cyclization of a chain so folded [57] leads to the ion [58], which by two rearrangements to [59] thence to [60] yields an intermediate properly arranged for a series of migrations and eventual proton loss to furnish lanosterol.

If, instead of being lost from the molecule, the C-10 hydrogen moves to C-9 followed by migration of the C-5 methyl group, which migration is intercepted by loss of a proton from the migrating methyl, cycloartenol [61] results.   An important point about the stereochemistry of cycloartenol is that the migration of the final methyl group occurs on the same side of the molecule as that on which the previous hydrogen has just moved—a situation that contravenes the generalization that the Wagner-Meerwein shifts occur in a sequentially *trans* fashion.   The production of cycloartenol cannot, therefore, be explained without the intervention of some nonbridged intermediate.

36. T. T. Tchen and K. Bloch, *J. Am. Chem. Soc.*, **77**, 6085 (1955).
37. R. B. Clayton and K. Bloch, *J. Biol. Chem.*, **218**, 319 (1956).

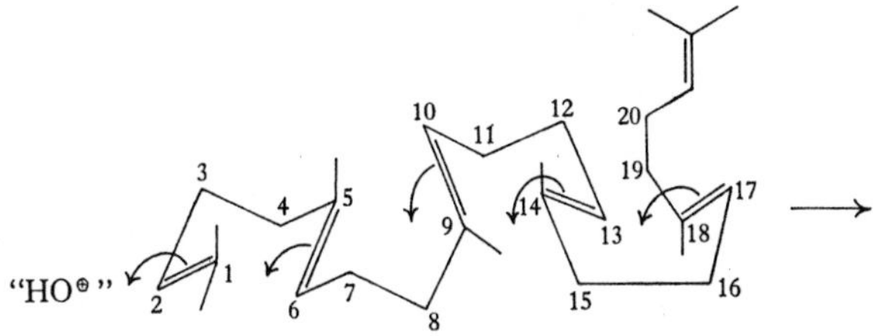
"HO⊕"
1
2
3
4
5
6
7
8
9
10
11
12
13
14
15
16
17
18
19
20

[57]

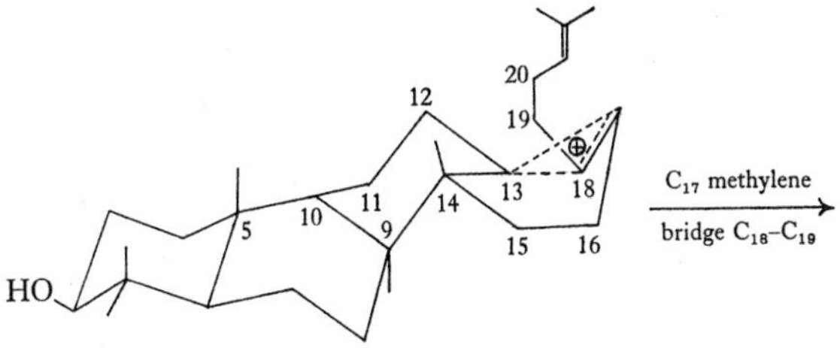
HO
5
9
10
11
12
13
14
15
16
18
19
20
C_{17} methylene
bridge C_{18}–C_{19}

[58]

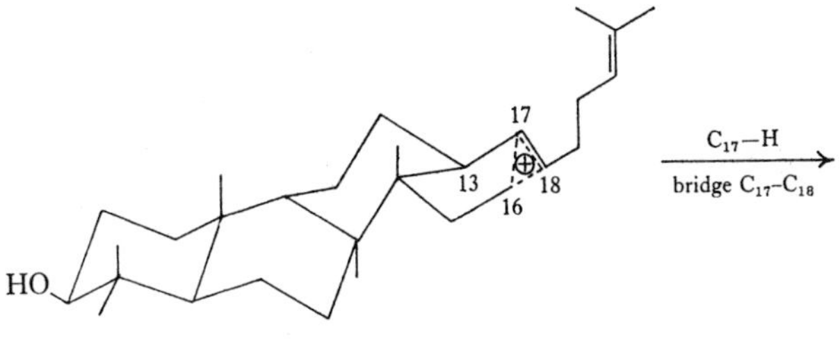
HO
13
16
17
18
C_{17}—H
bridge C_{17}–C_{18}

[59]

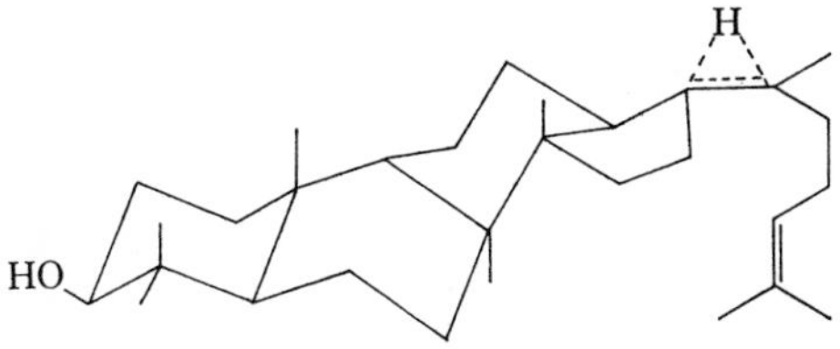
HO
H

[60]

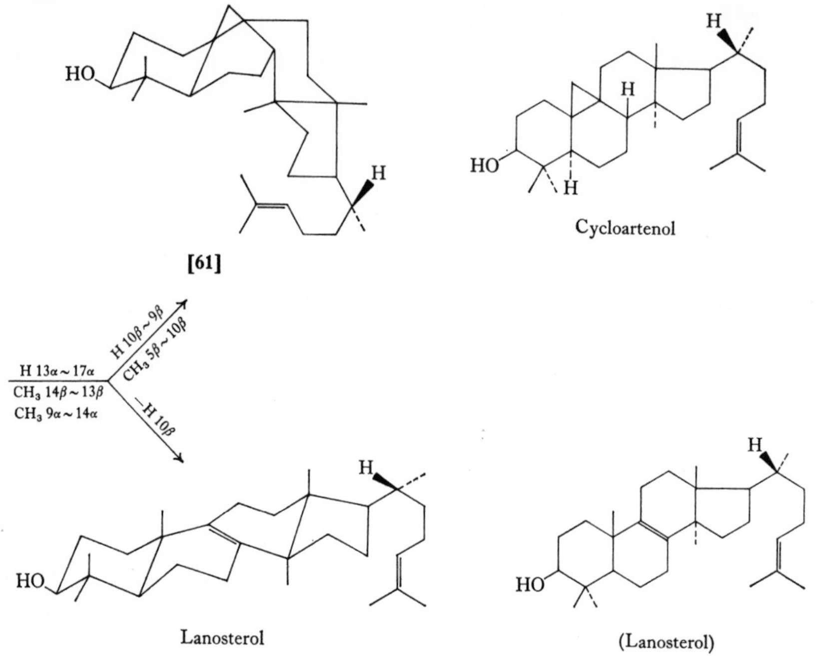
HO
H
[61]
HO
H
H
H
Cycloartenol
H 13α ~ 17α
CH3 14β ~ 13β
CH3 9α ~ 14α
H 10β ~ 9β
CH3 5β ~ 10β
—H 10β
H
HO
Lanosterol
H
HO
(Lanosterol)

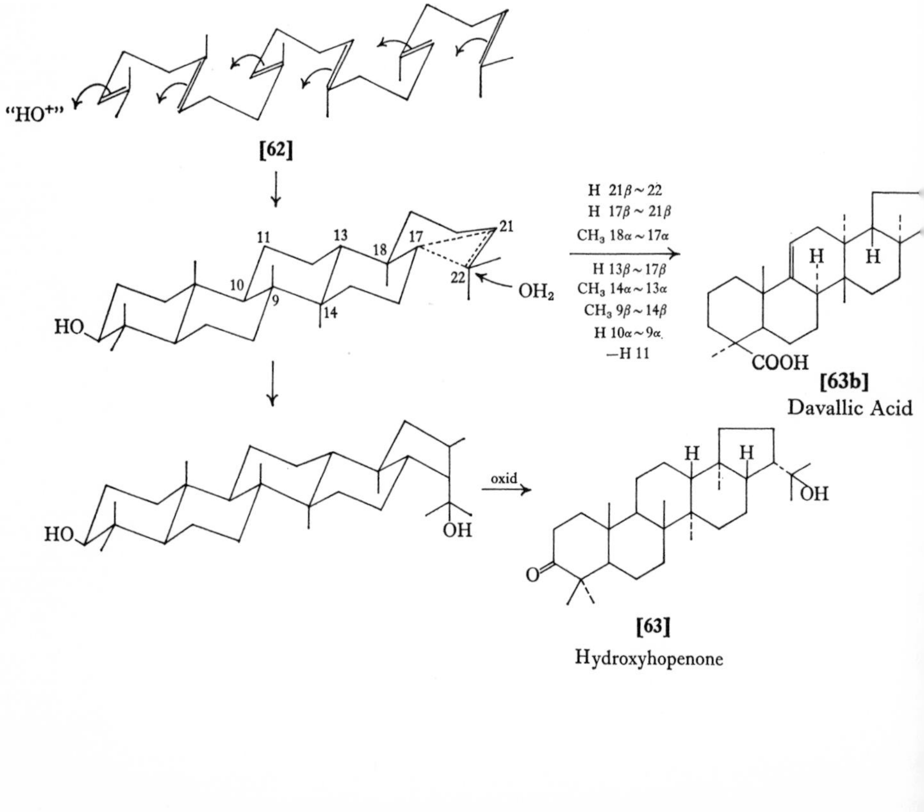
"HO+"
[62]
11
13
18
17
21
10
9
14
22
OH2
HO
H 21β ~ 22
H 17β ~ 21β
CH3 18α ~ 17α
H 13β ~ 17β
CH3 14α ~ 13α
CH3 9β ~ 14β
H 10α ~ 9α
—H 11
H
H
COOH
[63b]
Davallic Acid
HO
OH
oxid
H
H
OH
O
[63]
Hydroxyhopenone

10–10 HYDROXYHOPENONE
(CHAIR–CHAIR–CHAIR–CHAIR–CHAIR)

An unusual triterpene, hydroxyhopenone [63], has recently received attention.   It is particularly interesting as an example of the simplest kind of squalene cyclization, i.e., the cyclization of an all chair-folded chain [62] that terminates by the direct acquisition of a nucleophile.

The result of a sequential series of migrations down the backbone of this all-chair skeleton has recently been encountered in davallic acid [63b].   These migrations demonstrate the appropriate stereo-electronic control and terminate with proton loss from C-11.

10–11 ALTERNATE POSSIBILITIES

Although the general mechanisms just discussed are dramatic in their simplicity and over-all applicability, it is perhaps worthwhile pointing out that other possibilities, which are in a sense modifications of the Ruzicka proposal, do exist.   In the case of lanosterol, for example, the cyclization of an all-*trans* squalene, folded chair–boat–chair–boat as above and which ends by acquisition of a nucleophile, will produce a species that, by rotation about a carbon-carbon single bond followed by a concerted sequence of elimination, rearrangements, and proton loss,

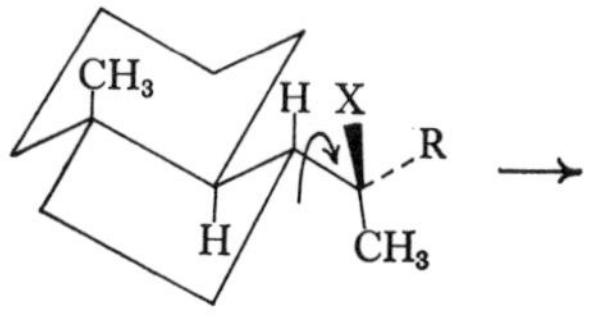

[64]

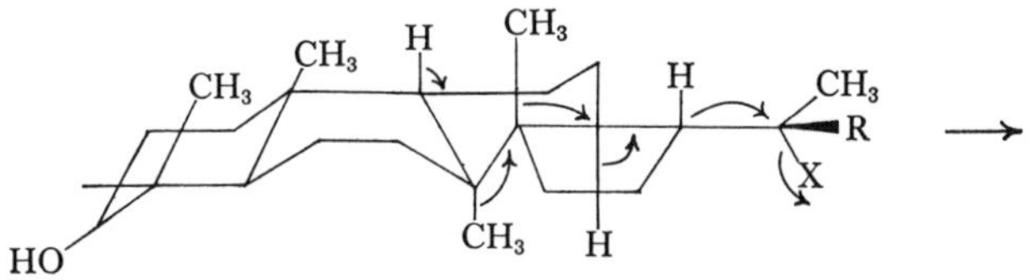

[65]

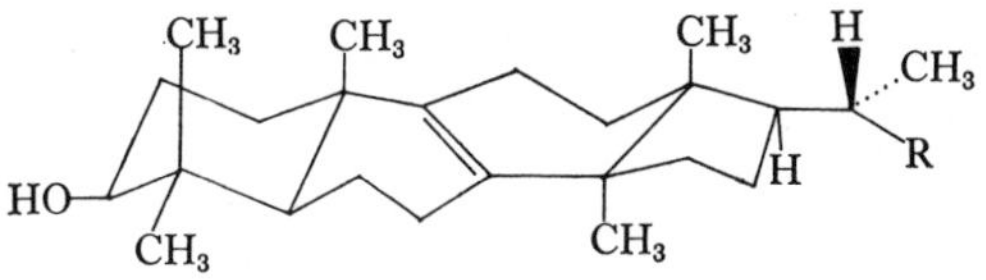

Lanosterol

will also yield lanosterol. Or, one can consider a prior isomerization of one of the squalene double bonds to a *cis* configuration, giving a stereochemically isomeric form of squalene that could also produce lanosterol by an appropriate cyclization. The former of these possibilities is indicated above (**[64]** → **[65]** → etc.).

It is entirely possible that the nucleophile that might be acquired in some of these alternate cyclization mechanisms is bound always to an enzyme surface. The possibility of the existence of these species, which have acquired a nucleophile, is thus not eliminated by the failure so far to isolate intermediates between squalene and lanosterol. The occurrence of them as structural types in nature is demonstrated, for example, by dammarenediol or hydroxyhopenone.

These remarks are not intended to detract from the postulate of a completely concerted cyclization of an all-*trans* squalene but should only emphasize that, although nature is surely aware of the fundamentals of organic chemistry, she may not always choose to follow the routes that appear to us, on paper, to be the most direct and economical.

10–12 MODIFIED TRITERPENES

There are a great many other triterpenes the structures of which represent secondary transformations (such as oxidation) on a presumably performed triterpene skeleton. Examples are cucurbitacin B **[66]** [38,39] and cactus triterpenes,[40] such as machaeric acid **[67]**. Nyctanthic acid

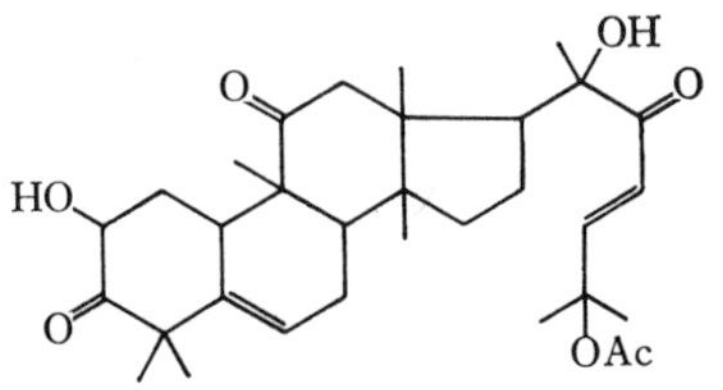

[66] 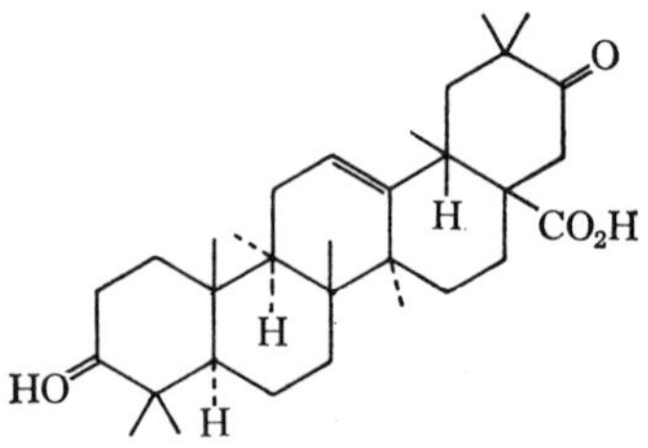   [67]

38. D. Lavie, T. Shvo, D. Willner, P. R. Enslin, J. M. Hugo, and K. B. Norton, *Chem. & Ind. (London)*, **1959**, 951.
39. W. T. deKoch, P. R. Enslin, K. B. Norton, D. H. R. Barton, B. Sklarz, and A. A. Bothner-By, *Tetrahedron Letters*, **1962**, 309.
40. For a review cf. C. Djerassi, *Festschr. Arthur Stoll*, **1957**, 330.

[68] [41–43] is of interest in that it contains the basic β-amyrin carbon skeleton, which has suffered an oxidative opening of ring A.

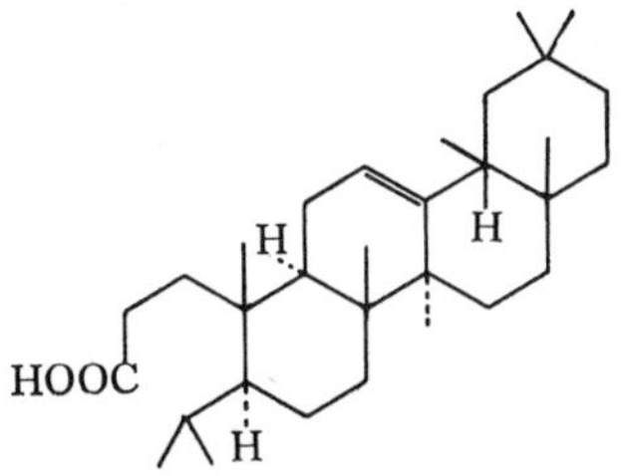

[68]

Nyctanthic Acid

Another interestingly altered triterpene is ceanothic acid [69],[44] a lupeol-type triterpene that has undergone a ring-A contraction analogous to that postulated for the diterpene giberellic acid.

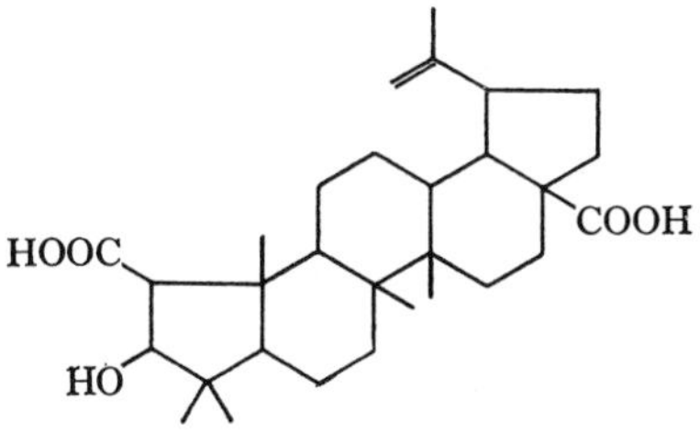

[69]

Since the types of reactions that are responsible for these further transformations are discussed for the conversion of lanosterol to cholesterol and for the further transformations of cholesterol to bile acids, etc., these substances will not be considered in detail. The central point is that, from the simple assumptions outlined earlier, it is possible

41. J. H. Turnbull, S. K. Vasistha, W. Wilson, and R. Woodger, *J. Chem. Soc.*, **1957**, 569.
42. G. H. Whitham, *Proc. Chem. Soc.*, **1959**, 271; *J. Chem. Soc.*, **1960**, 2016.
43. D. Arigoni, D. H. R. Barton, R. Bernasconi, C. Djerassi, J. S. Mills, and R. E. Wolff, *Proc. Chem. Soc.*, **1959**, 306; *J. Chem. Soc.*, **1960**, 1900.
44. P. de Mayo and A. N. Starratt *Tetrahedron Letters*, **1961**, 259.

to generate in a straightforward manner the skeletal and stereochemical features of the known triterpenes.

10–13 EXPERIMENTAL EVIDENCE FOR MECHANISM OF SQUALENE CYCLIZATION

Oxidative Cyclization

It will be well now to consider in detail the experimental evidence that supports this hypothetical scheme for triterpene genesis by various modes of squalene cyclization. There is now an impressive array of evidence in support of the type of cyclization mechanisms discussed above. Tchen and Bloch[45] have isolated an enzyme preparation from hog-liver homogenate that catalyzes the conversion of squalene to lanosterol, but not the further transformation of lanosterol to cholesterol. This enzyme preparation requires[46] air and reduced pyridine nucleotide (reduced nicotine adenine dinucleotide being more effective than reduced nicotine adenine dinucleotide phosphate). Moreover, O^{18} is incorporated into the lanosterol formed from squalene in the presence of O_2^{18} but not in the presence of H_2O^{18}. The requirement for reduced pyridine nucleotide is understandable if the reaction is catalyzed by an enzyme of the type that Mason[47] has termed *mixed function oxidases*, i.e., an enzyme that catalyzes the consumption of one molecule of oxygen per molecule of substrate; one atom of this oxygen molecule appears in the substrate, the other being reduced and appearing finally as the oxygen of water. The cyclization of squalene, catalyzed by an enzyme that Bloch has called *squalene oxidocyclase*, is of this type.

$$C_{30}H_{50} + O_2 + 2H^+ + 2e^- \rightarrow C_{30}H_{50}O + H_2O$$

The requirement for two electrons (and therefore reduced pyridine nucleotide) for the reduction of one atom of oxygen to water is evident.

A more detailed mechanism for this reaction has been proposed[48] and is analogous to Mason's formulation of phenolase action.[47] This mechanism postulates that the oxygenase, when active, contains two

45. T. T. Tchen and K. Bloch, *J. Biol. Chem.*, **226**, 921 (1957).
46. T. T. Tchen and K. Bloch, *J. Biol. Chem.*, **226**, 931 (1957).
47. H. S. Mason, *Advan. Enzymol.*, **19**, 79 (1957).
48. T. T. Tchen and K. Bloch, *Abs. 130th Meeting Am. Chem. Soc.*, Atlantic City, Sept. 16–21, 1956, p. 56C.

metal atoms in the reduced form.   These metal atoms are oxidized by the molecular oxygen, which is itself thereby reduced.   Finally, the enzyme is returned to the active state by a subsequent reduction of the metal atoms by reduced nicotine adenine dinucleotide phosphate. This mechanism is illustrated [Eq. (10–3)] for the case of a copper containing enzyme.   In support of this postulate, it has been found [49]

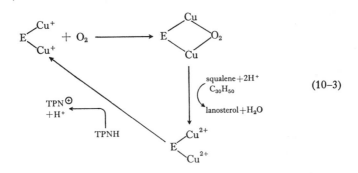

$$(10\text{–}3)$$

that chelating agents, such as o-phenanthroline, inhibit the oxidocyclase system.   The properties of this oxidocyclase are typical of reduced nicotinamide adenine dinucleotide phosphate-linked oxygenase reactions, which are important in other phases of steroid biogenesis and are to be considered subsequently.

It is extremely unlikely that any intermediate in the cyclization process is stabilized by loss of a proton.   This would almost surely necessitate the subsequent reacquisition of a proton from the medium unless the same proton that had previously been lost was re-added in some highly specific fashion, which gave no possibility for exchange with the medium.   Such a situation is, however, exceedingly remote, and therefore the finding [46] that no deuterium is incorporated into lanosterol when squalene is allowed to cyclize in a medium of D_2O virtually eliminates the occurrence of an intermediate formed by loss of a proton between squalene and lanosterol.

Migration of Methyl Groups

Another aspect of the cyclization mechanism that has been investigated in some detail concerns the migrations of the two methyl groups in the region of the C-D ring juncture.   Purely on structural grounds, there exist two possibilities: a single 1,3-methyl shift or a pair of 1,2-methyl migrations.   Although the latter situation is vastly

49. T. T. Tchen and K. Bloch, *J. Biol. Chem.*, **226**, 921 (1957).

more reasonable in a mechanistic sense, this consideration does not of itself eliminate the possibility of a 1,3-shift. However, the occurrence of a pair of 1,2-methyl migrations has recently been demonstrated by Bloch's group at Harvard[51] and by Cornforth's group in England.[52,53]

Bloch prepared squalene containing excess C^{13} in the positions indicated below by a sequence of reactions beginning with geranyl chloride **[70]** and ethyl acetoacetate **[71]** which contained excess C^{13} in C-3 and C-4. Cyclization of the squalene so labeled by a mechanism

Cl
CH₃COCH₂CO₂Et
or
+ CH₃COCH₂CO₂Et
[70]
[71]
A
B
C
D

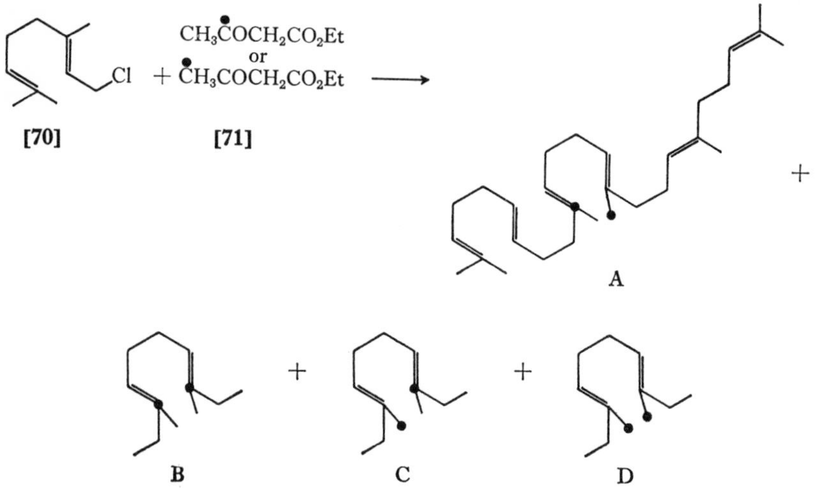

that involves two 1,2-methyl migrations will produce lanosterol with the C^{13} distribution shown in Eqs. (10–4). However, if the cyclization involved the alternate possibility [Eqs. (10–5)], a single 1,3-methyl shift, lanosterol with this distribution of excess C^{13} would result.

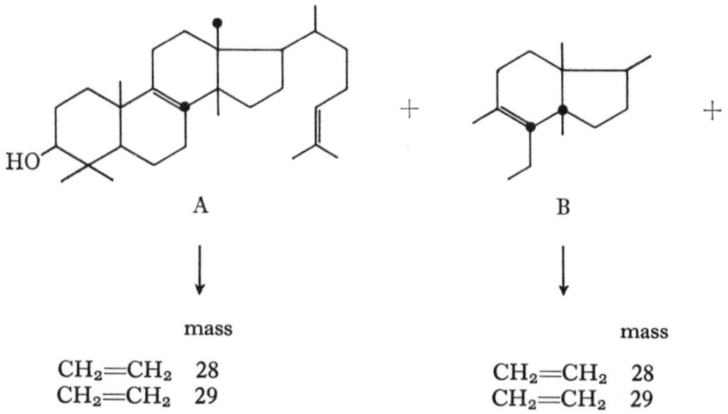

HO
A
B
mass
CH₂=CH₂ 28
CH₂=CH₂ 29
mass
CH₂=CH₂ 28
CH₂=CH₂ 29

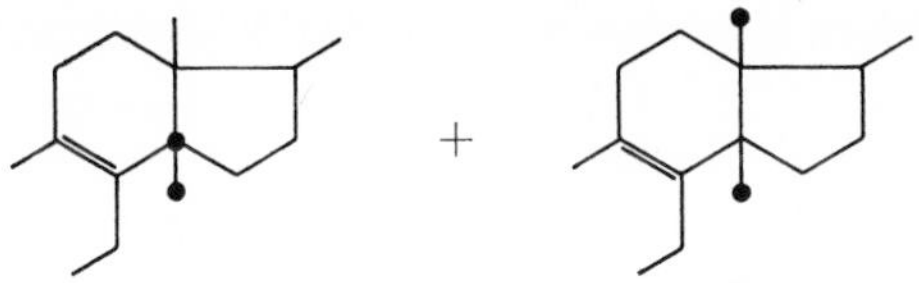

(10–4)

C   D

mass   mass
$CH_2=CH_2$ 28 $2CH_2=CH_2$ 29
$CH_2=CH_2$ 30

mass   28/29/30
ratio 3/4/1

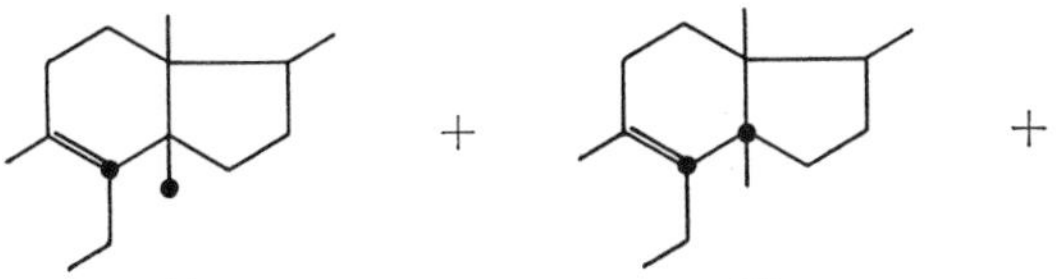

A′   B′

mass   mass
$CH_2=CH_2$ 28 $CH_2=CH_2$ 28
$CH_2=CH_2$ 29 $CH_2=CH_2$ 29

(10–5)

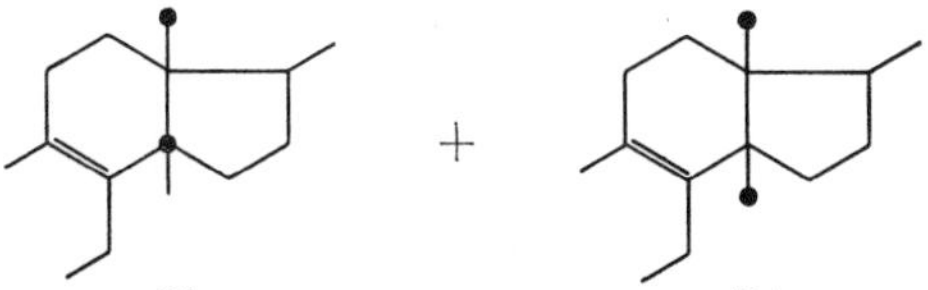

C′   D′

mass   mass
$2CH_2=CH_2$ 29 $2CH_2=CH_2$ 29

mass   28/29
ratio 2/6

51. R. K. Maudgal, T. T. Tchen, and K. Bloch, *J. Am. Chem. Soc.*, **80**, 2589 (1958).
52. J. W. Cornforth, R. H. Cornforth, A. Pelter, M. G. Horning, and G. Popják, *Proc. Chem. Soc.*, **1958**, 112.
53. J. W. Cornforth, R. H. Cornforth, A. Pelter, M. G. Horning, and G. Popják, *Tetrahedron*, **5**, 311 (1959).

The lanosterol produced from this C^{13}-labeled squalene by a liver homogenate was degraded first to acetic acid and then to ethylene. The acetic acid was obtained by a Kuhn-Roth oxidation procedure that extracts from the lanosterol molecules all the C-methyl groups, i.e., the gem-dimethyl groups of ring A and the sidechain, the three angular methyl groups, and the methyl substituent of the sidechain. Although the yield of acetic acid from these various potential sources is by no means uniform, this fact is unimportant in the subsequent argument. The amount of ethylene of various masses was determined by mass spectrometric analysis. It will be seen from the above discussion that ethylene of mass 30, i.e., containing two atoms of C^{13}, can result (from species C) only if the cyclization has involved two 1,2-methyl migrations. Further, the relative amount of masses 28 and 29 is different in the two cases. From the finding of ethylene with mass 30 and the relative amount of masses 28 and 29, it was abundantly clear that the rearrangement mechanism proceeds by a pair of 1,2-methyl shifts. This experiment conclusively demonstrates the conversion of synthetic[54] all-*trans* squalene (the natural stereoisomer) to lanosterol.

In their demonstration of this same point, Cornforth's group used mevalonate labeled with excess C^{13} as indicated. These three labeled species were used in a mixture with unlabeled mevalonate. The

$$\overset{\bullet}{C}H_3 \quad OH \qquad\qquad \overset{\bullet}{C}H_3 \quad OH \qquad\qquad CH_3 \quad OH$$

$$OHCH_2 \quad COOH \qquad OH\overset{\bullet}{C}H_2 \quad COOH \qquad OH\overset{\bullet}{C}H_2 \quad COOH$$

important point in this experiment is that a pair of 1,2-methyl shifts will result in cholesterol (by way of lanosterol) in which C-13 and C-18 have originated from the same mevalonate unit, whereas a single 1,3-methyl migration will produce cholesterol in which C-13 and C-18 have been derived from *different* mevalonate units. Clearly the statistical probability of finding two C^{13} atoms in adjacent positions is considerably greater in the former case. It was by a determination of the amount of cholesterol with adjacent carbon atoms (i.e., C-13 and C-18, both labeled with excess C^{13}) that led to the unambiguous conclusion that C-13 and C-18 do indeed both originate in the same mevalonate unit. This finding is both a necessary and sufficient condition for a mechanism which involves only 1,2-methyl shifts.

54. D. W. Dicker and M. C. Whiting, *Chem. & Ind. (London)*, **1956**, 351.

Squalene as an Obligatory Precursor

In apparent opposition to all the evidence that strongly implicates squalene as the obligatory precursor of lanosterol are results that might suggest that the rate of over-all squalene synthesis in isolated liver[55] and in yeast extracts[56] is too low for squalene to be an obligatory intermediate in steroid biosynthesis. It can be shown, however, in perfused pig liver,[57] in skin slices,[58] and in tissues of rats injected with C^{14}-acetate and killed shortly thereafter[54] that the specific activity of squalene exceeds that of cholesterol by a factor of 10 to 30, demonstrating that at least under these conditions the rate of squalene synthesis is entirely adequate to satisfy the criteria of a precursor-product relationship.

A beautiful investigation by Loud and Bucher[60] of the dynamic relations between squalene and cholesterol utilized a new technique of multiple liver biopsies on a single rat, which by removing errors produced by variations between different animals made it possible to follow the acetate-squalene-cholesterol metabolic process in vivo. It was found that the turnover rates in hepatic squalene were such as to indicate the metabolic separation of this compound into relatively active and relatively inert components, between which there is at best only very slow equilibration. It was shown that the active squalene component becomes labeled before cholesterol, that it possesses a rate of turnover sufficiently rapid to function as a direct precursor of cholesterol, and that it constitutes no more than a small fraction (less than 4 per cent) of the total hepatic squalene.

Thus the role of squalene as an obligatory precursor of cholesterol is assured, and the mechanism of its conversion to lanosterol proposed on purely structural and theoretical grounds now has firm experimental support.

10-14 EXPERIMENTAL STUDIES OF TRITERPENE BIOSYNTHESIS

A further experiment is of particular importance in indicating the involvement of the pathways just discussed in the biosynthesis of the

55. G. Popják, *Arch. Biochem. Biophys.*, **48**, 102 (1954).
56. L. M. Corwin, L. J. Schroeder, and W. G. McCullough, *J. Am. Chem. Soc.*, **78**, 1372 (1956).
57. E. Schwenk, D. Todd, and C. A. Fish, *Arch. Biochem. Biophys.*, **49**, 187 (1954).
58. R. B. Clayton and K. Bloch, *J. Biol. Chem.*, **218**, 319 (1956).
60. A. V. Loud and N. L. R. Bucher, *J. Biol. Chem.*, **233**, 37 (1958).

pentacyclic triterpenes and the stereospecificity of the steps in this pathway. Arigoni[61] has shown that 1-C^{14}-acetate, 2-C^{14}-acetate, and 2-C^{14}-mevalonate are all incorporated by soya beans into soyasapogenol [72] and squalene. By degradation techniques, it was shown that C_{24} is derived from the methyl group of mevalonate (i.e., is *not* labeled

[72]
Soyasapogenol

from 2-C^{14}-mevalonate precursor) and that all the label to be expected in the geminal substituent at C-4 is restricted to the equatorial methyl group C-23. Thus, in all precursors the two terminal methyl groups of the squalene chain retain a distinct identity, demanding that the isomerization of Δ^3-isopentenylpyrophosphate to the Δ^2-isomer be a stereospecific process. This demonstrates, in turn, that of the two terminal methyl groups it is the one *cis* to the hydrogen of the double bond that is derived from C-2 of the mevalonate precursor—a relation analogous to that between the internal isoprene units of the squalene chain.[62]

This fact also proves that, even during cyclization, no randomization of the isotope occurs, and the observed distribution of radioactivity clearly shows that ring A has been formed by a chair-type folding of the squalene chain (cf. [34]) and that at no time during the process has the configurational stability of the cationic structure [35] been lost. There is similar evidence in the case of the two diterpenes gibberellic acid and rosenonolactone (cf. Section 10–12).

Further studies of triterpene biosynthesis in plants have been reported. Mevalonate was shown to be incorporated into squalene,[63]

61. D. Arigoni, *Experientia*, **14**, 153 (1958).
62. J. W. Cornforth, R. H. Cornforth, G. Popják, and I. Y. Gore, *Biochem. J.*, **66**, 10P (1957).
63. E. Capstack, Jr., D. J. Baisted, W. W. Newschwander, G. Blondin, N. L. Rosin, and W. R. Nes, *Biochem.*, **1**, 1178 (1962).

β-amyrin[64] and β-sitosterol[64] by the pea, *Pisum sativum*; into β-sitosterol and oleanolic acid by *Salvia sclarea*;[65] into β-sitosterol, oleanolic acid, and ursolic acid(s) by *Salvia officinalis*;[66] into squalene, acidic triterpenes, and steam-volatile terpenes by cut sections of *Ocimum basilicum*;[67] into Δ^{22}-stigmasten-3β-ol by the slime mold *Dictyostelium discoideum*[68]; and into sterols and sapogenins of *Dioscorea spiculiflora*.[68b] In these cases it was generally found that the incorporation of mevalonate into the pentacyclic triterpenes was more efficient than into β-sitosterol [73], a cholesterol-like substance that possesses an

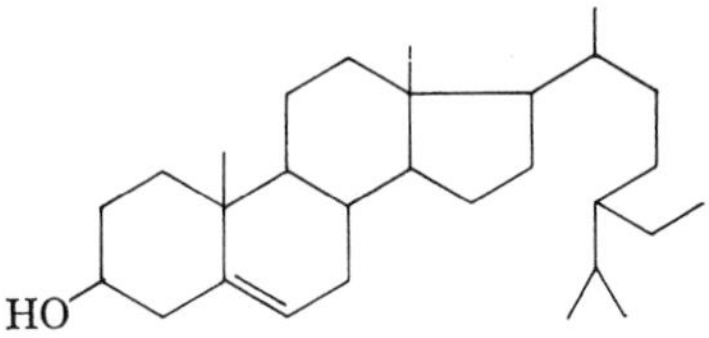

[73]

β-Sitosterol

ethyl substituent in the sidechain, and is analogous in this sense to ergosterol whose biosynthesis is discussed in Section 12–3.

The biosynthesis from labeled acetate of a triterpene, eburicoic acid [74], produced by the fungus *Polyporus anthrocophilus* Cooke has

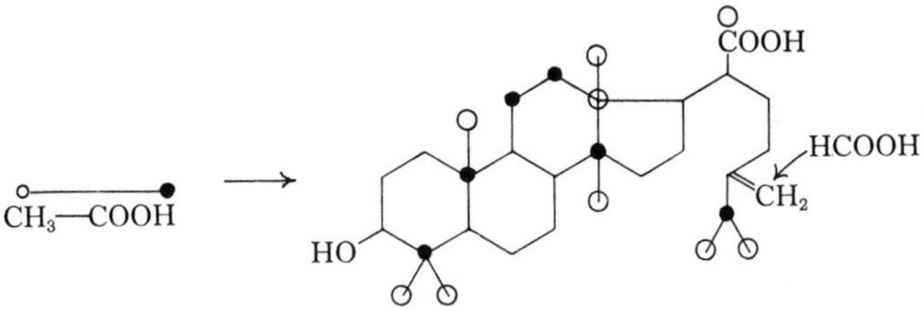

[74]

Eburicoic Acid

64. D. J. Baisted, E. Capstack, Jr., and W. R. Nes, *Biochem.*, **1**, 537 (1962).
65. H. J. Nicholas, *J. Biol. Chem.*, **237**, 1481 (1962).
66. H. J. Nicholas, *J. Biol. Chem.*, **237**, 1476 (1962).
67. H. J. Nicholas, *J. Biol. Chem.*, **237**, 1485 (1962).
68. D. F. Johnson, B. E. Wright, and E. Heftmann, *Arch. Biochem. Biophys.*, **97**, 232 (1962).
68b. R. D. Bennett, E. Heftman, W. H. Preston, Jr., and J. R. Haun, *Arch. Biochem. Biophys.*, **103**, 74 (1963).

been studied [69-71] and a pattern of labeling in the triterpene established that conforms to expectation. The single carbon unit attached to the sidechain was found to originate in formate, one of the members of the one-carbon metabolic pool. This is again analogous to the origin of a similar carbon in the ergosterol sidechain.

69. W. G. Dauben and J. H. Richards, *J. Am. Chem. Soc.*, **78**, 5329 (1956).
70. W. G. Dauben, Y. Ban, and J. H. Richards, *J. Am. Chem. Soc.*, **79**, 968 (1957).
71. W. G. Dauben, G. J. Fonken, and G. A. Boswell, *J. Am. Chem. Soc.*, **79**, 1000 (1957).

chapter | # Higher
eleven | # Terpenoids

11-1 CAROTENOIDS

The carotenoids represent a class of chemical compounds usually brightly colored in various hues of yellow to violet that account for the characteristic colors of many plants, e.g., the yellow-orange of carrots, the red of tomatoes. Chemically these substances are characterized by long unsaturated chains that are responsible for their colors and a skeleton usually composed of 40 carbon atoms that may hypothetically be derived from eight isoprene units. They represent a group of compounds analogous to the triterpenes in that they are probably derived from a dimerization of the C_{20} geranyl-geranyl pyrophosphate, the C_{40} substance so obtained being symmetrical in analogy to the symmetry of squalene. This dimerization probably occurs by a different mechanism than that discussed for the formation of squalene from farnesyl pyrophosphate.

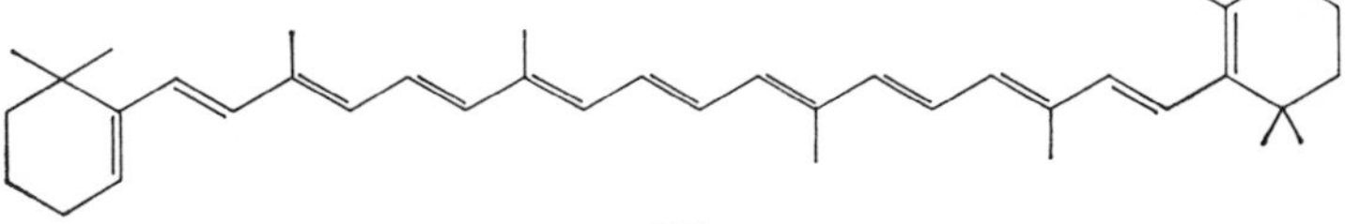

[1]

There are about 80 more or less well-characterized carotenoids that occur naturally. Examples of widely occurring carotenoids are β-carotene [1], from carrrots, and lycopene [2], found in tomatoes. Substances possessing less fully unsaturated skeletons are also known (e.g., phytofluene [3][1]). In addition there are carotenoid pigments

1. L. Zechmeister, *Experientia*, **10**, 1 (1954).

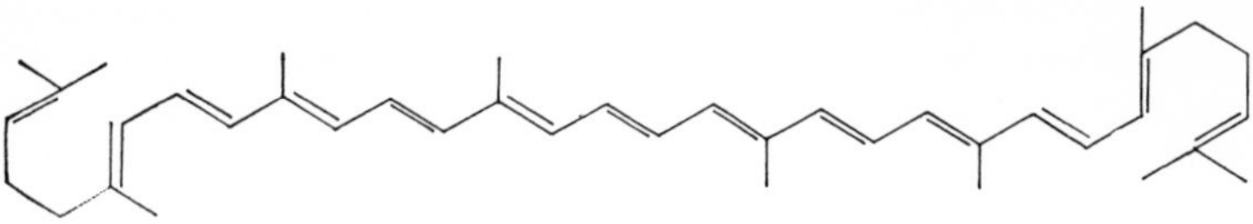

[2]

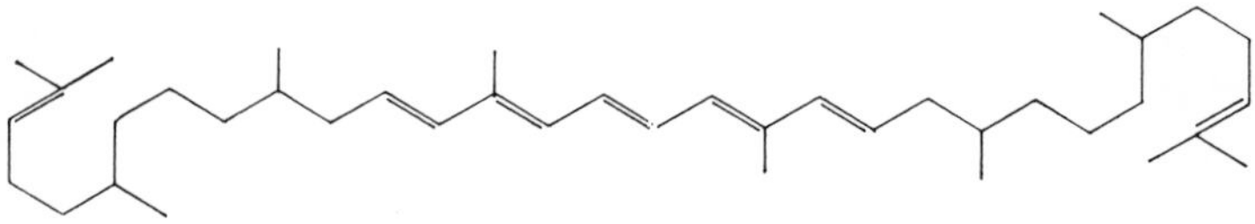

[3]

that have acquired oxygen atoms as part of their molecular composition, such as zeaxanthin **[4]** and capsanthin **[5]**, which possesses the interesting feature of a five-membered ring.[2]

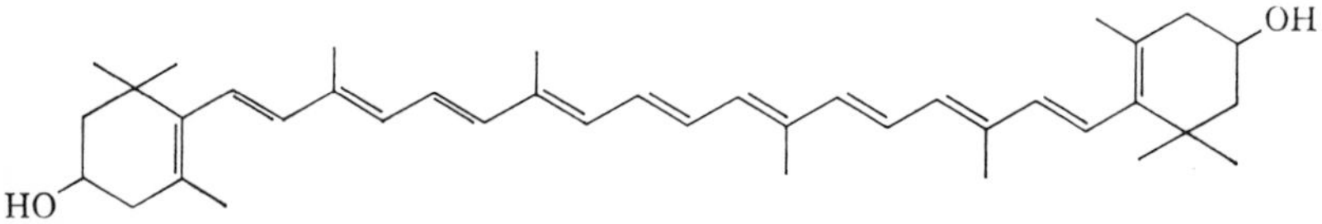

[4]

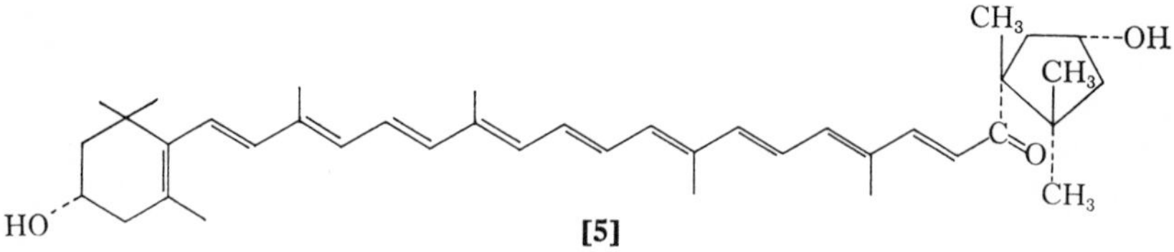

[5]

The overwhelming majority of the plant carotenoids possess an all-*trans* configuration about their many double bonds,[3,4] a situation reminiscent of the all-*trans* stereochemistry of squalene. It should be emphasized, however, that all the double bonds in squalene are present probably as a direct result of the polymerization of isopentenyl pyrophosphate. Thus a biogenetic process analogous to the synthesis of

2. H. Faigle and P. Karrer, *Helv. Chim. Acta,* **44**, 1904 (1961).
3. For a general review of carotenoid structure, cf. L. Zechmeister, *cis-trans Isomeric Carotenoids, Vitamin A and Arylpolyenes,* Springer-Verlag, Vienna and Academic, New York, 1962.
4. W. Karrer, *Konstitution und Vorkommen der Organische Pflanzenstoffe,* Birkhäuser, Basel, 1958.

squalene would yield an acyclic skeleton with eight olefinic linkages, none of them conjugated, whereas lycopene, for example, has 13 double bonds, 11 of them mutually conjugated.

Origin of Carbon Skeleton

The present state of knowledge of carotenoid biogenesis can be broken down into two main segments for discussion—the origin of the 40-carbon skeleton and the stages and mechanisms by which the various additional unsaturations are introduced. Many other aspects of carotenoid synthesis, such as quantitative and qualitative changes during growth, effects of nitrogen sources, light, oxygen, and temperature, have been adequately reviewed in detail by Goodwin[5,6] and will not be dealt with here.

The origin of the carbon skeletons of the carotenoids is similar to that for the lower terpenes. Acetate and mevalonate are incorporated in the expected way, and several experimental reports have confirmed this statement. Thus the mold *Phycomyces blakesleeanus* will synthesize β-carotene from 2-C^{14}-acetate[7,8] and 2-C^{14}-mevalonate[9,10] with the label in the expected position, though there is a report that the ring carbons are more highly labeled than the sidechain carbons.[10b]

Mevalonate and hydroxymethylglutarate are also incorporated into β-carotene in vitro by an extract from the mycelial mats of *P. blakesleeanus*.[11] As expected, mevalonate (and leucine) lose[12] the carboxyl before incorporation into β-carotene. Carbon dioxide is also incorporated by this mold but only in the presence of leucine as a nitrogen source.[10] This recalls the discussion of leucine metabolism and the route by which this amino acid can enter the group of interconvertible, branched five-carbon acids. The details of the incorporation of the carbon dioxide require comment, however, as the

5. T. W. Goodwin, *Advan. Enzymol.*, **21**, 295 (1959).
6. T. W. Goodwin in *Biosynthesis of Terpenes and Sterols*, Little, Brown, Boston, 1959, p. 279.
7. G. D. Braithwaite and T. W. Goodwin, *Biochem. J.*, **66**, 31P (1957).
8. F. J. Lotspeich, R. F. Krause, V. G. Lilly, and H. L. Barnett, *J. Biol. Chem.*, **234**, 3109 (1959).
9. G. D. Braithwaite and T. W. Goodwin, *Biochem. J.*, **67**, 13P (1957).
10. G. D. Braithwaite and T. W. Goodwin, *Biochem. J.*, **76**, 5 (1960).
10b. F. J. Lotspeich, R. F. Krause, V. G. Lilly, and H. L. Barnett, *Proc. Soc. Expt. Biol. Med.*, **114**, 444 (1963).
11. H. Yokoyama, C. O. Chichester, and G. Mackinney, *Nature*, **185**, 687 (1960).
12. C. O. Chichester, T. Nakayama, G. Mackinney, and T. W. Goodwin, *J. Biol. Chem.*, **214**, 515 (1955).

carboxyl group of the dimethylacrylic acid that is acylated with coenzyme A should eventually become the alcoholic carbon of the mevalonate; the carbon dioxide that is acquired will be present in the

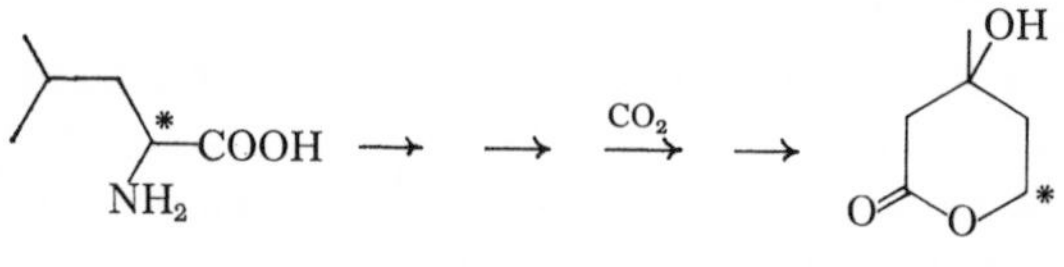

$$\text{(11-1)}$$

carboxyl carbon of the mevalonate.   The conversion of such mevalonate will *not* give rise to incorporation of the radioactivity present in the carbon dioxide into the carotenoid.   However, Goodwin[10] has suggested that a cleavage of the intermediate hydroxymethylglutarate to acetoacetate and acetyl coenzyme A will eventually lead to the observed result.   This is also in accord with other evidence on[13] the incorporation of leucine into carotenes.

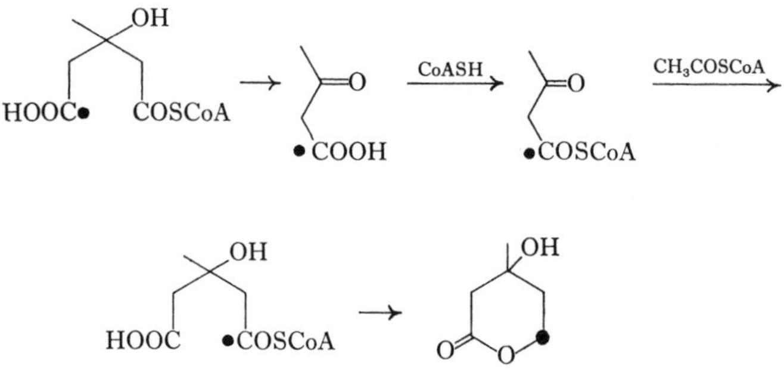

$$\text{(11-2)}$$

In the experiments with mevalonate incorporation in vitro by the extract of *P. blakesleeanus*, the reversion of the mevalonate to hydroxylmethylglutarate was observed.[11]

Steel and Gurin[14] have reported a study of the incorporation of acetate, mevalonate, β-hydroxy-β-methylglutarate, dimethylacrylate, and isovalerate, and several related branched-chain derivatives into β-carotene by *Euglena gracilis*.   The β-carotene was degraded and radioactivity was found in the anticipated positions.   The results obtained with 4,4'-C^{14}-isovalerate indicated that this substance was metabolized to smaller fragments before its incorporation into β-carotene.

13. C. O. Chichester, H. Yokoyama, T. O. M. Nakayama, A. Lukton, and G. Mackinney, *J. Biol. Chem.*, **234**, 598 (1959).
14. W. J. Steele and S. Gurin, *J. Biol. Chem.*, **235**, 2778 (1960).

A minor flap in carotenoid biogenesis was caused by a report[15] that incorporation of 1-C^{14}-acetate and 2-C^{14}-acetate into lycopene by ripening tomatoes (*Lycopersicon*) gave lycopene with a pattern of labeling not at all characteristic of terpenoid biogenesis. Happily, this indiscretion has been set right. More careful degradative techniques disclose[16] a well-disciplined incorporation of acetate by tomatoes. The incorporation of 2-C^{14}-mevalonate into lycopene[17-19] and other tomato carotenoids[18,20] has been reported. Homogenates of tomatoes that can synthesize radioactive lycopene from 2-C^{14}-mevalonate have been prepared.[19] For optimal incorporation of tracer, adenosine triphosphate, pyridine nucleotides, glutathione, manganese ion, and incubation in air are necessary.

In *Mucor hiemalis* Wehmer, the biogenesis of β-carotene from acetate[21] and mevalonate[22] has been shown to follow the expected course. Cultures of *Chromatium* incorporate C^{14}-acetate into a number of carotenoids.[23] Carrots have also been investigated[9,24] as agents for β-carotene biogenesis—a highly appropriate undertaking, as carrots are the classical source of β- (and α-) carotene. Carrot-root slices and gratings effectively incorporate 2-C^{14}-acetate and, with higher efficiency, DL-2-C^{14}-mevalonate. Radioactive carbon dioxide is not incorporated by these preparations.

An interesting aspect of the work with carrots is the isolation of a cell-free system[6,24,25] that will incorporate acetate and mevalonate into β-carotene and other components (mainly sterols) of the unsaponifiable matter of tissue extracts. The manner in which the cell-free system is prepared is of critical importance. For a successful preparation carrots are homogenized for 30 seconds, but disintegration of the carrot tissue for a longer period rapidly inactivates the preparation.

15. I. Zabin, *J. Biol. Chem.*, **226**, 851 (1957).
16. G. D. Braithwaite and T. W. Goodwin, *Biochem. J.*, **76**, 1 (1960).
17. E. A. Shneour and I. Zabin, *Abs.*, *113th Meeting, Am. Chem. Soc.*, San Francisco, April 13–18, 1958, p. 48C.
18. D. G. Anderson, D. W. Norgard, and J. W. Porter, *Biochem. Biophys. Res. Commun.*, **1**, 83 (1959).
19. E. A. Shneour and I. Zabin, *J. Biol. Chem.*, **234**, 770 (1959).
20. A. E. Purcell, G. A. Thompson, Jr., and J. Bonner, *J. Biol. Chem.*, **234**, 1081 (1959).
21. E. C. Grob and R. Bütler, *Helv. Chim. Acta*, **39**, 1975 (1956).
22. E. C. Grob, *Chimia (Aarau)*, **11**, 338 (1957).
23. C. R. Benedict, R. C. Fuller, and J. A. Bergeron, *Biochim. Biophys. Acta*, **54**, 525 (1961).
24. G. D. Braithwaite and T. W. Goodwin, *Biochem. J.*, **76**, 194 (1960).
25. T. W. Goodwin, *Proc. Intern. Congr. Biochem.*, *4th Vienna*, **1958**, 54.

This experience is analogous to that of Bucher[26] in preparing liver homogenates for the study of cholesterol biogenesis. The synthesis of carotenes by *Neurospora crassa* from a wide variety of labeled substrates has also been reported.[27] Again, 2-C^{14}-mevalonate was found to be the most efficient precursor and gave rise to labeling in all the C_{40} polyenes.

Suzue[28] has reported the enzymatic synthesis of bacterial phytoene from mevalonic acid with cell-free extracts of a mutant of *Staphylococcus aureus*, which is colorless because of a block in the pathway for the synthesis of the carotenoid pigment.[29] Adenosine triphosphate, reduced nicotinamide adenine dinucleotide phosphate, and Mn^{2+} were required as cofactors, and more recently flavine adenine dinucleotide has been found to be necessary in a partially purified enzyme preparation.[30] Suzue has also demonstrated[31] the enzymatic conversion of the phytoene so obtained into δ-carotene by a cell-free extract of the normal strain of *Staphylococcus aureus*.

Substances further along the biosynthetic pathway have also been shown to serve as precursors in carotenoid synthesis by various organisms. Tomato homogenates convert[32] C^{14}-isopentenyl pyrophosphate to lycopene with an efficiency estimated to be about 40 times that of mevalonate incorporation. C^{14}-citral and C^{14}-geraniol are also incorporated into β-carotene in carrot slices, although with poor efficiency.[33]

Thus there is a great body of experimental evidence supporting the origin of the C_{40} carotenoids from those precursors that have previously been shown to give rise to terpenes of smaller size.

Dimerization of Geranyl-Geranyl Pyrophosphate to Phytoene

The structure of the 40-carbon intermediate and the mechanism of its formation from a C_{20} precursor is clearly a question of great importance, and recently Anderson and Porter have reported the first

26. N. L. R. Bucher, *J. Am. Chem. Soc.*, **75**, 498 (1953).
27. L. F. Krzeminski and F. W. Quakenbush, *Arch. Biochem. Biophys.*, **88**, 287 (1960).
28. G. Suzue, *Biochim. Biophys. Acta*, **45**, 616 (1960).
29. G. Suzue, *Arch. Biochem. Biophys.*, **88**, 180 (1960).
30. G. Suzue, *J. Biochem.*, **51**, 246 (1962).
31. G. Suzue, *Biochim. Biophys. Acta*, **50**, 593 (1961).
32. T. N. R. Varma and C. O. Chichester, *Arch. Biochem. Biophys.*, **96**, 265 (1962).
33. T. N. R. Varma and C. O. Chichester, *Arch. Biochem. Biophys.*, **96**, 419 (1962).

work that begins to give a definitive answer to this question. Briefly the findings indicate with high probability that two moles of geranyl-geranyl pyrophosphate[34] combine and form phytoene—a dimer of geranyl-geranyl pyrophosphate with a double bond between those carbons that have just been joined. This dimerization is in contrast to the formation of squalene from two moles of farnesyl pyrophosphate, because here the dimerization is accompanied by a two-electron reduction so the newly formed bond is saturated.

The following results are experimental justification for this assertion. A mixture of terpenyl pyrophosphates were biosynthesized from C^{14}-mevalonate by a soluble rat-liver-enzyme system. The enzyme system was then inactivated by heating. Incubation of the components of the resulting mixture with carrot or tomato plastids led to the synthesis of phytoene (and other carotenoids as well, in the case with tomato plastids). In fact a mixture of terpenyl pyrophosphates isolated from the enzyme mixture also served as a substrate for phytoene synthesis. Gas chromatographic analysis of the terpenoids obtained by acid hydrolysis of the terpenyl pyrophosphates showed the presence of small amounts of radioactivity associated with the peak of geranyl-linaloöl, although most of the activity was associated with nerolidol. These results support the proposal of geranyl-geranyl pyrophosphate as the probable substrate in the synthesis of phytoene by carrot plastids.

Although the addition of pyridine nucleotides as cofactors to the incubation medium did not have a pronounced effect, the observed effects were consistent with the proposed biosynthetic route. Nicotin-amide adenine dinucleotide phosphate stimulated phytoene synthesis, whereas the reduced form of this coenzyme invariably inhibited the reaction slightly. The requirement for oxidized pyridine nucleotide is not evident from the stoichiometry of the reaction, as two moles of geranyl-geranyl pyrophosphate should produce one mole of phytoene and two pyrophosphate ions without either consumption or loss of electrons.

Moreover, Rilling has produced evidence that phytoene is formed by a nonoxidative reaction thereby excluding lycopersene as its precursor and supporting the view that phytoene is the first 40-carbon intermediate in carotenoid synthesis.[35] Attempts have been made to detect labeled lycopersene in higher plants in maize seedlings, carrot-root slides,[35b]

34. D. G. Anderson and J. W. Porter, *Arch. Biochem. Biophys.*, **97**, 509 (1962).
35. H. C. Rilling, *Biochim. Biophys. Acta*, **65**, 156 (1962).
35b. E. I. Mercer, B. H. Davies, and T. W. Goodwin, *Biochem. J.*, **87**, 317 (1963).

and *Neurospora crassa*.[35c]   None was found.   However, squalene is produced by carrot-root slices from acetate and mevalonate.   Also, carrot and tomato enzymes convert 2-C^{14}-mevalonate and 4,8,12-C^{14}-farnesyl pyrophosphate to squalene.[35d]

The production of such an intermediate with a central unsaturation may prevent the complete cyclization of the C_{40}-polyolefin in a manner analogous to that so characteristic of squalene.[36]   In no case, even when the reduced pyridine nucleotide was added, was evidence obtained for the formation of lycopersene, the C_{40} analog of squalene.

Dehydrogenation of Phytoene

The second general area of carotenogenesis, namely, the steps leading from the first C_{40} substance to the wide variety of compounds actually found in nature, is in a much less satisfactory state.   There has been a wide variety of genetic investigations of carotenoid biogenesis which have been reviewed by Goodwin.[5]

A particularly interesting case deals with various strains of *Neurospora crassa*.   Hungate[37] was able to obtain mutants that form a carotenoid-producing mycelium.   A number of *N. crassa* strains were examined and were divided into four main groups.   Group I mutants produced no acidogenic carotenoids; Group II produced almost no xanthophylls, and no carotenes but some phytofluene; Group III yielded no polyenes except phytoene; and Group IV gave rise to no polyenes at all.   The main mutant blocks could thus be located[38] as indicated in Eq. (11–5) on the assumption that phytoene is the precursor of the more unsaturated carotenoids.

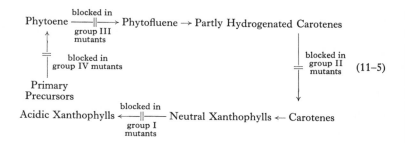

$$(11\text{–}5)$$

35c. B. H. Davies, D. Jones, and T. W. Goodwin, *Biochem. J.*, **87**, 326 (1963).

35d. D. A. Beeler, D. A. Anderson, and J. W. Porter, *Arch. Biochem. Biophys.*, **102**, 26 (1963).

36. B. H. Davies, *Biochem. J.*, **85**, 2P (1962).

37. Discussed by F. T. Haxo, *Fortschr. Chem. Org. Naturstoffe*, **12**, 169 (1956).

The speculation[39] that there exists a stepwise synthetic pathway from the less to the more unsaturated carotenoids has been widely discussed and conflicting claims have been made. For example, Grob[40] has studied the presence of carotenoids in *N. crassa* after exposure to light and he inferred support for the view that carotenoids are formed by progressive dehydrogenation of a saturated precursor. Haxo,[41] and later Zalokar,[42] found that the concentration of the colorless phytoene was not related to the formation of carotenoids. Light and oxygen are required for such formation.

Goodwin[43] found that addition of diphenylamine (1/40,000) to a culture medium on which *Phycomyces blakesleeanus* was growing almost completely inhibited the production of the more unsaturated carotenoids (α-, β-, and γ-carotene and lycopene) while stimulating production of the more saturated components, phytofluene, ζ-carotene, neurosporene, and possibly phytoene. Results[44] of experiments on diphenylamine inhibition of *Rhodospirillium rubrum* supported the conclusion that the more saturated substances were converted to lycopene and its oxidation product spirilloxanthin. A kinetic analysis of this endogenous system revealed a sequential relationship between the participating carotenoids. However, Villoutreix,[45] who made a study with mutants and inhibitors in *Rhodotorula mucilaginosa*, concluded that the different polyenes were not mutually related.

There has been a significant amount of work reported using the technique of determining the relative specific activities of various C_{40} terpenes after the administration of labeled substrate. An early report[20] claimed that phytoene could not be a general carotene precursor in the tomato fruit, since, after administration of 2-C^{14}-mevalonate to ripening tomatoes, the isolated phytoene had a much lower specific activity than any of the major carotenes. However, two reports[18,46] have disagreed with these experimental results pointing out that in the previous work the critical compounds were not carefully enough

38. F. T. Haxo, *Biol. Bull.*, **103**, 286 (1952).
39. J. W. Porter and R. E. Lincoln, *Arch. Biochem. Biophys.*, **27**, 390 (1950).
40. E. C. Grob, *Chimia (Aarau)*, **12**, 86 (1958).
41. F. T. Haxo, *Arch. Biochem. Biophys.*, **20**, 400 (1949).
42. M. Zalokar, *Arch. Biochem. Biophys.*, **70**, 561 (1957).
43. T. W. Goodwin, *Biochem. J.*, **50**, 550 (1952).
44. S. L. Jensen, G. Cohen-Bazire, T. O. M. Nakayama, and R. Y. Stanier, *Biochim. Biophys. Acta*, **29**, 477 (1958).
45. J. Villoutreix, *Biochim. Biophys. Acta*, **40**, 442 (1960).
46. D. G. Anderson, D. W. Norgard, and J. W. Porter, *Arch. Biochem. Biophys.*, **88**, 68 (1960).

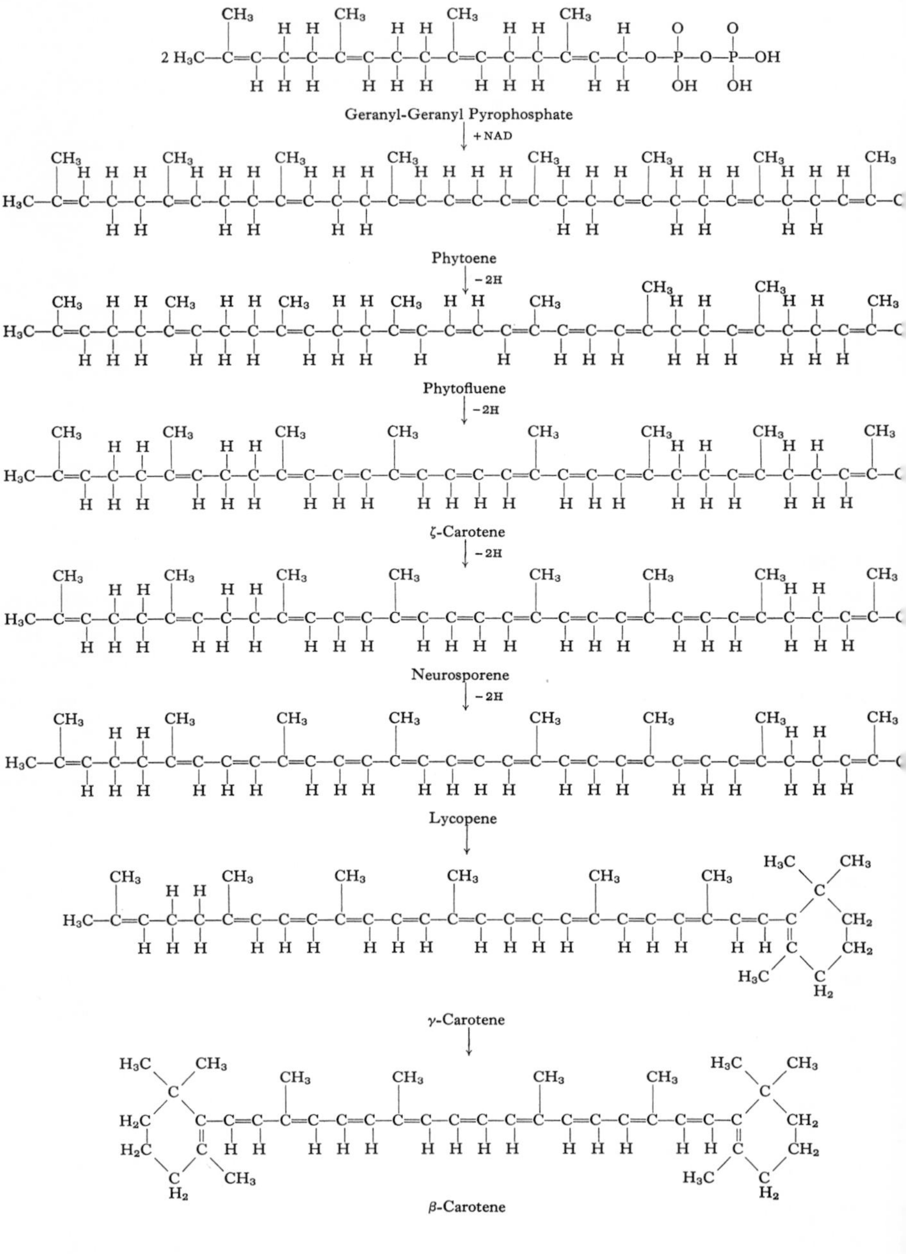
Geranyl-Geranyl Pyrophosphate
+NAD
Phytoene
-2H
Phytofluene
-2H
ζ-Carotene
-2H
Neurosporene
-2H
Lycopene
γ-Carotene
β-Carotene

Chart I

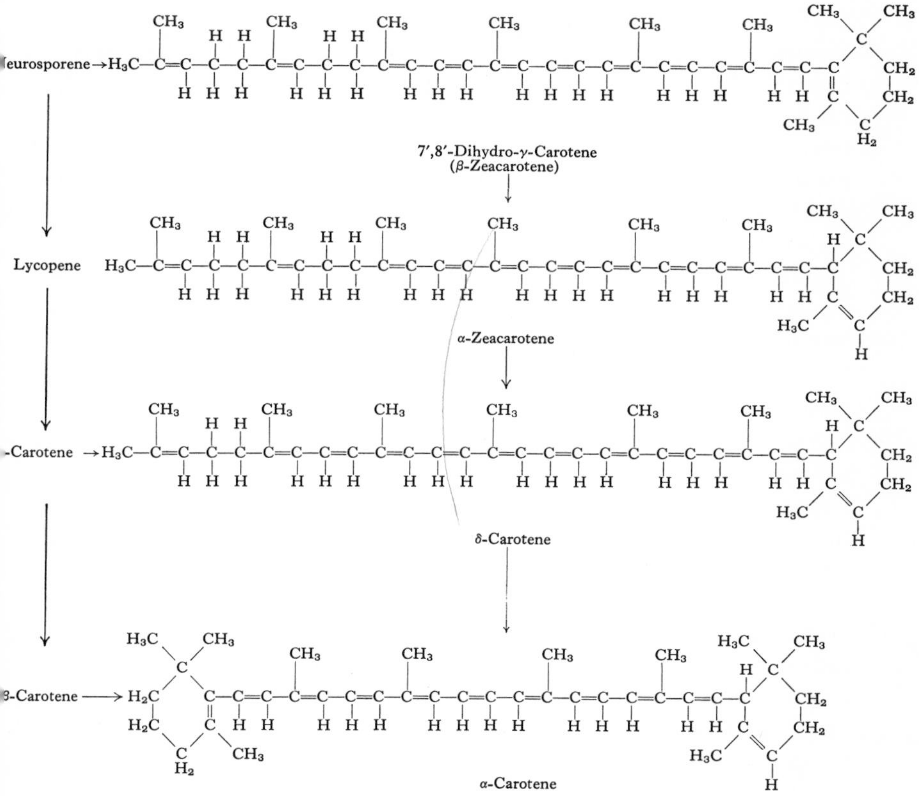

Chart II

purified. These later results are compatible with a precursor-product relationship for phytoene and the more unsaturated carotenoids. The latter workers also demonstrated that 3-C^{14}-dimethylacrylic acid serves as a substrate in the biosynthesis of β-carotene in *Chlorella pyrenoidosa* and *Blakeslea trispora* but not in ripening tomatoes. On the other hand, 2-C^{14}-mevalonate serves as a precursor for β-carotene in *Blakeslea trispora* and ripening tomato fruit, but not in *Chlorella pyrenoidosa*; the latter negative result is probably the result of a permeability barrier. In a similar study [27] in *Neurospora crassa* the evidence implied that the individual polyenes are synthesized independently rather than through a stepwise interconversion involving either hydrogenation or dehydrogenation.

The situation regarding the interrelations of the various carotenoids has been discussed anew by Porter with the conclusion that progressive unsaturation with cyclization where appropriate is the true pathway of carotenoid synthesis. In summary this pathway [47] is shown in Chart I. Chart II shows the proposed pathway for the synthesis of δ- and α-carotenes. The first reaction, the conversion of phytoene to phytofluene, has been demonstrated to occur in a system containing tomato plastids.[48] A study of the relative specific activities of various carotenoids biosynthesized from C^{14}-terpenylpyrophosphates supports a biosynthetic pathway involving a sequential desaturation of C_{40} polyolefins beginning at phytoene.[49] The only result not compatible with the proposed pathway was that the specific activity of the β-carotene was in some samples higher than that of lycopene. A pathway from neurosporene to β-carotene not involving lycopene was therefore proposed.

One does well to stress strongly the caveat that relative specific activities may be misleading guides to true biosynthetic interrelationships, and the cautious are reminded of the careful and elegant work [50] that eventually showed conclusively that, in rat liver, squalene is a direct and obligatory precursor of lanosterol, even though less than 4 per cent of the hepatic squalene is part of the metabolic pool. However, it does seem highly probable that the scheme proposed by Porter consisting of stepwise desaturation is essentially correct as the most important biosynthetic pathway for the formation of the carotenoids.

The chemical facility of these oxidative processes, which introduce additional unsaturation into an already highly unsaturated chain, is amply supported by the extensive investigations [51] of Zechmeister and his collaborators on in vitro conversions of naturally occurring carotenoids by many reagents; e.g., N-bromosuccinimide was found to effect the stepwise dehydrogenation of the colorless phytoene and phytofluene to carotenoid pigments.[52]

cis-trans Isomerizations

Thus far the discussion has dealt solely with the all-*trans* polyenes. Although these are the most widely occurring of the C_{40} terpenoids,

47. J. W. Porter and D. G. Anderson, *Arch. Biochem. Biophys.*, **97**, 520 (1962).
48. D. A. Beeler and J. W. Porter, *Biochem. Biophys. Res. Commun.*, **8**, 367 (1962).
49. D. A. Beeler and J. W. Porter, *Arch. Biochem. Biophys.*, **100**, 167 (1963).
50. A. V. Loud and N. L. R. Bucher, *J. Biol. Chem.*, **233**, 37 (1958).
51. L. Zechmeister, *Fortschr. Chem. Org. Naturstoffe*, **15**, 31 (1958).
52. L. Zechmeister and B. K. Koe, *J. Am. Chem. Soc.*, **76**, 2923 (1954).

some examples of carotenoids with one or more *cis* olefinic linkages do occur. For example, neo-γ-carotene P has been shown to be a genuine constituent of *Pyracantha* berries.[53] Some tomato varieties such as the "tangerine tomato" (so named because the ripe fruit is orange instead of red) contain a poly-*cis*-carotenoid, named prolycopene, because it substitutes for the lycopene of normal tomatoes.[54]

A particularly interesting example of *cis-trans* bioisomerization of carotenoids is that involving retinene. Rhodopsin, which is a protein joined to retinene, is of greatest importance in the process of seeing, and a fascinating event[55,56] in the evolution of polyene chemistry was the detection, in the retina, of a photoisomerase, *retinene isomerase*, that shifts the equilibrium between all-*trans*-retinene and the 11-*cis*-retinene in favor of the 11-*cis*-isomer. There also exists a protein, opsin, that binds 11-*cis*-retinene but releases all-*trans*-retinene. Retinene isomerase and opsin taken together thus complete the in vivo cycle[57,58] of Eq. (11–6).

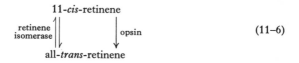

$$
\begin{array}{c}
11\text{-}cis\text{-retinene} \\
\underset{\text{isomerase}}{\overset{\text{retinene}}{\Big\updownarrow}} \qquad \Big\downarrow \text{opsin} \qquad\qquad (11\text{–}6)\\
\text{all-}trans\text{-retinene}
\end{array}
$$

Such isomerizations have recently been carried out also in vitro in the presence of synthetic photosensitizers such as benzophenone. For example, the photostationary state between *cis*- and *trans*-piperylene is attained much more rapidly in the presence of benzophenone than in its absence.[59] The photochemically induced in vivo isomerization of olefins undoubtedly makes use of suitable "biological photosensitizers."

Summary

In summary, the biosynthesis of the C_{40} terpenoids follows the general outlines of terpene biosynthesis developed for the other classes

53. L. Zechmeister and J. H. Pinckard, *J. Am. Chem. Soc.*, **69**, 1930 (1947).
54. L. Zechmeister, A. L. LeRosen, F. W. Went, and L. Pauling, *Proc. Natl. Acad. Sci. (U.S.)*, **27**, 468 (1941).
55. R. Hubbard, *Federation Proc.*, **14**, 229 (1955).
56. R. Hubbard, *J. Gen. Physiol.*, **39**, 935 (1956).
57. R. Hubbard, *J. Gen. Physiol.*, **42**, 259 (1958).
58. G. Wald and R. Hubbard, in *The Enzymes*, Vol. 3, 2d ed., Academic, New York, 1960, p. 369.
59. G. S. Hammond, P. A. Leermakers, and N. J. Turro, *J. Am. Chem. Soc.*, **83**, 2396 (1961).

in broad outline; the same substrates are effective precursors and their mode of incorporation parallels that for the other terpenes. The detailed steps between five-carbon fragments and the carotenoids, particularly the interconversions between 40-carbon intermediates, remain however to be filled in, and the discovery of cell-free systems sets the stage for a rapid development of these problems.

II–2 UBIQUINONES AND PLASTOQUINONES

For many years there appeared to be a gap in the size of terpenoid substances between the C_{40} carotenoids and rubber, which is a high polymer. However a series of compounds, the ubiquinones or co-enzyme Q group, of great importance in biological oxidation-reduction and phosphorylation processes, has recently received considerable attention. These substances[60] are 2,3-dimethoxy-5-methyl benzo-quinones with an unsaturated isoprenoid sidechain in the 6-position made up of six to ten isoprenoid units and are found in many plants, animals, and aerobic microorganisms. These substances are variously

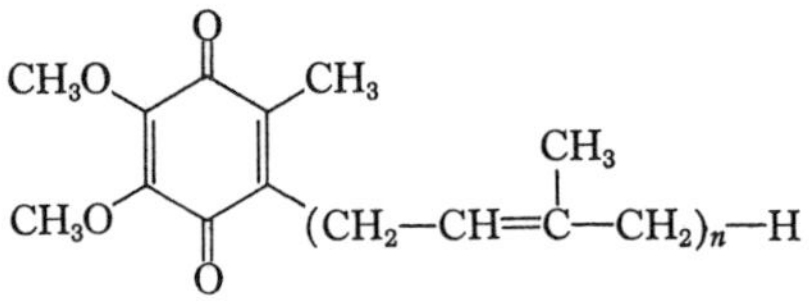

[6]
Ubiquinones $n = 6$–10

designated ubiquinone-30 or coenzyme Q_6 **[6]**, for that representative with a 30-carbon sidechain containing six isoprenoid units. The larger quinones with 45- or 50-carbon sidechains, i.e., coenzyme Q_9 and coenzyme Q_{10}, seem to be the most important in animal metabolism.

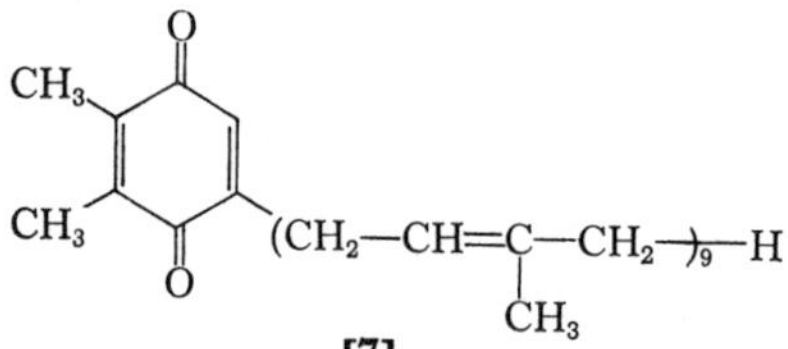

[7]
Plastoquinone
Kofler's Quinone

60. Cf. *Ciba Found. Symp. Quinones Electron Transport*, **1961**, Little, Brown, Boston.

A similar substance, plastoquinone or Kofler's quinone **[7]**, which has a 45-carbon isoprenoid sidechain appended at the 5-position of 2,3-dimethyl benzoquinone seems to function in photosynthetic electron transport.[61] Cyclized forms of these substances also exist, for example, ubichromene **[8]** and solanochromene **[9]**.

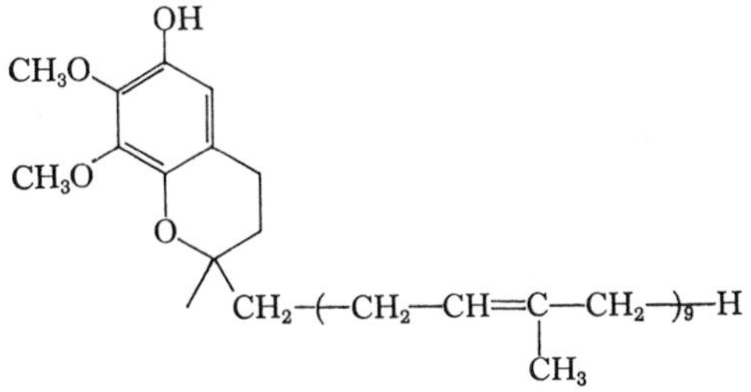

[8]
Ubichromene

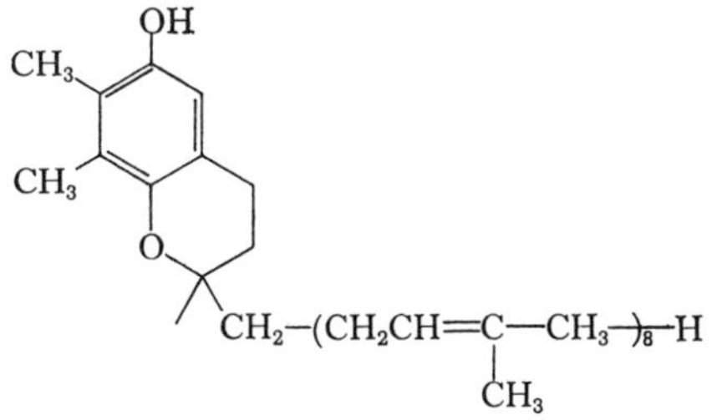

[9]
Solanochromene

Large sidechains are also found in the vitamin K series **[10]**, in which the terpenoid fragment is joined at the 3-position to a 2-methyl naphthoquinone nucleus. In human tissue the sidechain contains 20 carbons, but from putrified fish-meal derivatives with a 30- and 35-carbon chain have been isolated. Mycobacteria produce derivatives with 40-, 45-, and 50-carbon appendages.

The biosynthesis of the sidechains of these substances requires little comment, as they fit without the necessity of modification into the stepwise polymerization sequence, and the site of oxidation in these sidechains is just that expected. Experimental justification for this assertion comes from the findings that the usual substrates, mevalonate, acetate, etc., are incorporated in the expected manner.

61. N. I. Bishop, *Proc. Natl. Acad. Sci. (U.S.)*, **45**, 1696 (1959).

The attachment of the sidechain to the aromatic nucleus [Eq. (11-7)] is easily envisioned as an electrophilic attack of the allylic pyrophosphate onto the reduced quinone ring.

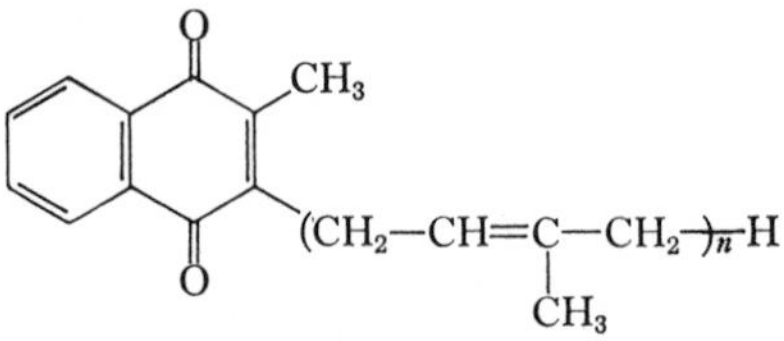

[10]

Vitamin K
$n = 4, 6, 7, 8, 9, 10$

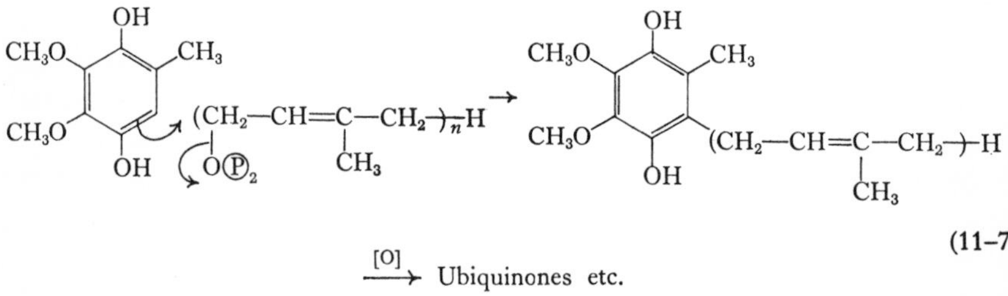

$$\xrightarrow{[O]} \text{ Ubiquinones etc.}$$

(11-7)

Last, the polymeric derivatives of the isoprene unit rubber and gutta percha—historically the first source of that ubiquitous five-carbon substance—are derived by an extended application of the polymerization sequence that is uninterrupted at any stage by dimerization, cyclization, or interception by an activated aromatic ring.

chapter | Cholesterol
twelve | Biogenesis

12–1 ORIGIN OF CARBON ATOMS

The study of the molecular events that result in the elaboration of steroids was begun over 20 years ago when it was found[1] that steroidal substances are fabricated from numerous small molecules and that acetate is the source of the carbon atoms of ergosterol in yeast[2] and of cholesterol in animal tissue.[3–5] This work took on an even greater significance with the realization that the biogenesis of cholesterol and steroids is but the variant of a vast biosynthetic panorama that now includes all terpenes and derived substances. Bloch's[6] pioneering work showed that acetic acid molecules are incorporated into the structure of cholesterol according to a definite pattern. The subsequent work, which has located the origin of every carbon atom of cholesterol in either the carboxyl or methyl carbon of acetate, stands as a brilliant achievement and is summarized in Eq. (12–1).

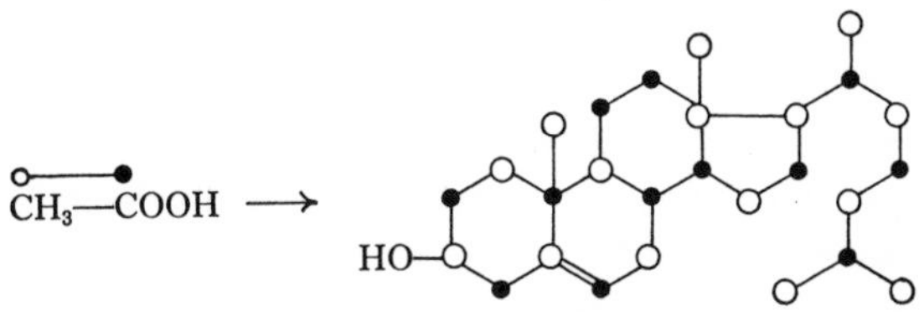

$$CH_3\text{—COOH} \longrightarrow \qquad \qquad (12\text{-}1)$$

1. D. Rittenberg and R. Schoenheimer, *J. Biol. Chem.*, **121**, 235 (1937).
2. R. Sonderhoff and H. Thomas, *Ann.*, **530**, 195 (1937).
3. K. Bloch, E. Borek, and D. Rittenberg, *J. Biol. Chem.*, **162**, 441 (1946).
4. K. Bloch and D. Rittenberg, *J. Biol. Chem.*, **145**, 625 (1942).
5. K. Bloch and D. Rittenberg, *J. Biol. Chem.*, **159**, 45 (1945).
6. H. N. Little and K. Bloch, *J. Biol. Chem.*, **183**, 33 (1950).

Bloch and co-workers determined the labeling pattern in the side-chain of cholesterol. Cholesterol was converted to cholestane,[6] which was oxidized to acetone and *allo*cholanic acid [see Eq. (12–2)]. The acetone was further oxidized with hypodite to iodoform, which allowed the determination of C-26 and C-27 and, by subtraction of the activity of the iodoform from that of the original acetone, the activity of C-25 was inferred. For the determination[7] of the origin of C-20 to C-24,

$$\text{Cholesterol} \longrightarrow \{ \} \quad \xrightarrow{\text{CrO}_3} \quad \{ \} \text{COOH} \quad +$$

26   25   27
Cholestane   *Allo*cholanic Acid

(12–2)

$$\begin{array}{c} ^{26,\,27}\text{CH}_3 \\ ^{25}\text{C}{=}\text{O} \\ ^{26,\,27}\text{CH}_3 \end{array} \xrightarrow{\text{NaOI}} {}^{26,\,27}\text{CH}_3\text{I}$$

inclusive, a sample of 3-β-acetoxy*allo*cholanic acid, derived from biosynthetic cholesterol, served as the starting material [follow Eq. (12–3)]. A series of Barbier-Wieland degradations gave C-22, C-23, and C-24 as the carbonyl group of benzophenone and a steroidal fragment that, after hydrolysis at C-3, yielded 5-α-pregnanolone. The 3-formate derivative was oxidized with perbenzoic acid to 3-β-formoxy-17-β-acetoxyandrostane, which was hydrolyzed to give acetic acid representing C-20 and C-21. The acetic acid was degraded by reaction of its silver salt with bromine; the carbon dioxide evolved in this reaction originates only from C-20 of the original steroid.

The origin of C-7 of cholesterol was determined both by Bloch[8] and by Dauben and Takemura[9] through essentially the same procedure. Ozonolysis of 7-ketocholest-5-ene produced a ketoacid [1] (6-nor-5,7-seco-5-keto-7-carboxycholestane). Wolff-Kishner reduction of the keto acid produced the corresponding desketo acid [2], which yielded carbon dioxide from C-7 and an amine [3] when treated with hydrazoic

7. J. R. Wüersch, R. L. Huang, and K. Bloch, *J. Biol. Chem.*, **195**, 439 (1952).
8. K. Bloch, *Helv. Chim. Acta*, **36**, 1611 (1953).
9. W. G. Dauben and K. H. Takemura, *J. Am. Chem. Soc.*, **75**, 6302 (1953).

acid under the conditions of the Schmidt reaction. In this way the origin of C-7 was found to be the methyl carbon of acetate.

Cornforth, Hunter, and Popják[10] developed an elegant degradative procedure that provided all the carbon atoms of ring A, as well as C-6

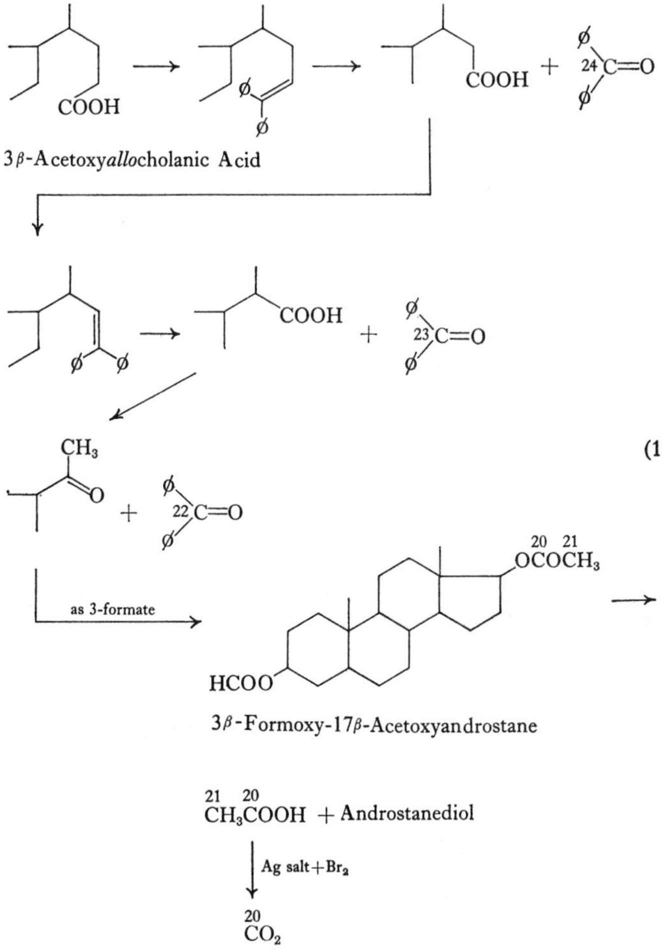
COOH
3β-Acetoxy*allo*cholanic Acid
COOH
24 C=O
COOH
23 C=O
CH₃
22 C=O
as 3-formate
20 21
OCOCH₃
HCOO
3β-Formoxy-17β-Acetoxyandrostane
21 20
CH₃COOH + Androstanediol
Ag salt+Br₂
20
CO₂

(12–3)

and C-19. Cholesterol was first converted to Δ^5-cholestene, which was then ozonized and the ozonide reduced with zinc and acetic acid to a ketoaldehyde **[4]**. On cyclization and subsequent ozonolysis there

10. J. W. Cornforth, G. D. Hunter, and G. Popják, *Biochem. J.*, **54**, 590 (1953).

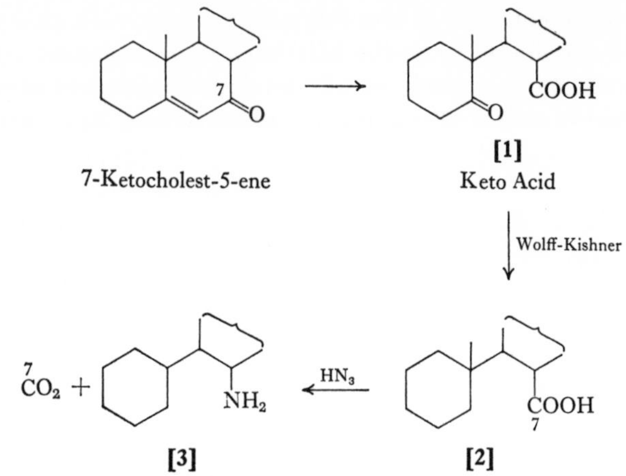
7
O
COOH
7-Ketocholest-5-ene
[1]
Keto Acid
Wolff-Kishner
7
CO2 +
NH2
HN3
COOH
7
[3]
[2]

resulted a diketoacid **[5]** that, upon heating at 200° or boiling with aniline, yielded a ketoaldehyde **[6]** and carbon dioxide from C-6. Heating of this ketoaldehyde **[6]** or its precursor with potassium carbonate at 450° caused a reverse Michael reaction, resulting in the extrusion of ring A as 2-methylcyclohexanone. Conversion of this ketone to the

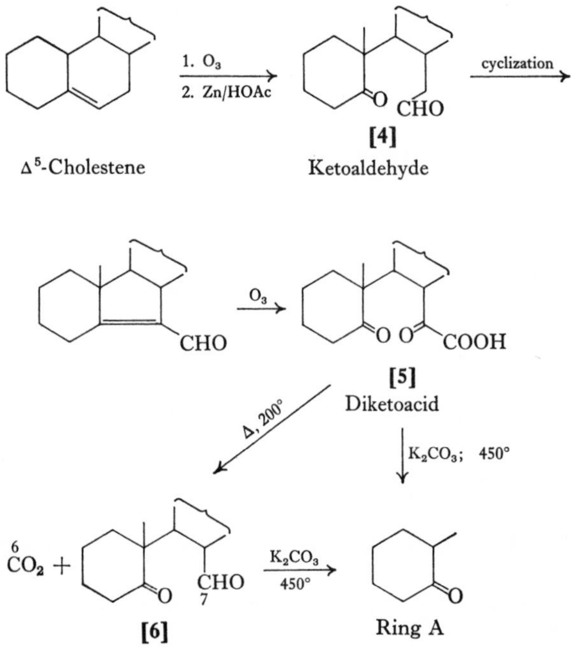
1. O3
2. Zn/HOAc
O
CHO
cyclization
[4]
Δ5-Cholestene
Ketoaldehyde
CHO
O3
O O
COOH
[5]
Diketoacid
Δ, 200°
K2CO3; 450°
6
CO2 +
O
CHO
7
K2CO3
450°
O
[6]
Ring A

corresponding lactam via a Schmidt reaction followed by hydrolysis and methylation led to a betaine [7] that on heating with potassium hydroxide gave rise to valeric and acetic acids by a series of steps involving elimination of trimethylamine, migration of the double bond to the α,β-position, hydration of the double bond, and, finally, a fission of the resulting β-hydroxyacid to acetic acid and valeraldehyde, which was then oxidized to valeric acid. Further stepwise degradations of these acids completed the sequence.

$$
\begin{array}{c}
\underset{\substack{\text{1. HN}_3 \\ \text{2. H}_2\text{O} \\ \text{3. CH}_3\text{I}}}{\longrightarrow}
\quad
\underset{\text{CH}_3}{\overset{\text{CH}_3\ \ \text{CH}_3}{\underset{+}{N}}}\!\!-\!\text{CH}\!-\!(\text{CH}_2)_4\text{COO}^- \rightarrow \left[\text{CH}_2\!=\!\text{CH}\!-\!(\text{CH}_2)_4\!-\!\text{COO}^- \xrightarrow{\ \sim\text{dbl. bond}\ }\right.
\end{array}
$$

[7]

$$
\text{CH}_3(\text{CH}_2)_3\!-\!\text{CH}\!=\!\text{CH}\!-\!\text{COO}^- \xrightarrow{+\text{H}_2\text{O}}
$$

$$
\underset{}{\text{CH}_3\!-\!(\text{CH}_2)_3\!-\!\overset{\text{OH}}{\underset{}{\text{CH}}}\!-\!\text{CH}_2\text{COOH}} \xrightarrow[\text{aldol}]{\text{reverse}} \left. \text{CH}_3(\text{CH}_2)_3\text{CHO}\right] \xrightarrow{[0]}
$$

$$
\overset{19}{\text{CH}_3}\!-\!\overset{10}{\text{CH}_2}\!-\!\overset{1}{\text{CH}_2}\!-\!\overset{2}{\text{CH}_2}\!-\!\overset{3}{\text{COOH}} + \overset{4\quad 5}{\text{CH}_3\text{COOH}}
$$

$$
\downarrow \text{stepwise degrd.} \qquad\qquad \downarrow \text{stepwise degrd.}
$$

C-1, C-2, C-3, C-10, C-19 $\qquad$ C-4, C-5

Cornforth, Gore, and Popják[11] established the origin of the remaining carbon atoms in rings C and D. Conversion of biosynthetic cholesterol to Δ^{14}-cholesterol was accomplished via the $\Delta^{5,7}$-diene and the $\Delta^{8(14)}$-ene. Ozonolysis of the Δ^{14}-ene followed by reduction of the ozonide yielded a ketoaldehyde [8] that upon pyrolysis at 220° underwent a reverse Michael with formation of an unsaturated aldehyde [9] and a tricyclic ketone [10]. The aldehyde, as its oxime, was oxidized to the corresponding unsaturated acid [11], and this acid was cleaved in base at 350° to a branched-chain C_9 acid [12] and acetic acid. Further appropriate degradations of these two acids established the origin of C-15, C-16, and C-17.

The tricyclic ketone [10] was converted to its unsaturated analog [13] by bromination and dehydrobromination and then to an anhydride [14] and acetic acid by ozonolysis. The acetic acid was then further degraded to determine the origin of C-13 and C-18.

11. J. W. Cornforth, I. Y. Gore, and G. Popják, *Biochem. J.*, **65**, 94 (1957).

It was not found possible to differentiate chemically between the two carboxyl groups in the dicyclic diacid **[15]** obtained by hydrolysis of the anhydride **[14]**. However, electrolysis of this diacid in aqueous pyridine afforded carbon dioxide, representing the sum of C-12 and C-14, in 70 per cent yield. Fortunately, such a degradation of cholesterol biosynthesized from methyl-labeled acetate yielded nonradioactive carbon dioxide, whereas a similar degradation of cholesterol originating

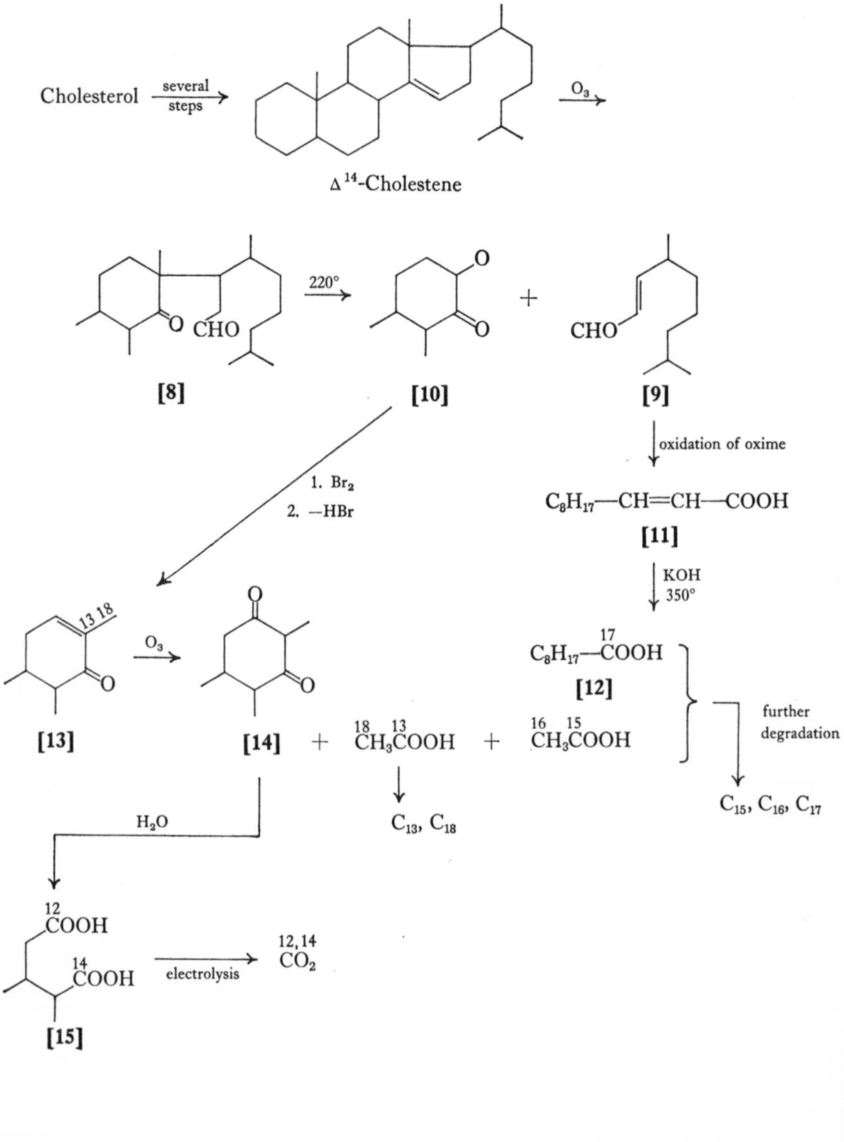

Cholesterol $\xrightarrow[\text{steps}]{\text{several}}$

Δ^{14}-Cholestene

$\xrightarrow{220°}$ +

[8]   **[10]**   **[9]**

$\downarrow$ oxidation of oxime

1. Br$_2$
2. —HBr

C_8H_{17}—CH=CH—COOH
[11]

$\downarrow$ $\begin{array}{c}\text{KOH}\\350°\end{array}$

$\overset{13}{}\overset{18}{}$

$\xrightarrow{O_3}$

$C_8H_{17}\overset{17}{—}COOH$
[12]

[13]   **[14]** + $\overset{18}{C}H_3\overset{13}{C}OOH$ + $\overset{16}{C}H_3\overset{15}{C}OOH$

$\left.\begin{array}{c}\\\\\end{array}\right\}$ further degradation

$\downarrow$

C_{15}, C_{16}, C_{17}

H$_2$O $\downarrow$

C_{13}, C_{18}

$\overset{12}{C}OOH$
$\overset{14}{C}OOH$ $\xrightarrow{\text{electrolysis}}$ $\overset{12,14}{CO_2}$

[15]

from carboxyl-labeled acetate yielded carbon dioxide of an appropriate activity, demonstrating that the origin of both C-12 and C-14 is the carboxyl carbon of acetate.

The origin of C-8, C-9, and C-11 was determined by ozonolysis of a $\Delta^{7,9(11)}$-diene, followed by treatment of the ozonide with hydrogen peroxide, which yielded a diacid [16] and a lactone acid [17]. Electrolysis of the diacid gave carbon dioxide derived from C-8 and C-11, and, by appropriate use of cholesterol biosynthesized from both methyl- and carboxyl-labeled acetate, it was possible to show that both C-8 and C-11 originate in the carboxyl group of acetate. Warming of the lactone acid [17] with sulfuric acid resulted in the liberation from the tertiary carboxyl of C-9 as carbon monoxide, which was oxidized and counted as barium carbonate.

$\Delta^{7,9(11)}$-Cholestadienyl Benzoate   [17]   [16]

12-2 CONVERSION OF LANOSTEROL TO CHOLESTEROL

After discussion of the origin of the various skeletal carbon atoms of cholesterol, we can return to the main biosynthetic pathway that was taken as far as lanosterol in previous chapters.

With the attainment of lanosterol, the biosynthesis of the structural feature most characteristic of the steroids, the cyclopentanoperhydrophenanthrene skeleton has been achieved. For the final transformation of lanosterol to cholesterol there remains only the removal of three superfluous methyl groups, the reduction of the Δ^{24} sidechain double bond and the relocation of the $\Delta^{8(9)}$ ring juncture double bond to $\Delta^{5(6)}$. There are undoubtedly many enzymatic reactions involved in these transformations, but to date only some of them have been elucidated in any detail. The over-all conversion of lanosterol [18] to cholesterol [19] was demonstrated by Langdon and Bloch.[12]

12. R. B. Clayton and K. Bloch, *J. Biol. Chem.*, **218**, 319 (1956).

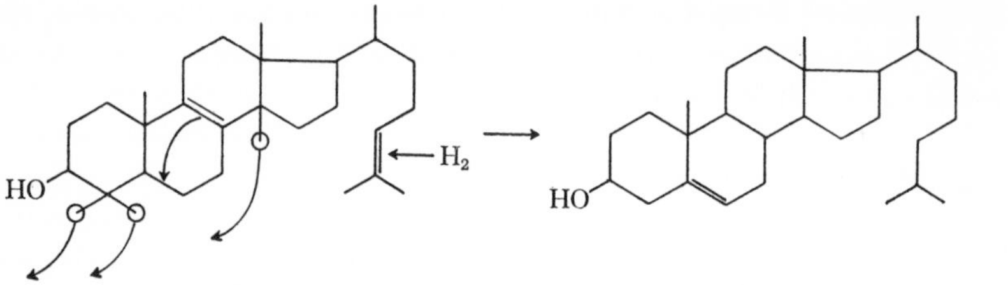

[18]   **[19]**
Lanosterol   Cholesterol

Removal of Methyl Groups

For the removal of the extra methyl carbons there are formally four possibilities: direct loss as a methyl group (for example, by a reversal of a reaction such as the transfer of the S-methyl group of methionine to carbon in the introduction of the C-24 methyl group in ergosterol biosynthesis)[13]; preliminary oxidation to a hydroxymethylene group and loss as formaldehyde (or a more complex biochemical transfer of a group at this oxidation level); further oxidation to a formyl group and loss as formic acid; or, finally, complete oxidation and loss of CO_2. It is the last of these possibilities that seems actually to occur [see Eq. (12–3)].

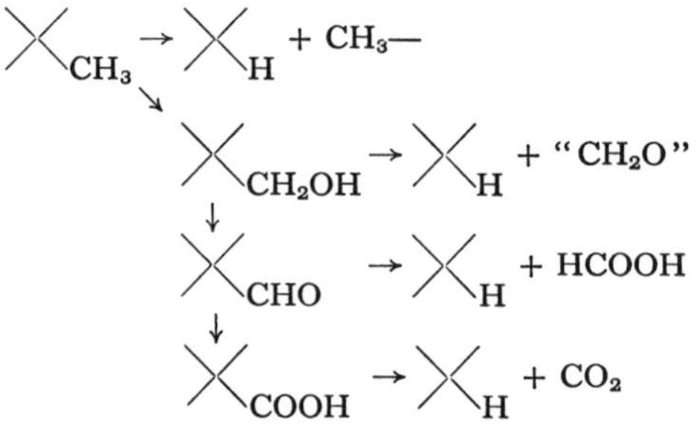

$$(12\text{–}3)$$

On the basis of the previous discussion it follows that lanosterol formed from 2-C^{14}-acetate will be labeled in the methyl carbons. The conversion of this "methyl-labeled" lanosterol to cholesterol results in the production of carbon dioxide and cholesterol with a ratio of total C^{14} activity between the carbon dioxide and cholesterol of about one to five.[14] This is just what would have been anticipated for the

13. G. J. Alexander and E. Schwenk, *J. Am. Chem. Soc.*, **79**, 4554 (1957).
14. J. A. Olson, Jr., M. Lindberg, and K. Bloch, *J. Biol. Chem.*, **226**, 941 (1957).

conversion of lanosterol with 18 labeled positions to cholesterol with 15 labeled carbons and three moles of labeled carbon dioxide. Under similar conditions lanosterol from 1-C^{14}-acetate or cholesterol from

$$\overset{*}{C}_{18}C_{12}H_{50}O \rightarrow \overset{*}{C}_{15}C_{12}H_{46}O + 3\overset{*}{C}O_2$$

1-C^{14}-acetate or from 2-C^{14}-acetate do not yield any active CO_2, demonstrating that the $C^{14}O_2$ produced in the methyl labeled lanosterol → cholesterol conversion does not originate from any part of the lanosterol skeleton except the three carbons expelled during the conversion.

The loss of the methyl carbons as methyl, formaldehyde, or formic acid is made unlikely, since one would expect the intermediacy of such a species to result in a dilution of C^{14} activity by the one-carbon pool in contrast to the almost quantitative recovery of the extra-methyl-group C^{14}-carbons as $C^{14}O_2$. Moreover, the addition of semicarbazide to a system that was converting methyl labeled lanosterol to cholesterol did not trap any active formaldehyde.

Bloch has reported[15] that fractionation of the products of lanosterol metabolism yielded a substance with the chromatographic characteristics of a diol. This metabolite was converted to cholesterol with the production of three moles of $C^{14}O_2$ and is, therefore, presumably a C_{30} diol containing one of the branched methyl groups (probably C-30) as a hydroxymethyl substituent.

Another intermediate in the sequence between lanosterol and cholesterol has been isolated. By a series of ingenious biochemical[16] and chemical[17] methods it has been shown to possess the structure $\Delta^{8(9),24}$-4,4-dimethylcholestadienol (i.e., 30-norlanosterol). It gives rise in turn to cholesterol, but produces only two moles of $C^{14}O_2$ in the process. Thus, it is established that C-30 is the first of the three extra methyl groups to be lost.

The location of the 8,9-double bond in lanosterol is attractive as an activating feature for the decarboxylation of the C-30 carboxylic acid. Such an activated decarboxylation usually results in the migration of the double bond, which would, in this case, form the $\Delta^{8(14),24}$-diene. It is possible that this substance is indeed an intermediate but that it rapidly rearranges to the thermodynamically more stable $\Delta^{8(9),24}$-isomer or that, in the reaction, C-9 acquires an electrophile from an enzyme

15. K. Bloch, *Vitamins Hormones*, **15**, 119 (1957).
16. F. Gautschi and K. Bloch, *J. Am. Chem. Soc.*, **79**, 684 (1957).
17. F. Gautschi and K. Bloch, *J. Biol. Chem.*, **233**, 1343 (1958).

surface that initiates the loss of CO_2. The enzyme-steroid complex is then cleaved by attack of a proton at C-14 producing the isolated intermediate. Such a mechanism will lead to a product with the correct stereochemistry about the D/E ring juncture [Eq. (12-4)].

(12-4)

The loss of the two "extra" methyl groups at C-4 can be activated by the presence at C-3 of a carbonyl group that can be easily derived from the 3-hydroxyl function by the action of an appropriate dehydrogenase. Such a possibility was suggested long ago by Robinson,[18] and recently Bloch has provided evidence[19] that the two C-4 methyl groups are indeed lost from a C-3 ketone. The existence of such a ketonic intermediate in the demethylation process was first indicated by the chromatographic behavior of lanosterol metabolites and later confirmed by the observation that [3-α-H^3]-lanosterol and [3-α-H^3],14-norlanosterol suffer a complete loss of the tritium label when converted to cholesterol. On the other hand, the conversion of [3-α-H^3]-zymosterol to cholesterol proceeds with complete retention of the tritium. Also, $\Delta^{8,24}$-4,4-dimethylcholestadien-3-one is as effectively metabolized to cholesterol as the corresponding alcohol $\Delta^{8,24}$-4,4-dimethylcholestadienol, whereas lanostadienone is inert. It is therefore concluded that the 3-ol to 3-one oxidation occurs after the loss of the C-14 methyl group and that the ensuing reduction to a 3-β-ol occurs directly after the loss of the two C-4 methyl groups. The product of this series of reaction is zymosterol.

The exact order of events resulting in loss of the C-4 methyl groups is not known with certainty, but a rather tenuous argument based upon the recently determined structures of some 4-monomethyl steroids, e.g., cycloeucalenol [20],[20] citrostadienol [21],[21] and methostenol [22]

18. R. Robinson, *J. Soc. Chem. Ind.*, **53**, 1062 (1934).
19. K. Bloch, in *The Biosynthesis of Terpenes and Sterols*, Little, Brown, Boston, 1959, p. 4.
20. J. S. G. Cox, F. E. King, and T. J. King, *Proc. Chem. Soc.*, **1957**, 290.
21. Y. Mazur, A. Weizmann, and F. Sondheimer, *J. Am. Chem. Soc.*, **80**, 1007 (1958).

(*lophenol*)[22] (which has also apparently been isolated from rat feces),[23] would suggest that one methyl group is completely oxidized and lost prior to the onset of the oxidation sequence in the remaining one. The fact that these substances have the 3-β-ol-4-α-dimethyl configuration (i.e., a diequatorial arrangement) taken together with the proposed intermediacy of a 3-keto compound in the loss of methyl groups makes it difficult to say which of the two methyl groups is first lost, since the mechanism of decarboxylation will produce an enol from which the most stable 4-α-methyl steroid will result. The occurrence of a 4,14-dimethylsteroid, such as cycloeucalenol, is of interest and points up the individuality of various biological systems. Not always is the C-14 methyl group lost prior to removal of the methyl groups at C-4.

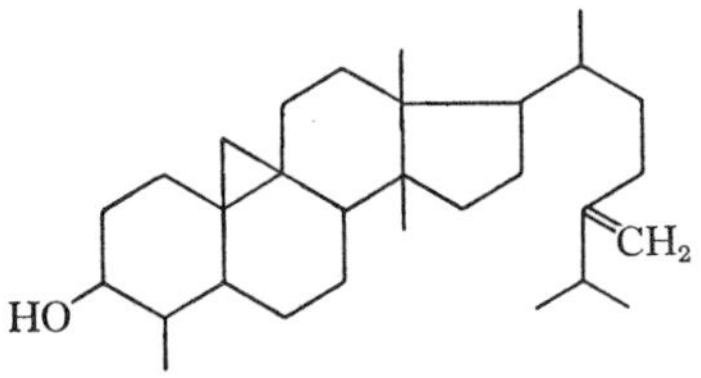

[20]

Cycloeucalenol

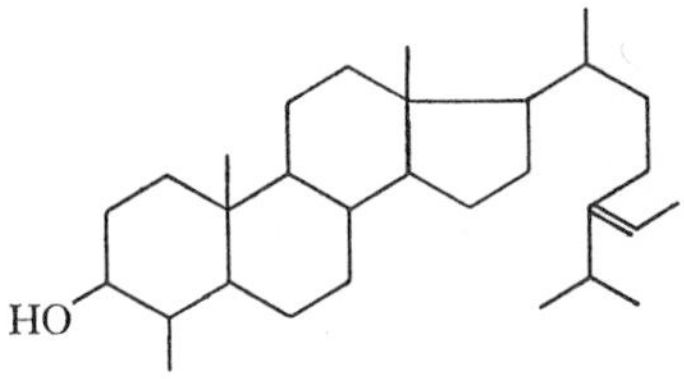

[21]

Citrostadienol

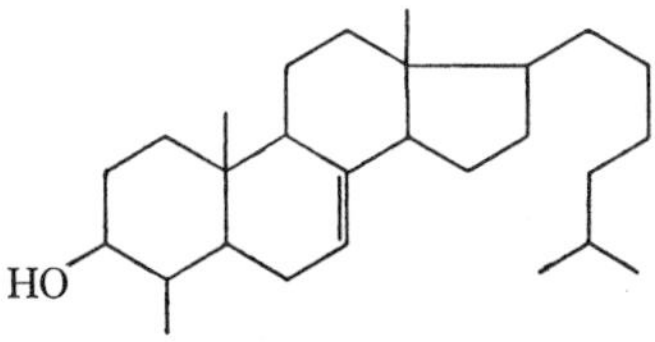

[22]

Lophenol

The C-4 monomethyl sterol, methostenol (4-α-methyl-Δ⁷-cholesten-3-β-ol) [23] has recently been identified in mammalian tissue.[23,24]

22. C. Djerassi, G. W. Krakower, A. J. Lemin, L. H. Liu, J. S. Mills, and R. Villotti, *J. Am. Chem. Soc.*, **80**, 6284 (1958).
23. W. W. Wells and D. H. Neiderhiser, *J. Am. Chem. Soc.*, **79**, 6569 (1957).
24. D. H. Neiderhiser and W. W. Wells, *Arch. Biochem. Biophys.*, **81**, 300 (1959).

The presence of this C-4 monomethyl sterol in the skin of rodents can be demonstrated by direct analysis.

It has also been possible to show [25,26] that 1-C^{14}-acetate injected into rats intracardially was incorporated rapidly into the methostenol of combined liver and intestinal tissue and skin of the rat. After this

[23]

Methostenol

injection the rate of incorporation of C^{14} was such that the specific activity of methostenol was 11 and 3 times that of cholesterol in 5 minutes and 3 hours, respectively. It was also shown that synthetic 4-C^{14}-methostenol administered orally was quickly absorbed by the rat and efficiently converted to cholesterol.

Zymosterol to Cholesterol

The exact details of the interconversions of C_{27} intermediates that give rise to cholesterol is, at present, somewhat uncertain, although there are apparently two available pathways distinguished by the presence or absence of the sidechain double bond. The occurrence of zymosterol as an intermediate in cholesterol biogenesis via the former pathway seems likely. Schwenk et al.[27] have demonstrated the incorporation of C^{14} acetate into zymosterol by resting yeast cells and have also shown that a conversion of zymosterol to cholesterol occurs in the intact animal.[28] It has also been found [29] that 24,25-dihydrozymosterol can be converted by Bucher-type homogenates to cholesterol at the same rate as zymosterol itself. But, in Waring-Blendor homogenates, which

25. W. W. Wells and C. L. Lorah, *J. Biol. Chem.*, **235**, 978 (1960).
26. I. D. Frantz, Jr., M. Ener, and M. L. Mobberley, *Federation Proc.*, **19**, 240 (1960).
27. E. Schwenk, G. J. Alexander, T. H. Stoudt, and C. A. Fish, *Arch. Biochem. Biophys.*, **55**, 274 (1955).
28. E. Schwenk, G. J. Alexander, C. A. Fish, and T. H. Stoudt, *Federation Proc.*, **14**, 752 (1955).
29. J. D. Johnston and K. Bloch, *J. Am. Chem. Soc.*, **79**, 1145 (1957).

generally show a narrower range of metabolic activities, no conversion of 24,25-dihydrozymosterol was observable, whereas zymosterol itself is transformed to cholesterol at an undiminished rate.

A more recent report,[30] however, claims that both C^{14}-zymosterol and 24,25-diH^3-zymosterol are converted to cholesterol by both Bucher and Waring-Blendor homogenates, the latter substance being more readily converted to cholesterol. Moreover, there was evidence against the oxidation of the 24,25-dihydro compound to an intermediate with Δ^{24}. The dihydro compound was efficiently converted to cholesterol after intraportal administration to rats treated with triparanol (cf. subsequent discussion), whereas zymosterol was not, indicating that triparanol apparently inhibited the reduction of the Δ^{24} double bond.

The mechanism by which the 8,9-double bond vanishes and a double bond is created at C-5,6 seems not to be simply a series of hydride migrations, as the conversion of zymosterol to cholesterol in vitro by a liver homogenate system that catalyzes various phases of cholesterol biogenesis requires oxygen. The over-all conversion of zymosterol to cholesterol is, stoichiometrically, a reduction, and the oxygen requirement suggests either that a hydroxyl group is introduced into ring B, which in turn gives rise to a double bond by elimination of water, or that a direct dehydrogenation of ring B to a diene occurs. If these processes are followed by reduction of the unwanted double bond, an intermediate with the correct oxidation site in ring B results.

In this connection, it has been found that the requirements for the conversion of Δ^7-cholestenol to cholesterol[31] are an oxygen atmosphere and cellular factors found to reside in the $105,000 \times g$ supernatant and in the microsomes.[32] This conversion has also been demonstrated for cell-free homogenates of rat liver.[33] It has also been possible to demonstrate the conversion of 4-C^{14}-7-dehydrocholesterol to cholesterol; 4-C^{14}-Δ^6-cholesterol was not detectably converted to cholesterol by rats. This reductive reaction does not require oxygen. The enzyme system for the reaction has been studied and an apparent requirement was found for reduced nicotinamide adenine dinucleotide phosphate.[34] The major product of this reaction was cholesterol.

30. G. J. Shroepfer, Jr., *J. Biol. Chem.*, **236**, 1668 (1961).
31. M. W. Biggs, R. M. Lemmon, and F. T. Pierce, Jr., *Arch. Biochem. Biophys.*, **51**, 155 (1954).
32. I. D. Frantz, Jr., A. G. Davidson, E. Dulit, and M. L. Mobberley, *J. Biol. Chem.*, **234**, 2290 (1959).
33. G. J. Shroepfer, Jr. and I. D. Frantz, Jr., *J. Biol. Chem.*, **236**, 3137 (1961).
34. A. A. Kandutsch, *J. Biol. Chem.*, **237**, 358 (1962).

The product so obtained is $\Delta^{5,24}$-cholestadiene-3β-ol (desmosterol), which has been isolated from developing chick embryos by Stokes et al.[35] Desmosterol has also been found as a companion to cholesterol in rat skin[36,37] and the barnacle. When C^{14}-acetate was present during incubation, the desmosterol was found to have a specific activity 20 times that of cholesterol. The conversion of desmosterol, which was injected intraportally into rats, to cholesterol has been demonstrated[36] and the distribution of activity among cholesterol, desmosterol, and other higher counting companions at different time periods after injection suggested that desmosterol is a final precursor of cholesterol.[38]

The metabolic fate of desmosterol in the brain of chick embryos has been investigated. The substance, which can account for up to 11 per cent of the total sterol was found to have a turnover time of about 1 day, and the distribution of activity indicated that this desmosterol was the major source of newly synthesized cholesterol. That there are other pathways to cholesterol that do not involve desmosterol was shown by the observation that the desmosterol pool in the remainder of the embryo (approximately 1.5 per cent of the total sterol) was comparatively inert.[39]

The reductase system in liver responsible for the saturation of the sidechain double bond has been investigated.[40] A rapid conversion of desmosterol to cholesterol was demonstrated in washed rat-liver mitochondria and microsomes. The reaction requires reduced nicotinamide adenine dinucleotide phosphate, the hydrogen of which is incorporated into the cholesterol formed. Agents which block sulfhydryl groups inhibit the reduction, and this inhibition is reversed by reduced glutathione.

Alternate Pathway

Although the major pathway to cholesterol may involve the route just discussed in which the final step is the saturation of the sidechain double bond of desmosterol, there is accumulating evidence that a

35. W. M. Stokes, W. A. Fish, and F. C. Hickey, *J. Biol. Chem.*, **220**, 415 (1956).
36. W. M. Stokes, F. C. Hickey, and W. A. Fish, *J. Biol. Chem.*, **232**, 347 (1958).
37. U. H. M. Fagerlund and D. R. Idler, *J. Am. Chem. Soc.*, **79**, 6473 (1957).
38. W. M. Stokes and W. A. Fish, *J. Biol. Chem.*, **235**, 2604 (1960).
39. W. A. Fish, J. E. Boyd, and W. M. Stokes, *J. Biol. Chem.*, **237**, 334 (1962).
40. J. Avigan and D. Steinberg, *J. Biol. Chem.*, **236**, 2898 (1961).

series of conversions may exist in which the intermediates possess from the outset a saturated sidechain. Thus Δ^7-cholesterol,[31,41] 24,25-dihydrolanosterol and 24,25-dihydro-14-norlanosterol[15] are convertible to cholesterol.

That the conversion of 24,25-dihydrolanosterol to cholesterol does not involve prior oxidation of the sidechain is clearly shown by the observation that 24,25-diH^3,C^{14}-lanosterol gives rise to cholesterol with the same tritium-to-C^{14} ratio[15] as that present in the starting material.

Methostenol, which was discussed previously, also provides an example of a steroid with a saturated sidechain that can be converted to cholesterol.

Various steroids with saturated sidechains, e.g., 24,25-dihydrolanosterol, 4-α-methyl-Δ^8-cholesterol, Δ^7-cholesterol, and 7-dehydrocholesterol, have been isolated from preputial gland tumors.[42] In another study[43] the conversion of both Δ^7-cholestenol and 7-dehydrocholesterol to cholesterol by liver homogenates at a fairly rapid rate was observed. The specific activities of Δ^7-cholesterol and 7-dehydrocholesterol isolated from preputial tumor slices incubated with labeled acetate were high compared to the specific activity of the isolated cholesterol, making it likely that the former two substances precede cholesterol in the metabolic pathways. Additional evidence for the roles of Δ^7-cholesterol and 7-dehydrocholesterol as precursors of cholesterol is the conversion by tumor homogenates of labeled dihydrolanosterol and 4-α-methyl-Δ^8-cholesterol to Δ^7-cholesterol and 7-dehydrocholesterol more rapidly than into cholesterol and the earlier demonstration[44] that the specific activities of Δ^7-cholesterol and 7-dehydrocholesterol were considerably higher than that of cholesterol after incubation of skin with labeled acetate. The precursor-product relationships of lanosterol, 24,25-dehydrolanosterol, and 4-α-methyl-Δ^8-cholesterol are obvious from a consideration of their structures. If 4-α-methyl-Δ^7-cholesterol, which is present in intestine and skin,[24] is included as an intermediate between its Δ^8-isomer and Δ^7-cholesterol, a series of reactions that result in the conversion of lanosterol to cholesterol via a sequence whose intermediates possess a saturated sidechain is possible.

Gaylor[45] has studied the conversion of squalene to sterols by rat

41. R. G. Langdon and K. Bloch, *J. Biol. Chem.*, **202**, 77 (1953).
42. A. A. Kandutsch and A. E. Russell, *J. Biol. Chem.*, **234**, 2037 (1959).
43. A. A. Kandutsch and A. E. Russell, *J. Biol. Chem.*, **235**, 2256 (1960).
44. J. L. Gaylor and C. A. Baumann, *Federation Proc.*, **18**, 233 (1959).
45. J. L. Gaylor, *J. Biol. Chem.*, **238**, 1643, 1649 (1963).

skin and isolated lanosta-7,24,dien-3β-ol, which may be an intermediate in cholesterol formation. Arsenite inhibited the conversion of lanosterol to cholesterol and resulted in an accumulation of this Δ^7-isomer of lanosterol.

More evidence has been presented indicating that, in rat liver, the reduction of the sidechain double bond may occur many points in the normal pathway from lanosterol to cholesterol. Thus, an enzyme system, associated mostly with microsomes, has been prepared[46] from rat liver homogenates which catalyzes the reduction of lanosterol to 24,25-dihycholanosterol. This reduction is inhibited by MER-29.[47] A detailed study[48] of the time course of the distribution of radioactivity in rat liver nonsaponifiables at short intervals after administration of 2-C[14]-mevalonate supported the conclusion that reduction of the sidechain double bond does not occur exclusively at one point.

Inhibitors of Cholesterol Synthesis

A particularly interesting aspect of cholesterol biosynthesis is the recent discovery of a compound 1-[p-(β-diethylaminoethoxy)-phenyl]-1-(p-toly)-2-(p-chlorophenyl)ethanol (MER-29 or triparanol [24]), which apparently interferes with the last stage in cholesterol synthesis, the reduction of the sidechain double bond of desmosterol.

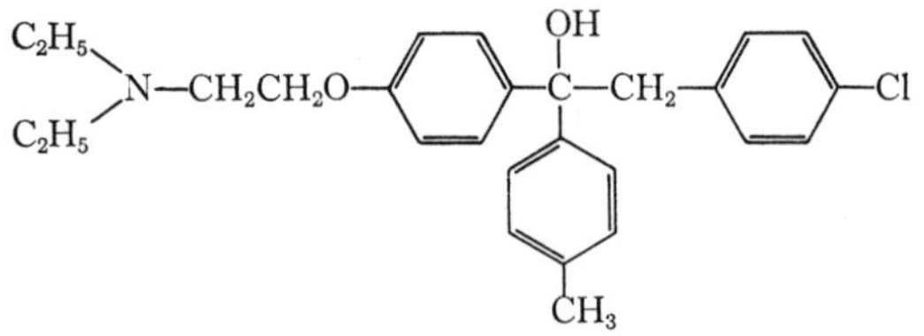

[24]
Triparanol or MER-29

Thus Blohm and MacKenzie have shown[49] that, under the influence of MER-29 the incorporation of 1-C[14]-acetate into cholesterol

46. J. Avigan, D. S. Goodman, and D. Steinberg, *J. Biol. Chem.*, **238**, 1283 (1963).
47. J. L. Gaylor, *Arch. Biochem. Biophys.*, **101**, 108 (1963).
48. D. S. Goodman, J. Avigan, and D. Steinberg, *J. Biol. Chem.*, **238**, 1287 (1963).
49. T. R. Blohm and R. D. MacKenzie, *Arch. Biochem. Biophys.*, **85**, 245 (1959).

was much diminished, even though the amount of radioactivity appearing in the total nonsaponifiable material and in the digitonin precipitable fraction was comparable to that obtained with control rats. Evidence was also obtained that the inhibition acted after the formation of the steroid nucleus,[50] and desmosterol has been found to be the major sterol component in tissues of rats treated with this drug.[51] Evidence has also been presented for the formation of the hitherto undetected sterol $\Delta^{5,7,24}$-cholestatrien-3-β-ol, in the intestinal tissues of guinea pigs treated with triparanol.[52]

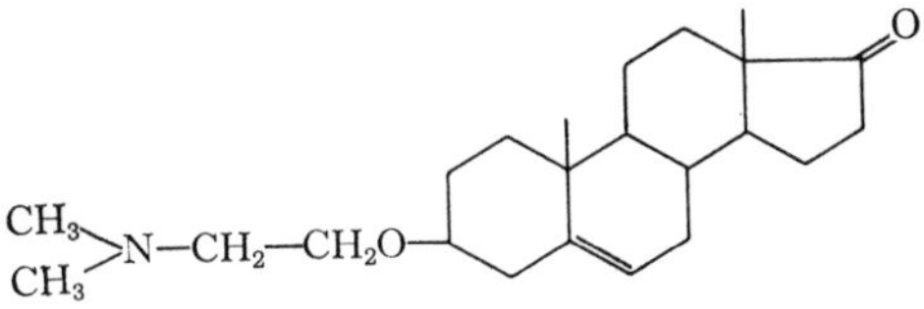

[25]

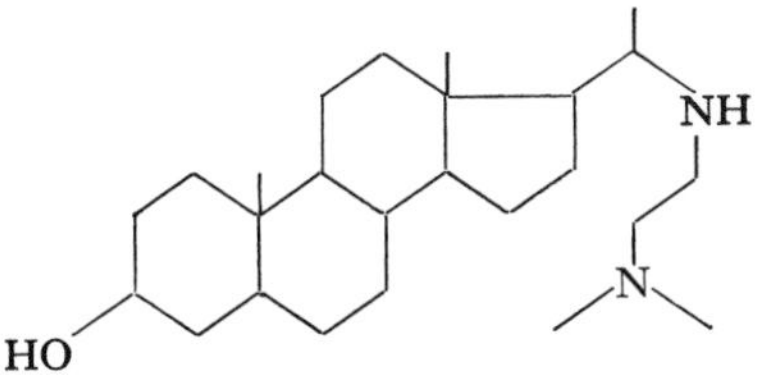

[25b]

Another substance, 3-β-(β-dimethylaminoethoxy)-androst-5-en-17-one [25] has been reported also to inhibit the conversion of desmosterol to cholesterol.[53] 22,25-Diazacholestanol, 20α-(2-dimethyl aminoethyl) amino-5α-pregnane-3β-ol dihydrochloride [25b] also acts in vivo in normal rats and hypercholesterolemic humans as an inhibitor of the conversion of desmosterol to cholesterol.[54,55] In a rat liver

50. T. R. Blohm, T. Kariya, and M. W. Laughlin, *Arch. Biochem. Biophys.*, **85**, 250 (1959).
51. J. Avigan, D. Steinberg, H. E. Vroman, M. J. Thompson, and E. Mosettig, *J. Biol. Chem.*, **235**, 3123 (1960).
52. I. D. Frantz, Jr., A. T. Sanghvi, and R. B. Clayton, *J. Biol. Chem.*, **237**, 3381 (1962).
53. S. Gordon, E. W. Cantrall, W. P. Cekleniak, H. J. Albers, R. Littell, and S. Bernstein, *Biochem. Biophys. Res. Commun.*, **6**, 359 (1961).
54. D. Dvornik and M. Kramel, *Proc. Soc. Exptl. Biol. Med.*, **112**, 1012 (1963).
55. B. A. Sachs and L. Wolfman, *Circulation*, **26**, 669 (1961).

homogenate[56] 22-25,diazacholestanol interfered with the synthesis of mevalonate by inhibiting β-hydroxy-β-methylglutaryl coenzyme A reductase.

Other agents have also been investigated as inhibitors of cholesterol biosynthesis, and although some of them act even before the formation of squalene, their discussion here in one place may not be too out of order. Thus, hepatocatalase (Caperase) inhibits cholesterol between mevalonate and squalene.[57] Phenethylbiguanide interferes with the conversion of isopentenyl pyrophosphate to squalene and the aryl-sulfonylureas, tolbutamide, chlorpropamide, and metahexamide, interfere with some step subsequent to squalene formation.[58] Arsenite inhibits virtually every stage in the biosynthesis of skin sterols; the formation of mevalonate from acetate, the formation of squalene from mevalonate, the conversion of squalene to lanosterol and of lanosterol to cholesterol.[59]

The role of desmosterol as a precursor in cholesterol biosynthesis has been demonstrated[60] in man treated with the drug MER-29. Thus it was found that desmosterol has a higher specific activity than cholesterol when these substances are isolated either from the liver of a MER-29–treated rat given 1-C^{14}-acetate or from the serum of a MER-29–treated man given 2-C^{14}-mevalonic acid.

Summary

The sequence from lanosterol thus consists of a series of demethylation processes and appropriate alteration of the two olefinic centers in the lanosterol. There are apparently two major pathways by which these changes are effected. One pathway has as its terminal step the saturation of the sidechain double bond. The alternate route involves earlier reduction of the sidechain double bonds. There is of course the distinct possibility of intermediates crossing from one of these pathways to the other. In liver both pathways apparently operate, whereas in preputial gland tumor and probably in skin and intestine that pathway involving intermediates with saturated sidechains seems to be the more important. See Chart III.

56. R. E. Ranney and R. E. Counsell, *Proc. Soc. Exptl. Biol. Med.*, **109**, 820 (1962).
57. J. Caravaca, M. D. May, and E. G. Dimond, *Biochem. Biophys. Res. Commun.*, **10**, 189 (1963).
58. H. J. McDonald and J. E. Dalidowicz, *Biochem.*, **1**, 1187 (1962).
59. J. L. Gaylor, *Arch. Biochem. Biophys.*, **101**, 409 (1963).
60. D. Steinberg and J. Avigan, *J. Biol. Chem.*, **235**, 3127 (1960).

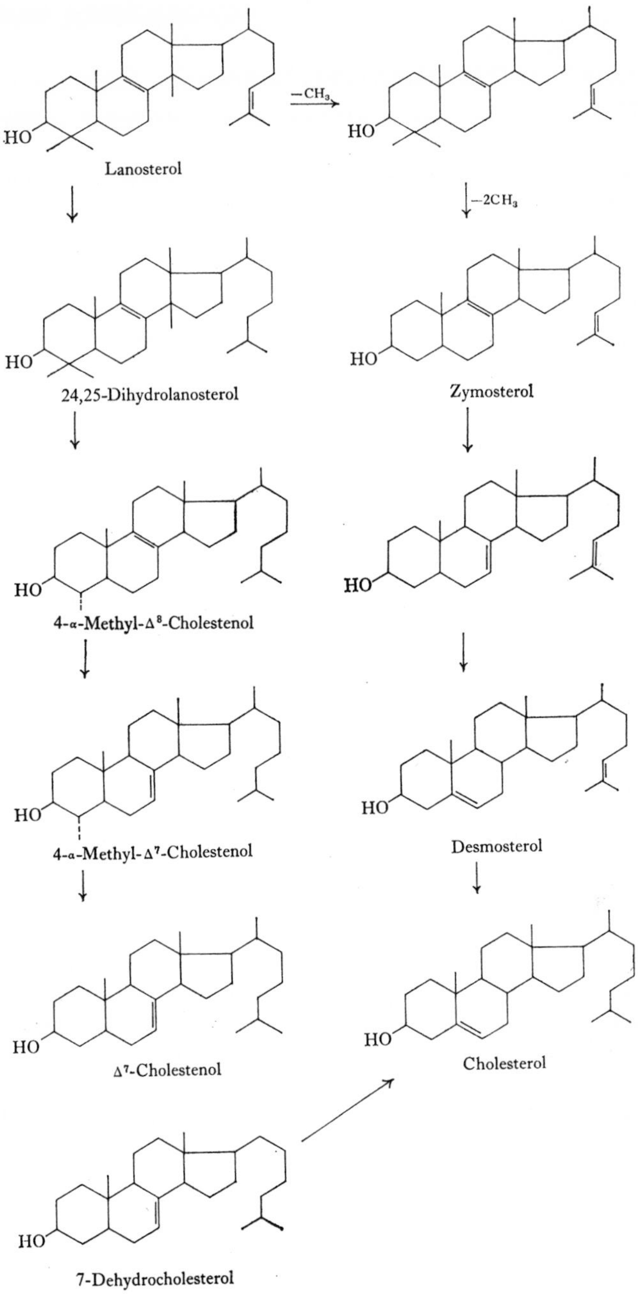

Lanosterol $\xrightarrow{-CH_3}$

$\Big\downarrow -2CH_3$

24,25-Dihydrolanosterol

Zymosterol

4-α-Methyl-Δ^8-Cholestenol

4-α-Methyl-Δ^7-Cholestenol

Desmosterol

Δ^7-Cholestenol

Cholesterol

7-Dehydrocholesterol

Chart III

12–3 ERGOSTEROL

There is a continually increasing body of evidence indicating that ergosterol [26] arises in yeast by a sequence of transformations that parallel those leading to cholesterol, except for some modification in the terminal stages. The results of Sonderhoff and Thomas[2] with deuterioacetate were the first to show clearly the importance of acetate in ergosterol synthesis by yeast. By the use of $C^{14}H_3C^{13}O_2H$ and an acetate-requiring strain of *Neurospora crassa* it was possible to demonstrate[62] that at least 26 of the 28 carbon atoms of ergosterol must have been derived from acetate. By chemical degradation, the same type of distribution of carboxyl and methyl carbons of acetate has been found in the sidechain[63] and in C-11 and C-12[64] of ergosterol, as was previously seen to be characteristic of cholesterol biosynthesized from appropriately labeled acetate.

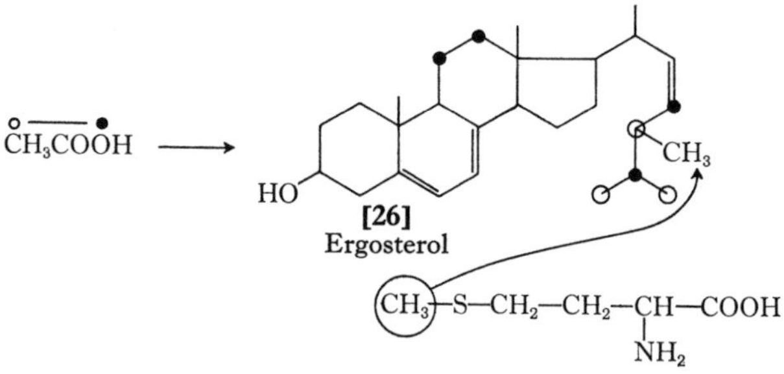

[26]
Ergosterol

[27]
Methionine

The extra methyl carbon of ergosterol [26] has recently been shown to be derived from the one carbon pool, e.g., formate.[65] More extensive experiments[66] with one-carbon donors indicates that C-28 of ergosterol is derived through a transmethylation reaction from the S-methyl group of methionine. Thus, it was found that methionine [27] doubly labeled with tritium and C^{14} in the S-methyl group gave rise to ergosterol, in which the H^3/C^{14} ratio was about 90 per cent that in the

62. R. C. Ottke, E. L. Tatum, I. Zabin, and K. Bloch, *J. Biol. Chem.*, **189**, 429 (1951).
63. D. J. Hanahan and S. J. Wakil, *J. Am. Chem. Soc.*, **75**, 273 (1953).
64. W. G. Dauben and T. W. Hutton, *J. Am. Chem. Soc.*, **78**, 2647 (1956).
65. H. Danielsson and K. Bloch, *J. Am. Chem. Soc.*, **79**, 500 (1957).
66. G. J. Alexander and E. Schwenk, *J. Am. Chem. Soc.*, **79**, 4554 (1957).

original methionine. Furthermore, it was found that propionate was not incorporated into the ergosterol sidechain.

Other work by Schwenk and Alexander[67] has demonstrated that the following conversions can occur in a cell-free yeast homogenate: $1\text{-}C^{14}$-acetate → ergosterol, lanosterol, and zymosterol; C^{14}-squalene and H^3-lanosterol → ergosterol; but C^{14}-zymosterol does *not* produce cholesterol. On the basis of this evidence it can be concluded that the biosynthetic pathway to ergosterol probably parallels that to cholesterol at least as far as lanosterol, but that somewhere before zymosterol the paths diverge. Whether the C-28 methyl group is acquired at a C_{30} stage or at a C_{27} stage is unknown.

There is evidence that the intracellular site of ergosterol biosynthesis in *Torulopsis lipofera* is the mitochondria or large microsomes.[68]

It is interesting to note that certain varieties of fungi produce a C_{31} metabolite, eburicoic acid [28], whose biosynthesis has many[69-71] features in common with ergosterol, e.g., distribution of carboxyl and methyl carbons of precursor acetate (cf. Sec. 10-13).

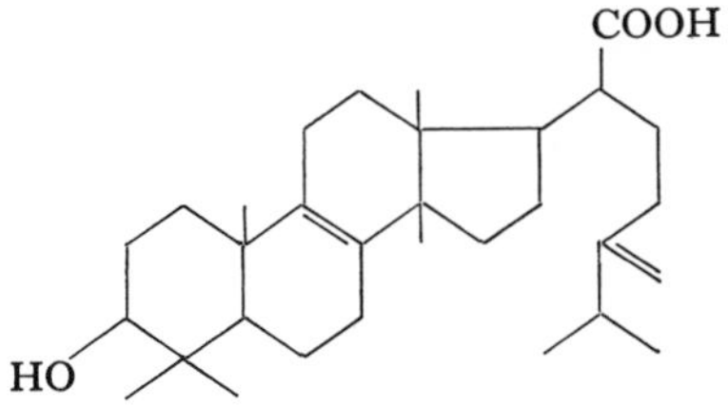

[28]

67. E. Schwenk and G. J. Alexander, *Arch. Biochem. Biophys.*, **76**, 65 (1958).
68. C. G. Schuytema and G. F. Lata, *Arch. Biochem. Biophys.*, **75**, 40 (1958).
69. W. G. Dauben and J. H. Richards, *J. Am. Chem. Soc.*, **78**, 5329 (1956).
70. W. G. Dauben, Y. Ban, and J. H. Richards, *J. Am. Chem. Soc.*, **79**, 968, (1957).
71. W. G. Dauben, G. J. Fonken, and G. A. Boswell, *J. Am. Chem. Soc.*, **79**, 1000, (1957).

chapter thirteen | Further Transformations of Cholesterol

Cholesterol occupies a central position in steroid metabolism. It is, therefore, appropriate to inquire into the kinds of further transformations in which cholesterol can participate and from which arise the 24-carbon bile acids, the 21-carbon cortical hormones, the 19-carbon androgens, and the 18-carbon estrogens. It is manifestly impossible to discuss in detail the many reactions that connect all these physiologically important substances, so the purpose of this section is not to attempt a comprehensive treatment but, rather, by discussion of some of these processes to indicate the wide scope of the biochemical reactions of the steroids. Nor will this section include a discussion of the many reactions of steroids that are effected by various microbiological systems —an area that has been reviewed.[1]

13-1 REACTION TYPES

It will be useful to outline, initially, the kinds of reactions involved in the conversion of cholesterol to its metabolic successors. One of the most important is the scission of carbon–carbon bonds.[2] Such a scission removes an appropriate number of carbon atoms from the isooctyl sidechain of cholesterol for the formation of its degradation products.

1. A. Wettstein, *Experientia*, **11**, 465 (1955).
2. M. Hayano, N. Saba, R. I. Dorfman, and O. Hechter, *Recent Progr. Hormone Res.*, **12**, 79 (1956).

326

A further reaction type of great importance is the hydroxylation of saturated carbon atoms that are unactivated in any classical sense.

$$\rangle C-H \rightarrow \rangle C-OH$$

As in the case of the oxido-cyclization of squalene to lanosterol, these hydroxylation processes utilize molecular oxygen[3] and require reduced nicotinamide adenine nucleotides.[3-9] The enzymes involved are therefore of the mixed-function oxidase type.[10] The hydroxylation reaction in adrenal tissue has been shown[11] to require probably three distinct enzymes and a heat-stable cofactor in addition to molecular oxygen and reduced nicotinamide adenine dinucleotide phosphate. The stereochemistry of these reactions has been shown to involve retention of configuration in all cases so far investigated,[12-15] i.e., the hydroxyl group occupies the same steric location as the hydrogen which it replaces. This stereochemical result is finding increasing analogy in studies of electrophilic substitution reactions at saturated carbon. For example, the cleavage by bromine of optically active sec-butylmercuric

3. M. Hayano, M. C. Lindberg, R. I. Dorfman, J. E. H. Hancock, and W. von E. Doering, *Arch. Biochem. Biophys.*, **59**, 529 (1955).
4. B. B. Brodie, J. Axelrod, J. R. Cooper, L. Gaudette, B. N. La Du, C. Mitoma, and S. Udenfriend, *Science*, **121**, 603 (1955).
5. O. Hayaishi, M. Katagiri, and S. Rothberg, *J. Am. Chem. Soc.*, **77**, 5450 (1955).
6. H. S. Mason, W. L. Fowlks, and E. Peterson, *J. Am. Chem. Soc.*, **77**, 2914 (1955).
7. C. Mitoma, H. S. Posner, H. C. Reitz, and S. Udenfriend, *Arch. Biochem. Biophys.*, **61**, 431 (1956).
8. K. J. Ryan, *Federation Proc.*, **15**, 344 (1956).
9. M. L. Sweat, R. A. Aldrich, C. H. de Bruin, W. L. Fowlks, L. R. Heiselt, and H. S. Mason, *Federation Proc.*, **15**, 367 (1956).
10. H. S. Mason, *Adv. Enzymol.*, **19**, 79 (1957).
11. G. M. Tomkins, J. F. Curran, and P. J. Michael, *Biochim. Biophys. Acta*, **28**, 449 (1958).
12. S. Bergström, S. Lindstedt, B. Samuelson, E. J. Corey, and G. A. Gregoriou, *J. Am. Chem. Soc.*, **80**, 2337 (1958).
13. E. J. Corey, G. A. Gregoriou, and D. H. Peterson, *J. Am. Chem. Soc.*, **80**, 2338 (1958).
14. M. Hayano, M. Gut, R. I. Dorfman, A. Schubert, and R. Siebert, *Biochim. Biophys. Acta*, **32**, 269 (1959).
15. M. Hayano, M. Gut, R. I. Dorfman, O. K. Sebek, and D. H. Peterson, *J. Am. Chem. Soc.*, **80**, 2336 (1958).

bromide[16] or of *cis*- or *trans*-4-methylcyclohexylmercuric bromides[17] proceeds with retention of configuration.

Another close chemical analog of this type of biological reaction is to be found in the recent demonstration[18] of the formation [Eq. (13-1)] of a cyclic ether from a hydroperoxide tosylate, which involves attack on a carbon unactivated in any classical fashion.

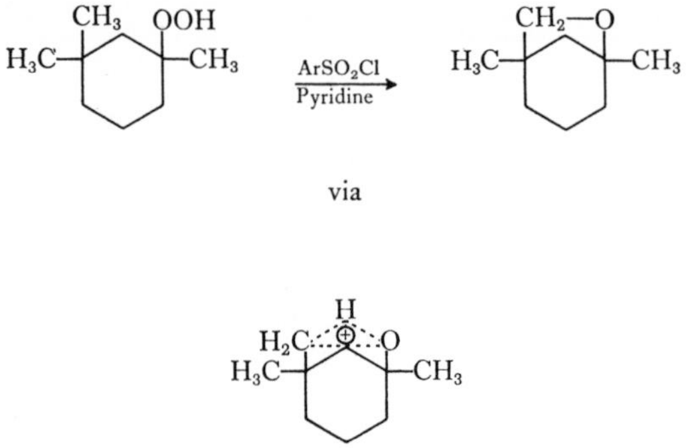

via

(13-1)

One important feature of the reaction in this case is its steric facilitation, owing to the geographic proximity of the methyl group and hydroperoxide function.   Surely, one can ascribe to an enzyme the property of bringing two centers sufficiently close together so that reactions that, in classical chemistry, derive assistance by virtue of being intramolecular can, under the influence of an enzyme, occur intermolecularly with corresponding ease.

Although it is possible that the biologically operative electrophile is a positive oxygen bonded to carbon, it is more likely that the positive oxygen is linked to a metal, such as iron in the form of a chelated ferryl oxide.   Thus the over-all biological process might be represented as in Eq. (13-2).

$$l_5Fe^{2+} + O_2 + 2H^+ + 2e^- = (l_5FeO)^{2+} + H_2O$$

$$(l_5FeO)^{2+} + {>}C{-}H \rightarrow \left[C \overset{\cdot \cdot H \cdot \cdot}{\cdots} O{-}Fel_5 \right]^{2+} \rightarrow {>}C{-}OH + l_5Fe^{2+} \quad (13\text{-}2)$$

16. F. R. Jensen, L. D. Whipple, D. K. Wedegaertner, and J. A. Landgrebe, *J. Am. Chem. Soc.*, **81**, 1262 (1959).
17. F. R. Jensen and L. H. Gale, *J. Am. Chem. Soc.*, **81**, 1261 (1959).
18. E. J. Corey and R. W. White, *J. Am. Chem. Soc.*, **80**, 6686 (1958).

Yet another reaction of importance is the introduction, removal, and rearrangement of double bonds. The first may involve prior hydroxylation and subsequent loss of water. Rearrangement of double bonds may in some cases eventuate as a result of a series of oxidations and reductions—as in the case of the movement of $\Delta^{8,9}$-unsaturation of zymosterol to $\Delta^{5,6}$-in cholesterol.

Also significant in steroid metabolism is the interconversion of hydroxyl and keto functions by appropriate dehydrogenases. In this as in any other area of enzymatic interconversions, it is probable that a variety of enzymes is involved, each being specific for keto or hydroxyl groups in a given chemical environment For example an 11-β-hydroxysteroid dehydrogenase has been localized in mammalian liver microsomes,[19] where it is closely associated with, but distinct from, a 3-α-hydroxysteroid dehydrogenase.

13-2 BILE ACIDS

Cholic acid [1], chenodesoxycholic acid [2], desoxycholic acid [3], and lithocholic acid [4] represent the end products of the major pathway of cholesterol metabolism in higher animals. In addition to their occur-

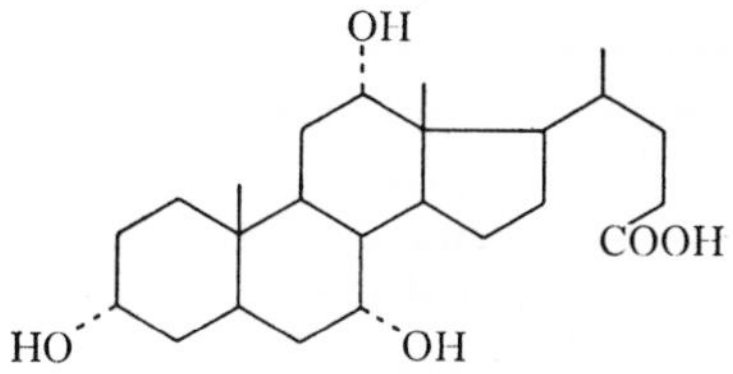

[1]
Cholic Acid

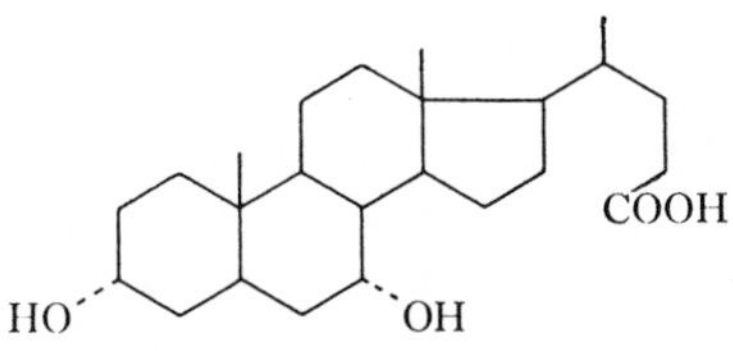

[2]
Chenodesoxycholic Acid

19. B. Hurlock and P. Talalay, *Arch. Biochem. Biophys.*, **80**, 468 (1959).

rence as free acids, the bile acids are frequently conjugated by formation of amides with glycine as in glycocholic acid (cholylNHCH$_2$CO$_2$H), or with taurine in taurocholic acid (cholylNHCH$_2$CH$_2$SO$_3$H).

| [3] | [4] |
| Desoxycholic Acid | Lithocholic Acid |

Synthesis from Cholesterol

The first evidence that cholesterol can be converted into cholic acid came in 1943 with the observation [20] that the intravenous administration of an emulsion of H^2-cholesterol to a dog led to the isolation of deuterium-labeled cholic acid with a concentration of deuterium such as to suggest that two-thirds or more of the cholic acid had been derived from the plasma cholesterol. Chaikoff and co-workers [21] found that the rat could oxidize a large amount of 26-C^{14}-cholesterol to radioactive carbon dioxide. Nineteen per cent of the C^{14} dose was recovered in the form of respiratory C^{14}O$_2$ in the first 24 hours and 40 per cent by the end of 84 hours. On the other hand, no C^{14}O$_2$ was obtained when 4-C^{14}-cholesterol was administered. Much work [22-24] on the quantitative aspects of cholesterol metabolism leads to the generalization that, in the rat, cholesterol is ultimately excreted 85 per cent as fecal steroidal acids, 10 per cent as fecal sterols, and 1 per cent in the urine, largely as steroid hormones and their metabolites. In man, cholesterol is converted primarily to glycocholic acid, although some taurocholic acid and a small amount of conjugated dihydroxy bile acid, possibly glycodesoxycholic acid, is formed.[25] In agreement with this statement,

20. K. Bloch, B. N. Berg, and D. Rittenberg, *J. Biol. Chem.*, **149**, 511 (1943).
21. I. L. Chaikoff, M. D. Siperstein, W. G. Dauben, H. L. Bradlow, J. F. Eastham, G. M. Tomkins, J. R. Meier, R. W. Chen, S. Hotta, and P. A. Srere, *J. Biol. Chem.*, **194**, 413 (1952).
22. S. Bergström and A. Norman, *Proc. Soc. Exptl. Biol. Med.*, **83**, 71 (1953).
23. M. D. Siperstein and I. L. Chaikoff, *Federation Proc.*, **14**, 767 (1955).
24. M. D. Siperstein, M. E. Jayko, I. L. Chaikoff, and W. G. Dauben, *Proc. Soc. Exptl. Biol. Med.*, **81**, 720 (1952).
25. M. D. Siperstein and A. W. Murray, *J. Clin. Invest.*, **34**, 1449 (1955).

it is found that after the administration of 4-C^{14}-cholesterol to human patients over 95 per cent of the activity in the bile appeared as bile acids. An unexpectedly large fraction (34 to 81 per cent) of fecal radioactivity was present in sterols.[26]

The question of whether cholesterol is an obligatory precursor of bile acids is still somewhat unsettled. There are reports that the administration of labeled acetate led to bile acids, which, during 3 days[27] and 1 day,[28] had initially higher specific activities than did the biliary cholesterol. On the other hand, a study using C^{14}- and tritium-labeled acetate and cholesterol on human patients with a complete bile fistula showed that the specific activity of the cholic acid was always lower than that of both plasma-free cholesterol and bile cholesterol.[29]

It is important to note, however, that these results were obtained only on animals with a bile fistula in which the rate of bile acid synthesis is 10 times higher than in normal rats.[30] Bergström[31] has pointed out the quite reasonable possibility that, under these abnormal conditions, there is not sufficient time for the newly formed cholesterol in the liver to equilibrate with that circulating in the blood before this newly formed cholesterol is degraded to bile acids, a situation which would produce bile acids of higher specific activity than that of the total cholesterol.

Trihydroxycoprostane

The conversion of cholesterol to cholic acid involves three types of transformations: the degradation of the sidechain by three carbons, reduction of the nuclear double bond, and hydroxylation of the ring. The question of the sequence of events leading between these two substances has been extensively examined by the Scandinavian group who have presented convincing evidence[32] that nuclear transformations precede sidechain degradation in the conversion of cholesterol to cholic acid. Using C^{14}- and tritium-labeled precursors in the rat, they observed cholic acid formation from 7-α-hydroxycholesterol,[33]

26. J. Avigan and D. Steinberg, *Federation Proc.*, **18**, 5 (1959).
27. E. Staple and S. Gurin, *Biochim. Biophys. Acta*, **15**, 372 (1954).
28. S. Dayton, E. H. Mosbach, F. Drimmer, and F. E. Kendall, *Federation Proc.*, **14**, 460 (1955).
29. R. S. Rosenfeld, L. Hellman, and T. F. Gallagher, *Federation Proc.*, **14**, 271 (1955).
30. S. Eriksson, *Proc. Soc. Exptl. Biol. Med.*, **94**, 578 (1957).
31. S. Bergström, personal communication.
32. S. Bergström and B. Borgström, *Ann. Rev. Biochem.*, **25**, 177 (1956).
33. S. Lindstedt, *Acta Chem. Scand.*, **11**, 417 (1957).

3-α,7-α-dihydroxycoprostane,[34]   and   3-α,7-α,12-α-trihydroxycopros-
tane.[35]

Cholic acid, is, however, not formed from 3-β-hydroxy-Δ[5]-cholenic
acid (the C-24 carboxylic acid corresponding to cholesterol),[36] from 25-
or 26-hydroxycholesterol,[37] or from any known bile acid except
desoxycholic acid.[38]

Some recent studies of bile acid synthesis in the alligator (*Alligator
mississippiensis*) have shed light on the question of bile acid synthesis
in mammals.   Trihydroxycoprostanic acid [5] is formed from cholesterol

[5]

by the alligator.[39]   Further studies[40] in vitro provided evidence
favoring trihydroxycoprostanic acid as an intermediate in bile acid
formation in mammals.   These showed that trihydroxycoprostanic
acid inhibited the production of $C^{14}O_2$ from 26-C^{14}-cholesterol by rat
liver mitochondria, that $C^{14}O_2$ is formed from 26,27-C^{14}-trihydroxy-
coprostanic acid in vitro, and that 4-C^{14}-cholic acid is produced
from 4-C^{14}-trihydrosoprostanic acid in vitro.

Moreover, rat liver mitochondria readily oxidize[41] 3-α-,7-α-,
12-α-trihydroxycoprostane and to a lesser degree its 24-hydroxy and
24-keto derivatives.   Coincubation of these compounds with each other
indicated that 3α,7α,12α-trihydroxycoprostane is the most nearly
related to, if not actually on, the pathway from cholesterol to cholic

34. S. Bergström and S. Lindstedt, *Biochim. Biophys. Acta*, 19, 556 (1956).
35. S. Bergström, K. Pääbo, and J. A. Rumpf, *Acta Chem. Scand.*, 8, 1109
    (1954).
36. S. Bergström and K. Pääbo, *Acta Chem. Scand.*, 9, 699 (1955).
37. D. S. Fredrickson and K. Ono, *Biochim. Biophys. Acta*, 22, 183 (1956).
38. S. Bergström, M. Rottenberg, and J. Sjövall, *Z. Physiol. Chem.*, 295, 278
    (1953).
39. T. Briggs, M. W. Whitehouse, and E. Staple, *Ar ch. Biochem. Biophys.*,
    85, 275 (1959).
40. T. Briggs, M. W. Whitehouse, a nd E. Staple, *J. Biol. Chem.*, 236,
    688 (1961).
41. M. W. Whitehouse, E. Staple, and S. Gurin, *J. Biol. Chem.*, 236, 73
    (1961).

acid. This work supplements the Scandinavian work mentioned above in which the same conversion of 3α,7α,12α-trihydroxycoprostane to cholic acid was demonstrated in rats with bile fistulas.

Another piece of evidence in support of the contention that nuclear hydroxylation precedes sidechain oxidation is the reported isolation[42] of what is probably a C_{27}-trihydroxy steroid from cholesterol metabolism by mouse-liver mitochondria.

Last, an enzyme system has been found[42b] in rat liver which is capable of converting cholesterol to 3α,7α,12α-trihydroxycoprostane, reinforcing the role of this substance as an obligatory intermediate between cholesterol and the bile acids.

These results thus prove that nuclear hydroxylation is complete before the sidechain oxidation commences. The exact sequence of the events by which the nucleus is converted from a 3-β-ol-5-ene, as in cholesterol, to a 3α,7α,12α-triol, as in cholic acid, is not known in detail. The primary occurrence of an epimerization of the 3-β-ol to a 3-α-ol and a reduction of the 5-ene function has been eliminated, since none of the intermediates (3-α-hydroxycholest-5-ene, 3-β-hydroxy-coprostane, 3-α-hydroxycoprostane, nor Δ⁴- or Δ⁵-cholestenone) expected for such a series of transformations is converted to cholic acid.[43-45] Bergström[46] has pointed out a generalization that the 12-α-hydroxylase enzyme is only effective when the normal-isoöctyl sidechain is intact, and considers that the 7-α-hydroxylation may well be the rate-determining step, as all 7-α-hydroxy derivatives are more rapidly metabolized to cholic acid than cholesterol itself (Chart I).

Reduction of Cholesterol

An interesting study has been made of the reduction of the cholesterol double bond.[47] The reduction of 6-H³-4C¹⁴-cholesterol by bile fistula rats gave chenodeoxycholic acid with an unchanged H^3/C^{14} ratio.

42. H. Danielsson and M. G. Horning, *Biochim. Biophys. Acta*, **34**, 596 (1959).
42b. D. Mendelsohn and E. Staple, *Biochem.*, **2**, 577 (1963).
43. S. Bergström, *Record Chem. Progr. Kresge-Hooker Sci. Lib.*, **16**, 63 (1955).
44. F. M. Harold, D. D. Chapman, and I. L. Chaikoff, *J. Biol. Chem.*, **224**, 609 (1957).
45. F. M. Harold, M. E. Jayko, and I. L. Chaikoff, *J. Biol. Chem.*, **216**, 439 (1955).
46. S. Bergström, *Biosynthesis of Terpenes and Sterols*, Little, Brown, Boston, 1959, p. 185.
47. B. Samuelsson, *J. Biol. Chem.*, **234**, 2852 (1959).

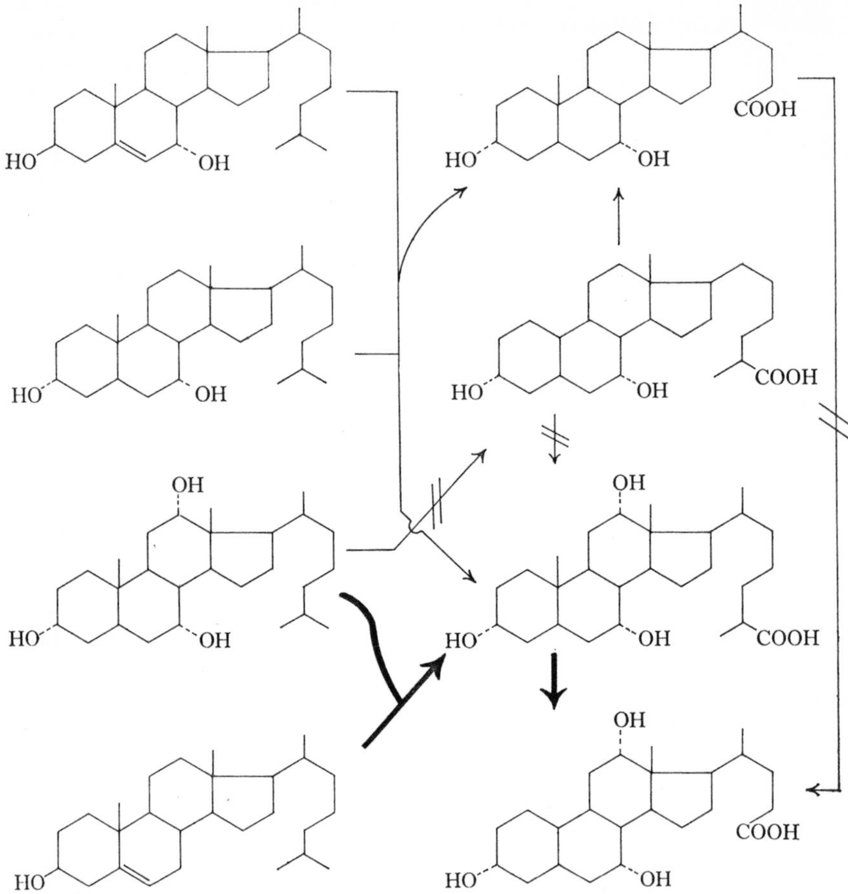

Chart I *Summary of metabolic interconversions in bile-fistula rats of possible intermediates between cholesterol and cholic acid.*

With the aid of specific enzymatic 6-α- and 6-β-hydroxylations it was found that the 6-H³ label was in the 6-α-position. Thus the reduction of the cholesterol double bond takes place by a stereospecific process in which the two newly acquired hydrogens are *cis* and in a β orientation [Eq. (13–3).]

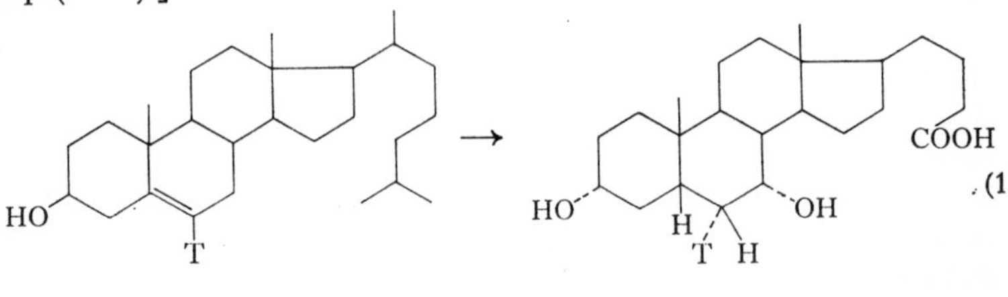

$$(13\text{–}3)$$

Pathway not Involving Cholic Acid

In addition to the metabolic pathway involving cholic acid, there exists a pathway in which lithocholic acid, chenodesoxycholic acid, and trihydroxycholanic acids other than cholic acid participate. For example, 3-β-hydroxy-Δ^5-cholenic acid, Δ^5-cholestenone, 3-β-hydroxy-coprostane, and 3-α-cholesterol all yield acidic products similar to, but not identical with, cholic acid.[48,49] Also, lithocholic and chenodesoxycholic acids give rise to substances similar to cholic acid.[48] The isolation of one of these trihydroxycholanic acids (acid I, 3α,6β,7β-trihydroxycholanic acid[50,51]) from the bile of normal rats[52] and from the urine of surgically jaundiced rats[53] has been reported. Its appearance as a distinct metabolite of chenodesoxycholic acid has also been observed.[54]

Also participating in this area of bile acid metabolism are hyodesoxycholic acid[55,56] and 7-ketolithocholic acid.[57,58] The former gives rise to acid I, acid II, (3α,6β,7α-trihydroxycholanic acid),[59] acid IV,

48. S. Bergström, *Record Chem. Progr. Kresge-Hooker Sci. Lib.*, **16**, 63 (1955).
49. F. M. Harold, M. E. Jayko, and I. L. Chaikoff, *J. Biol. Chem.*, **216**, 439 (1955).
50. S. L. Hsia, J. T. Matschiner, T. A. Mahowald, W. H. Elliott, E. A. Doisy, Jr., S. A. Thayer, and E. A. Doisy, *J. Biol. Chem.*, **225**, 811 (1957).
51. S. L. Hsia, J. T. Matschiner, T. A. Mahowald, W. H. Elliott, E. A. Doisy, Jr., S. A. Thayer, and E. A. Doisy, *J. Biol. Chem.*, **230**, 573 (1958).
52. J. T. Matschiner, T. A. Mahowald, W. H. Elliott, E. A. Doisy, Jr., S. L. Hsia, and E. A. Doisy, *J. Biol. Chem.*, **225**, 771 (1957).
53. T. A. Mahowald, J. T. Matschiner, S. L. Hsia, E. A. Doisy, Jr., W. H. Elliott, and E. A. Doisy, *J. Biol. Chem.*, **225**, 795 (1957).
54. T. A. Mahowald, J. T. Matschiner, S. L. Hsia, R. Richter, E. A. Doisy, Jr., W. H. Elliott, and E. A. Doisy, *J. Biol. Chem.*, **225**, 781 (1957).
55. J. T. Matschiner, T. A. Mahowald, S. L. Hsia, E. A. Doisy, Jr., W. H. Elliott, and E. A. Doisy, *J. Biol. Chem.*, **225**, 803 (1957).
56. J. T. Matschiner, R. L. Ratliff, T. A. Mahowald, E. A. Doisy, Jr., W. H. Elliott, S. L. Hsia, and E. A. Doisy, *J. Biol. Chem.*, **230**, 589 (1958).
57. T. A. Mahowald, M. W. Yin, J. T. Matschiner, S. L. Hsia, E. A. Doisy, Jr., W. H. Elliott, and E. A. Doisy, *J. Biol. Chem.*, **230**, 581 (1958).
58. B. Samuelsson, *Acta Chem. Scand.*, **13**, 236 (1959).
59. S. L. Hsia, J. T. Matschiner, T. A. Mahowald, W. H. Elliott, E. A. Doisy, Jr., S. A. Thayer, and E. A. Doisy, *J. Biol. Chem.*, **230**, 597 (1958).

(3α,6α,7β-trihydroxycholanic acid),[60] 3α,6β-dihydroxycholanic acid, and 6-ketoallolithocholic acid. The metabolites of 7-ketolithocholic acid are acid I, acid II, 3α,7β-dihydroxycholanic acid, and chenodesoxycholic acid. In short, this metabolic area is characterized by the absence of a hydroxyl group at C-12 and the occurrence of 6-hydroxyl functions, whereas the participants in the cholic acid pathway have no oxygen function at C-6 and either possess or acquire a hydroxyl group at C-12.

Conversion of Trihydroxycoprostane to Cholic Acid; Sidechain Scission

With the completion of nuclear transformations the cholesterol nucleus is now present as 3α,7α,12α-trihydroxycoprostane. There remains the amputation of three carbons of the isoöctyl sidechain to complete the conversion to cholic acid. The first steps in this process are the sequential oxidation of one of the terminal methyl groups to a carboxyl function as suggested by Fieser and Fieser.[61] Thus Danielsson found that mouse-liver mitochondria oxidize 3α,7α,12α-trihydroxycoprostane to derivatives with a new hydroxyl group at C-26, i.e., 3α,7α,12α,26-tetrahydroxycoprostane, or more drastically to a derivative with this carbon present as a carboxyl group i.e., 3α,7α,12α-trihydroxycoprostanic acid. Rat liver mitochondria produced only the 27-hydroxy substance.[62] Oxidation of the dihydroxycoprostane (3α,7α-dihydroxycoprostane) to its 26-hydroxy analog (3α,7α,26-trihydroxycoprostane) by mouse-liver mitochondria has been observed.[62b] The conversion of the acid 3α,7α,12α-trihydroxycoprostanic acid to cholic acid has been demonstrated.[63]

These three terminal carbons are cleaved from the steroid sidechain as an intact three-carbon unit that appears as propionyl coenzyme A.[64] The preparation that catalyzed this cleavage consisted of rat liver mitochondria, supplemented with 105,500 × g supernatant fluid, adenosine triphosphate, nicotine adenine dinucleotide, nicotinamide,

60. S. L. Hsia, J. T. Matschiner, T. A. Mahowald, W. H. Elliott, E. A. Doisy, Jr., S. A. Thayer, and E. A. Doisy, *J. Biol. Chem.*, **226**, 667 (1957).

61. L. F. Fieser and M. Fieser, *Steroids*, Reinhold, New York, 1959, p. 442.

62. H. Danielsson, *Acta Chem. Scand.*, **14**, 348 (1960).

62b. O. Bersius and H. Danielsson, *Acta, Chem. Scand.*, **17**, 1293 (1963).

63. T. Briggs, M. W. Whitehouse, and E. Staple, *J. Biol. Chem.*, **236**, 688 (1961).

64. H. M. Suld, E. Staple, and S. Gurin, *J. Biol. Chem.*, **237**, 338 (1962).

and glutathione. Incubation of 26,27-C^{14}-3α,7α,12α,26-tetrahydroxy-coprostane with carrier propionyl coenzyme A led to the recovery of labeled propionyl coenzyme A.

This identification of propionyl coenzyme A as the major cleavage product from the steroid sidechain agrees with the observation that only 10 to 15 per cent of the isotope of 26-C^{14}-cholesterol was oxidized to carbon dioxide after long incubation periods and that carbon dioxide production was suppressed by reagents that inhibit the tricarboxylic acid cycle.[65]

The mechanism of Eq. (13–4) has been suggested for the loss of the three sidechain carbon atoms.

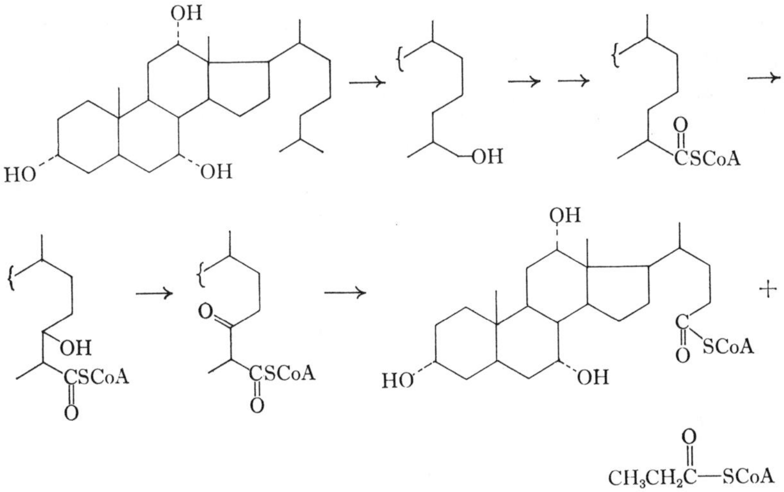

$$(13\text{–}4)$$

Bile Acid Influence on Steroid Synthesis

The interesting observation[66] has recently been made that the addition of cholic acid to the diet of rats results in an initial elevation of total liver cholesterol but a constantly decreasing incorporation of 1-C^{14}-acetate into cholesterol, i.e., a constantly decreasing rate of cholesterol synthesis. Thus there would seem to be a negative feed-back mechanism by which cholic acid inhibits its own production

65. M. W. Whitehouse, E. Staple, and S. Gurin, *J. Biol. Chem.*, **234**, 276 (1959).
66. W. T. Beher and G. D. Baker, *Federation Proc.*, **18**, 189 (1959).

leading to a build up in the concentration of its precursor, cholesterol. The high concentration of cholesterol so induced then, in turn, represses the further synthesis of cholesterol. Other aspects of this question have been investigated using a single injection of 2-C^{14}-mevalonate to bile acid- and cholesterol-treated mice. The results revealed a complex interrelationship between the various metabolic products indicating that the synthesis of any one was markedly influenced by the presence and concentrations of the others.[67]

The oral administration of the antibiotic, neomycin, has an interesting effect on cholesterol and bile acid metabolism in man.[67b] It lowers the serum cholesterol level and causes an increase in the fecal excretion of bile acids. Desoxycholic acid is normally the preponderant bile acid excreted in human feces. Neomycin, however, inhibits the reduction of cholic acid to desoxycholic acid by the intestinal bacteria, but does not affect the bacteria that hydrolyse the conjugated bile acids.

Conjugation of Bile Acids with Amino Acids

The conjugation of free bile acids with glycine and taurine has been reported[68] to involve the intermediate formation of cholyl CoA in a manner analogous to the formation of acetyl CoA:

$$\text{cholic acid} + \text{ATP} + \text{CoASH} \rightarrow \text{cholylCoA} + \text{AMP} + \text{PP}$$

$$\text{cholylCoA} + \text{glycine} \rightarrow \text{—glycocholate} + \text{CoASH}$$

The enzymes concerned in the coupling show a specificity toward the amino acid. In the presence of both glycine and taurine, rat microsomes give more taurocholate than glycocholate; chicken microsomes form only taurocholate; and rabbit liver microsomes only glycocholate.

Species Differences in Bile Acids

Other interesting aspects of bile acid metabolism concern the differences in bile acids produced by different species of animals, which have recently been discussed by Haslewood.[69] By examination of bile salts produced by various species of animals, he has concluded

67. W. T. Beher, G. D. Baker, M. E. Beher, and W. L. Anthony, *Proc. Soc. Exptl. Biol. and Med.*, **108**, 555 (1961).
67b. J. G. Hamilton, *Arch. Biochem. Biophys*, **101**, 7 (1963).
68. J. Bremer, *Acta Chem. Scand.*, **10**, 56 (1956).
69. G. A. D. Haslewood, *Biosynthesis of Terpenes and Sterols*, Little, Brown, Boston, 1959, p. 206.

that there exists an evolutionary pattern that mirrors the steps just discussed for the removal of three carbons from the sidechain. Thus the older animals, in an evolutionary sense (e.g., coelacanth, shark) have

etc.

(13-5)

I   II   III   IV

substances largely of group II structure, the reptiles synthesize mainly group III substances, and the mammals produce the familiar bile acid derivatives of group IV [see Eq. (13-5)]. This chemical evolution has apparently been gradual and seems to have gone hand in hand with morphological changes leading to ascent up the evolutionary ladder by the animal type.

Bile Acid Interconversion by Intestinal Microorganisms

Also of great significance is the role of the intestinal microorganisms in effecting metabolic interconversion between bile acids, discussed by Bergström.[70]

Of particular interest in this connection is the conversion of cholic acid to desoxycholic acid by the intestinal flora of the rabbit. Thus, rabbit bile contains almost pure desoxycholic acid conjugated with glycine. In rabbits with a bile fistula, however, Lindstedt and Sjövall found[71] that cholic acid becomes the main component in the fistula bile soon after the fistula is opened. Also, if labeled cholic acid is given to an intact rabbit, labeled desoxycholic acid is formed from it in the gut. In the rat, the desoxycholic acid so formed is rehydroxylated in the liver. This rehydroxylation however does not occur in the rabbit.[70]

The bile acid metabolism of normal python and constrictor snakes apparently follows[73] the same general pattern:

$$\text{Cholesterol} \xrightarrow{\text{liver}} \text{Cholic Acid} \xrightarrow[\text{microorganisms}]{\text{intestinal}} \text{Deoxycholic Acid}$$

70. S. Bergström, *Biosynthesis of Terpenes and Sterols*, Little, Brown, Boston, 1959, p. 185.
71. S. Lindstedt and J. Sjövall, *Acta Chem. Scand.*, **11**, 421 (1957).
73. S. Bergström, H. Danielsson, and T. Kazuno, *J. Biol. Chem.*, **235**, 983 (1960).

These animals show a family specificity, however, in the final 16α-hydroxylation of the desoxycholic acid, which is formed in the intestine from the "primary" bile acid, cholic acid. As a result, these snakes excrete phytocholic acid (3α,12α,16α-trihydroxycholanic acid). The mechanism of loss of the 7α-hydroxyl function has been studied[74] using administration of 7β-H³-24-C¹⁴-cholic acid to intact rabbits in which bile fistulas were made after various intervals. The desoxycholic acid so isolated had the same H³/C¹⁴ ratio as the original cholic acid, demonstrating that the removal of the 7α-hydroxyl group does not involve intervention of a 7-keto function but proceeds either by a direct displacement or by elimination to an alkene followed by reduction. The configuration of the tritium is inverted from β in cholic acid to α in desoxycholic acid.[75,76] This over-all conversion is summarized in Eq. (13-6).

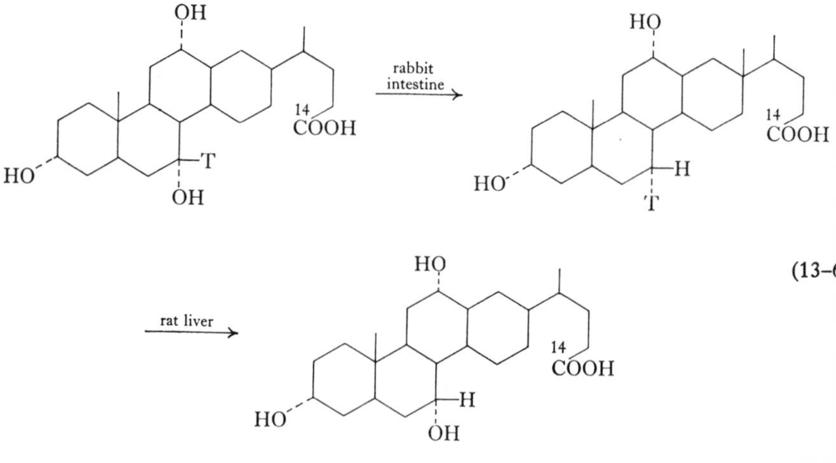

(13-6)

Moreover, it was found[76] that 50 per cent of the total cholic acid pool is converted into desoxycholic acid per day during the enterohepatic circulation; the greater part of this acid is subsequently rehydroxylated in the liver of some species, but not in rabbits. Recall also the observation in Section 13-36 that oral administration of neomycin, by inhibition of the bacteria which normally effect the reduction of cholic to desoxycholic acid, can cause cholic acid to be the main fecal bile acid.

74. S. Bergström, S. Lindstedt, and B. Samuelsson, *Acta Chem. Scand.*, in press.
75. S. Bergström, S. Lindstedt, and B. Samuelsson, *J. Biol. Chem.*, **234**, 2022 (1959).
76. S. Lindstedt and B. Samuelsson, *J. Biol. Chem.*, **234**, 2026 (1959).

Further work[77] has clarified the dehydroxylation reaction as an elimination-reduction process. The evidence supporting this proposal is that, during the conversion $6\alpha,6\beta$-8β-H^3,24-C^{14}-cholic acid to desoxycholic acid in the rabbit or rat intestine, the tritium label in the 6β position is eliminated. The remaining tritium label at C-6, originally in the 6α position, is brought into the 6β position. The proposed mechanism of desoxycholic acid formation from cholic acid consists of diaxial *trans* elimination of the elements of water followed by reduction of the resulting Δ^6-olefin. The two hydrogens (6α and 7β) thus introduced are equatorial and in the *trans* position.

The metabolism of the intermediate olefin 24-C^{14}-$3\alpha,12\alpha$-dihydroxy-Δ^6-cholenic acid has been investigated. The unsaturated acid is reduced in the intestine to desoxycholic acid and both labeled desoxycholic acid and cholic acids are present in the bile, as in Eq. (13–7).[78]

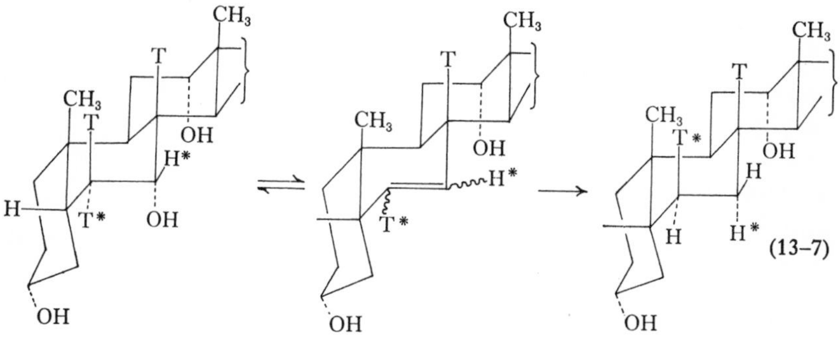

(13–7)

13–3   CORTICOIDS

Although a great many hormones have been isolated that are secreted by the adrenal cortex, the most important in a physiological sense are cortisol, corticosterone, and aldosterone. We shall, therefore, dwell on the biogenesis of corticosterone [6], cortisol [7], and aldosterone [8] in this section.

Synthesis from Cholesterol and Acetate

In 1945, Bloch[79] showed that the administration of deuterium-labeled cholesterol gave rise in the urine to labeled pregnanediol, a 21-carbon steroid. It has also been shown that 4-C^{14}-cholesterol

77. B. Samuelsson, *J. Biol. Chem.*, **235**, 361 (1960).
78. B. Matkovics and B. Samuelsson, *Acta Chem. Scand.*, **16**, 683 (1962).
79. K. Bloch, *J. Biol. Chem.*, **157**, 661 (1945).

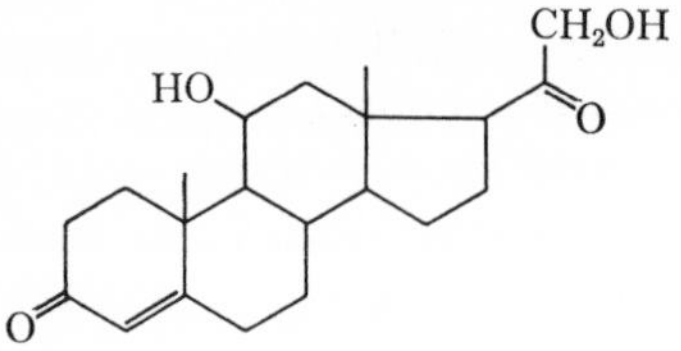

[6]
Corticosterone

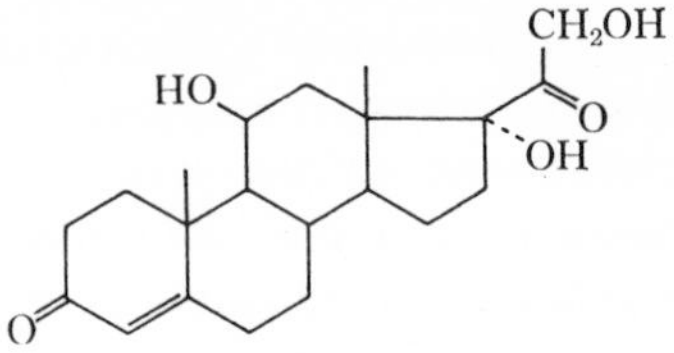

[7]
Cortisol

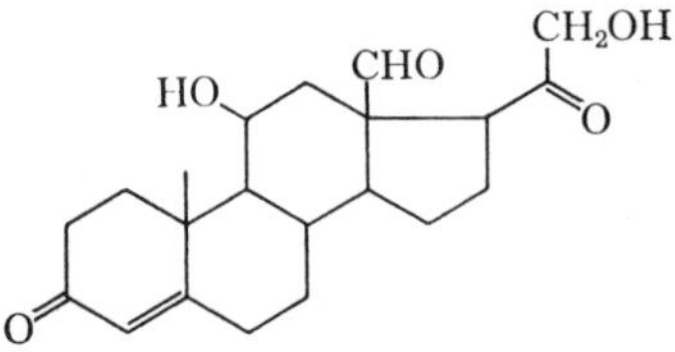

[8]
Aldosterone

can be converted to cortisol and corticosterone in a variety of systems that includes isolated perfused cow adrenal,[80,81] cell-free homogenate of cow adrenal cortex,[82,83] and hog adrenal homogenates.[84] In man, the in vivo administration of cholesterol doubly labeled with C^{14} and tritium produced the characteristic urinary metabolites of cortisol.[85,86] The conversion of tritium-labeled cholesterol to H^3-cortisol has been observed[87] in guinea pigs. The biosyntheses of progesterone[88] and other hormones[89] from 1-C^{14}-acetate in vitro by human ovarian tissue have also been demonstrated.

80. O. Hechter, M. M. Solomon, A. Zaffaroni, and G. Pincus, *Arch. Biochem. Biophys.*, **46**, 201 (1953).
81. A. Zaffaroni, O. Hechter, and G. Pincus, *J. Am. Chem. Soc.*, **73**, 1390 (1951).
82. M. Hayano, N. Saba, R. I. Dorfman, and O. Hechter, *Recent. Progr. Hormone Res.*, **12**, 79 (1956).
83. N. Saba and O. Hechter, *Federation Proc.*, **14**, 775 (1955).
84. R. D. H. Heard, E. G. Bligh, M. C. Cann, P. H. Jellinck, V. J. O'Donnell, B. G. Rao, and J. L. Webb, *Recent Progr. Hormone Res.*, **12**, 45 (1956).
85. H. Werbin and G. V. LeRoy, *J. Am. Chem. Soc.*, **76**, 5260 (1954).
86. H. Werbin and G. V. LeRoy, *Federation Proc.*, **14**, 303 (1955).
87. H. Werbin, I. L. Chaikoff, and E. E. Jones, *J. Biol. Chem.*, **234**, 282 (1959).
88. M. L. Sweat, D. L. Berliner, M. J. Bryson, C. Nabors, Jr., J. Haskell, and E. G. Holmstrom, *Biochim. Biophys. Acta*, **40**, 289 (1960).
89. K. J. Ryan and O. W. Smith, *J. Biol. Chem.*, **236**, 2207 (1961).

In contrast to these expectedly positive results 2-C^{14}-mevalonate was *not* incorporated into corticosteroids by bovine adrenal tissue preparations under conditions when 1-C^{14}-acetate was efficiently converted to a variety of corticosteroids. The evidence for a similar biosynthetic pathway for steroids and cholesterol is so compelling however that this result must be taken to indicate that there was some permeability barrier to the exogenous mevalonate or that the D-isomer was a very effective inhibitor in the adrenal tissue.[90]

Clearly, if cholesterol is to be considered the precursor of the cortical hormones, a predictable pattern of labeling should be observed in hormones biosynthesized from labeled acetate. This has been demonstrated for C-20 (derived from the carboxyl carbon of acetate) and for C-21 (derived from the methyl carbon of acetate) in the sidechain of cortisol, corticosterone, and 3α,17α,21-trihydroxy-pregnane-20-one.[91,92] Other work has shown that 1-C^{14}-acetate is incorporated in the expected fashion into cortisol by calf adrenals. Thus C-2, C-4, C-6, and C-20 were radioactive and each had a specific activity one-tenth of that of the cortisol.[93]

Influence of Physiological Conditions of Corticoid Synthesis

General physiological conditions should influence corticoid synthesis. In this connection, it has been found that adenosine-3′,5′-monophosphate added to rat adrenal glands incubated in vitro elicits a response in corticosteroid production equal to or greater than that produced by adrenocorticotropic hormone.[94] This finding supports the theory[95] that one of the initial changes brought about by adrenocorticotropic hormone in its stimulation of corticosteroid synthesis is the activation of adrenal phosphorylase. It had previously been suggested[96] that the action of adrenocorticotropic hormone is localized at the cholesterol to pregnenolone step in corticoid biosynthesis. In addition Ca^{2+} seems to be[97] specifically involved in the action of

90. M. J. Bryson and M. L. Sweat, *Arch. Biochem. Biophys.*, **96**, 1 (1962).
91. E. Caspi, G. Rosenfeld, and R. I. Dorfman, *J. Org. Chem.*, **21**, 814 (1956).
92. E. Caspi, F. Ungar, and R. I. Dorfman, *J. Org. Chem.*, **22**, 326 (1957).
93. E. Caspi, R. I. Dorfman, B. T. Khan, G. Rosenfeld, and W. Schmid, *J. Biol. Chem.*, **237**, 2085 (1962).
94. R. C. Haynes, Jr., S. B. Koritz, and F. G. Péron, *J. Biol. Chem.*, **234**, 1421 (1959).
95. R. C. Haynes, Jr. and L. Berthet, *J. Biol. Chem.*, **225**, 115 (1957).
96. D. Stone and O. Hechter, *Arch. Biochem. Biophys.*, **51**, 457 (1954).
97. F. G. Péron and S. B. Koritz, *J. Biol. Chem.*, **233**, 256 (1958).

adrenocorticotropic hormone. Further, it has been shown[98] that Ca^{2+} and freezing will stimulate the corticoid production of rat adrenal homogenates in the presence of nicotinamide adenine dinucleotide phosphate and glucose-6-phosphate. The suggestion has been made[98] that these various types of stimulation may involve a common basic reaction, which is proteolytic in nature.

Sidechain Scission

The structural modifications necessary to convert cholesterol to the corticosteroids include removal from the sidechain of six superfluous carbon atoms and appropriate nuclear and sidechain oxidations. The first step in the conversion of cholesterol to the corticoids is the cleavage of the six unwanted carbons from the sidechain. The immediate products of this cleavage are pregnenolone[99–101] and isocaproaldehyde,[102] which is rapidly oxidized to isocaproic acid, the product usually isolated from this reaction.

This cleavage reaction has been widely investigated and a prior oxidation of cholesterol to 20α-hydroxy cholesterol seems to be the first step. Thus the cleavage requires reduced nicotinamide adenine dinucleotide phosphate[102,103] and oxygen,[104] which suggests a hydroxylation reaction. Furthermore, the intermediacy in this process of 20-hydroxysteroids is supported by the finding[105] that cow adrenal homogenates can hydroxylate cholesterol at C-20 and that 20α-hydroxycholesterol with bovine adrenal preparations yield C_{21} steroids[106] and isocaproic acid.[107]

98. S. B. Koritz and F. G. Péron, *J. Biol. Chem.*, **234**, 3122 (1959).
99. W. S. Lynn, Jr., E. Staple, and S. Gurin, *J. Am. Chem. Soc.*, **76**, 4048 (1954).
100. W. S. Lynn, Jr., E. Staple, and S. Gurin, *Federation Proc.*, **14**, 783 (1955).
101. E. Staple, W. S. Lynn, Jr., and S. Gurin, *J. Biol. Chem.*, **219**, 845 (1956).
102. G. Constantopoulos and T. T. Tchen, *J. Biol. Chem.*, **236**, 65 (1961).
103. I. D. K. Halkerston, J. Eichhorn, and O. Hechter, *Arch. Biochem. Biophys.*, **85**, 287 (1959).
104. I. D. K. Halkerston, J. Eichhorn, and O. Hechter, *J. Biol. Chem.*, **236**, 374 (1961).
105. S. Solomon, P. Levitan, and S. Lieberman, *Proc. Can. Physiol. Soc.*, 20th Meeting, Montreal, 1956, p. 54.
106. K. Shimizu, M. Hayano, M. Gut, and R. I. Dorfman, *J. Biol. Chem.*, **236**, 695 (1961).
107. K. Shimizu, R. I. Dorfman, and M. Gut, *J. Biol. Chem.*, **235**, PC25 (1960).

In addition to the isolation of prenenolone and progesterone by the cleavage of 20α-hydroxycholesterol a "compound X" was found[106] that has been shown to be 20α-22ξ-dihydroxycholesterol.[108] Moreover, Tchen[109] has reported evidence that 20α-hydroxy-22-keto-cholesterol is not an obligatory intermediate in the loss of the sidechain carbons. These results lead to Eq. (13-8) for sidechain cleavage.

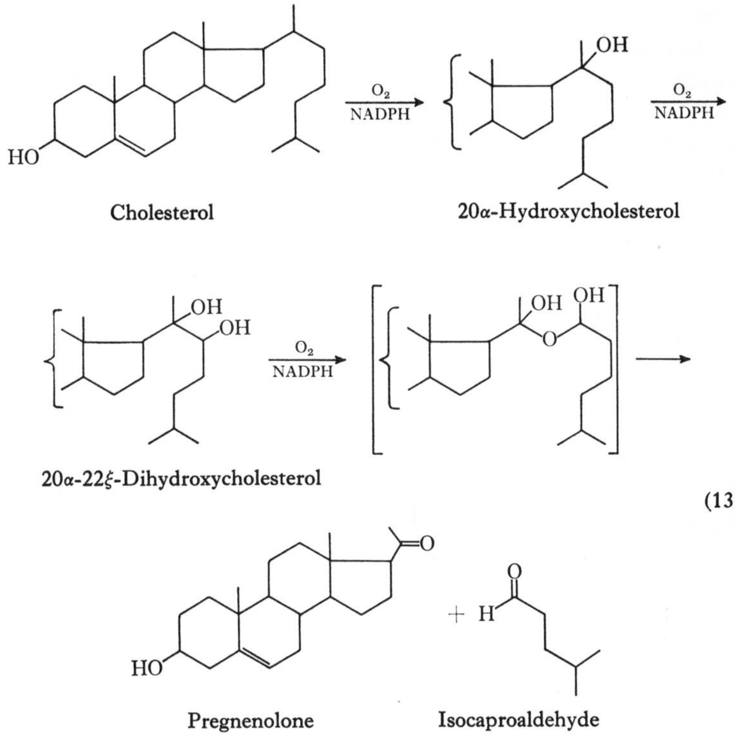

Cholesterol   20α-Hydroxycholesterol

20α-22ξ-Dihydroxycholesterol

(13-8)

Pregnenolone   Isocaproaldehyde

Other oxidized derivatives of cholesterol have also been investigated. An adrenal enzyme preparation was found to oxidize 3α-H³-22-hydroxycholesterol to H³-pregnenolone in a yield greater than that obtained from cholesterol under the same conditions.[110] Only starting material was recovered when 3α-H³-22-ketocholesterol was tried as

108. K. Shimizu, M. Gut, and R. I. Dorfman, *J. Biol. Chem.*, **237**, 699 (1962).
109. G. Constantopoulos, P. S. Satoh, and T. T. Tchen, *Biochem. Biophys. Res. Commun.*, **8**, 50 (1962).
110. A. C. Chaudhuri, Y. Harada, K. Shimizu, M. Gut, and R. I. Dorfman, *J. Biol. Chem.*, **237**, 703 (1962).

a substrate. Indeed, 22-ketocholesterol was found to be cleaved by guinea pigs between C-22 and C-23 to yield isovaleric acid.[111]

Conversion of Pregnenolone to Progesterone

The conversion of pregnenolone to progesterone is effected by a 3β-hydroxysteroid dehydrogenase system that is found in the microsomal fraction of adrenal tissue.[112] Concurrently with the oxidation of the 3β-hydroxyl function the Δ^5 double bond moves into conjugation with the newly formed keto group, a position of greater chemical stability. This conversion is also catalyzed by preparations from placenta, corpus luteum, testis, and ovary.[113] The enzyme system is dependent on nicotinamide adenine dinucleotide as a cofactor and is unable to catalyze the reverse reaction; i.e., Δ^4-3-keto steroids are not converted to Δ^5-3-hydroxy compounds in the presence of the enzyme system and excess reduced nicotinamide adenine dinucleotide. This enzyme system is also effective in catalyzing a similar structural change in steroids other than pregnenolone; it can convert dehydroepiandrosterone to androstenedione. In some cases, it has been possible to separate the isomerase enzyme from the enzyme catalyzing the oxidation.[114,115]

The mechanism of the isomerization of the double bond from the Δ^5- to the Δ^4-position was shown[115] probably to involve an intramolecular hydrogen transfer, for when the isomerization of 5-androstene-3,-17-dione to 4-androstene-3,17-dione was allowed to proceed in a medium of deuterium oxide or tritium oxide, none of the label was found in the rearranged product. On the other hand, acetone-washed beef adrenal mitochondria converts 4-C^{14},4-βH^3-cholesterol to pregnenolone with tritium retention and to progesterone with loss of tritium.[115b]

A crystalline steroid isomerase was subsequently isolated from *Pseudomonas testosteroni*.[116] This enzyme has a broad pH optimum

111. G. J. Kautsky, C. J. Bouboulis, R. R. Becker, and C. G. King, *J. Biol. Chem.*, **233**, 1340 (1958).
112. K. F. Beyer and L. T. Samuels, *J. Biol. Chem.*, **219**, 69 (1956).
113. W. H. Pearlman, E. Cerceo, and M. Thomas, *J. Biol. Chem.*, **208**, 231 (1954).
114. P. Talalay and M. M. Dobson, *J. Biol. Chem.*, **205**, 823 (1953).
115. P. Talalay and V. S. Wang, *Biochim. Biophys. Acta*, **18**, 300 (1955).
115b. H. Wertin and J. L. Charkoff, *Biochim. Biophys. Acta*, **71**, 471 (1963).
116. F. S. Kawahara and P. Talalay, *J. Biol. Chem.*, **235**, PCl (1960).
    F. S. Kawahara, S. Wang, and P. Talalay, *J. Biol. Chem.*, **237**, 1500 (1962); S. Wang, F. S. Kawahara, and P. Talalay, *J. Biol. Chem.*, **238**, 576 (1963).

between 6 and 8 and is competitively inhibited by low concentrations of various steroids such as 17β-estradiol, 17-dihydroequilenin, and 19-nortestosterone.

Oxidation of Progesterone to Corticoids

Progesterone apparently occupies a central position in corticoid biosynthesis. The reactions remaining to complete the synthesis of the corticoids involve hydroxylations at one or more of the following positions: C-11, C-17, C-21, and, in the case of aldosterone, the oxidation also of the C-18 angular methyl group. The paths to cortisol and corticosterone diverge after progesterone. The route to corticosterone proceeds through a sequential series of oxidations, first at C-21 and then at C-11β. Cortisol, however, arises by oxidation first at C-17α, then at C-21, and finally at C-11β. The enzymes that catalyze these reactions have been reviewed,[117,118] and will not be discussed in detail here. On the pathway to cortisol, a 17α-hydroxylase system introduces the 17α-hydroxyl group yielding 17α-hydroxyprogesterone.[119,120] There exists another enzyme system, 21-hydroxylase, that converts 17α-hydroxyprogesterone and progesterone to their 21-hydroxy analogues— 17α-hydroxydesoxycorticosterone and desoxycorticosterone, respectively.[121] The final introduction of the 11β-hydroxyl function is mediated by an 11β-hydroxylase present in the mitochondrial fraction of adrenal tissue.[122–125] A soluble steroid 11β-hydroxylase has been isolated from bovine adrenal cortex,[127] and such an enzyme system has been separated into two components by differential precipitation from ammonium sulfate solutions.[128]

117. J. K. Grant, *Ann. Rept. Progr. Chem. (Chem. Soc. London)*, **52**, 316 (1955).
118. M. Hayano, N. Saba, R. I. Dorfman, and O. Hechter, *Recent Progr. Hormone Res.*, **12**, 79 (1956).
119. H. Levy, R. W. Jeanloz, R. P. Jacobsen O. Hechter, V. Schenker, and G. Pincus, *J. Biol. Chem.*, **211**, 867 (1954).
120. J. E. Plager and L. T. Samuels, *J. Biol. Chem.*, **211**, 21 (1954).
121. K. J. Ryan and L. L. Engle, *J. Biol. Chem.*, **225**, 103 (1957).
122. A. C. Brownie and J. K. Grant, *Biochem. J.*, **62**, 29 (1956).
123. A. C. Brownie, J. K. Grant, and D. W. Davidson, *Biochem. J.*, **58**, 218 (1954).
124. J. K. Grant, *Biochem. J.*, **64**, 559 (1956).
125. M. Hayano and R. I. Dorfman, *J. Biol. Chem.*, **211**, 227 (1954).
127. D. C. Sharma, E. Forchielli, and R. I. Dorfman, *J. Biol. Chem.*, **237**, 1495 (1962).
128. M. L. Sweat and M. J. Bryson, *Arch. Biochem. Biophys.*, **96**, 186 (1962).

These enzyme systems are similar to the other oxidases in that they utilize molecular oxygen and require reduced nicotinamide adenine dinucleotide phosphate. Some studies have been made on the inhibition of 11β-hydroxylation by androgens. In particular Δ⁴-androstene-3,17-dione was found to be a competitive inhibitor for the 11β-hydroxylation of 11-deoxycorticosterone. Dehydroepiandrosterone and testerone also inhibited the hydroxylation, but 11β-hydroxy-Δ⁴-androstene-3,17-dione, progesterone, and 17α-hydroxyprogesterone had no such effect.[129]

The stoichiometry of the C-21 hydroxylation process of 17-hydroxyprogesterone by bovine adrenocortical microsomes has been studied.[129b] The stoichiometry anticipated from the discussion of Section 13-1 was confirmed; the hydroxylation of one mole of steroid consumes one mole of oxygen and one mole of reduced nicotinamide adenine dinucleotide phosphate.

Route to Corticoids Not Involving Progesterone

An alternative sequence in which all possible orders of hydroxylation are operative has been proposed by Dorfman[130] and supported by Heard.[131] Hechter has discussed in some detail various aspects of this alternative pathway.[132] More specifically Eichhorn and Hechter[133] have investigated the role of 11β-hydroxyprogesterone as an intermediate in the biosynthesis of cortisol and corticosterone. They find that, although both substances can arise from 11β-hydroxyprogesterone, the rates of these reactions are far too low when compared to the rates for conversion of known precursors (progesterone and desoxycorticosterone) for the pathway from 11β-hydroxyprogesterone to have much quantitative significance.

The most definitive work that strongly implies a route to the adrenal cortical steroids and that does not involve the intermediacy of proges-

129. D. C. Sharma, E. Forchielli, and R. I. Dorfman, *J. Biol. Chem.*, **238**, 572 (1963).

129b. D. Y. Cooper, R. W. Estabrook, and O. Rosenthal, *J. Biol. Chem.*, **238**, 1320 (1963).

130. R. I. Dorfman, in G. Pincus and K. V. Thimann (eds.), *The Hormones*, Academic, New York, 1955, Vol. 3, p. 293.

131. R. D. H. Heard, E. G. Blight, M. C. Cann, P. H. Jellinck, V. J. O'Donnell, B. G. Rao, and J. L. Webb, *Recent Progr. Hormone Res.*, **12**, 45 (1956).

132. O. Hechter, in R. P. Cook (ed.), *Cholesterol*, Academic, New York, 1958, p. 309.

133. J. Eichhorn and O. Hechter, *Proc. Soc. Exptl. Biol. Med.*, **97**, 614 (1958).

terone is due to Engel,[134] who incubated 4-C^{14}-progesterone and 7α-H^3-17-hydroxypregnenolone with slices of human adrenal cortical tumor and found that both substances were converted to cortisol, progesterone in 17 per cent yield, and 17-hydroxypregnendone in a yield of 63 per cent.

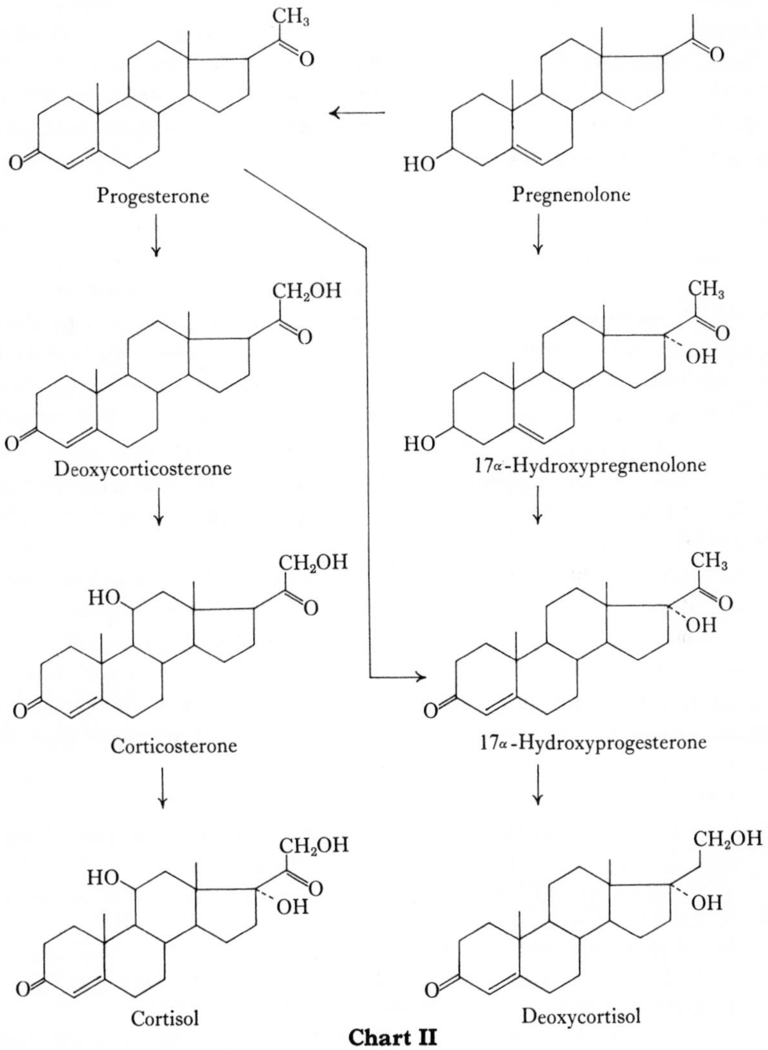

Chart II

134. I. Weliky and L. L. Engel, *J. Biol. Chem.*, **237**, 2089 (1962).

In an extension of this work, Engel showed that incubation of pregnenolone with human hyperplastic adrenal cortical slices led to cortisol, apparently via 17-hydroxypregnenolone, 17-hydroxyprogesterone, and desoxycortisol. Progesterone was also converted to corticosterone and cortisol. However, pregnenolone did *not* give rise to progesterone or desoxycorticosterone; this emphasizes the presence of a pathway from pregnenolone to cortisol that does not include progesterone.[135] These results also explain the unequal incorporation of 4-C^{14}-cholesterol and 4-C^{14}-progesterone into corticosterone and cortisol,[136] there being a route from cholesterol to pregnenolone to cortisol that does not include either progesterone or corticosterone. For a summary, see Chart II.

Aldosterone

The synthesis of aldosterone requires an additional oxidation at C-18, and the presently available work indicates that progesterone, desoxycorticosterone, and corticosterone can all be converted to aldosterone, but no definitive conclusion as to the sequence of events is yet possible. 4-C^{14}-Progesterone, 21-C^{14}-desoxycorticosterone, and 4-C^{15}-corticosterone are all converted to aldosterone by capsule strippings of ox adrenals. Moreover, there was a reasonable agreement between the specific activities of the corticosterone and aldosterone, which were isolated.[137] A similar conversion of progesterone to aldosterone by perfused calf adrenals has been observed.[138] In fortified bovine adrenal homogenates the conversion of desoxycorticosterone to aldosterone has been demonstrated.[139] However, neither progesterone nor corticosterone yields any detectable aldosterone under similar conditions.[140] Incubation of desoxycorticosterone with bovine adrenal homogenates has led to the isolation of 18-hydroxydesoxycorticosterone.[141] Finally, it has been shown[142] in man that al-

135. I. Weliky and L. L. Engel, *J. Biol. Chem.*, **238**, 1302 (1963).
136. J. Eichhorn and O. Hechter, *Arch. Biochem. Biophys.*, **84**, 196 (1959).
137. P. J. Ayres, O. Hechter, N. Saba, S. A. Simpson, and J. F. Tait, *Biochem. J.*, **65**, 22P (1957).
138. P. S. Chen, Jr., H. P. Schedl, G. Rosenfeld, and F. C. Bartter, *Proc. Soc. Exptl. Biol. Med.*, **97**, 683 (1958).
139. F. W. Kahnt, R. Neher, and A. Wettstein, *Experientia*, **11**, 446 (1955).
140. A. Wettstein and G. Anner, *Experientia*, **10**, 397 (1954).
141. F. W. Kahnt, R. Neher, and A. Wettstein, *Helv. Chim. Acta*, **38**, 1237 (1955).
142. H. S. Seltzer and D. A. Clark, *Proc. Soc. Exptl. Biol. Med.*, **98**, 674 (1958).

dosterone can originate from corticosterone. The metabolism of aldosterone in man is stereospecific.[143] Thus after administration of DL-aldosterone the unnatural L-enantiomorph was not accounted for among the urinary products of aldosterone metabolism, implying a stereospecificity inherent in the mechanism for aldosterone excretion.

Reduction at C-20

The sidechain carbonyl group of progesterone and related compounds can be reduced by a 20-hydroxysteroid dehydrogenase. Thus progesterone[144] is reduced [Eq. (13-8)] by rat ovarian tissues in vitro to 4-pregnen-20-α-ol-3-one.

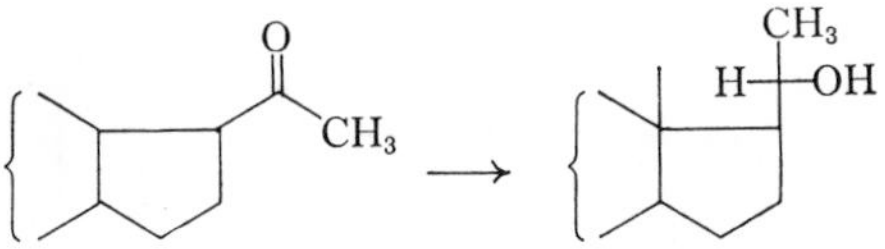

$$(13-8)$$

The purification and some properties of this enzyme, which require reduced nicotinamide adenine dinucleotide phosphate have been reported.[145] A similar enzyme has been found in rabbit skeletal muscle, where an in vitro reduction of 3β, 17α-dihydroxy-Δ⁵-pregnen-20-one (17α-hydroxypregnenolone) to Δ⁵-pregnene-3β,17α,20α-triol and Δ⁵-pregnene-3β,17α,20β-triol has been observed.[146]

13-4 ANDROGENS

Sidechain Scission

The formation of the 19-carbon testicular androgens in the rat and in human testis by further degradation of progesterone has been demonstrated. The pathway involves a preliminary oxidation of progesterone to 17α-hydroxyprogesterone, which is cleaved to acetic acid and

143. S. Ulick, *J. Biol. Chem.*, **236**, 680 (1961).
144. W. G. Wiest, *J. Biol. Chem.*, **234**, 3115 (1959).
145. W. G. Wiest and R. B. Wilcox, *J. Biol. Chem.*, **236**, 2425 (1961).
146. P. Z. Thomas, E. Forchielli, and R. I. Dorfman, *J. Biol. Chem.*, **235**, 2797 (1960).

androstenedione which is then reduced to testosterone.[147-153]   However, rat testicular particles, which can convert 17α-hydroxyprogesterone to acetic acid and androgens, do not cleave the sidechain of 17-hydroxy-desoxycorticosterone.[154]

In a study of the conversion of progesterone to androgens by testis, Lynn and Brown[155] also found that the actual substrate for the cleavage was 17α-hydroxyprogesterone. The stoichiometric requirements of the reaction were such as to indicate that one mole of oxygen and one mole of reduced pyridine nucleotide were required Eq. (13–9)]. In

$$(13–9)$$

support of this mechanism, it was never possible to isolate any acetaldehyde, acetic acid being the only two-carbon product. At least four enzymes were found to be involved in the production of testosterone and Δ⁵-pregnene-17α,20β-diol-3-one from progesterone in testes. These enzymes are androstenedione reductase, 20-keto reductase, 17α-hydroxy-20-keto cleavage enzyme, and 17α-hydroxylase. All require reduced nicotinamide adenine dinucleotide phosphate (reduced nicotinamide adenine dinucleotide was inactive) and two require oxygen.

147. H. Breuer, L. Nocke, and R. Knuppen, *Biochim. Biophys. Acta*, **33**, 254 (1959).
148. W. S. Lynn, Jr., *Federation Proc.*, **15**, 305 (1956).
149. W. S. Lynn and R. Brown, *Biochim. Biophys. Acta*, **21**, 403 (1956).
150. W. R. Slaunwhite, Jr. and L. T. Samuels, *J. Biol. Chem.*, **220**, 341 (1956).
151. K. Savard, R. I. Dorfman, B. Baggett, and L. L. Engel, *J. Clin. Endocrinol. Metab.*, **16**, 1629 (1956).
152. H. H. Wotiz, J. W. Davis, and H. M. Lemon, *J. Biol. Chem.*, **216**, 677 (1955).
153. E. Bloch, B. Tissenbaum, and K. Benirschke, *Biochim. Biophys. Acta*, **60**, 182 (1962).
154. O. Hechter, in R. P. Cook (ed.), *Cholesterol*, Academic, New York, 1958, p. 309.
155. W. S. Lynn and R. Brown, *Biochim. Biophys. Acta*, **21**, 403 (1956).

The two that require oxygen, 17α-hydroxylase and 17α-hydroxy-20-keto cleavage enzyme, are found in the microsomes and were appreciably active only in the presence of particles. However the two reductases, androstenedione reductase and the 20-keto reductase, are active in the soluble state but their activity was impressively stimulated by the presence of washed inactive particles.

Androgen Synthesis from Pregnenolone

A second pathway exists that involves the conversion of pregnenolone to dehydroepiandrosterone—a pathway analogous to that just discussed with the difference that the ring A and B transformations necessary in the production of testosterone have not yet been brought about. Thus a conversion of both pregnenolone and cholesterol to dehydroepiandrosterone by a homogenate from human adrenocortical adenoma has been demonstrated.[156] This transformation has also been demonstrated in a virilized woman bearing an adrenal adenoma by injection of 7-H^3-pregnenolone and isolation of 7-H^3-dehydroepiandrosterone. Also the conversion in vivo by a woman with adrenocortical metastases of 17α-hydroxypregnenolone to dehydroisoandrosterone (3β-hydroxy-Δ^5-androstene-17-one) and other androgenic hormones has been observed.[157]

The two pathways just discussed for testosterone formation both involve a preliminary oxidation at C-17 with the introduction of an alcohol function at this position. After further oxidative cleavage of the two-carbon sidechains, C-17 is present as a keto-group in, for example Δ^4-androstene-3,17-dione. The reduction of this 17-keto function, then produces testosterone.

Pathway Not Involving Preliminary Oxidation at C-17

The existence of a third pathway for testosterone formation that does not involve a preliminary oxidation at C-17 but proceeds directly from progesterone to testosterone has been indicated. Indeed, Dorfmann considers this mechanism may be the most significant one for testosterone formation in the adult.

The evidence supporting this third pathway is the finding that incubation of 7-H^3-progesterone and 4-C^{14}-17α-hydroxyprogesterone with a homogenate prepared from human polycystic ovaries, yielded

156. M. Goldstein, M. Gut, and R. I. Dorfman, *Biochim. Biophys. Acta*, **38**, 190 (1960).
157. S. Soloman, A. C. Carter, and S. Lieberman, *J. Biol. Chem.*, **235**, 351 (1960).

testosterone with a higher H^3/C^{14} ratio than that of the Δ^4-androstene-3,17-dione formed simultaneously, strongly indicating that testosterone could be formed without the intermediacy of Δ^4-androstene-3-17-dione.[158] The aerobic conversion of progesterone to testosterone

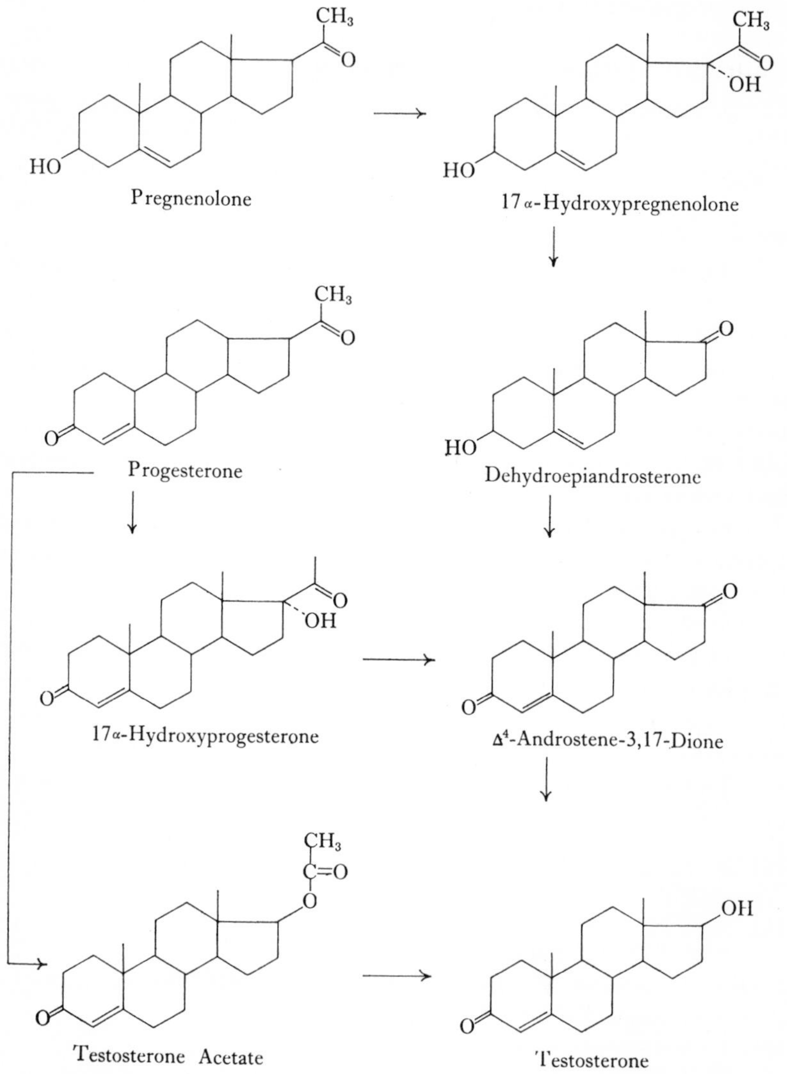

Pregnenolone

17α-Hydroxypregnenolone

Progesterone

Dehydroepiandrosterone

17α-Hydroxyprogesterone

Δ^4-Androstene-3,17-Dione

Testosterone Acetate

Testosterone

Chart III

158. N. Kase, E. Forchielli, and R. I. Dorfman, *Acta Endocrinol.*, **37**, 19 (1961).

acetate, in which the two acetate carbons are the acetyl sidechain carbons of the progesterone substrate, has been demonstrated in the microorganism *Cladosporium resinae*.[159] A fourth alternative route to adrenal androgens envisages the cleavage of cholesterol directly to dehydroepiandrosterone, a reaction analogous to that forming pregnenolone. The dehydroepiandrosterone so formed can then give rise to androsterone by the action of the 3β-hydroxydehydrogenase system and so lead to the other androgens. Although the direct conversion of cholesterol to the C_{19} androgens has not been demonstrated, Dorfman[160] considers that this pathway remains an interesting hypothesis. The three established pathways are indicated in Chart III.

Enzymes Mediating Oxidation-Reduction Processes

An interesting aspect of steroid hormone biosynthesis, which has received considerable attention, is the problem of enzymes concerned with the oxidation-reduction reactions at carbonyl and olefin centers.

In the case of some of the hydroxysteroid dehydrogenases, the stereochemistry of the process linked with pyridine nucleotides has been investigated. The nicotinamide adenine dinucleotide-linked interconversion of 17β-hydroxysteroids, e.g., 4-androstene-3,17-dione and testosterone, has been shown to involve side β[161] of the pyridine nucleotide (that side *not* utilized in the dehydrogenases for alcohol, L-lactate or L-malate).[162–164] Jarabak and Talalay[165] have also shown that side β is involved in a 3β-hydroxysteroid dehydrogenase from *Pseudomonas testosteroni*, which catalyzes the reaction of epiandrosterone [9] to androstane-3,17-dione [10]. Some studies of inhibition of β-hydroxy steroid dehydrogenase from *Pseudomonas sistosteroni* have been reported.[165b]

159. G. S. Fonken, H. C. Murray, and L. Reineke, *J. Am. Chem. Soc.*, **82**, 5507 (1960).
160. R. I. Dorfman, *Comp. Biochem. Physiol.*, **4**, 319 (1962).
161. P. Talalay, F. A. Loewus, and B. Vennesland, *J. Biol. Chem.*, **212**, 801 (1955).
162. H. F. Fisher, E. E. Conn, B. Vennesland, and F. H. Westheimer, *J. Biol. Chem.*, **202**, 687 (1953).
163. F. A. Loewus, P. Ofner, H. F. Fisher, F. H. Westheimer, and B. Vennesland, *J. Biol. Chem.*, **202**, 699 (1953).
164. F. A. Loewus, T. T. Tchen, and B. Vennesland, *J. Biol. Chem.*, **212**, 787 (1955).
165. J. Jarabak and P. Talalay, *J. Biol. Chem.*, **235**, 2147 (1960).
165b. R. A. Ferrari and A. Arnold, *Biochim. Biophys. Acta*, **77**, 349, 357 (1963).

As well as reactions centered around secondary hydroxyl and carbonyl groups, there are enzymes that catalyze reduction of the Δ^4 double bonds. There are a great many distinct Δ^4-reductases in the rat liver.[166] The products can possess either a 5α- or 5β-configuration [Eq. (13–10)]. 5α-Reductase activity has been found[167] in the micro-

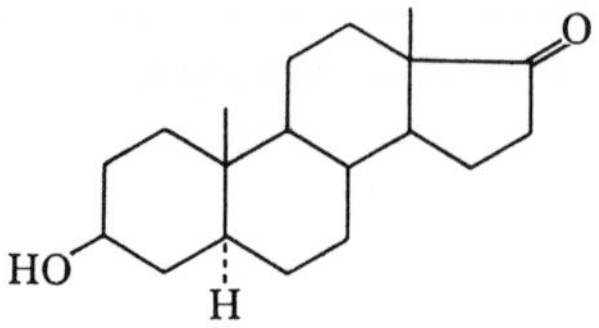

+ NAD+

[9]
Epiandrosterone

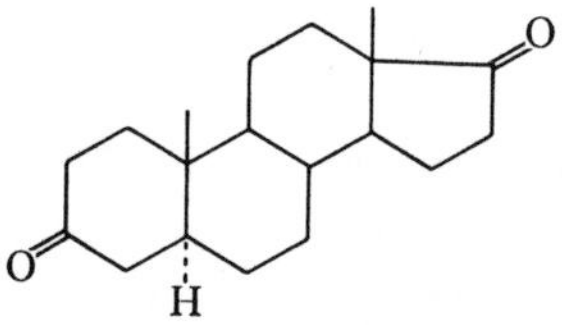

+ NADH + H+

[10]

Androstane-3,17-dione

somal fraction of the rat liver cell, whereas the 5β-activity was entirely soluble.[168] Moreover, it has been shown[169] that each series of Δ^4-3-ketosteroid-reductase-5α and -5β contains multiple enzymes by which small variations in the steroid molecule can be discerned.

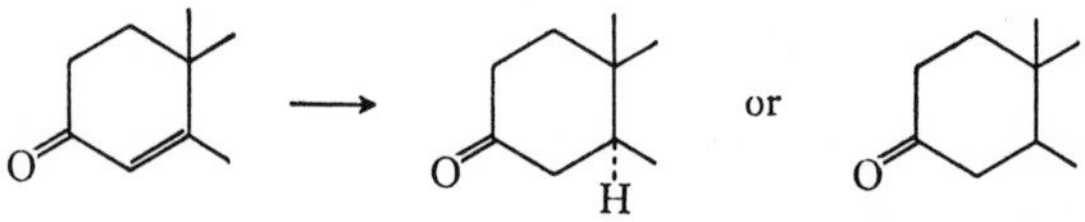

or   (13–10)

166. J. S. McGuire, Jr. and G. M. Tomkins, *J. Biol. Chem.*, **235**, 1634 (1960).
167. E. Forchielli, K. Brown-Grant, and R. I. Dorfman, *Proc. Soc. Exptl. Biol. Med.*, **99**, 594 (1958).
168. G. M. Tomkins, *J. Biol. Chem.*, **225**, 13 (1957).
169. J. S. McGuire and G. M. Tomkins, *Arch. Biochem. Biophys.*, **82**, 476 (1959).

Among several species, the guinea pig is unique in that the adrenal glands possess very high levels of Δ^4-reductases, whereas the liver of this species contains barely detectable amounts of these enzymes.[170]

Some of the properties of the microsomal steroid reductases (5α) of rat liver have been studied.[171] These enzymes have a high-substrate specificity, an absolute requirement for reduced nicotinamide adenine dinucleotide phosphate as a cofactor, and they catalyze an apparently irreversible reduction. The reduction of a given steroid can be competitively inhibited by a smaller less-substituted steroid.

13–5 ESTROGENS

The estrogens, such as estrone **[11]**, represent the final stage in the degradative removal of fragments from the 30-carbon precursor lanosterol; in estrone only slightly over half of these original carbons

[11]
Estrone

are present. The precursors of these 18-carbon substances are the 19-carbon androgens, such as Δ^4-androstene-3,17-dione (in turn, of course derived from cholesterol), and the changes necessary to convert this substance to estrone are the appropriate modifications to allow the aromatization of ring A, namely, the insertion of an additional double bond and the removal of the angular methyl group.

The in vivo conversion in humans of cholesterol to estrone has been demonstrated.[172] Also, the biosynthesis of estrone and related estrogens has been reported to occur from acetate in biological systems, such as perfused testes of a stallion primed with gonadotropin[173]

170. K. Brown-Grant, E. Forchielli, and R. I. Dorfman, *J. Biol. Chem.*, **235**, 1317 (1960).
171. J. S. McGuire, Jr., V. W. Hollis, Jr., and G. M. Tomkins, *J. Biol. Chem.*, **235**, 3112 (1960).
172. H. Werbin, J. Plotz, G. V. LeRoy, and E. M. Davis, *J. Am. Chem. Soc.*, **79**, 1012 (1957).
173. M. A. Nyman, J. Geiger, and J. W. Goldzieher, *J. Biol. Chem.*, **234**, 16 (1959).

and in the pregnant mare.[174]   An in vitro system prepared from human ovarian tissue has been demonstrated[175] to convert acetate to estrone and estradiol, and a possible precursor role for cholesterol was suggested from quantitative considerations of relative specific activities. Further, the conversion of cholesterol to estrogens in vitro by human ovarian tissue has been demonstrated.[176]

The pathway from cholesterol to estrone includes[177–179] pregnenolone, 17α-hydroxyprogesterone, and androstenedione. The conversion by human ovarian tissue of progesterone to estrone and estradiol has been observed.[180]   The results of this and other work[181–184] are consistent with the sequence of Eq. (13–11). The conversion of

$$\text{Cholesterol} \rightarrow \text{Pregnenolone} \rightarrow \text{Progesterone} \rightarrow$$

$$17\alpha\text{-Hydroxyprogesterone} \rightarrow \text{Androstenedione} \rightleftharpoons \text{Testosterone} \quad (13\text{--}11)$$
$$\downarrow \qquad\qquad \downarrow$$
$$\text{Estrone} \rightleftharpoons \text{Estradiol}$$

testosterone to estradiol in dog ovary slices is accelerated by follicle-stimulating hormone.[185] Ryan has recently described[186] an enzyme system consisting of human placental microsomes and a supernatant fraction that requires reduced nicotinamide adenine dinucleotide phosphate and can convert C_{19} androgens to the corresponding estrogens; e.g., androstenedione to estrone.

174. K. Savard, K. Andrec, B. W. L. Brooksbank, C. Reyneri, R. I. Dorfman, R. D. H. Heard, R. Jacobs, and S. S. Solomon, *J. Biol. Chem.*, **231**, 765 (1958).
175. K. J. Ryan and O. W. Smith, *J. Biol. Chem.*, **236**, 705 (1961).
176. K. J. Ryan and O. W. Smith, *J. Biol. Chem.*, **236**, 2204 (1961).
177. A. S. Meyer, *Experientia*, **11**, 99 (1955).
178. A. S. Meyer, *Biochim. Biophys. Acta*, **17**, 441 (1955).
179. S. Solomon, R. V. Wiele, and S. Lieberman, *J. Am. Chem. Soc.*, **78**, 5453 (1956).
180. K. J. Ryan and O. W. Smith, *J. Biol. Chem.*, **236**, 710 (1961).
181. B. Baggett, L. L. Engel, K. Savard, and R. I. Dorfman, *Federation Proc.*, **14**, 175 (1955).
182. B. Baggett, L. L. Engel, K. Savard, and R. I. Dorfman, *J. Biol. Chem.*, **221**, 931 (1956).
183. R. D. H. Heard, P. H. Jellinck, and V. J. O'Donnell, *Endocrinology*, **57**, 200 (1955).
184. C. D. West, B. L. Damast, S. D. Sarro, and O. H. Pearson, *J. Biol. Chem.*, **218**, 409 (1956); S. R. Stitch, R. E. Oakey, and S. S. Eccles, *Biochem. J.*, **88**, 70 (1963).
185. N. Hollander and V. P. Hollander, *J. Biol. Chem.*, **233**, 1097 (1958).
186. J. K. Ryan, *J. Biol. Chem.*, **234**, 268 (1959).

Loss of C-19

There are two types of transformations necessary to convert ring A to the aromatic system characteristic of the estrogens—introduction of a new double bond and loss of C-19. The oxidation at C-19 precedes introduction of new unsaturation into ring A. Evidence that loss of C-19 is not completed before dehydrogenation of ring A is provided by the finding that 19-nortestosterone is converted to estrogens more slowly than androstenedione, although there is evidence that 19-nortestosterone can give rise to estrone.[187]

The intermediacy of 19-oxygenated derivatives of androstenedione is well authenticated. Oxidation of C-19 to a carbinol has been demonstrated by Meyer, who isolated 19-hydroxyandrostenedione, a derivative that was more rapidly converted to estrogens than androstenedione.[188,189]

More detailed work by Dorfman has shown that 19-ketoandrostenedione is more rapidly converted to estrone by human placental microsomes than was 19-hydroxyandrostenedione under identical conditions. Both these conversions had an absolute requirement for oxygen and reduced nicotinamide adenine dinucleotide phosphate.[190] The analogous carboxy derivative, Δ^4-androsten-3,17-dione-19-oic acid, and 19-norandrostenedione were converted to estrone only in small yield, indicating that the 19-carboxy or 19-nor analog are not normal intermediates and suggesting Eq. (13–12).

Androstenedione → 19-Hydroxyandrostenedione →

19-Ketoandrostenedione → → Estrone   (13–12)

The form in which C-19 appears after cleavage has been studied. Breuer and Grill[191] found that incubation of either testosterone, androstenedione, or 19-hydroxyandrostenedione with human placental microsomes in the presence of reduced nicotinamide adenine dinucleotide phosphate gave rise to formaldehyde and the corresponding estrogen.

187. L. L. Engel, J. Alexander, and M. Wheeler, *J. Biol. Chem.*, **231**, 159 (1958).
188. A. S. Meyer, *Experientia*, **11**, 99 (1955).
189. A. S. Meyer, *Biochim. Biophys. Acta*, **17**, 441 (1955).
190. T. Morato, M. Hayano, R. I. Dorfman, and L. R. Axelrod, *Biochem. Biophys. Res. Commun.*, **6**, 334 (1961).
191. H. Breuer and P. Grill, *Z. Physiol. Chem.*, **324**, 254 (1961).

Another study[192] showed that the 19-hydroxy substance yields both formaldehyde and formic acid, whereas the 19-keto derivative gives mostly formic acid.

The stereochemistry of loss of the C-1 hydrogen in the conversion of androstenedione to estrone was investigated using tritium labeling, and it was found that the β-(equatorial)-hydrogen is the one lost in the conversion. This conclusion is contrary to one reached in studies[193] with androstenedione incubation with baboon and human ovaries in which the α-hydrogen seemed to be eliminated. However, this latter conclusion rested on some unfortunate assumptions and is to be regarded skeptically.[194]

In contrast to the finding that it is the equatorial β-hydrogen which is lost in the formation of estrogens in humans is the finding that bacterial dehydrogenation involves diaxial loss of the 1α- and 2β-hydrogen atoms.[195]

Dorfman has discussed some of the mechanistic pathways possible to accommodate the above findings. Many are possible that are essentially modifications in timing of the various steps. As the oxidation state of the 19-carbon after elimination seems no higher than when this carbon is still attached to the steroid molecule, it would seem that the oxidation process must occur at the C-1 hydrogen. The requirement for oxygen and reduced pyridine nucleotide would seem to make the enzyme that catalyzes the oxidation step of the mixed function oxidase type and therefore may suggest " $^+$OH " or more probably ferryl iron. Equation (13-13) may then represent this transformation, although many other detailed descriptions are possible. A central

$$+ \text{ HCOOH} \qquad (13\text{-}13)$$
$$+ \text{ H}_2\text{O}$$
$$+ l_5\text{Fe}^{2+}$$

192. R. I. Dorfman, C. Gual, T. Morato, M. Hayano, and M. Gut, *Abs. Intern. Congr. Hormonal Steroids*, Milan, Italy, 1962, p. 270.

193. L. R. Axelrod and J. W. Goldzieher, *J. Clin. Endocrinol. Metab.*, **22**, 537 (1962).

194. T. Morato, K. Raab, H. J. Brodie, M. Hayano, and R. I. Dorfman, *J. Am. Chem. Soc.*, **84**, 3764 (1962).

195. M. Hayano, H. J. Ringold, V. Stefanovic, M. Gut, and R. I. Dorfman, *Biochem. Biophys. Res. Commun.*, **4**, 454 (1961).

point in any mechanism is certainly the driving force for the formation of the estrogens provided by the aromatization of ring A.

Reduction at C-17

Estrone and estradiol are two of the more important estrogenic hormones and differ only in the state of oxidation at C-17; estrogen has a carbonyl group and estradiol has a 17β-hydroxyl function. The reduction of estrone produces estradiol-17β **[12]**, which can give rise to estriol both in a human liver slice[196] and isolated rat liver.[197] It has been reported[198] that there exist enzyme systems in liver that in vitro can reduce a 16-keto group to either an α- or β-hydroxyl, whereas a 17-keto group always yields a 17β-alcohol. Thus, 16α-hydroxyestrone yields only estratriol-16α,17β, whereas 16-oxo-estradiol-17β gives rise both to estratriol-16α, 17β and estratriol-16β,17β.

A nicotinamide adenine dinucleotide-linked estradiol-17β-dehydrogenase that catalyzes the interconversion of the two substances has been partially purified from human term placenta.[199] Talalay et al.[200,201]

$$+ \text{NADH} \rightleftharpoons$$

$$+ \text{NAD}^+$$

[12]

Estrone   Estradiol-17β

confirmed several previous observations on its characteristics; a requirement for sulfhydryl groups, stabilization by estradiol, and almost constant initial reaction velocity from pH 6 to pH 9. The kinetics and

196. L. L. Engel, B. Baggett, and M. Halla, *Biochim. Biophys. Acta*, **30**, 435 (1958).
197. M. Hagopian and L. K. Levy, *Biochim. Biophys. Acta*, **30**, 641 (1958).
198. H. Breuer, L. Nocke, and R. Knuppen, *Biochim. Biophys. Acta*, **33**, 254 (1959).
199. L. J. Langer and L. L. Engel, *J. Biol. Chem.*, **233**, 583 (1958).
200. P. Talalay and H. G. Williams-Ashman, *Proc. Natl. Acad. Sci. (U.S.)*, **44**, 15 (1958).
201. P. Talalay, B. Hurlock, and H. G. Williams-Ashman, *Proc. Natl. Acad. Sci. (U.S.)*, **44**, 862 (1958).

substrate specificities of this enzyme preparation have also been investigated.[202]   The enzyme preparation has absolute specificity for 17β-hydroxyl group, and the steroid substrate must possess a highly planar ring A or ring B or both.   Furthermore, the enzyme interacts with the entire steroid surface.

13–6 SUMMARY

Cholesterol is a substrate for the production of two biologically important groups of substances, the bile acids and the steroid hormones.

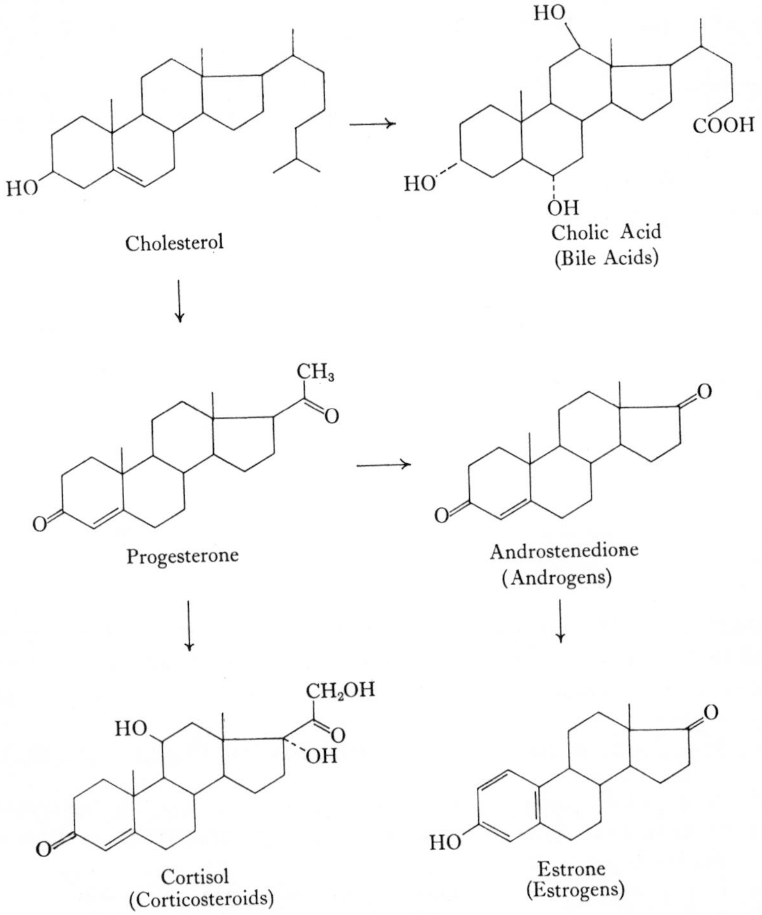

Chart IV

202. L. J. Langer, J. A. Alexander, and L. L. Engel, *J. Biol. Chem.*, **234** 2609 (1959).

Nuclear transformations of cholesterol and loss of the three terminal carbons from the isoöctyl sidechain give the bile acids. See Chart IV. The hormones are formed by a fundamentally different sequence which begins with the removal of six of the sidechain carbons. Appropriate nuclear transformations yield the corticosteroids. The androgens arise by loss of the remaining two sidechain carbon atoms, and the estrogens by ejection of the angular C-19 methyl group and aromatization of ring A.

13-7 STEROIDAL ALKALOIDS

A final word is appropriate about a class of alkaloids from diverse plant sources whose carbon skeletons show a clear relationship to cholesterol. This relation is evident in the aglycone portion of *Solanum* alkaloids such as solanidine [13] and tomatidine [14], which are produced by potatoes and tomatoes. Some tracer experiments have been reported for these substances. Sprouting potato[203,204] or tomato

[13]   [14]

plants[205] incorporated labeled acetate mainly into the aglycone portion of these glycoalkaloids. The incorporation of 2-C^{14}-mevalonate was several-fold more efficient than the incorporation of acetate.[206]

The aglycone portions of the ester alkaloids of *Veratrum* species contain a slightly perturbed cholesterol carbon skeleton, in which the C and D rings have exchanged sizes, the C ring being five- and the D ring six-membered. Examples of such substances are jervine [15] and cevine [16].

The requisite rearrangement[207] can be considered analogous to

203. A. R. Guseva and V. A. Paseshnichenko, *Biokhimiyo*, **23**, 412 (1958).
204. A. R. Guseva, M. G. Borikhina, and V. A. Paseshnichenko, *Biokhimiya*, **25**, 282 (1960).
205. H. Sander and H. Grisebach, *Z. Naturforsch.*, **13B**, 755 (1958).
206. A. R. Guseva, V. A. Paseshnichenko, and M. G. Borikhina, *Biokhimiya*, **26**, 723 (1961).
207. E. Leete, in *Biogenesis of Natural Compounds*, P. Bernfield (ed.), Pergamon, New York, 1963, p. 787.

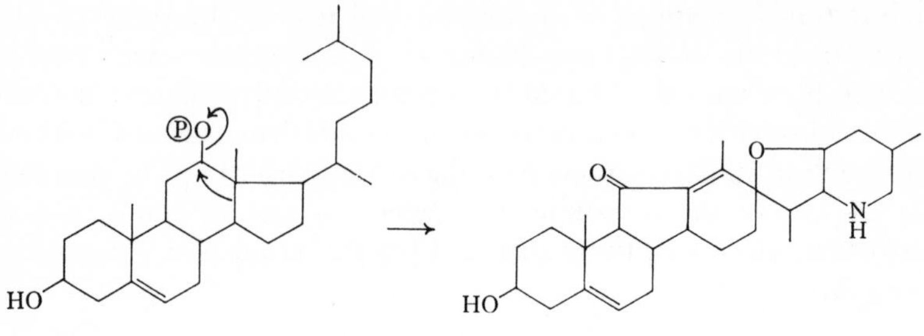

[15]

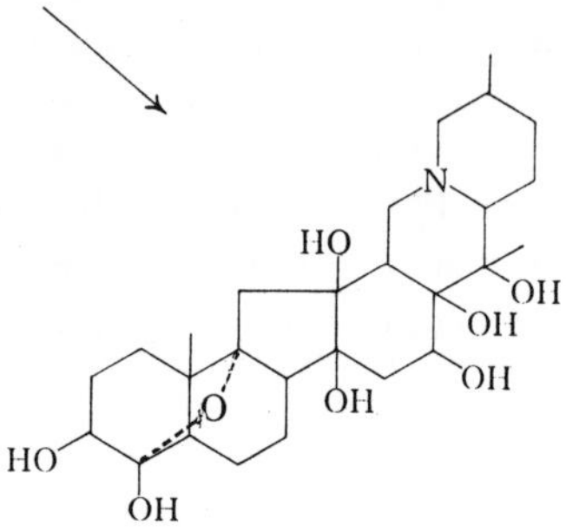

[16]

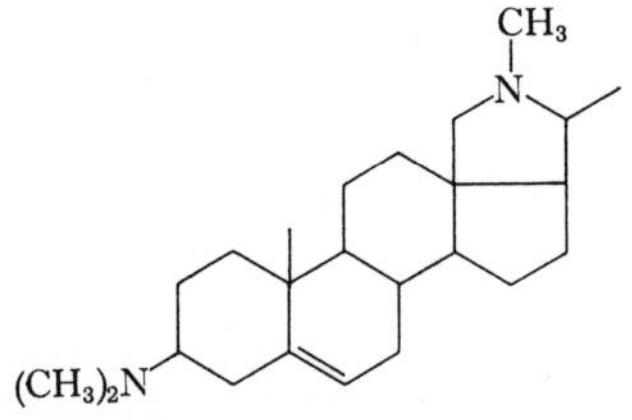

[17]

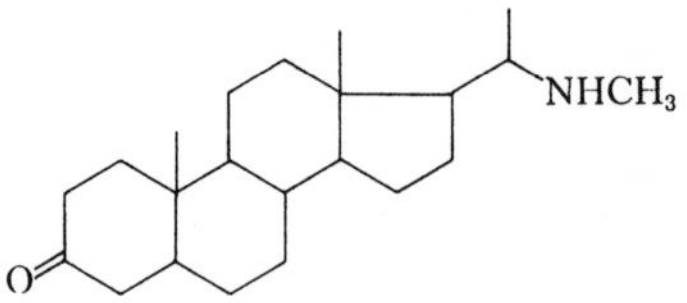

[18]

that which contracts the six-membered ring of a normal diterpene to the five-membered ring present in gibberellic acid.

A final structural type found in the *Apocyanaceae* family is clearly related to the amputated skeleton characteristic of the C_{21} steroid hormones such as pregnenolone. Conessine **[17]** and funtumafrine B **[18]** are examples of this group of substances, and bear an interesting relationship to aldosterone in their common possession of an oxidized C-18 angular methyl group.

Appendix

The following list of compounds was used in the statistical examination of acetogenins presented in Chapter 4. Compounds not otherwise referenced will be found in one or more of the major compendia, Karrer,[1] Miller,[2] and Geissman.[3]

Macrolides

Erythromycin
Erythromycin B
Filipin [4]
Lagosin [4]
Magnamycin B
Magnamycin (Carbomycin)

Methymycin
Narbomycin
Neomethymycin
Oleandomycin
Picromycin
Pimaricin

φ-C$_2$ Compounds

2,5-Dihydroxyphenylglyoxylic acid
Ethyl-guiacol
Homogentisic acid
Homoprotocatechuic acid
o-Hydroxyphenylacetic acid
p-Hydroxyphenylacetic acid

Mandelic acid
Phenylacetic acid
m-Phlorol
m-Phlorol methyl ether
2,4,5-Trihydroxy-phenylglyoxylic acid
Tropic acid

1. W. Karrer, *Konstitution und Vorkommen der Organischen Pflanzenstoffe*, Birkhauser, Basel, 1958.
2. M. W. Miller, *The Pfizer Handbook of Microbial Metabolites*, McGraw-Hill, New York, 1961.
3. T. A. Geissman, *The Chemistry of Flavonoid Compounds*, Macmillan, New York, 1962.
4. M. L. Dhar, V. Thaller, and M. C. Whiting, *Proc. Chem. Soc.*, **1960**, 310.

φ-C₃ *Compounds*

Acetyleugenol
Allyl-pyrocatechol
Allyl-tetramethoxybenzene
Anethole
Anise ketone
Anisoxide[5]
Anthricin
Apiole
1-Arctigenin
Asarone
Caffeic acid[6,7]
Chavibetol
Chavicol
Chlorogenic acid
Cinnamaldehyde
Cinnamic acid
Cinnamyl alcohol
Conidendrin
Coniferyl alcohol
o-Coumaric acid
p-Coumaric acid
Croweacin
Cubebin
Dehydrodieugenol
Dehydropodophyllotoxin
Dihydrocinnamyl alcohol
Dill apiole
Elemicin
Esdragol
Ethyl p-methoxycinnamate
Eudesmin
Eugenol
Eugenol methyl ether
Ferulic acid

Foeniculin
Forsythigenol
Galbacin
Galbulin[8]
Galcatin
Galgravin
Gmelinol[9]
Guaiaretic acid
Hernandia lignane
Hinokinin
Hydrocaffeic acid
Hydrocinnamaldehyde
Hydrocinnamic acid
Hydroxy-propiosyringone
Hydroxy-propiovanillone
Isoapiole
Isoeugenol
Isoeugenol methyl ether
Isoferulic acid
Isomyristicin
Isoölivil
Isosafrole
Isotaxiresinol
Lariciresinol
Lubanol benzoate
Lyoniside[10]
Magnolol
Matairesinol[11]
Melilotic acid
o-Methoxycinnamaldehyde
p-Methoxycinnamaldehyde
p-Methoxycinnamic acid
Methyl cinnamate
Methyl p-methoxycinnamate

5. D. H. R. Barton, A. Bhati, P. deMayo, and G. A. Morrison, *J. Chem. Soc.*, **1958**, 4393.
6. W. W. Reid, *Chem. & Ind.* (*London*), **1958**, 1439.
7. T. A. Geissman and T. Swain, *Chem. & Ind.* (*London*), **1957**, 984.
8. G. K. Hughes and E. Ritchie, *Australian J. Chem.*, **7**, 104 (1954).
9. A. J. Birch, G. K. Hughes, and E. Ritchie, *Australian J. Chem.*, **7**, 83 (1954).
10. M. Yasue and Y. Kato, *Yakugaku Zasshi*, **80**, 1013 (1960); **81**, 529 (1961).
11. R. D. Haworth and L. Wilson, *J. Chem. Soc.*, **1950**, 71.

Myristicin
Nordihydro guaiaretic acid
Olivil
α-Peltatin
β-Peltatin
Picropodophyllin[12]
Safrole

Savinin
seco-Isolariciresinol[13]
Sesamin
Sinapic acid
Sinapin
Syringenin
Truxillic acids

Coumarins

Aculeatin
Alloxanthoxyletin
Ammoresinol
Angelicin
Angelicone
Athamantin[14]
Aurapten (7-geranyloxy-coumarin)
Avicennin[15]
Ayapin
Bergamotin
Bergaptene
Bergaptol
Brayleyanin[16]
Braylin
Byak-angelicin
Byak-angelicol
Calophyllolide[17]
Collinin
Coumarin
Dalbergin[18]

Daphnetin
Demethyl-suberosin
Dicoumarol
Dihydrosamidin
Edultin[19]
Esculetin
Esculetin dimethyl ether
Fabiatrin
Farnesiferol-a[20]
Farnesiferol-b[20]
Farnesiferol-c[20]
Fraxetin
Fraxidin
Fraxinol
Geijerin[21]
5-Geranyloxy-7-methoxy-coumarin
8-Geranyloxy-psoralene[22]
Glabra lactone[23]
Glucosido-furocoumaric acid
Halfordin[24]

12. A. W. Schrecker and J. L. Hartwell, *J. Am. Chem. Soc.*, **76**, 752 (1954).
13. L. H. Briggs, R. C. Cambie, and J. L. Hoare, *Tetrahedron*, **7**, 262 (1959).
14. H. Schmid, *Sci. Proc. Roy. Dublin Soc.*, **27**, 145 (1956).
15. H. R. Arthur and C. M. Lee, *J. Chem. Soc.*, **1960**, 4654.
16. F. A. L. Anet, G. K. Hughes, and E. Ritchie, *Australian J. Sci.*, **2**, 608 (1949).
17. J. Polonsky, *Bull. Soc. Chim.*, **1956**, 914; **1958**, 929.
18. V. K. Ahluwalia, A. C. Mehta, and T. R. Seshadri, *Proc. Indian Acad. Sci.*, **A45**, 15 (1957); *Tetrahedron*, **4**, 271 (1958).
19. H. Mitsuhasiji and T. Itoh, *Chem. Pharm. Bull.*, **9**, 170 (1961).
20. L. Caglioti, H. Naef, D. Arigoni, and O. Jeger, *Helv. Chim. Acta.*, **41**, 2278 (1958); **42**, 2557 (1959).
21. F. N. Lahey and D. J. Wluka, *Australian J. Chem.*, **8**, 125 (1955).
22. W. L. Stanley and S. H. Vannier, *J. Am. Chem. Soc.*, **79**, 3488 (1957).
23. K. Hata and A. Nita, *Yakugaku Zasshi*, **77**, 941 (1957).
24. M. P. Hegarty and F. N. Lahey, *Australian J. Chem.*, **9**, 120 (1956).

Coumarins—continued

Herniarin
8-Hydroxy-bergaptene [25]
Imperaturin
Inophyllolide [17]
Isobergaptene
Isobyak-angelicolic acid
Isofraxidin
Isohalfordin [24]
Isoimperatorin
Isopimpinellin
Limettin
Luvangetin
Mammein [26]
Marmesin
Marmin [27]
Melilotin
Meranzin (aurapten)
Novobiocin [28]
Osthenol
Osthol
Ostruthin
Ostruthol
Oxypeucedanin

Peucedanin
Phellopterin
4-Phenyl-5,7-dihydroxy-6-isovaleryl-
   8-isopentenyl coumarin [29]
Pimpinellin
Prangenin
Psoralene (Ficusin)
Psoralidin
Samidin [30,31]
Scopoletin [32]
Seselin
Sphondin
Suberosin
Toddalolactone
6,7,8-Trimethoxy-coumarin
Umbelliferone
Umbelliprenin
Visnadin [33]
Xanthotoxin
Xanthotoxol
Xanthoxyletin
Xanthyletin

Terphenyls and Pulvic Acids

Atromentin
Aurantiacin

Calycin
Epanorin

25. F. A. Kincle, J. Romo, G. Rosenkranz, and F. Sondheimer, *J. Chem. Soc.*, **1956**, 4163.
26. C. Djerassi, E. J. Eisenbraun, R. A. Finnegan, and B. Gilbert, *Tetrahedron Letters*, **1**, 10 (1959); *J. Org. Chem.*, **25**, 2165 (1960).
27. A. Chatterjee and A. Bhattacharya, *J. Chem. Soc.*, **1959**, 1922.
28. J. W. Hinman, E. L. Caron, and H. Hoeksema, *J. Am. Chem. Soc.*, **79**, 3789 (1957).
29. C. Djerassi and R. A. Finnegan, *Tetrahedron Letters*, **13**, 11 (1959); R. A. Finnegan, M. P. Morris, and C. Djerassi, *J. Org. Chem.*, **26**, 1180 (1961).
30. E. Smith, N. Hosansky, W. G. Bywater, and E. E. van Tamelen, *Chem. & Ind.* (*London*), **1956**, 718; *J. Am. Chem. Soc.*, **79**, 3534 (1957).
31. W. Bencze, O. Halpern, and H. Schmid, *Experientia*, **12**, 137 (1956); *Ber.*, **92**, 2338 (1959).
32. W. W. Reid, *Chem. & Ind.* (*London*), **1958**, 1439.
33. H. D. Schroeder, W. Bencze, O. Halpern, and H. Schmid, *Chem. Ber.*, **92**, 2338 (1959).

Leprapic acid
Leprapinic acid[34]
Leucomelone
Muscarufin
Pinastric acid[35]
Polyporic acid

Pulvic acid
Pulvic anhydride
Rhizocarpic acid
Thelephoric acid[36]
Volucrisporin[37]
Vulpinic acid

ϕ-C_n Compounds ($n > 3$)

Ageratochromene
Anibine[38]
Aureothin
Betuligenol
Campnosperma diketone[39-41]
Campnospermonol[39-41]
Chaetomium acid
Cortisalin
Curcumin
5,6-Dehydrokawain[42]
Dicinnamoylmethane
Diferulylmethane
Dihydrokawain (marindinin)
Dihydromethysticin
Dihydrourushiol
Embelin
Glutarenghol
Hispidin[43]
Kawain
Laccol
Maesaquinone

Methoxy-paracotoin[38,44]
Methyl gingerol
Methyl phenethyl ketone
3-Methyl-6-phenyl-2,3-dihydro-γ-
  pyrone
Methysticin
Paracotoin
Phenylcoumalin
Piperic acid
Piscidic acid
Rapanone
Renghol
Rheosmin[45]
Shogaol
Tetrahydropiperic acid
Thitsiol
Trachelogenin[46]
Urushiol[47]
Yangonin
Zingerone

34. O. P. Mittal and T. R. Seshadri, *J. Chem. Soc.*, **1955**, 3053.
35. P. K. Grover and T. R. Seshadri, *Tetrahedron*, **6**, 312 (1959).
36. J. Gripenberg, *Tetrahedron*, **10**, 135 (1960).
37. P. V. Divekar, G. Read, and L. C. Vining, *Chem. & Ind. (London)*, **1959**, 731.
38. W. B. Mars, O. R. Gottlieb, and C. Djerassi, *J. Am. Chem. Soc.*, **79**, 4507 (1957).
39. L. K. Dalton and J. A. Lamberton, *Australian J. Chem.*, **11**, 46 (1958).
40. A. S. Birch and F. W. Donovan, *Australian J. Chem.*, **6**, 360 (1955).
41. J. A. Lamberton, *Australian J. Chem.*, **11**, 73 (1958).
42. O. R. Gottlieb and W. B. Mors, *J. Org. Chem.*, **24**, 17 (1959).
43. R. L. Edwards, D. C. Lewis, and D. V. Wilson, *J. Chem. Soc.*, **1961**, 4995.
44. O. R. Gottlieb and W. B. Mors, *J. Am. Chem. Soc.*, **80**, 2263 (1958).
45. L. Bauer, A. J. Birch, and A. J. Ryan, *Australian J. Chem.*, **8**, 534 (1955).
46. T. Takano, *Yakugaku Zasshi*, **79**, 1449 (1959).
47. R. F. Dawson, *Rec. Chem. Progr.*, **15**, 39 (1954).

Acetophenones and Phloroglucinols

Acetophenone
Acetovanillone
Adhumulone
Albaspidin
Allo-evodione [48]
Allo-evodionol
Allo-evodionol methyl ether
Ammiol
Angustifolionol [49]
Angustione
Aspidin
Aspidinol
Baeckeol [49]
Butanofilicinic acid [50]
Clavatol [51,52]
Cohumulone
Colupulone
Conglomerone
Dehydroangustione [53]
2,6-Dihydroxyacetophenone [54]
3,4-Dihydroxyacetophenone [55]
2,6-Dihydroxybutyrophenone [54]
Eugenin [56]
Eugenitin (eugenitol) [56]
Eugenone
Evodionol [56]

Evodione [57]
Evodionol methyl ether
Euparin
Filicin (filixic acid)
Flavaspidic acid [56]
2-Hydroxyacetophenone
5-Hydroxy-2-methyl-chromanone [54]
5-Hydroxy-2-methyl-chromone [54]
Hydroxy-paeonol [58]
Humulone
Isoeugenitin
Isoeugenitol [56]
Khellin
Khellinol [14]
Khellol
α-Kosin [59]
β-Kosin [59]
Leptospermone [60]
Lupulone
4-Methoxy-acetophenone
Muellitol [61]
Paeonol
Peucenin
Phloroacetophenone
Phloroacetophenone dimethyl ether
  (xanthoxylin)

48. K. D. Kirby and M. D. Sutherland, *Australian J. Chem.*, **9**, 411 (1956).
49. A. J. Birch, P. Elliott, and A. R. Penfold, *Australian J. Chem.*, **7**, 169 (1954).
50. A. J. Birch and P. Elliott, *Australian J. Chem.*, **9**, 98 (1956).
51. A. J. Birch, P. Elliott, and A. R. Penfold, *Australian J. Chem.*, **7**, 171 (1954).
52. R. Kuhn and H. A. Staab, *Angew. Chem.*, **65**, 371 (1953).
53. A. J. Birch and P. Elliott, *Australian J. Chem.*, **9**, 95 (1956).
54. D. C. Allport and J. D. Bu'Lock, *J. Chem. Soc.*, **1960**, 654.
55. M. Takanashi, T. Itox, and A. Mizutani, *Yakugaku Zasshi*, **80**, 782 (1960).
56. A. J. Birch, P. Elliott, and A. R. Penfold, *Australian J. Chem.*, **7**, 170 (1954).
57. K. D. Kirby and M. D. Sutherland, *Australian J. Chem.*, **9**, 411 (1956).
58. A. J. Birch and P. Hextall, *Australian J. Chem.*, **8**, 263 (1955).
59. A. J. Birch and A. R. Todd, *J. Chem. Soc.*, **1952**, 3102.
60. A. J. Birch and P. Elliott, *Australian J. Chem.*, **9**, 98 (1956).
61. F. N. Lahey in lecture, UCLA, 1961.

Phloroacetophenone trimethyl ether
Piceol
Protokosin
Quinacetophenone methyl ether
Sorbicillin [52,53]
Tasmanone [60]

Torquatone [62]
Tremetone [63]
Usnic acid
Visnagin
Visnamminol
Xanthostemone [64]

Benzophenones

Cotoin
Griseophenone
Griseophenone Y [65]
Hydrocotoin
p-Hydroxybenzophenone

Maclurin
Methyl-hydrocotoin
Methyl-protocotoin
Protocotoin
Sulochrin

Xanthones

Asperxanthone
Decussatin
Dehydrogriseofulvin [65]
Deschloro-griseofulvin
Desmethyl-deschloro-griseofulvin
Desmethyl-swertianol [66]
Erdin [67]
Euxanthone
Gentisin
Geodin [67]
Griseofulvin [68]
Griseoxanthone C [65,69]

Isogentisin
Jacareubin [70]
Lichexanthone
Mangiferin [66]
Mangostin [71]
Pinselic acid
Pinselin
Ravenelin
Sterigmatocystin
Swerchirin
Swertianol
Swertinin

62. R. C. Bowyer and P. R. Jefferies, *Australian J. Chem.*, **12**, 442 (1959).
63. W. A. Bonner, J. I. DeGraw, D. M. Bowen, and V. R. Shah, *Tetrahedron Letters*, **12**, 417 (1961).
64. A. J. Birch and P. Elliott, *Australian J. Chem.*, **9**, 238 (1956).
65. W. J. McMaster, A. I. Scott, and S. Trippett, *J. Chem. Soc.*, **1960**, 4628.
66. J. C. Roberts, *Chem. Revs.*, **61**, 591 (1961).
67. D. H. R. Barton and A. I. Scott, *J. Chem. Soc.*, **1958**, 1767.
68. A. J. Birch, R. A. Massy-Westropp, R. W. Rickards, and H. Smith, *J. Chem. Soc.*, **1958**, 360.
69. A. Rhodes, B. Boothroyd, M. P. McGonagle, and G. A. Somerfield, *Biochem. J.*, **81**, 28 (1961).
70. F. E. King, T. J. King, and L. C. Manning, *J. Chem. Soc.*, **1957**, 563.
71. P. Yates and G. H. Stout, *J. Am. Chem. Soc.*, **80**, 1691 (1958).

Linear φ-C₃-φ Compounds

Asebogenin
Butein
Carthamone [72]
Ceroptene [73]
2',6'-Dihydroxy-4,4'-dimethoxy-dihy-
    drochalcone [74]
2',4-Dihydroxy-4'-methoxy-chalcone
2,6'-Dihydroxy-4-methoxy-β-phenyl-
    propiophenone
2-Hydroxy-4,6-dimethoxy-chalcone
Hyssopin
Iso-liquiritigenin
Isosalipurpol

Lanceolatin
Lonchocarpin
Methylpedicinin
Okanin
Pedicellin
Pedicin
Pedicinin
Phloretin
Pongamol (lanceolatin C)
Rottlerin
Stillopsidin (neoplathymenin)
Xanthohumol [75]

Aurones and Hydro-Aurones

Alphitonin [76]
Aureusidin
2-Benzyl-2,6,3',4'-tetrahydroxy-
    coumaran-3-one [77]
2-Benzyl-2,6,3'-trihydroxy-4'-
    methoxycoumaran-3-one [77]

Leptosidin
Maesopsin [78]
Maritimetin
Sulfuretin

3-Hydroxy-Flavanes

Afzelechin [79]
Arachidose
Butea-leucocyanidin [80]
Cacao-leucocyanidin [81]

Catechin
Fisetinidol [82]
Gallocatechin
Leucodelphinidin [80]

72. T. R. Seshadri and R. S. Thakur, *Current Sci.* (*India*), **29**, 57 (1960).
73. M. Nilsson, *Acta Chem. Scand.*, **13**, 750 (1959); S. Forsen and M. Nilsson, *ibid.*, **13**, 1383 (1959).
74. M. Nilsson, *Acta Chem. Scand.*, **15**, 154 (1961).
75. H. Hubner and W. Riedl, *Ber.*, **93**, 312 (1960).
76. A. J. Birch, E. Ritchie, and R. N. Speake, *J. Chem. Soc.*, **1960**, 3593.
77. H. G. C. King, T. White, and R. B. Hughes, *J. Chem. Soc.*, **1961**, 3234.
78. N. F. James, F. E. King, and J. W. W. Morgan, *Chem. & Ind.* (*London*), **1961**, 346.
79. W. E. Hillis and A. Carle, *Australian J. Chem.*, **3**, 390 (1960).
80. A. K. Ganguly and T. R. Seshadri, *Tetrahedron*, **6**, 21 (1959).
81. C. C. Forsyth and J. B. Roberts, *Biochem. J.*, **74**, 374 (1960).
82. D. G. Roux and E. Paulus, *Biochem. J.*, **78**, 120 (1961).

Leucofisetinidin [83]
Leucopelargonidin [84]
Leucorobinetidin [83]

Melacacidin [83]
Pro-anthocyanidin [85]
Teracacidin [86]

Anthocyanins

Cyanidin
Delphinidin
Gesneridin
Hirsutidin
Luteolinidin [87]
Malvidin

Nudicaulin
Pelargonidin
Peonidin
Petunidin
Rosinidin [88]
Salvianin

Flavanones

Alpinetin
Angophorol [89]
Butin
Citronetin
Cryptostrobin [90]
Cyrtominetin [91]
Desmethoxy-matteucinol
Dihydrowogonin [92]
5,4'-Dihydroxy-7,3'-dimethoxy-
flavanone [93]
Eriodictyol
Farrerol (cyrtopterinetin)
Hesperetin
Homoeriodictyol
Isopedicin

Isoakuranetin
Isoökanin [94,95]
Isorottlerin
Liquiritigenin
Matteucinol
Melicope flavanone [93]
8-Methoxy-butin
Naringenin
Pinocembrin (dihydrochrysin) [44,90]
Pinostrobin [90]
Plathymenin
Sakuranetin
Strobopinin [90]
6,7,3',4'-Tetramethoxy-flavanone

83. J. W. Clark-Lewis and G. F. Katekar, *Proc. Chem. Soc.*, **1960**, 345.
84. A. K. Ganguly and T. R. Seshadri, *J. Chem. Soc.*, **1961**, 2787.
85. K. Freudenberg and K. Weinges, *Tetrahedron Letters*, **8**, 267 (1961).
86. J. W. Clark-Lewis, G. F. Katekar, and P. I. Mortimer, *J. Chem. Soc.*, **1961**, 499.
87. J. B. Harborne, *Chem. and Ind. (London)*, **1960**, 229.
88. J. B. Harborne, *Nature*, **181**, 26 (1958).
89. A. J. Birch, D. G. Pettit, A. J. Ryan, and R. N. Speake, *J. Chem. Soc.*, **1960**, 2063.
90. G. Lindstedt, *Acta Chem. Scand.*, **5**, 121, 129 (1951).
91. Y. Kishimoto, *Yakugaku Zasshi*, **76**, 250 (1956).
92. J. Chopin, D. Molho, H. Pacheco, and C. Mentzer, *Bull. Soc. Chim. France*, **1957**, 192.
93. T. A. Geissman, *Australian J. Chem.*, **11**, 376 (1958).
94. F. E. King and T. J. King, *J. Chem. Soc.*, **1951**, 569.
95. M. Shimokoriyama, *J. Am. Chem. Soc.*, **79**, 214 (1957).

374

3-Hydroxy Flavanones

Ampelopsin
Aromadendrin dimethyl ether [96]
Aromadendrin (dihydrokaempferol) [97]
Dihydrorobinetin
Fustin
Keyakinol [98]
Leaserone [99]
Padmatin [100]

Phellamuretin
Pinobanksin
Pinobanksin acetate
Pinobanksin dimethyl ether [101]
Pinobanksin monomethyl ether [90]
Strobobanksin [90]
Taxifolin

Flavones

Acacetin (Buddleoflavonol)
Acrammerin
Apigenin
Artocarpin [102]
Baicalein
Chrysin
Chrysoeriol
Chrysoeriol-8-glucoside [103]
5-O-Desmethyl-nobiletin [104]
Dimethoxy-flavone
Diometin
Flavone
Fukugetin
Gamatin [105]
Genkwanin

Ginkgetin [106]
Hinokiflavone [107]
5-Hydroxy-4',7-dimethoxy-flavone
5-Hydroxy-flavone
Isoginkgetin [106]
Kayaflavone [106,108]
Lanceolatin B
Lotoflavin
Luteolin
Nobiletin
Orientin [109]
Oroxylin A
Pectolinarigenin
5,6,7,3',4'-Pentamethoxy-flavone [110]

96. W. E. Hillis, *Australian J. Sci.*, **A5**, 379 (1952).
97. N. F. James and J. W. W. Morgan, *J. Chem. Soc.*, **1960**, 2560.
98. K. Funaoka and M. Tanaka, *Nippon Mokuzai Gakkasishi*, **3**, 144, 173, 218 (1957).
99. W. D. Ollis, private communication, 1961.
100. R. N. Goel and T. R. Seshadri, *Tetrahedron*, **5**, 91 (1959).
101. G. Linstedt, *Acta Chem. Scand.*, **4**, 772 (1950).
102. K. G. Dave and K. Verkatoraman, *J. Sci. Ind. Res. (India)*, **15B**, 183 (1956); *C.A.*, **51**, 386 (1957).
103. E. C. Bate-Smith and T. Swain, *Chem. & Ind. (London)*, **1960**, 1132.
104. P. S. Sarin and T. R. Seshadri, *Tetrahedron*, **8**, 67 (1960).
105. S. K. Pavanaram and L. R. Row, *Australian J. Chem.*, **9**, 132 (1956).
106. W. Baker, A. C. M. Finch, W. D. Ollis, and K. W. Robinson, *Proc. Chem. Soc.*, **1959**, 91, 269.
107. Y. Fukui and N. Kawano, *J. Am. Chem. Soc.*, **81**, 6331 (1959).
108. N. Kawano, *Chem. Pharm. Bull. (Tokyo)*, **9**, 358 (1961).
109. L. Hörhammer and H. Wagner, in W. D. Ollis (ed.), *Chemistry of Natural Phenolic Compounds*, Pergamon, London, 1961, p. 187ff.
110. R. Born, *Chem. & Ind. (London)*, **1960**, 264.

Pinnatin [111]
Primetin
Sciadopitysin [106,112]
Scutellarein
Sotetsuflavone [113]
Strobochrysin [90]
Tangeretin (Ponkanetin)
Tectochrysin
5,7,3',4'-Tetrahydroxy-6,8-dimethyl-
    flavone [114]

Tricin
5,7,4'-Trihydroxy-6,8-dimethyl-
    flavone [114]
2',5-6-Trimethoxy-flavone [115]
Vitexin (saponaretin) [116]
Wogonin
Zapotin [115]
Zaputinin [115]

3-Hydroxyflavones

Amarbelin
Artemetin
Atanasin [117]
Auranetin
Ayanin
Azaleatin
Calycopterin (thapsin)
Casticin [118]
Chrysoplenetin
Datiscetin
Desmethoxy-kanugin
O-Desmethyl-icaritin
Distemonanthin
Erianthin
Fisetin
Flindulatin [119]
Galangin

Galangin methyl ether
Gardenin
Gossypetin
Herbacetin
Hibiscetin
5-Hydroxyauranetin [120]
Icaritin
Isorhamnetin
Izalpinin
Kaempferide
Kaempferol
Karanjin [111]
Kanugin
Keyakinin [98]
Limocitrin [121,122]
Limocitrol [122]
Melisimplexin

111. S. K. Pavanaram and L. R. Row, *Australian J. Chem.*, **9**, 132 (1956).
112. N. Kawano, *Chem. Pharm. Bull.* (*Tokyo*), **7**, 698, 821 (1959).
113. N. Kawano and M. Yamada, *J. Am. Chem. Soc.*, **82**, 1505 (1960); *Yakugaku Zasshi*, **80**, 1577 (1960).
114. Y. Kishimot, *Chem. Pharm. Bull.* (*Tokyo*), **4**, 24 (1956).
115. F. Sondheimer and A. Meisels, *Tetrahedron*, **9**, 139 (1960).
116. W. R. N. Williamson, *Chem. & Ind.* (*London*), **1961**, 1168.
117. S. E. Flores and J. Herran, *Chem. & Ind.* (*London*), **1960**, 291.
118. I. Belic, J. Bergant, S. Dolar, and R. A. Morton, *J. Chem. Soc.*, **1961**, 2523.
119. G. K. Hughes and E. Ritchie, *Australian J. Chem.*, **7**, 184 (1954).
120. P. S. Sarin and T. R. Seshadri, *Tetrahedron*, **8**, 64 (1960).
121. R. M. Horowitz and B. Gentili, *J. Org. Chem.*, **26**, 2899 (1961).
122. R. M. Horowitz and B. Gentili, *J. Org. Chem.*, **25**, 2183 (1960).

3-Hydroxyflavones—continued

Melisimplin
Meliternatin
Meliternin
4-O-Methyl-fisetin [123]
Morin (myricetin)
Ombuin
Oxyayanin A
Oxyayanin B
Patuletin
Penduletin [124]
3,7,8,3',4'-Pentahydroxy-flavone [125]
Pinomyricetin
Pinoquercetin
Polycladin [126]
Pongapin [111]
Pratoletin
Ptaeroxylol

Quercetagetin
Quercetin
Quercetin-3,3'-dimethyl ether [127]
Quercetin-3-methyl ether [127]
Rhamnazin
Rhamnetin
Rhamnocitrin
Robinetin
Sericetin [128]
Spinacetin [129]
Tamarixetin
Tambuletin
Tambulin
Ternatin
3,7,4'-Trihydroxy-flavone [123]
Vogeletin [130]
Wharangin

Miscellaneous Flavonoids

Carajurin
Cyanomaclurin [131]
Dracorhodin

Dracorubin
Peltogynol [132,133]

Isoflavonoids

Afromosin [134]
Angolensin

Biochanin A
Cabreuvin [135]

123. K. S. Kirby and T. White, *Biochem. J.*, **60**, 582 (1955).
124. S. E. Flores, J. Herian, and H. Menchaca, *Tetrahedron*, **4**, 132 (1958).
125. F. E. King and W. Bottomley, *J. Chem. Soc.*, **1954**, 1399.
126. G. B. Marini-Bettolo, S. Chiavarelli, and C. G. Casinovi, *Gazz. Chim. Ital.*, **87**, 1185 (1957).
127. C. H. Yang, H. D. Braymer, E. L. Murphy, W. Chorney, N. Scully, and S. H. Wender, *J. Org. Chem.*, **25**, 2063 (1960).
128. B. F. Burrows, W. D. Ollis, and L. M. Jackman, *Proc. Chem. Soc.*, **1960**, 177.
129. A. Zane and S. H. Wender, *J. Org. Chem.*, **26**, 4718 (1961).
130. S. Rangaswami and K. H. Rao, *Proc. Indian Acad. Sci.*, **49A**, 241 (1959).
131. K. Freudenberg and K. Weinges, *Ann.*, **613**, 61 (1958).
132. W. G. C. Forsyth, C. H. Hassall, and J. B. Roberts, *Chem. & Ind. (London)*, **1958**, 656.
133. W. R. Chan, W. G. C. Forsyth, and C. H. Hassall, *J. Chem. Soc.*, **1958**, 3174.
134. T. B. H. McMurray and C. Y. Theng, *J. Chem. Soc.*, **1960**, 1491.
135. O. R. Gottlieb and M. T. Magalhaes, *Anais Assoc. Brasileira Quim.*, **18**, 89 (1959).

Caviunin [136]
Coumestrol [137]
Deidzein [138]
Equol [139]
Erosnin [140]
Ferreirin
Formononetin
Genistein
Homoferreirin
Homopterocarpin
Irigenin
Jamaicin [141]
Maxima-substance A [142]
Maxima-substance B [142]
Maxima-substance C [143]
Mundulone [144]
Munetone [145]
Muningin
Ononetin [146]

Orobol
Osajin
Pachyrrhizin [147]
Padmakastein
Podospicatin [148]
Pomiferin
Pratensein [149]
Prunetin
Pseudo-baptigenin
Psoralidin [150]
Pterocarpin
Puerarin [151]
Santal
Sophorol [152]
Tectorigenin
Tlatlancuayin [153]
Toxicarol isoflavone [154]
Trifolirhzin [155]
Wedelolactone

136. O. R. Gottlieb and M. T. Magalhaes, *J. Org. Chem.*, **26**, 2449 (1961).
137. E. M. Bickoff, R. L. Lyman, A. L. Livingston, and A. N. Booth, *J. Am. Chem. Soc.*, **80**, 3969 (1958).
138. T. Murskami, Y. Nishikawa, and T. Ando, *Chem. Pharm. Bull. (Tokyo)*, **8**, 688 (1960).
139. F. Wessely and F. Prillinger, *Ber.*, **72**, 629 (1939).
140. J. Eisenbeiss and H. Schmid, *Helv. Chim. Acta*, **42**, 61 (1959).
141. O. A. Stamm, H. Schmid, and J. Buchi, *Helv. Chim. Acta*, **41**, 2006 (1958).
142. S. Rangaswami and B. V. R. Sastry, *Current Sci. (India)*, **24**, 13, 337 (1955); *C.A.*, **50**, 13008 (1956).
143. S. Rangaswami and B. V. R. Sastry, *Arch. Pharm.*, **292**, 170 (1959).
144. B. R. Burrows, N. Finch, W. D. Ollis, and I. O. Sutherland, *Proc. Chem. Soc.*, **1959**, 150.
145. N. L. Dutts, *J. Indian Chem. Soc.*, **36**, 165 (1959).
146. F. Wessely and F. Lechner, *Monatsh.*, **57**, 395 (1931); **63**, 201 (1933).
147. E. Simonitsch, H. Frei, and H. Schmid, *Monatsh.*, **88**, 541 (1957).
148. H. R. Briggs and T. P. Cebalo, *Tetrahedron*, **6**, 145 (1959).
149. E. Wong, *Chem. & Ind. (London)*, **1961**, 1963.
150. P. C. Duttagupta, H. N. Khastgir, and P. Sengupta, *Chem. & Ind. (London)*, **1960**, 937.
151. T. Murakamii, Y. Nishikawa, and T. Andro, *Chem. Pharm. Bull. (Tokyo)*, **8**, 688 (1960).
152. H. Suginome, *Tetrahedron Letters*, **19**, 16 (1960).
153. P. Crabbe, P. R. Leeming, and C. Djerassi, *J. Am. Chem. Soc.*, **80**, 5285 (1958).
154. S. H. Harper, *J. Chem. Soc.*, **1940**, 1178.
155. J. B. Bredenberg and P. K. Hietala, *Acta Chem. Scand.*, **15**, 696 (1961).

Rotenoids

Dehydrodeguelin
Dehydrorotenone
Dehydrotoxicarol
Deguelin
Elliptone
Malaccol
Munduserone [156]

Pachyrrhizon
Rutenolon I [157]
Rotenone
Sermundone [99]
Sumatrol
Tephrosin [157]
Toxicarol

Depsides and Depsidones

Alectoronic acid
Anziaic acid
Atronorin
Baeomycesic acid
Barbatic acid
Barbatolic acid
Boninic acid
Chloroatronorin
α-Collatolic acid
Deschloro-nornidulin [158]
Didymic acid
Diffractaic acid
Diploicin
Diploschistesic acid
Divaricatic acid
Erythrin
Evernic acid
Fumarprotocetraric acid
Gangaleoidin
Geodoxin
Glomelliferic acid
Gyrophoric acid
Hiascic acid
Homosekikaic acid
Hypothamnolic acid
Imbricaric acid

Lecanoric acid
Lobaric acid
Microphyllic acid
Nidulin [158]
Norolobaridone
Nornidulin [158]
Norstictic acid
Obtusatic acid
Olivetoric acid
Pannaric acid [159]
Pannarin
Perlatolic acid
Physodalic acid
Physodic acid
Picrolichenic acid [160]
Porphyrilic acid
Protocetraric acid
Psoromic acid
Ramalinolic acid
Salazinic acid
Sekikaic acid
Sphaerophorin
Squamatic acid
Stictic acid
Strepsilin
Tenuiorin

156. N. Finch and W. D. Ollis, *Proc. Chem. Soc.*, **1960**, 176.
157. M. Miyano and M. Matsui, *Ber.*, **92**, 1438 (1959).
158. F. M. Dean, D. S. Dearha, A. D. T. Erni, D. W. Hughes, and J. C. Roberts, *J. Chem. Soc.*, **1960**, 4829.
159. B. Akermark, H. Erdtman, and C. A. Wachtmeister, *Acta Chem. Scand.*, **13**, 1855 (1958).
160. C. A. Wachtmeister, *Acta Chem. Scand.*, **12**, 147 (1958).

Thamnolic acid
Umbilicaric acid
Variolaric acid

Vicanicin [161]
Virensic acid [162]

Orcinol Derivatives

α-Acetyl-orsellinic acid
Agrimonolide [163]
Anacardic acids [40,47]
Aurantiogliocladin
Auroglaucin [164]
Bergenin [165]
Bilobol
Cannabidiol
Cannabinol
Cardols [40,47]
Chebulic acid
Coenzymes Q
Cyclopaldic acid
Cyclopolic acid
Dihydrogladiolic acid
Dihydro-ligusticum-lactone
4,6-Dihydroxy-3-methoxyphthalic
  acid
3,5-Dihydroxyphthalic acid
3,4-Dimethyl-8-hydroxy-
  isocoumarin [166]
Flavipin
Flavoglaucin

Ginkgol
Ginkgolic acid
Gladiolic acid
Gliorosein
Haematommic acid [167]
α-Hydroxy-α-acetyl-orsellinic acid
8-Hydroxy-3-methyl-isocoumarin
α-Keto-α-acetyl-orsellinic acid
Ligusticumic acid
Ligusticum-lactone
Ligustilide [168]
Meconin
Mellein
Methoxy-mellein [169]
Methylsalicylic acid
Montagnetol
Mycophenolic acid
Orcinol
β-Orcinol
Orsellinic acid
Pelandjuaic acid
Pirolagenin
Quadrilineatin [170]

161. S. Neelakantan, T. R. Seshadri, and S. S. Subramanian, *Tetrahedron Letters*, **9**, 1 (1959).
162. K. Agnoramurthy, K. G. Sarma, and T. R. Seshadri, *Tetrahedron*, **12**, 173 (1961).
163. N. Yamato, *Yakugaku Zasshi*, **79**, 129, 1069 (1959).
164. A. J. Birch, J. Schofield, and H. Smith, *Chem. & Ind. (London)*, **1958**, 1321.
165. J. E. Hay and L. J. Haynes, *J. Chem. Soc.*, **1958**, 2231.
166. I. Yamamoto and Y. Yamamoto, *Bull. Agr. Chem. Soc. (Japan)*, **24**, 628 (1960).
167. D. Hess, *Naturforsch.*, **146**, 345 (1959).
168. H. Mitsuhashi, U. Magai, and T. Muramatsu, *Chem. Pharm. Bull. (Tokyo)*, **9**, 115 (1961).
169. E. Sondheimer, *J. Am. Chem. Soc.*, **79**, 5036 (1957).
170. J. H. Birkinshaw, P. Chaplen, and R. Lahoz-Oliver, *Biochem. J.*, **67**, 155 (1957).

Sedanolide
Sedanonic acid
Sparassol

Tetrahydrocannabinol
Tocopherols [171]
Ustic acid

Stilbenes and Dihydrostilbenes

Chlorophorin
Dihydropinosylvin [90]
Dihydropinosylvin monomethyl
   ether [90]
Hydrangeol
Hydrangic acid
Hydroxy-resveratrol
4-Hydroxy-stilbene
4-Methoxy-stilbene

3,4,5,3',5'-Pentahydroxy-stilbene
Phylloeuldin
Pinosylvin
Pinosylvin dimethyl ether
Pinosylvin monomethyl ether
Pterostilbene
Resveratrol
Rhapontigenin
3,4,3',5'-Tetrahydroxy-stilbene

Naphthalenes and Dimeric Naphthyls

Alkannan
Alkannin
Chartreusin
Chimaphillin
Cordeauxia quinone
1,8-Dihydroxynaphthalene mono-
   methyl ether [54]
Dihydroxyperylene quinone [172]
Dimethoxynaphthoquinone
1,8-Dimethoxynaphthene [54]
Diospyrol [173]
Diosquinone
Droserone
Dunnione
Echinochrome A
Eleutherin
Eleutherinol [174]
Eleutherol

Erythroaphin [175]
Flaviolin
Fusarubin
Hydroxy-droserone
5-Hydroxy-7-methyl-naphtho-
   quinone [176]
Javanicin
Juglone
Lapachenole
Lapachol
Lawsone
Lomatiol
2-Methoxy-naphthoquinone
Methyl juglone
6-Methyl-naphthoquinone
Mollisin
Musizin (nepodin) [177,178]
Phthlocol

171. J. Green, P. Mamalis, S. Marcinkiewile, and D. McHale, *Chem. & Ind.* (*London*), **1960**, 73.
172. D. C. Allport and J. D. Bu'Lock, *J. Chem. Soc.*, **1958**, 4090.
173. J. W. Loder, S. Mongolsu, A. Robertson, and W. B. Whalley, *J. Chem. Soc.*, **1957**, 2233.
174. A. J. Birch and F. W. Donovan, *Australian J. Chem.*, **6**, 373 (1953).
175. A. R. Todd, *Experientia*, **18**, 433 (1962).
176. R. G. Cooke and H. Dowd, *Australian J. Sci.*, **5A**, 760 (1952).
177. C. J. Covell, F. E. King, and J. W. W. Morgan, *J. Chem. Soc.*, **1961**, 702.
178. T. Murakami and A. Matsushima, *Chem. Pharm. Bull.* (*Tokyo*), **9**, 654 (1961).

Piceatannol [179]
Plumbagin
Protoactinorhodin
Rubrofusarin [180,181]
α-Sorigenin
β-Sorigenin
Spinochrome D

Spinochrome E [182]
Spinochrome N [183]
Tetrahydroxy-dinaphthyl [172]
1,2,4-Trihydroxy-5,6,7,8-tetrahydro-
 naphthalene [184]
Vitamin K_1
Vitamin K_2

Anthraquinones

Aklavinone [185]
Alaternin [186]
Alizarin
Alizarin methyl ether
Aloe-emodin
Anthragallol and methyl ethers
Anthraquinone-2-carboxaldehyde [187]
Anthraquinone-2-carboxylic acid [187]
Asperthecin
Aurantio-obtusin [188]
Barbaloin [189]
1,2-Bis-O-methyl-anthragallol
1,3-Bis-O-methyl-anthragallol
Boletol
Carminic acid [190]
Catenarin
Chryso-obtusin [188]
Chrysophanol

Citreorosein
Copareolatin dimethyl ether
Copareolatin
Cyclo-pseudo-hypericin
Cynodontin
Damnacanthal
Damnacanthol
Denticulatol
7-Deoxyaklavinone [185]
Dermocybin [191]
Digitoluteine
Emodic acid
Emodin
Endocrocin
Erythroglaucin
Erythrolaccin [192]
Fagopyrin
Fallacinal

179. H. Endres and F. Leppmeier, Ber., **94**, 419 (1961).
180. H. Tanaka and T. Tamura, Tetrahedron Letters, **4**, 151 (1961).
181. G. H. Stout, D. L. Dreyor, and L. H. Jensen, Chem. & Ind. (London), **1961**, 289.
182. J. Smith and R. H. Thomson, Tetrahedron Letters, **1**, 10 (1960).
183. J. Smith and R. H. Thomson, J. Chem. Soc., **1961**, 1008.
184. H. Endres, K. Merkle, and H. Bauriede, Ber., **94**, 438 (1961).
185. W. D. Ollis and I. O. Sutherland, in Chemistry of Natural Phenolic Compounds, Pergamon, London, 1961, p. 213ff.
186. J. C. Lovie and R. H. Thomson, J. Chem. Soc., **1961**, 485.
187. P. Rudman, Chem. & Ind. (London), **1960**, 1356.
188. M. Takido, Chem. Pharm. Bull. (Tokyo), **8**, 246 (1960).
189. A. J. Birch and F. W. Donovan, Australian J. Chem., **8**, 523 (1955).
190. M. A. Ali and L. J. Haynes, J. Chem. Soc., **1959**, 1033.
191. J. H. Birkinshaw and R. Gourlay, Biochem. J., **80**, 387 (1961).
192. K. G. Dave, B. S. Joshi, A. V. Patwardhan, and K. Venkataraman, Tetrahedron Letters, **6**, 22 (1959).

Anthraquinones—continued

Flavoskyrin [193]
Fusaroskyrin [194]
Helminthosporin
Homonataloin [195]
Hydroxyanthraquinone
2-Hydroxymethyl-anthraquinone [187]
Hydroxy-skyrin
Hydroxy-skyrin B
Hypericin
Hystazarin methyl ether
Iridoskyrin
Islandicin
Islandicum-compound A
δ-Isorhodomycinone [185]
ϵ-Isorhodomycinone [185,196]
Kermesic acid
Lucidin
Luteoskyrin
Macrosporin
2-O-Methyl-anthragallol
2-Methyl-3-hydroxy-anthraquin-
one [187]
Methyl xanthopurpurin
1-O-Methyl-xanthopurpurin
3-O-Methyl-xanthopurpurin
Morindone
Munjistin
Nalgiolaxin
Nalgiovensin
Obtusin [188]

Pachybasin
Parietinic acid
Penicillopsin
Physicion
Proto-hypericins
Pseudo-hypericin
Pseudo-purpurin
Purpurin
δ-Pyrromycinone [185]
ϵ-Pyrromycinone (rutilantinone) [185]
η-Pyrromycinone [185,197]
Rhamnus alaternus pigment
Rhein
Rhodocladonic acid
Rhodocomatulin [198]
Rhodocomatulin methyl ether [198]
β-Rhodomycinone [199]
Roseopurpurin
Rubiadin
Rubiadin methyl ether
Rubroskyrin [200]
Rugulosin
Sennosides A and B
Skyrin
Solorinic acid
Soranjidiol
Tectoquinone
Teloschistin
Tritisporin
Xanthopurpurin

193. S. Shibata, *Chem. Pharm. Bull.* (*Tokyo*), **4**, 303 (1956); *Chem. Pharm. Bull.* (*Tokyo*), **8**, 889 (1960).
194. S. Fujisi, S. Hishida, S. Shibata, and S. Matsueda, *Chem. & Ind.* (*London*), **1961**, 1754.
195. L. J. Haynes and J. I. Henderson, *Chem. & Ind.* (*London*), **1960**, 50.
196. H. Brockmann and P. Boldt, *Ber.*, **94**, 2174 (1961).
197. H. Brockmann and W. Link, *Ber.*, **92**, 1880 (1959).
198. M. D. Sutherland and J. W. Wells, *Chem. & Ind.* (*London*), **1959**, 291.
199. H. Brockmann, Stanford symposium lecture, 1961; H. Brockmann and H. Brockmann, Jr., *Ber.*, **94**, 2681 (1961).
200. S. Shibata and I. Kitagawa, *Chem. Pharm. Bull.* (*Tokyo*), **8**, 884 (1960).

Polycyclic Aromatics

Alternariol
Atrovenetin [201]
Aureomycin
7-Bromotetracycline
Citrinin
Citromycetin
Curvularin
Dehydroaureomycin
6-Demethyl-aureomycin
6-Demethyl-tetracycline
Fulvic acid [202]
Fuscin [203]

Haemocorin [204]
Monascin [205]
Monascorubin
Purpurogenone [204]
Resistomycin
Rotiorin [206]
Rubropunctatin [207]
Sclerotiorin [206]
Siphulin [208]
Terramycin
Terramycin X
Tetracycline

Cyclopentane Derivatives

Adhulupone [209]
Alepric acid
Aleprylic acid
Aleprestic acid
Aleprolic acid
Brevifolin-carboxylic acid
Caldariomycin
Calythrone [210]
Chaulmoogric acid
Cinerolone
Cohulupone [209]
Cyclopentanone
Gorlic acid

Hulupone [209]
Hydnocarpusic acid
Jasmone
Keto-chaulmoogric acid
Keto-hydnocarpusic acid
Linderone [211]
Methyl-cyclopentenone
Methyl-linderone [211]
Methyl-reductinic acid
Pyrethrolone
Sarkomycin
Terrein
Trimethyl-cyclopentanone

201. D. H. R. Barton, P. deMayo, G. A. Morrison, and H. Raistrick, *Tetrahedron*, **6**, 48 (1959).
202. F. M. Dean, R. A. Eade, R. A. Moubasher, and A. Robertson, *Nature*, **179**, 366 (1957).
203. D. H. R. Barton and J. B. Hendrickson, *J. Chem. Soc.*, **1956**, 1028.
204. R. G. Cooke and R. H. Thomson, *Rev. Pure Appl. Chem.*, **8**, 85 (1958).
205. B. C. Fielding, J. S. E. Holker, D. F. Jones, A. D. G. Powell, K. W. Richmond, A. Robertson, and W. Whalley, *J. Chem. Soc.*, **1961**, 4579.
206. F. M. Dean, J. Stauton, and W. B. Whalley, *J. Chem. Soc.*, **1959**, 3004.
207. E. J. Haws, J. S. E. Holker, A. Kelley, A. D. G. Powell, and A. Robertson, *J. Chem. Soc.*, **1959**, 3598.
208. T. Bruun, *Tetrahedron Letters*, **4**, 1 (1960).
209. R. Stevens and D. Wright, *Proc. Chem. Soc.*, **1960**, 417.
210. A. J. Birch and P. Elliott, *Australian J. Chem.*, **9**, 95 (1956).
211. A. K. Kiang, H. H. Lee, and K. Y. Sim, *Proc. Chem. Soc.*, **1961**, 455.

Tetronic Acids, Tropolones, and Lichen Poly-Acids

Acetomycin
Agaricic acid
Ascorbic acid
Biglandulic acid
Caperatic acid
3-Carboxy-2,4,-pentadienal lactol
Carlic acid
Carlosic acid
Carolic acid
Carolinic acid
Dehydrocarolic acid
Dryophantin
Lichesterinic acid
γ-Methyl-tetronic acid
Minioluteic acid
Nephromopsic acid

Nephrosteranic acid
Nephrosterinic acid
Penicillic acid
Protolichesterinic acid
Puberulic acid
Puberulonic acid
Rangiformic acid
Roccellic acid
Spiculisporic acid
Stipitatic acid
Stipitatonic acid [212]
Tenuazonic acid
Terrestric acid
Viridicatic acid
Zymonic acid

Miscellaneous Compounds

4-Acetoxy-actidione
Actidione
Actiphenol
Alternaric acid [213]
Asterric acid [214]
Brazilin
Dalbergiones [215]
Egonol
Erythrocentaurin [216]
Frequentin [217]
Fumagillin

α-Guttiferin [218]
β-Guttiferin [218]
Hematoxylin
Holigarnalactone
Hyptolide
Inactone
Miroestrol [219]
Morellin [220]
Oleuropeic acid [221]
Palitantin [217]
Patulin

212. W. Segal, *J. Chem. Soc.*, **1959**, 2847.
213. J. R. Bartels-Keith and J. F. Grove, *Proc. Chem. Soc.*, **1959**, 398.
214. R. F. Curtis, C. H. Hassall, D. W. Jones, and T. W. Williams, *J. Chem. Soc.*, **1960**, 4838.
215. W. B. Eyton, W. D. Ollis, I. O. Sutherland, L. M. Jackman, O. R. Gottlieb, and M. T. Magalhaes, *Proc. Chem. Soc.*, **1962**, 301.
216. T. Kubota and Y. Tomita, *Chem. & Ind. (London)*, **1958**, 230.
217. K. Bowden, B. Lythgoe, and D. J. S. Marsden, *J. Chem. Soc.*, **1959**, 1662.
218. K. V. N. Rao and P. L. N. Rao, *Experientia*, **17**, 213 (1961).
219. D. G. Bounds and G. S. Pope, *J. Chem. Soc.*, **1960**, 3696.
220. D. V. K. Murthy and P. L. N. Rao, *Experientia*, **17**, 445 (1961).
221. B. Shasha and J. Leibowitz, *J. Org. Chem.*, **26**, 1948 (1960).

Streptimidone
Streptovitacin A
Streptovitacin B

Streptovitacin C_2
Trimesic acid
"Yeast benzofuran"[222]

222. M. A. P. Meisinger, F. A. Kuehl, E. L. Rickes, N. G. Brink, K. Folkers, M. Forbes, F. Zilliken, and P. Gyorgy, *J. Am. Chem. Soc.*, **81**, 4979 (1959).

Author Index

Abraham, S., 174, 273
Acerbo, S. N., 156
Achenbach, H., 139
Agnoramurthy, K., 379
Agranoff, B. W., 198, 207
Agurell, S., 198
Ahluwalia, V. K., 40, 367
Akazawa, T., 226
Akazawa, Y., 226
Akermark, B., 378
Albers, H. J., 321
Aldrich, R. A., 327
Alexander, G. J., 147, 312, 316, 324, 325
Alexander, J., 359
Alexander, J. A., 362
Ali, M. A., 90, 381
Ali Khan, M., 75
Ali Qureshi, A., 75
Allport, D. C., 79, 138, 151, 370, 380
Amdur, B. H., 192
Anderson, D. A., 296
Anderson, D. G., 293, 295, 297, 300
Ando, T., 377
Andrec, K., 358
Aneja, R., 23, 111
Anet, F. A. L., 116, 367
Anliker, R., 240
Anner, G., 350
Anthony, W. L., 338
ApSimon, J. W., 249, 253

Arigoni, D., 13, 114, 185, 188, 254, 256, 263, 264, 266, 279, 286, 367
Arnold, A., 355
Arnold, W., 10
Arnstein, H. R. V., 96
Arthur, H. R., 367
Artom, C., 122
Asahina, Y., 35
Ashton, D. M., 185
Asselineau, J., 140
Avadhani, P. N., 162
Avigan, J., 318, 320–322, 330
Avizonis, P. V., 199
Axelrod, J., 327
Axelrod, L. R., 359, 360
Ayer, W. A., 116
Ayres, P. J., 350

Babin, D. R., 250
Bachelor, F. W., 250
Bachhawat, B. K., 178–180
Baddeley, G. V., 266
Baggett, B., 352, 358, 361
Baisted, D. J., 286, 287
Baker, G. D., 337, 338
Baker, W., 171, 374
Baltrush, H. A., 196
Ban, Y., 288, 325
Bank, S., 258
Barltrop, J. A., 242, 247

Barnes, C. S., 237
Barnett, H. L., 291
Baronowsky, P., 134
Barron, E. S., 140
Bartels-Keith, J. R., 102, 384
Bartlett, P. D., 258
Barton, D. H. R., 26, 44, 75, 81, 84,
    226, 233, 236, 240, 248, 249, 263,
    278, 279, 366, 371, 383
Bartter, F. C., 350
Bassett, E. W., 143, 167
Bate-Smith, E. C., 374
Battaile, J., 193, 213
Bauer, L., 369
Baumann, C. A., 319
Bauriede, H., 381
Bawden, K., 73
Baxter, B. M., 197
Bayerle, H., 10
Beak, P., 245
Beaton, J. M., 265
Becker, R. R., 346
Beckwith, J. R., 165
Beeler, D. A., 296, 300
Beher, M. E., 338
Beher, W. T., 337, 338
Belic, I., 375
Bell, R. A., 245
Bellis, D. M., 158
Bencze, W., 368
Benedict, C. R., 293
Benirschke, K., 352
Bennett, R. D., 287
Bentley, R., 96, 165, 166, 168
Berg, B. N., 330
Bergant, J., 375
Bergeron, J. A., 293
Bergstrom, S., 327, 330-333, 339, 340
Beriger, E., 240
Berliner, D. L., 342
Bernasconi, R., 279
Bernfield, P., 363
Bernstein, S., 321
Beroza, M., 212
Bersius, O., 336
Berthet, L., 343
Beyer, K. F., 346
Bhate, D. S., 165
Bhati, A., 366
Bhattacharji, S., 197

Bhattacharya, A., 368
Bickelhaupt, F., 250
Bickoff, E. M., 377
Biederbick, K., 124
Biggs, M. W., 317
Bigley, D. B., 242, 247
Birch, A. J., 10, 12, 17, 41, 42, 44, 62,
    65, 79, 81, 86, 88, 92, 138, 142-147,
    149-155, 166, 188, 189, 197, 198,
    207, 208, 210, 222, 233, 234, 253,
    254, 256, 366, 369-373, 379-381,
    383
Birkinshaw, J. H., 66, 144, 208, 379,
    381
Bishop, N. I., 303
Blair, J., 62
Blance, G. E., 166, 198
Blanchard, M. L., 179
Blight, E. G., 342, 348
Bloch, E., 352
Bloch, K., 134-137, 174, 177, 192-195,
    209, 273, 274, 280, 283, 285, 305,
    306, 311-314, 316, 319, 324, 330, 341
Blohm, T. R., 320, 321
Blondin, G., 286
Bloomfield, D. K., 135
Böckman, O. C., 236
Boldt, P., 382
Bonner, J., 188, 293
Bonner, W. A., 371
Booth, A. N., 377
Boothroyd, B., 371
Bopp, M., 161
Borek, E., 305
Borikhina, M. G., 363
Born, R., 374
Boswell, G. A., 288, 325
Bothner-By, A. A., 278
Bottomley, W., 376
Bouboulis, C. J., 346
Bouchardat, A., 173
Boulter, A. J., 207
Bounds, D. G., 102, 384
Bowden, K., 384
Bowen, D. M., 371
Bowyer, R. C., 42, 371
Boyd, J. E., 318
Bradley, R. M., 125, 126
Bradlow, H. L., 174, 273, 330
Brady, R. O., 123, 125, 126

Braithwaite, G. D., 291, 293
Branch, A., 197
Brandner, G., 163
Brandt, C. W., 242
Braymer, H. D., 376
Bredenberg, J. B., 377
Bremer, J., 338
Bressler, R., 125, 130
Breuer, H., 352, 359, 361
Briggs, H. R., 377
Briggs, L. H., 243–245, 249, 367
Briggs, T., 332, 336
Brink, N. G., 103, 385
Britt, J. J., 254
Brockmann, H., Jr., 89, 94, 382
Brodie, B. B., 327
Brodie, H. J., 360
Brodie, J. D., 175, 187
Brooksbank, B. W. L., 358
Brown, R., 352
Brown, R. F. C., 250
Brown, S. A., 156, 158
Brown-Grant, K., 356, 357
Brownie, A. C., 347
Brownlee, G., 263, 265
Brucker, W., 160
Brummer, W., 124
Bruns, K., 229
Bruun, T., 94, 383
Bryson, M. J., 342, 343, 347
Bublitz, C., 176
Bucher, N. L. R., 176, 185, 285, 294, 300
Buchi, G., 61, 100, 222, 250, 377
Bu'Lock, J. D., 79, 131, 137, 138, 143, 151, 370, 380
Burger, M., 81
Burgstahler, A. W., 260
Burn, D., 248
Burrows, B. F., 376, 377
Burstein, S., 237
Busch, H., 196
Butler, N. L., 159
Butler, R., 293
Butte, J. C., 139
Bywater, W. G., 368

Caglioti, L., 114, 367
Cain, B. F., 222, 243, 244, 249

Cais, M., 247
Caldwell, I. C., 181
Cambie, R. C., 244, 245, 249, 367
Cameron, D. W., 155, 256
Cann, M. C., 342, 348
Canonica, L., 223
Cantrall, E. W., 265, 321
Capstack, E., 286, 287
Caravaca, J., 322
Carle, A., 372
Carmack, M., 250
Caron, E. L., 368
Carter, A. C., 353
Casinovi, C. G., 376
Caspi, E., 343
Cassera, A., 143, 149
Cava, M. P., 246
Cavill, G. W. K., 221
Cebalo, T. P., 377
Cekleniak, W. P., 321
Cerceo, E., 346
Chadha, M. S., 221
Chaikoff, I. L., 174, 333, 335, 342
Chamberlin, J. W., 244
Chambers, K., 38, 159
Chan, W. R., 246, 376
Channon, H. J., 273
Chaplen, P., 66, 379
Chapmann, D. D., 333
Chapon, S., 265
Charkoff, I. L., 273, 330, 333, 335, 342
Chatterjee, A., 368
Chaudhuri, A. C., 345
Chaykin, S., 193
Chen, P. S., Jr., 350
Chen, R. W., 330
Cheung, H. T., 249
Chiavarelli, S., 376
Chichester, C. O., 291, 292, 294
Chopin, J., 373
Chorney, W., 376
Christophe, J., 197
Church, R. F., 244
Clark, D. A., 350
Clark, K. J., 223
Clark, L. C., 177
Clark-Lewis, J. W., 373
Clarke, F. H., 227
Clarke, L. C., 209
Clarkoff, J. L., 346

Clayton, R. B., 274, 285, 311, 321
Cleland, M., 182
Cocker, W., 248
Codner, R. C., 154
Cohen-Bazire, G., 297
Cohen, T., 26
Cohnen, E., 193
Collie, J. N., 10, 16
Collins, D. J., 234
Conn, E. E., 157, 158, 355
Conroy, H., 116
Constantopoulos, G., 344, 345
Cook, R. P., 348, 352
Cooke, R. G., 81, 380, 383
Cookson, R. C., 250
Coon, M. J., 177–181, 183
Cooper, D. Y., 348
Cooper, J. R., 327
Corcoran, J. W., 139
Corey, E. J., 263, 265, 327, 328
Cornforth, J. W., 185, 190, 201, 204,
    206, 283, 286, 307, 309
Cornforth, R. H., 185, 190, 201, 204,
    283, 286
Corwin, L. M., 285
Counsell, R. E., 321
Covell, C. J., 81, 380
Crabbe, P., 377
Cramer, F. J., 215
Cresson, E. L., 181
Crombie, L., 61, 97
Cross, A. D., 249
Cross, B. E., 245, 253
Crowley, K. J., 218
Crowley, P. J., 211
Curcumelli-Rodostamo, M., 116
Curran, J. F., 327
Curtis, R. F., 384

Dalgliesh, C. E., 19
Dalidowicz, J. E., 322
Dalton, L. K., 62, 369
Damast, B. L., 358
Danielsson, H., 324, 333, 336, 339
Dauben, W. G., 174, 273, 288, 306,
    324, 325, 330
Dave, K. G., 374, 381
David, S., 198, 265
Davidson, A. G., 317

Davidson, D. W., 347
Davies, B. H., 295, 296
Davis, B. D., 19
Davis, B. R., 244, 249
Davis, E. M., 357
Davis, J. W., 352
Dawson, C. R., 62
Dawson, R. F., 369
Day, A. C., 81
Dayton, S., 331
Dean, F. M., 66, 76, 81, 171, 378, 383
Dearha, D. S., 378
de Bruin, C. H., 327
Deflorin, A. M., 44
DeGraw, J. I., 371
Dekker, E. E., 178, 181
DeKoch, W. T., 278
del Campillo-Campbell, A., 178
de Mayo, P., 84, 226, 231, 233, 236,
    279, 366, 383
Deorha, D. S., 66
Dev, S., 228
deWaard, A., 193, 195
Dhar, M. L., 30, 365
Dicker, D. W., 284
Dimond, E. G., 322
Dituri, F., 190
Divekar, P. V., 369
Djerassi, C., 31, 40, 61, 138, 222, 237,
    247, 249, 278, 279, 315, 368, 369,
    377
Dobson, M. M., 346
Doerr, N., 163
Doisy, E. A., 335, 336
Dolar, S., 375
Donninger, G., 204
Donovan, F. W., 10, 17, 62, 65, 79,
    86, 369, 380, 381
Dorfman, R. I., 326, 327, 342–345,
    347, 348, 351–360
Dowd, H., 380
Dreyer, D. L., 83, 381
Drimmer, F., 331
Drummond, G. I., 181
Dulit, E., 317
Dünnenberger, M., 263
Durr, I. F., 181–184
Dutcher, J. D., 138
Dutler, H., 263
Dutta, B. N., 182

Duttagupta, P. C., 377
Dutts, N. L., 377
Dvornik, D., 321

Eade, R. A., 81, 383
Eastbrook, R. W., 348
Eastham, J. F., 330
Eberhardt, G., 156
Eberle, M., 185
Ebnöther, A., 81, 85
Eccles, S. S., 358
Eder, H. A., 190
Edward, J. T., 248
Edwards, O. E., 44, 249, 253
Edwards, P. N., 119, 223
Edwards, R. L., 369
Eggerer, H., 125, 193, 198, 207
Ehrensvärd, G., 165
Eichhorn, J., 344, 348, 350
Eisenbeiss, J., 377
Eisenbraun, E. J., 40, 222, 368
Eisenhuth, W., 102
Eisner, T., 221
Elad, D., 248
Elliott, P., 42, 44, 370, 371, 383
Elliott, W. H., 335, 336
Endres, H., 381
Ener, M., 316
Engel, L. L., 242, 347, 349, 350, 352, 358, 359, 361, 362
English, R. J., 81, 145, 208
Enslin, P. R., 278
Erdtman, H., 26, 34, 66, 216, 378
Eriksson, S., 331
Erni, A. D. T., 66, 378
Erxleben, H., 171
Eschenmoser, A., 13, 174, 260, 261, 264
Eugster, C. H., 81
Eyton, W. B., 41, 384

Fagerlund, U. H. M., 318
Faigle, H., 290
Falk, K., 10
Fass, W. E., 215
Faulds, W. F., 145
Fazakerley, H., 265, 266

Ferguson, G., 246
Ferguson, J. J., Jr., 176, 182–184
Ferrari, R. A., 355
Ferreti, L. D., 168
Ferris, J. P., 250
Fielding, B. C., 76, 383
Fiertel, A., 192
Fieser, L. F., 336
Fieser, M., 336
Finch, A. C. M., 374
Finch, N., 377, 378
Finnegan, R. A., 40, 368
Fischer, A., 217
Fischer, F. G., 241
Fischer, J. E., 179
Fischer, R., 197
Fish, C. A., 285, 316
Fish, W. A., 318
Fisher, H. F., 355
Fishman, J., 188, 238
Fitton, P., 147, 149
Flores, S. E., 375, 376
Floss, H. G., 189
Folkers, K., 103, 181, 182, 385
Fonken, G. J., 288
Fonken, G. S., 355
Forbes, M., 103, 385
Forchielli, E., 347, 348, 351, 354, 356, 357
Forsen, S., 54, 372
Forsyth, W. G. C., 74, 372, 376
Fouken, G., 325
Fowler, L. R., 116, 250
Fowlks, W. L., 327
Francis, J. E., 116
Frantz, I. D., 316, 317, 321
Fray, G. I., 223
Fredrickson, D. S., 332
Freeman, G. G., 238
Frei, H., 377
French, W. N., 116
Freudenberg, K., 373, 376
Frey, A. J., 261
Fryer, R. I., 150, 153, 207
Fujisi, S., 89, 222, 382
Fukui, Y., 374
Fuller, R. C., 293
Fumagalli, R., 190
Funaoka, K., 374
Furin, S., 123

Gaglioti, E., 266
Gale, L. H., 328
Gallagher, T. F., 331
Galt, R. H. B., 245
Gamboni, G., 260
Ganguly, A. K., 372, 373
Ganguly, J., 123
Garattini, S., 190
Gascoigne, R. M., 233
Gastambide-Odier, M., 140
Gatenback, S., 143, 144, 152
Gaudette, L., 327
Gautschi, F., 313
Gaylor, J. L., 319, 320, 322
Geiger, J., 357
Geissman, T. A., 27, 156, 163, 365, 366, 373
Gentili, B., 375
Gey, K. F., 190
Ghosal, S., 119, 223
Gibbs, M. H., 189, 190
Gibson, D. M., 123
Gidez, L. I., 190
Gilbert, B., 40, 368
Gilfillan, J. L., 182
Gill, J. E., 238
Gilner, D., 139
Gloor, U., 189
Godin, P. J., 61, 211
Goel, R. N., 374
Goldfine, H., 134, 137
Goldman, P., 126
Goldstein, M., 353
Goldzieher, J. W., 357, 360
Goodman, D. S., 201, 204, 320
Goodwin, T. W., 291, 293, 295–297
Gordon, S., 321
Gore, I. Y., 190, 196, 286, 309
Gorz, H. J., 158
Gottlieb, O. R., 31, 41, 369, 376, 377, 384
Götz, M., 250
Gough, J., 236
Gould, E., 185
Gould, R. G., 189
Gourlay, R., 381
Gowlland, A., 144
Grant, F. W., Jr., 242
Grant, J. K., 346
Green, B., 253

Green, J., 380
Gregory, H., 137
Grill, P., 359
Grimshaw, J., 222, 233
Gripenberg, J., 171, 369
Grisebach, H., 38, 40, 100, 139, 160, 161, 163, 363
Grob, E. C., 188, 293, 297
Grossi, E., 190
Grove, J. F., 102, 253, 384
Grover, P. K., 369
Gual, C., 360
Gupta, G. S., 233
Gurin, S., 190, 194, 292, 331, 332, 336, 337, 344
Guseva, A. R., 363
Gut, M., 327, 344, 345, 353, 360
Gyorgy, P., 103, 385

Haber, R. G., 78
Haegele, W., 222
Hager, L. P., 165
Hagopian, M., 361
Hahn, G., 10
Halkerston, I. D. K., 344
Halla, M., 361
Halpern, O., 368
Halsall, T. G., 237, 265, 266
Hamilton, G. A., 179
Hamilton, J. G., 338
Hammond, G. S., 217, 301
Hamor, T. A., 249
Hanahan, D. J., 324
Hancock, J. E., 327
Hanson, J. R., 245
Harada, Y., 345
Harary, I., 177, 209
Harborne, J. B., 373
Harold, F. M., 333, 335
Harper, S. H., 97, 377
Harris, A., 253, 254
Harrison, J. A., 116
Hartwell, J. L., 367
Hasegawa, M., 160
Haskell, J., 342
Haskins, F. A., 158
Haskins, R. H., 156
Haslewood, G. A. D., 338
Hassall, C. H., 44, 74, 76, 81, 376, 384

Hata, K., 367
Hatch, M. D., 140
Hauge, S. M., 182
Haun, J. R., 287
Haworth, R. D., 36, 366
Haws, E. J., 76, 383
Haxo, F. T., 296, 297
Hay, J. E., 95, 379
Hayaishi, O., 327
Hayano, M., 326, 327, 342, 344, 347, 359, 360
Haynes, L. J., 90, 95, 246, 379, 381, 382
Haynes, R. C., 343
Heard, R. D., 342, 348, 358
Hechter, O., 326, 342–344, 347, 348, 350, 352
Heftmann, E., 287
Hegarty, M. P., 367
Heilbron, I. M., 273
Heiselt, L. R., 327
Helg, R., 260
Hellig, H., 193
Hellman, L., 331
Hellyer, R. O., 233
Hemming, R., 171
Henderson, J. L., 90, 382
Hendrickson, J. B., 13, 75, 174, 225, 383
Henning, U., 176, 193, 198, 207
Henry, J. A., 265
Herbert, E. J., 252
Herian, J., 376
Herout, V., 236
Herran, J., 375
Herz, W., 233
Hess, D., 144, 379
Heusser, H., 240
Hextall, P., 41, 370
Hiasiwetz, H., 173
Hickey, F. C., 318
Hietala, P. K., 377
Hildebrand, R. P., 228
Hillis, W. E., 160, 372, 374
Hilz, H., 180
Hinman, J. W., 368
Hinreiner, E., 27
Hinterberger, F., 173, 221
Hirata, Y., 100
Hishida, S., 89, 382

Hoare, J. L., 367
Hochstein, F. A., 93, 154
Hockenhull, D. J., 145
Hoeksema, H., 368
Hoffman, C. H., 181
Hoffmann, C. E., 179
Hoffmann, E. G., 236
Hofheinz, W., 139
Hofmann, A., 197
Hofmann, K., 137
Holker, J. S. E., 76, 149, 383
Hollander, N., 358
Hollander, V. P., 358
Holley, T. F., 248
Holmstrom, E. G., 342
Holzapfel, C. W., 256
Hörhammer, L., 24, 374
Horning, M. G., 125, 283, 333
Horowitz, R. M., 375
Hosansky, N., 368
Hosking, J. R., 242
Hösli, H., 240
Hotta, S., 174, 273, 330
Howton, D. B., 136
Hsia, S. L., 335, 336
Hsiu, H. C., 266
Hsü, H., 266
Huang, R. L., 306
Hubbard, R., 301
Hubner, H., 372
Huebner, C. F., 39
Huff, J. W., 182, 189
Hughes, D. W., 66, 378
Hughes, G. K., 366, 367, 375
Hughes, R. B., 372
Hugo, J. M., 278
Hullin, R. P., 190
Hunter, G. D., 307
Hurlock, B., 329, 361
Hurst, J. J., 221
Hutchinson, A., 162
Hutton, T. W., 324

Ibrahim, R. K., 160
Idler, D. R., 318
Ikekawa, T., 153
Inglis, H. S., 211
Ipatiev, W., 173
Ireland, R. E., 243–245

Irie, T., 171
Irvine, D. S., 265
Isler, O., 190
Itoh, T., 367, 370
Iverbach, G. G., 116

Jackman, L. M., 41, 249, 376, 384
Jacobsen, R. P., 347
Jacobson, M., 212
Jaeger, R. H., 223
James, A. N., 222
James, N. F., 372, 374
Jänecke, J., 171
Janot, M. M., 242
Jarabak, J., 355
Jayaraman, P., 233
Jayko, M. E., 330, 333, 335
Jeanloz, R. W., 347
Jefferies, P. R., 371
Jeger, O., 13, 114, 240, 263–266, 367
Jellinck, P. H., 342, 348, 358
Jensen, F. R., 328
Jensen, L. H., 83, 381
Jensen, S. L., 297
Johnson, B. L., 163
Johnson, D. F., 287
Johnson, D. H., 75, 103
Johnson, L. F., 246
Johnson, W. S., 262
Johnston, J. D., 316
Jommi, G., 223
Jones, D., 296
Jones, D. F., 383
Jones, D. W., 76, 384
Jones, E. E., 342
Jones, E. R. H., 188, 238, 265, 266
Jorgensen, E. C., 163
Joshi, B. S., 381
Jukes, T. H., 179
Juneja, H. R., 222
Jutting, G., 124

Kach, K., 10
Kahnt, F. W., 350
Kakisawa, H., 266
Kaltenbronn, J. S., 61

Kamal, A., 75
Kamm, E. D., 273
Kandel, S. I., 197
Kandutsch, A. A., 317, 319
Kaneda, T., 139
Kaplan, F., 222
Kariya, T., 321
Karmel, M., 321
Karmen, A., 125
Karrer, P., 81, 241, 290
Karrer, W., 27, 290, 365
Kase, N., 354
Katagiri, M., 327
Katekar, G. F., 373
Kato, Y., 366
Kautsky, G. J., 345
Kawahara, F. S., 346
Kawai, S., 102
Kawano, N., 374, 375
Kazior, Y., 124
Kazuno, T., 339
Keil, J. G., 165, 166
Keilich, G., 197
Kelly, A., 76, 383
Kendall, F. E., 331
Kenner, G. W., 38, 159
Kessel, I., 193
Kessel, T., 125
Kesztler, F., 39
Khan, B. T., 343
Khastgir, H. N., 377
Kiang, A. K., 98, 383
Kincle, F. A., 368
King, C. G., 346
King, F. E., 48, 81, 314, 371–373, 376, 380
King, H. G. C., 372
King, T. J., 48, 314, 371, 373
Kirby, G. W., 252
Kirby, K. D., 370
Kirby, K. S., 376
Kirkwood, S., 147
Kirtley, M. E., 181
Kishimot, Y., 375
Kishimoto, Y., 373
Kitagawa, I., 89, 382
Klein, H. P., 123, 192
Klenk, E., 136
Klyne, W., 245
Knappe, J., 124, 178, 180

Knauss, H. J., 182
Knight, S. A., 263
Knuppen, R., 352, 361
Kobel, H., 197
Kocor, M., 144, 210
Kodicek, E., 192
Kögl, F., 171
Koritz, S. B., 343, 344
Kosuge, T., 158
Koukol, J., 157
Krakower, G. W., 315
Krause, R. F., 291
Kremer, G., 136
Krupka, R. M., 156
Krzeminski, L. F., 294
Kubota, T., 223, 384
Kuehl, F. A., 103, 385
Kuhn, R., 370

La Du, B. N., 37, 327
Lahey, F. N., 44, 367, 370
Lahoz-Oliver, R., 66, 379
Lamberton, J. A., 62, 369
Landgrebe, J. A., 328
Langdon, R. G., 122, 319
Langer, L. J., 361, 362
Lata, G. F., 325
Laughlin, M. W., 321
Lavie, D., 278
Law, J., 193
Lawrence, W. J. C., 56
Lawton, R. G., 258
Lechner, F., 377
Lederer, E., 30, 140, 240
Lee, A. K., 383
Lee, C. M., 367
Lee, H. H., 98, 383
Leeming, P. R., 377
Leermakers, P. A., 301
Leete, E., 59, 119, 169, 223, 363
Lehman, G., 10
Leibowitz, J., 384
Lemin, A. J., 315
Lemmon, R. M., 317
Lemon, H. M., 352
Lennarz, W. J., 134, 137
Leppmeier, F., 381
LeQuesne, P. W., 222
LeRoy, G. V., 342

Levin, J. G., 19
Levisalles, J. E. D., 233
Levitan, P., 344
Levy, C. C., 157
Levy, H. R., 193, 206, 347
Levy, L. K., 361
Lewis, D. C., 369
Lieberman, S., 344, 353, 358
Light, R., 134, 137
Lilly, V. G., 291
Lin, Y., 266
Lincoln, R. E., 297
Lindberg, M., 195, 312, 327
Lindstedt, G., 373
Lindstedt, S., 327, 331, 332, 339, 340
Link, K. P., 39
Link, W., 382
Linn, B. O., 182
Linstedt, G., 374
Lipscomb, W. N., 237
Lister, J. H., 81
Littell, R., 321
Little, H. N., 305
Liu, L. H., 315
Liu, T. Y., 137
Livingston, A. L., 377
Loder, J. W., 237, 380
Loewus, F. A., 355
Loomis, W. D., 193, 213
Lorah, C. L., 316
Lorch, E., 124
Lotspeich, F. J., 291
Loud, A. V., 185, 285, 300
Louden, M. L., 59
Lovie, J. C., 381
Lowe, G., 188, 238
Lukton, A., 292
Lybing, S., 165
Lyman, R. L., 377
Lynen, F., 122, 124–126, 140, 175, 176, 178, 180, 182, 185, 193, 198, 207
Lynn, W. S., 344, 352
Lythgoe, B., 73, 384

Machleidt, H., 193
MacKenzie, R. D., 320
Mackinney, G., 291, 292

MacLean, D. B., 116
MacRae, G. D. E., 181
Magalhaes, M. T., 41, 376, 377, 384
Mahowald, T. A., 335, 336
Mamalis, P., 380
Manitto, P., 223
Manning, L. C., 48, 371
Manning, R. E., 222
Manske, R. H. F., 117
Marakami, M., 171
Marcinkiewile, S., 380
Marini-Bettolo, G. B., 376
Marion, L., 250
Markley, K., 193, 194
Marsden, D. J. S., 73, 384
Marshall, D., 247
Martin, D. B., 125
Mason, H. S., 280, 327
Massy-Westropp, R. A., 81, 92, 142, 145, 208, 371
Matkovics, B., 341
Matschiner, J. T., 335, 336
Matsueda, S., 89, 382
Matsui, M., 378
Matsushima, A., 81, 380
Maudgal, R. K., 283
May, M. D., 322
Mayer, R., 213
Mayo, D. W., 250
Mazur, Y., 314
McCalla, D. R., 155
McCapra, B. F., 246, 253
McCloskey, P., 253
McCullough, W. G., 285
McDonald, H. J., 322
McGarrahan, K., 185
McGhie, J. F., 263
McGold, A., 147
McGonagle, M. P., 371
McGuire, J. S., 356, 357
McHale, D., 380
McLoughlin, J., 189
McMaster, W. J., 371
McMurray, T. B. H., 376
Mead, J. F., 136
Mehler, A., 179
Mehta, A. C., 40, 367
Meier, J. R., 330
Meier, P. J., 240
Meinwald, J., 221

Meisels, A., 375
Meisinger, M. A. P., 103, 385
Menchaca, H., 376
Mendelsohn, D., 333
Mentzer, C., 373
Mercer, E. I., 295
Merkle, K., 381
Meyer, A. S., 358, 359
Michael, P. J., 327
Migicovsky, B. B., 185
Miller, G. A., 154
Miller, G. E., 180
Miller, M. W., 27, 365
Mills, J. S., 265, 279, 315
Mitoma, C., 327
Mitscher, L. A., 247
Mitsuhashi, H., 367, 379
Mittal, O. P., 369
Miyano, M., 378
Mizutani, A., 370
Mobberley, M. L., 316, 317
Mohrhaver, H., 136
Molho, D., 373
Mongolsu, S., 380
Morato, T., 360
Morf, R., 241
Morgan, J. W. W., 81, 372, 374, 380
Morris, M. P., 368
Morrison, G. A., 84, 366, 383
Mors, W. B., 31, 369
Morton, R. A., 375
Mosbach, E. H., 331
Mosbach, K., 143, 166
Moslein, E. M., 198, 207
Mothes, K., 189, 198
Moubasher, R. A., 81, 383
Moye, C. J., 142
Mudd, J. B., 140
Mukerjee, S. K., 23, 111
Mulholland, C. P., 253
Murai, K., 93
Murakami, T., 81, 377, 380
Muramatsu, T., 379
Murphy, E. L., 376
Murray, A. W., 330
Murray, H. C., 355
Murthy, D. V. K., 102, 384
Murty, N. L., 136
Musgrave, O. C., 88, 150

Nabney, J., 81
Nabors, C., 342
Naef, H., 114, 367
Nagai, U., 379
Nakamura, S., 191
Nakamura, T., 102
Nakanishi, K., 266
Nakano, T., 222
Nakata, H., 100
Nakayama, T., 291, 292, 297
Naves, Y. R., 212
Nechvatal, A., 261
Neelakantan, S., 379
Neher, R., 350
Neiderhiser, D. H., 315
Neish, A. C., 155, 156, 157, 161
Nemeth, K. E., 169
Nes, W. R., 286, 287
Newbold, G. T., 62
Newman, H., 253
Newschwander, W. W., 286
Nicholas, H. J., 287
Nicolson, A., 253
Nikuni, J., 78
Nilsson, M., 54, 171, 372
Nishikawa, Y., 377
Nita, A., 367
Nocke, L., 352, 361
Nord, F. F., 156
Norgard, D. W., 293, 297
Norin, T., 219
Norman, A., 330
Norris, A. T., 134
Norton, J. S., 182
Norton, K. B., 278
Novak, A. F., 182
Nyman, M. A., 357

Oakey, R. E., 358
Obara, H., 222
Ochoa, S., 124, 179
O'Donnell, V. J., 342, 348, 358
Oechler, F., 10
Ofner, P., 355
Ohloff, G., 236
Okany, A., 197
O'Leary, W. M., 137
Ollis, W. D., 19, 23, 38, 41, 61, 93, 103, 111, 146, 154, 171, 374, 376–378, 381, 384

Olson, J. A., 312
Ono, K., 332
Orth, H. D., 197
Ottke, R. C., 324
Ourisson, G., 265
Overath, P., 176, 185
Overum, J. C., 83
Owens, W. M., 273
Oxford, A. E., 208

Pääbo, K., 332
Pacheco, H., 373
Paech, K., 11
Paoletti, P., 190
Papadopoulos, S., 98
Pardee, A. B., 185
Park, R. B., 188
Partyka, R. A., 245
Paseshnichenko, V. A., 363
Patrick, J. B., 30
Patwardhan, A. V., 381
Paul, I. C., 84, 249
Paulus, E., 372
Pavanaram, S. K., 374, 375
Pearlman, W. H., 346
Pearson, O. H., 358
Pelizzoni, F., 223
Pelter, A., 283
Penfold, A. R., 42, 234, 236, 370
Perlman, D., 138
Péron, F. G., 343, 344
Peterson, D. H., 327
Peterson, E., 327
Pettit, D. G., 373
Phillips, A. H., 122, 193, 195
Pierce, F. T., Jr., 317
Pinckard, J. H., 301
Pincus, G., 342, 347, 348
Plager, J. E., 347
Plaut, G. W. E., 179
Pletscher, A., 190
Plieninger, H., 197
Plotz, J., 357
Podesva, C., 98
Poggi, M., 190
Polonsky, J., 40, 367
Pope, G. S., 102, 384
Popják, G., 185, 189, 190, 193, 196, 197, 201, 204, 206, 283, 285, 286, 307, 309

Porter, J. W., 175, 177, 182, 187, 193, 293, 295–297, 300
Posner, H. S., 327
Powell, A. D. G., 76, 383
Powell, V., 236
Pradhan, M. K., 263
Preston, W. H., 287
Price, J. R., 56
Pride, E., 138, 147
Prillinger, F., 377
Przybylska, M., 250
Purcell, A. E., 188, 293

Quakenbush, F. W., 294

Raab, K., 360
Rabindran, K., 233
Rabinowitz, J. L., 180, 190
Raistrick, H., 81, 84, 208, 383
Ramanathan, J. D., 48
Ramstad, E., 189, 198, 221
Rangaswami, S., 376, 377
Ranney, R. E., 321
Rao, B. G., 342, 348
Rao, K. H., 376
Rao, K. V. N., 102, 384
Rao, M. V., 116
Rao, P. L. N., 102, 384
Ratliff, R. L., 335
Read, G., 156, 369
Regan, M., 179
Reid, W. W., 158, 366, 368
Reineke, L., 355
Reio, L., 165
Reiser, R., 136
Reitsema, R. H., 215, 247
Reitz, H. C., 327
Reyneri, C., 358
Reznik, H., 159
Rhodes, A., 371
Richards, J. H., 168, 223, 288, 325
Richards, R. W., 88, 150
Richmond, K. W., 383
Richter, R., 335
Rickards, R. W., 138, 142, 143, 146, 155, 208, 253, 254, 256, 371
Rickes, E. L., 103

Riedl, W., 372
Rigby, W., 248
Rilling, H. C., 179, 192, 194, 295
Ringelmann, E., 124, 180
Ringold, H. J., 360
Ritchie, E., 366, 367, 372, 375
Rittenberg, D., 305, 330
Roberts, J. B., 74, 372, 376
Roberts, J. C., 66, 81, 371, 378
Robertson, A., 75, 76, 81, 103, 253, 380, 383
Robertson, J. M., 249
Robinson, F. M., 182
Robinson, Mrs. G. M., 56
Robinson, J. D., 126
Robinson, J. R., 231
Robinson, K. W., 374
Robinson, M. J. T., 38, 159
Robinson, R., 10, 56, 116, 173, 223, 236, 273, 314
Robinson, W. G., 178, 180
Rodwell, V., 184
Rogers, E. F., 117
Rohde, W. A., 233
Romo, J., 368
Rosenfeld, G., 343, 350
Rosenfield, R. S., 331
Rosenkranz, G., 368
Rosenthal, O., 348
Rosin, N. L., 286
Ross, D. J., 208
Rossmann, M. G., 237
Rothberg, S., 327
Rottenberg, M., 332
Roux, D. G., 372
Row, L. R., 374, 375
Rudman, P., 88, 381
Rudney, H., 175–177, 180–184
Rueff, L. K., 176
Rüegg, R., 190
Rumpf, J. A., 332
Russell, A. E., 319
Russell, R. C., 61
Rutledge, P. S., 245
Ruzicka, L., 10, 13, 174, 213, 225–227, 240, 242, 243, 258, 263, 264
Ryan, A. J., 147, 152, 369, 373
Ryan, K. J., 327, 342, 347, 358
Ryback, G., 204
Ryhage, R., 201

Saba, N., 326, 342, 347, 350
Sachs, B. A., 321
Samuels, L. T., 346, 347, 352
Samuelsson, B., 204, 327, 333, 335, 340, 341
Sander, H., 363
Sandermann, W., 209, 219, 229
Sanghvi, A. T., 321
Sarin, P. S., 374, 375
Sarma, K. G., 379
Sarro, S. D., 358
Sastry, B. V. R., 377
Satoh, P. S., 345
Savard, K., 352, 358
Saxton, J. E., 117
Scaife, J. F., 185
Schaeffer, G. W., 158
Schaffner, K., 266
Schedl, H. P., 350
Schenker, V., 347
Scheverbrandt, G., 134
Schiess, P. W., 243
Schinz, H., 260
Schlesinger, M. J., 181, 183
Schlittler, E., 118
Schmid, H., 78, 81, 85, 100, 102, 222, 367, 368, 377
Schmid, W., 343
Schmidt, C., 123
Schmidt, O. T., 95
Schoenheimer, R., 305
Schofield, J., 146, 379
Schöpf, C., 10
Schöpp, K., 241
Schrecker, A. W., 367
Schroeder, H. D., 368
Schroeder, L. J., 285
Schroepfer, G. J., 204, 206, 317
Schuber, W. J., 156
Schubert, A., 327
Schulze, E., 160
Schuytema, C. G., 325
Schweers, W., 219
Schwenk, E., 147, 285, 312, 316, 324, 325
Scott, A. I., 44, 81, 246, 253, 371
Scribney, M., 147
Scully, N., 376
Sebek, O. K., 327
Segal, W., 384

Seidel, C. F., 242
Seltzer, H. S., 350
Sengupta, P., 377
Seshadri, T. R., 23, 40, 48, 111, 367, 369, 372–375, 379
Shah, V. R., 371
Sharma, D. C., 347, 348
Shasha, B., 384
Shaw, P. D., 165
Sheppard, N., 210
Sheth, K., 221
Shibata, S., 35, 89, 153, 382
Shimazono, H., 156
Shimizu, K., 344, 345
Shimokoriyama, M., 162, 373
Shinoda, J., 171
Shiro, T., 191
Shneour, E. A., 188, 293
Shoolery, J. N., 222
Shreeve, W. W., 190
Shunk, C. H., 182
Shvo, T., 278
Siddalingaiah, K. S., 61
Siddiqi, M. A., 184
Siebert, R., 327
Siegelman, H. W., 159
Sim, G. A., 84, 246, 249, 253
Sim, K. Y., 98, 383
Simmons, D. L., 250
Simon, H., 189
Simonitsch, E., 102, 377
Simonsen, J. L., 236
Simpson, S. A., 350
Siperstein, M. D., 330
Sjövall, J., 332, 339
Skeggs, H. R., 181, 182
Sklarz, B., 278
Slaunwhite, W. R., 352
Slaytor, M., 81, 145
Smalley, H. M., 138, 143
Smallman, E., 193
Smith, D. C. C., 197
Smith, E., 368
Smith, G. N., 143
Smith, H., 12, 81, 88, 142, 145–147, 149, 150, 152, 153, 166, 188, 189, 197, 198, 208, 253, 254, 371, 379
Smith, J., 381
Smith, M. M., 249
Smith, O. W., 342, 358

Snarey, M., 211
Snell, J. F., 154
Solomon, M. M., 342
Solomon, S., 344, 353, 358
Soloway, A. H., 174, 273
Somerfield, G. A., 371
Sonderhoff, R., 305
Sondheimer, F., 314, 368, 375, 379
Sörbo, B., 176
Sorm, F., 236
Späth, E., 39
Speake, R. N., 233, 372, 373
Spencer, E. Y., 231
Spring, F. S., 263, 265
Springson, D. B., 19
Sprinson, D. B., 19
Squires, C. C., 123, 140
Srere, P. A., 330
Srinivasan, P. R., 139
Staab, H. A., 370
Stadler, P. A., 261
Stahmann, M. A., 39
Stamm, O. A., 100, 102, 377
Stanier, R. Y., 297
Stanley, R. G., 218
Stanley, W. L., 367
Stanton, J., 76, 383
Stanway, D. N., 76
Staple, E., 331–333, 336, 337, 344
Starratt, A. N., 279
Staunton, J., 171
Steele, W. J., 292
Stefanovic, V., 360
Stein, R. P., 246
Steinberg, D., 318, 320–322, 331
Stern, B. K., 206
Stern, J. R., 180
Sternbach, L., 240
Stevens, D. F., 147
Stevens, R., 98, 383
Stevenson, R., 263, 265
Stever, H., 10
Stewart, J. L., 265
Stewart, J. M., 191
Stickings, C. E., 81, 165
Stockman, H., 209
Stoffel, W., 136
Stoker, J. R., 158
Stokes, W. M., 318
Stone, D., 343

Stork, G., 227, 253, 260
Stoudt, T. H., 316
Stout, G. H., 48, 83, 371, 381
Strachan, W. S., 263, 265
Stumpf, P. K., 122, 123, 140
Subramanian, S. S., 379
Suchy, M., 236
Suginome, H., 377
Sugiyama, N., 102
Sukhov, G. V., 218
Suld, H. M., 336
Sutherland, I. O., 23, 41, 93, 111, 154,
    377, 381, 384
Sutherland, M. D., 92, 228, 236, 370,
    382
Suzue, G., 294
Swain, T., 366, 374
Sweat, M. L., 156, 327, 342, 343, 347

Tait, J. F., 350
Takahashi, T., 265
Takai, M., 191
Takanashi, M., 370
Takano, T., 102, 369
Takemura, K. H., 306
Takido, M., 381
Talalay, P., 206, 329, 346, 355, 361
Tamura, G., 191
Tamura, S., 191
Tamura, T., 381
Tanaka, M., 374, 381
Tanebaum, S. W., 143, 167
Tanner, F. W., 93
Tatum, E. L., 324
Taubman, S. B., 139
Tavormina, P. A., 189, 190
Taylor, E. H., 189
Taylor, W. I., 118
Tchen, T. T., 192–194, 274, 280, 283,
    344, 345, 355
Ternbah, M., 117
Thain, E. M., 211
Thakur, R. S., 372
Thaller, V., 30, 365
Thayer, S. A., 335, 336
Theng, C. Y., 376
Theobald, D. W., 237
Thimann, K. V., 348
Thomann, N. G., 227

Thomas, H., 305
Thomas, M., 346
Thomas, P. Z., 351
Thomas, R., 81, 118, 149, 223
Thompson, G. A., Jr., 149, 188, 293
Thompson, M. J., 321
Thompson, P. J., 138, 153, 154, 207
Thompson, R. H., 27, 81, 381, 383
Thorne, K. J. I., 192
Tietz, A., 177
Tilden, W., 173
Tissenbaum, B., 352
Titchener, E. B., 123
Todd, A. R., 79, 226, 370, 380
Todd, D., 285
Tomita, Y., 223, 384
Tomkins, G. M., 327, 330, 356, 357
Towers, G. H. N., 156, 158, 160, 162
Townsend, R. J., 165
Trams, E. G., 125
Treibs, W., 237
Trevett, M. E., 250
Trippett, S., 371
Tschesche, R., 193
Turnbull, J., 234, 279
Turner, W. B., 138
Turro, N. J., 217, 301

Uda, H., 222
Udenfriend, S., 327
Ueda, S., 171
Ulery, H., 261
Ulick, S., 351
Underhill, E. W., 161
Ungar, F., 343
Urban, R., 159
Uritani, I., 226
Ursprung, J. J., 263, 265

Vagelos, P. R., 125, 126
Valenta, Z., 98, 116, 117, 249, 250
van der Kerk, G. J. M., 83
Vannier, S. H., 367
van Tamelen, E. E., 368
Varma, T. N. R., 294
Vasistha, S. K., 279
Venkataraman, K., 381
Vennesland, B., 206, 355

Verkatoraman, K., 374
Villotti, R., 315
Villoutreix, J., 297
Vining, L. C., 156, 297, 369
Viswanathan, N., 233
Viterbo, R., 263
von E. Doering, W., 327
von Wittenau, M. S., 93
Vorbrüggen, H., 249
Vroman, H. E., 321

Wachtmeister, C. A., 26, 34, 66, 378
Wagner, H., 24, 374
Wagner, R. L., 154
Waite, M., 124
Wakil, S. J., 123–125, 130, 324
Wald, G., 301
Waldmann, H., 240
Wang, V. S., 346
Waring, W. S., 238
Warren, C. W. H., 81
Wasson, G. W., 175, 182, 187
Waters, O. J., 228
Webb, J. L., 342, 348
Webb, J. S., 30
Webster, B. R., 38, 159
Wedegaetner, D. K., 328
Weinges, K., 373, 376
Weinstein, B., 246
Weizmann, A., 314
Weliky, I., 349, 350
Wells, J. W., 92, 382
Wells, W. W., 315, 316
Wender, S. H., 376
Wendt, H., 158
Wenkert, E., 14, 116, 118, 223, 244, 245
Werbin, H., 342, 357
Werner, A. E. A., 265
Werner, H., 10
Wertin, H., 346
Wessely, F., 176, 377
West, C. D., 358
Westheimer, F. H., 179, 355
Wettstein, A., 326, 350
Weürsch, J. R., 306
Weygand, F., 158, 160, 189
Whalley, W. B., 38, 75, 76, 100, 103, 147–149, 171, 249, 253, 254, 380, 383

Wheeler, M., 359
Whipple, L. D., 328
White, R. W., 231, 328
White, T., 372, 376
Whitehouse, M. W., 332, 336, 337
Whitham, G. H., 279
Whiting, D. A., 61
Whiting, M. C., 30, 188, 238, 284, 365
Wieland, O., 176
Wiele, R. V., 358
Wiesner, K., 116, 117, 249, 250
Wiest, W. G., 351
Wilcox, R. B., 351
Williams-Ashman, H. G., 361
Williams, G., 173
Williams, R. P., 30
Williams, T. W., 384
Williamson, W. R. N., 375
Willis, C., 246
Willis, J. L., 207
Willner, D., 223, 278
Wilmshurst, J. K., 243, 249
Wilson, D. V., 369
Wilson, L., 366
Wilson, W., 279
Winkler, K., 198
Winter, J., 197, 210
Wiss, O., 189
Witting, L. A., 193
Wittorf, N., 173
Wittreich, P. E., 182
Wluka, D. J., 367
Woessner, J. F., Jr., 179
Wolf, D. E., 181
Wolff, R. E., 279
Wolfman, L., 321
Wolinsky, J., 221
Wong, E., 377
Woodger, R., 279
Woodward, R. B., 28, 116, 174, 273

Wooley, D. W., 191
Wotiz, H. H., 352
Wright, B. E., 287
Wright, D., 98, 158, 383
Wright, L. D., 181, 182, 191
Wriston, J. C., 199
Würsch, J., 190
Wyngaarden, J. B., 185

Yamada, K., 100
Yamada, M., 375
Yamamoto, I., 379
Yamamoto, R. T., 212
Yamamoto, Y., 379
Yamato, N., 379
Yamato, M., 73
Yang, C. H., 376
Yasue, M., 366
Yates, P., 48, 371
Yates, R. A., 185
Yin, M. W., 335
Yogi, K., 78
Yoho, C. W., 137
Yokoyama, H., 291, 292
Yoshimura, H., 117
Young, D. W., 246, 253
Yuan, C., 136, 194, 195

Zabin, I., 188, 293, 324
Zaffaroni, A., 342
Zalkor, L. H., 222
Zalokar, M., 297
Zane, A., 376
Zannoni, V. G., 37
Zechmeister, L., 289, 290, 300, 301
Zeiss, H. H., 242
Zilliken, F., 103, 385
Zucker, M., 157

Subject Index

Abietadiene, 244
  from pimaric acid, 244
Abietic acid, 240, 243
Acetate, incorporation into mevalonate, 182
Acetate replacing factor, 181
Acetoacetate, decarboxylation of, 179
  synthesis of, 180
Acetoacetic acid, 128
Acetoacetyl coenzyme A, 4, 176
  from acetyl coenzyme A, 175
Acetogenin, definition, 2
2-Acetonaphthone, 218
Acetone, from mevalonate, 183
Acetophenone, 32
Acetovanillone, 32
Acetoxy-actidione, 104
3β-Acetoxyallocholanic acid, 306
Acetyl coenzyme A, 4
N-Acetylcysteamine, 128
Acid I, 335
Acid II, 335
Acid IV, 335
Acrifoline, 117
Actidione, 104
Actidione antibiotics, 104
Actinidine, 221
Actinomycetes, 93
Actiphenol, 104
Acylphloroglucinol, 19

Acylphloroglucinol derivatives, 41
Adenosine triphosphate, 124
Ageratochromene, 95
Agrimololide, 73
Ajmaline, 119
Aklavinone, 93
Aldosterone, 341
  from corticosterone, 350
  from desoxycorticosterone, 350
  from progesterone, 350
Alkaloid biosynthesis, 116
Allyl benzenes, 33
Alpinetin, 55
Alternaric acid, 30, 102
Alternariol, 81, 149
Ambrein, 265, 266
Ammi visnaga, 44, 109
Ammiol, 44
Ammoresinol, 39, 114
α-Amyrin, 265, 271
β-Amyrin, 265, 272
Anabine, 31
Anacardiaceae, 62
Anacardic acid, 62
Androgens, from progesterone, 352
Andrographolide, 246
Androstane-3,17-dione, 356
  from epiandrosterone, 355
Δ⁴-Androstene-3,17-dione, 346, 353, 354, 356–359, 362
  from Δ⁵-androstene-3,17-dione, 346

from cholesterol, 8
from dehydroepiandrosterone, 346
from   17α-hydroxyprogesterone,
   352
as inhibitor for 11β-hydroxylation,
   348
Δ⁴-Androstene-3,17-dione-19-oic acid,
   359
Δ⁵-Androstene-3,17-dione, 346
Androstenedione reductase, 353
Angelica species, 109
Angelicin, 109
Angolensin, 59
Angustifolionol, 42
Angustione, 42
Anisomorphal, 221
Anisoxide, 113
Annofoline, 117
Annotinine, 117
Anthocyanins, 50, 56
Anthragallol, 90
Anthraquinone dimers, 89
Anthraquinones, 87
Antirrhinum flowers, 163
Aphid pigments, 79
Apigenin, 53
cis-Apogeranic acid, 260
trans-Apogeranic acid, 260
Arachidonic acid, 134
Aromadendrene, 233
Aromadendrin, 53
Artemisia ketone, 211
4-Arylcoumarins, 40, 104
4-Aryl-coumarins, 100
Ascaridole, 213
Asperigillus species, 71
Asperigillus terreus, 81
Asperuloside, 98, 222
Aspidinol, 44
Aspidium species, 44
Asterric acid, 81
Athamantin, 111
Atisine, 249
Atrovenetin, 84, 108, 113
Aucubin, 222
Aurantiogliocladin, 150
Aureomycin, 94
Aureothin, 101
Auroglaucin, 71, 108, 146
Aurones, 50

Bacteria, aerobic, 137
   anaerobic, 137
Baeckeol, 44
Benzophenone, 301, 306
Benzophenones, 47
Benzoquinones, 64
Bergamotin, 114
Bergenin, 95
Betuligenol, 32
Bile acids, conjugation of, 338
Bilobol, 62
Biochanin-A, 58
Biogenetic isoprene rule, 174
Biological isoprene unit, 4, 193
Biotin, 124, 178
Bisabolene, 226
Bis-anthrones, 89
Bis-flavones, 53
Borneol, 217
Brazilin, 100
Brevifolin, 96
Bromination, 257
Butadiene, 218
Butanofilicinic acid, 44
sec-Butylmercuric bromide, 377
2-Butyl mevalonate, 191
Byak-angelicin, 109
Byak-angelicol, 109

Cactus triterpenes, 278
Cafestol, 246, 247
Caffeic acid, 21, 33, 155
Caldariomycin, 97, 108, 165
Calophyllolide, 40, 114
Calythrone, 98
Camphene, 220
Camphor, 217
Campnosperma brevipetiolata, 62, 90
Campnospermol, 62
Cannabidiol, 71
Cannabinol, 71
Cannabis phenols, 114
Cannabis species, 71
Caoutchouc, 173
Caperase, 322
Capsanthin, 290
Carajurin, 56
Carbon dioxide, 123
Cardol, 62

Δ^4-Carene, 213
Carlic acid, 100
Carlosic acid, 100, 165
Carminic acid, 90
Carolic acid, 100, 165
Carolinic acid, 100
α-Carotene, 299
β-Carotene, 289, 298
 from acetate, 291–293
 from carbon dioxide, 291
 from citral, 294
 from β-dimethylacrylate, 292, 297
 from geraniol, 294
 from hydroxymethyl glutarate, 291, 292
 from isovalerate, 292
 from leucine, 291
 from mevalonate, 188, 291–293, 299
 from neurosporene, 300
δ-Carotene, 299
 from phytoene, 294
γ-Carotene, 298
ζ-Carotene, 298
Carotenoid biogenesis: cell-free system, 293
 effects of light, 291
 effects of nitrogen sources, 291
 effects of oxygen, 291
 effects of temperature, 291
 in *Neurospora crassa*, 296
Carotenoids, 7
Caryophyllene, 228, 230
Catechins, 50, 56
Cativic acid, 242
Ceanothic acid, 279
Cedrol, 227
Ceroptene, 53
Cevine, 363
Chaetomium diacid, 103
Chalcone glycosides, 162
Chartreusin, 102
Chaulmoogric acid, 97
Chebulic acid, 95
Chenodesoxycholic acid, 335, 336, 392
 from cholesterol, 333
Chimaphilline, 155
Chloride ion, 165
Chlorine in biosynthesis, 108, 165
Chloroatronorin, 65
δ-Chlorolevulinic acid, 165

Chlorophorin, 74, 114
Chlorpropamide, 322
allo-Cholanic acid, 306
$\Delta^{5,24}$-Cholestadiene, 318
Cholestane, 306
$\Delta^{5,7,24}$-Cholestatrien-3-β-ol, 321
Δ^5-Cholestene, 307
Δ^{14}-Cholestene, 310
Δ^{14}-Cholestenol, 309
Δ^4-Cholestenone, 333
 as cholesterol inhibitor, 185
Δ^5-Cholestenone, 333, 335
Cholesterol, 310, 345, 358
 from Δ^7-cholesterol, 317, 319
 from 7-dehydrocholesterol, 319
 from desmosterol, 318
 from 24,25-dihydrolanosterol, 319
 from dimethylacrylate, 177, 209
 from isopentyl pyrophosphate, 194
 from lanosterol, 8, 264, 311, 312
 from methostenol, 319
 from mevalonate: quantitative aspects of, 189
 as obligatory precursor of bile acids, 331
 physiological control of synthesis, 184
 from zymosterol, 316, 317
3α-Cholesterol, 335
Δ^7-Cholesterol, 319
 from dihydrolanosterol, 319
 from 4α-methyl-Δ^8-cholesterol, 319
Cholic acid, 329, 337, 362
 from cholesterol, 8, 330
 from desoxycholic acid, 332
 from $3\alpha,7\alpha,12\alpha$-trihydroxycoprostanic acid, 336
Cholyl coenzyme A, 338
Chrysanthemum carboxylic acid, 211
 from mevalonate, 211
Chrysin, 53, 105
Chrysophanol, 88
Cinchonamine, 118
Cineole, from mevalonate, 215
Cinerolone, 97
Cinnamic acid, 21, 31, 157
Citric acid cycle, 98
Citrinin, 75, 147
Citromycetin, 81, 148
Citronellal, from acetate, 207

Citronellol, 207
Citrorosein, 88
Citrostadienol, 314, 315
Clavatol, 41
Clerodin, 249
Coelacanth, 339
Coenzyme Q, 71, 72, 108, 302
Coenzyme Q_6, 302
Cogeijerene, 234
Cohumulone, 44
Colchicine, 169
Columbin, 248
Colupulone, 44
Conessine, 364
Conglomerone, 44
Coniferyl alcohol, 33, 159
Cordeauxiaquinone, 81
Corticoid biosynthesis, 347
    from acetate, 343
    effect of adenosine-3′,5′-monophosphate on, 343
    effect of adrenocorticotropic hormone on, 344
    from mevalonate, 343
Corticosteroids, 362
Corticosterone, 341, 348
    from acetate, 343
    from cholesterol, 342
    from 11β-hydroxyprogesterone, 348
    from progesterone, 347
Cortisalin, 31
Cortisol, 341, 347, 348
    from acetate, 343
    from cholesterol, 342
    from 17-hydroxypregnenolone, 350
    from 11β-hydroxyprogesterone, 348
    from progesterone, 348
Corynomycolic acid, 30, 140
o-Coumaric acid, 51, 61
p-Coumaric acid, 21, 157
Coumarin, 36, 158
o-Coumaryl β-glucoside, 158
Crotonase, 179
Crotonic acids, 128
Cryptostrobin, 55
Cucurbitacin B., 278
Curcumin, 99
Curvularia species, 75
Curvularin, 86, 149
Curvulin, 76

Curvulinic acid, 76
Curvulol, 75
Cyanidin, 160
Cycloartenol, 265, 274
Cycloeucalenol, 314, 315
Cyclopaldic acid, 4, 70, 144
Cyclopentanes, 97
2-(Δ^3-Cyclopentenyl)ethyl tosylate, 258
2-Cyclopentylethyl tosylate, 258
Cyclopolic acid, 70
Cynodontin, 153
Cyperone, 233

Dalbergin, 40
Dalbergiones, 41
Daldinia concentrica, 79, 151
Dammarenediol, 265, 267
Davallic acid, 265
Deacylase enzymes, 181
Decussatin, 49
Deguelin, 109
Dehydracetic acid, 16
Dehydroangustione, 42
7-Dehydrocholesterol, 319
Dehydroepiandrosterone, 346, 353, 354
    from cholesterol, 355
    inhibition of hydroxylation by, 348
    from pregnenolone, 353
Dehydrogenase, 3α-hydroxysteroid, 329
    3β-hydroxysteroid, 346, 355
    11β-hydroxysteroid, 329
    20-hydroxysteroid, 351
Dehydrogriseofulvin, 80
Dehydroisoandrosterone, from 17α-hydroxypregnenolone, 353
Dehydroquinic acid, 20
Dehydrorotenoids, 61
Dehydroshikimic acid, 20
Delphinine, 250
Deltaline, 250
6-Demethyltetracycline, 94
Denticulatol, 89
Deoxyaklavinone, 93
Depsides, 65
Depsidones, 65
Derris elliptica, 109
Deschlorogriseofulvin, 80

Deschloro nornidulin, 67
Desmethoxy matteucinol, 55
Desmosterol, 318, 320
Desoxycholic acid, 329
 from cholic acid, 339
11-Desoxycorticosterone, 348
 from progesterone, 347
17α-Desoxycorticosterone, from 17α-hydroxyprogesterone, 347
Diacetylacetone, 16, 155
"Diaminobiotin," 124
Dicumarol, 39
Didymic acid, 69
Dihydro-γ-carotene, 299
17-Dihydroequilenin, 347
Dihydrogladiolic acid, 70
24,25-Dihydrolanosterol, 319
24,25-Dihydro-14-norlanosterol, 319
Dihydropinosylvin, 155
Dihydrosamidin, 109
3,4-Dihydroxyacetophenone, 157
3,4-Dihydroxybenzoic acid, 156
3α,6β-Dihydroxycholanic acid, 336
3α,7β-Dihydroxycholanic acid, 336
3α,12α-Dihydroxy Δ⁶-cholenic acid, 341
20α-22ξ-Dihydroxycholesterol, 345
3α,7α-Dihydroxycoprostane, 332
3,5-Dihydroxy-3-methylpentanoic acid (see Mevalonate)
1,8-Dihydroxynaphthalene, 79
3β,17α-Dihydroxy-Δ⁵-pregnen-20-one, reduction to Δ⁵-pregnen-3β, 11α, 20α-triol and Δ⁵-pregnen-3β, 17α,20β-triol, 351
24,25-Dihydrozymosterol, 316
2,3-Dimethoxy-5-methyl benzoquinone, 302
1,8-Dimethoxynaphthalene, 151
Dimethylacrylyl coenzyme A, carboxylation of, 178
 from isovaleryl coenzyme A, 177
 from methylvinylacetyl coenzyme A, 179
3,3-Dimethylallyl pyrophosphate, alkylation of, 111
 from Δ³-isopentenyl pyrophosphate, 198
3β-(β-Dimethylaminoethoxy)-androst-5-17-one, 321

2,3-Dimethyl benzoquinone, 303
Δ⁸⁽⁹⁾,²⁴-4,4-Dimethylcholestadienol, 313, 314
Δ⁸,²⁴-4,4-Dimethylcholestadien-3-one, 314
2,3-Dimethyl-3,4-dihydroxybutyric acid, 191
2,2-Dimethyl-3-isopropylidene cyclopropyl propionate, 212
2,2-Dimethyl mevalonate, 191
2,6-Dimethyl-2,6-octadiene, 208
Diospyros, 79
Diospyros species, 79
5,7-Dioxycoumarins, 38, 170
Dipentene, from isoprene, 173
Diphenylamine, inhibitor of carotenoid biogenesis, 297
α,β-Diphenylbutyric acid, 191
Distemonanthin, 74
Divinyl methane rhythm, 134
Double olefiant, 173
Dracorhodin, 56
Droserones, 78
Dunnione, 113

Eburicoic acid, from acetate, 287, 325
Echinulin, 113, 198
Economy, principle of, 12
Edultin, 114
Egonol, 102
Electrophilic substitutions, at saturated carbon, 327
δ-Elemene, 234
Elemol, 234
Eleutherin, 85
Eleutherine bulbosa, 85
Eleutherinol, 85
Eleutherol, 81, 85
Ellagic acid, 96
Elliptone, 109
Embelin, 64
Emodic acid, 88
Emodin, 88, 152
Emodin anthrone, 88, 89
Endocrocin, 88
Enzyme control, 13
Eperuic acid, 247
Epiandrosterone, 356
Erdin, 81

Eremophilone, 174, 235
Ergosterol, 288
  from acetate, 305, 324
  from lanosterol, 325
  from methionine, 324
  origin of C-24 methyl group, 312
  from zymosterol, 325
Erianthin, 54
Eriodictyol, 53
Erosnin, 58
Erythroaphin, 4, 80
Erythromycin, 29, 139
Estradiol, 347, 358, 361
  from testosterone, 358
Estrone, 357–359, 361, 362
  from androstenedione, 358
  from cholesterol, 8
  from 17α-hydroxyprogesterone, 358
  from pregnenolone, 358
β-Ethyl-β-hydroxy-δ-valerolactone,
  191
2-Ethyl mevalonate, 191
Eudesmol, 233
Eugenia caryophyllata, 42
Euparin, 44, 109
Euphenol, 263
Euphol, 265, 268
Evernic acid, 65, 67
Evodia species, 44
Evodionol, 44

Fallacinal, 88
Farnesiferols, 114
Farnesinic acid, 191
Farnesol, 174
Farnesyl pyrophosphate, 7, 198, 200,
  225
  reductive dimerization of, 7, 201
  stereochemistry of reductive dimer-
    ization of, 204
Fatty acid biosynthesis, 2, 125
Fatty acid cycle, 122
Fatty acid metabolism, 121
Fatty acid synthetase, 126, 130
Fatty acids, 21, 28, 122
Felinine, 199
Fenchyl alcohol, 220
Fern constituents, 44, 54
Ferryl iron, 360

Ferryl oxide, 328
Ferulic acid, 157
Filicin, 44
Filipin, 30
Flabelliformine, 117
Flavanone synthease, 162
Flavanones, 53, 55
Flavaspidic acid, 44
Flavin mononucleotide, 129
Flaviolin, 79
Flavipin, 71
Flavoglaucin, 71, 108
Flavones, 53
Flavonoid biosynthesis, 160
Flavonoids, 50
Folic acid, 14
Formaldehyde, 14, 22
Formaldehyde equivalent, 44
Formononetin, 59, 163
3β-Formoxy-17β-acetoxyandrostane,
  306
Frangula-emodin, 88
Frequentin, 73
Friedelin, 248, 263, 265, 272
Fukugetin, 171
Fulvic acid, 81
Fumigatin, 64
Fungal terphenyls, 35, 108
Funtumafrine B, 364
Furfural, 97
Fusaroskyrin, 91
Fusarubin, 81
Fuscin, 75, 108, 109, 149

Galagin, 53
Gallic acid, 95
Gamatin, 54
Gangaleoidin, 65, 171
Geigerin, 233
Genetic experiments, 163
Genipin, 222
Genistein, 58
Gentiana species, 48
Gentiopicrin, 223
Gentisaldehyde, 167
Gentisic acid, 48, 167
Geodin, 81
Geodoxin, 81
Geraniol, 207

Geranyl-geranyl-pyrophosphate, 7,
    200
    dimerization of, 289
Geranyl linaloöl, 7, 240
Geranyl pyrophosphate, 6, 200
Germacrone, 236
Germanicol, 265, 272
Gesneria anthocyanins, 56
Gesneridin, 56
Gibberellic acid, 253, 286, 364
    from acetate, 254
    from mevalonate, 188, 254
Gingketin, 53
Ginkgo biloba, 62
Ginkgol, 62
Ginkgolic acid, 62
Glabra lactone, 109
Gladiolic acid, 70
Gliorosein, 150
Glucose, in macrolide biosynthesis, 140
Glutamic acid, 94, 154
Glutinone, 265, 272
Glycine, 338
    in phomarizin biosynthesis, 153
Glycocholate, 330, 338
    from cholesterol, 330
Glycodesoxycholic acid, 330
C-Glycosidation, 90
C-Glycosides, 24, 53
Gonadotropin, 357
Griseofulvin, 3, 141
    from dimethylacrylic acid, 209
Griseophenone, 47, 80
Griseophenone Y, 47, 82, 84
Griseoxanthone, 80
Gutta percha, 201, 303
Guttiferin, 102, 171
Guttiferins, 114

Haematommic acid, 144
Haemocorin, 84
Hagenia species, 44
Häufigkeitsregel, 11
Helminthosporal, 231
    from mevalonate, 231
Helminthosporin, 151
Hematoxylin, 101
Hepatocatalase, 322
Hildebrandt's acid, 210
Homogentisic acid, 37

Homonataloin, 90
Homopterocarpin, 59
Hop constituents, 98
Hulupone, 98
Humulene, 230
Humulone, 44, 47
Hydrangea macrophylla, 160
Hydrangeol, 73, 160
19-Hydroxyandrostenedione, 359
3β-Hydroxy-Δ^5-androstene-17-one,
    353
p-Hydroxybenzaldehyde, 160
p-Hydroxybenzophenone, 47
β-Hydroxybutyric acid, 128
Hydroxybutyryl coenzyme A, 177
    from acetoacetyl-coenzyme A, 176
3β-Hydroxy-Δ^5-cholenic acid, 332, 335
3α-Hydroxycholest-5-ene, 333
7α-Hydroxycholesterol, 331
20α-Hydroxycholesterol, 244, 345
25-Hydroxycholesterol, 332
26-Hydroxycholesterol, 332
3α-Hydroxycoprostane, 333
3β-Hydroxycoprostane, 333, 335
3β-Hydroxydehydrogenase, 355
17-Hydroxydesoxycorticosterone, 352
18-Hydroxydesoxycorticosterone,
    from desoxycorticosterone, 350
Hydroxydihydroeremophilone, 236
Hydroxyeremophilone, 236
Hydroxyflavanones, 50, 53
3-Hydroxyflavones, 53
Hydroxyhopenone, 265, 276, 277
β-Hydroxyisovaleryl coenzyme A,
    from dimethylacrylyl coenzyme
    A, 178
Hydroxylation, requirement for mole-
    cular oxygen, 327
    requirement for reduced nicotin-
    amide adenine nucleotides, 327
5-Hydroxymethyl-2-furoic acid, 97
Hydroxymethylglutarate, 191
Hydroxymethylglutaryl coenzyme A, 4
    from acetoacetyl coenzyme A and
    acetyl coenzyme A, 176
    cleavage enzyme, 176, 180, 183, 184
    condensing enzyme, 176, 184
    from β-hydroxyisovaleryl coenzyme
    A, 178
    from leucine, 177

from malonyl coenzyme A, 175
from β-methylglutaconyl coenzyme A, 179
reductase, 182, 184
reduction, 182
Hydroxy-peonol, 41
2-Hydroxyphenylacetic acid, 103
p-Hydroxyphenyllactic acid, 20
17α-Hydroxypregnenolone, 354
11β-Hydroxyprogesterone, 348
17α-Hydroxyprogesterone, 347, 352, 354, 358
from progesterone, 351
11β-Hydroxy steroid dehydrogenase, 329
p-Hydroxystyryl system, oxidative coupling of, 34
Hyodesoxycholic acid, 335
Hypericin, 89
Hypericum performatum, 89
Hyssopin, 56

Icartitin, 53, 109
Inactone, 104
N-(Ind)-methylharman, 119
Indole alkaloids, 117
Inophyllolide, 40, 114
Inositol, 160
Ipomeamarone, 226
from acetate, 226
from mevalonate, 226
Iridomyremecine, 221
Iridoskyrin, 91
Islandicin, 152
Isobutyric acid, 22, 44
Isobutyryl group by enol methylation, 22, 44
Isobyak-angelicolic acid, 109
Isocaproaldehyde, 344, 345
Isocaproic acid, 344
Isoeuphenol, 263
from euphenol, 263
Isoflavone, 51, 57, 100
biosynthesis, 163
Isoimperatorin, 111
Isoleucine, 165
Isopentenyl pyrophosphate, 4, 5, 23, 193
isomerization of, 198, 199

polymerization of, 198
stereochemistry of, 199
synthesis of, 194
Isopentenyl pyrophosphate isomerase, 198
Isophyllocladene, 244, 249
Isoprene, 173
dimerization, 173
from turpentine oil, 173
Isoprene units in acetogenins, 23, 108
Isorhodomycinones, 93
Isorottlerin, 54
Isovaleric acid from 22-ketocholesterol, 346
Isovaleryl coenzyme A, oxidation of, 177
from leucine, 177
Isovanillic acid, 160
Itaconic acid, 165

Jacareubin, 48, 65
Jasmone, 97
Javanicin, 81
Jervine, 363

Kaempferol, 53
Kaurene, 245, 249
Kawain, 32
Kermesic acid, 92
β-Ketoadipic acid, 165
6-Ketoallolithocholic acid, 336
19-Ketoandrostenedione, 359
Ketochaulmoogric acid, 97
7-Ketocholest-5-ene, 306
α-Ketoglutaric acids, 104
7-Ketolithocholic acid, 335, 336
20-Keto reductase, 352, 353
Δ⁴-3-Ketosteroid reductase, 356
Khellin, 44, 109
Khellol, 38, 44
Kofler's quinone, 303
Kojic acid, 97
Krebs cycle, 1

Laccol, 62
Lactic acid, 165
Lagosin, 30
Lanceolatin B, 57

Lanceolatin C, 57
Lanostadienone, 314
Lanosterol, 8, 265
    from mevalonate, 189
    from squalene, 8, 264, 273, 285, 300
Lapachol, 79
Lavandulal, 212
Leptospermone, 47
Leucine, metabolism of, 177
Leucoanthocyanins, 50, 56
Lichen lactone-acids, 165
Lichen polyacids, 98
Lichens, 44, 62, 65, 144
Lichexanthone, 49, 80
Lignanes, 33
Lignin biosynthesis, 156
Ligusticum root derivatives, 73
Ligusticumic acid, 73
Limonene, 213
Linaloöl, 207
Linderone, 98
Linoleic acid, 134
Lithocholic acid, 329, 335
Loganin, 221
Longifolene, 229
Lophenol, 315
Lucidin, 90
Lupeol, 265, 270, 271
Lupulone, 47
Luteolin, 53
Lycodine, 117
Lycopene, 289, 298
    from acetate, 93
    from isopentenyl pyrophosphate, 294
    from mevalonate, 293
Lycopersene, 295
Lycopodine, 4, 117
Lycopodium species, 116
Lysergic acid, from mevalonate, 189, 197
    from tryptophan, 197

Machaeric acid, 278
Maclurin, 48
Macrolides, 28, 138
Maesaquinone, 64, 171
Magnamycin, 29, 139
Magnesium ion, 124

Magnolol, 34
Malic acid, 165
Malonate, to mevalonate, 187
Malonyl coenzyme A, incorporation into hydroxymethylglutaryl coenzyme A, 175
Mammea americana, 40
Mammein, 40
Mangiferin, 48
Mangostin, 48, 65
Manoöl, 242
Marmesin, 111
Marmin, 114
Marrubin, 248
Matricaria ester, 138
Matricarianol, 138
Meconin, 64, 65
Melilotic acid, 158
Mellein, 62
Menthofuran, 215, 247
Menthol, 213, 215
    from carbon dioxide, 213
Menthone, 215
MER-29, 320, 322
    as cholesterol inhibitor, 317
Metahexamide, 322
Methostenol, 314, 315
    from acetate, 316
p-Methoxyacetophenone, 21
Methoxy-paracotoin, 31
p-Methoxytoluquinone, 151
4α-Methyl-Δ^7-cholesten-3-β-ol, 315
4α-Methyl-Δ^8-cholesterol, 319
β-Methylcrotonic acid, 191
β-Methylcrotonyl coenzyme A (*see* Dimethylacrylyl coenzyme A)
2-Methylcyclohexanone, 308
cis-4-Methylcyclohexylmercuric bromide, 328
trans-4-Methylcyclohexylmercuric bromide, 328
3-Methyl-3,4-dihydroxybutyric acid, 191
3-Methyl-3,4-dihydroxyvaleric acid, 191
Methylenedioxy group, origin, 147
Methyl-gingerol, 31
β-Methylglutaconase, 179
β-Methylglutaconyl coenzyme A, from dimethylacrylyl coenzyme A, 178

Methyllinderone, 98
2-Methyl mevalonate, 191
4-Methyl mevalonate, 191
Methyl phenethyl ketone, 32
6-Methylsalicylic acid, 62, 142, 167
Methylvinylacetyl isomerase, 179
Methymycin, 29, 138
Methysticin, 32
Mevaldehyde dehydrogenase, 183
  hemithioacetal, 184
  precursor for mevalonate, 182
  reduction of, 183
Mevaldic acid (see Mevaldehyde)
Mevaldic dehydrogenase, 182
Mevaldic reductase, 183
Mevalonate, 4
  from acetate, 182
  antimetabolites of, 191
  bacterial metabolism of, 192
  configuration of, 185
  discovery, 181
  from hydroxymethylglutaryl co-
    enzyme A, 182
  incorporation into cholesterol, 190
  incorporation into squalene, 190
  from malonate, 187
  from mevaldehyde, 182
  monophosphorylation of, 192
  5-phosphate, 193
  5-pyrophosphate, 193
  role in terpene biosynthesis, 189
  utilization of in cholesterol bio-
    synthesis, 189
Mevalonic dehydrogenase, 183
Mevalonic kinase, from higher plants,
  193
  from hog liver, 193
  from rabbit liver, 193
  from yeast extract, 193
Mevalonolactone, synthesis, 185
Microphyllic acid, 67
Mirene, 249
Miroestrol, 102
Mixed-function oxidase, 280, 327
Mollisin, 83, 108
Monascin, 76, 104, 149
Monascus species, 76
Monoascorubin, 76
Morellin, 102, 114, 171
Moss, 116

Muellitol, 44, 47
Munetone, 58, 60, 109
Muscarufin, 35, 171
Musk, 30
Musizin, 81
Mycelianamide, 12, 108, 146, 156, 208
  from dimethylacrylic acid, 209
  from mevalonate, 209
"Mycinone" antibiotics, 93
Mycobacteria, 140
Mycolic acids, 140
Mycophenolic acid, 71, 108, 144, 208
  from acetate, 210
  from dimethylacrylic acid, 210
  from mevalonate, 211

Nalgiolaxin, 92
Nalgiovensin, 92
Naphthalenes, 75, 78
Naphthoquinones, 75, 78
Narbomycin, 29
Naringenin, 53
Nemotinic acid, 137
Neo-γ-carotene P, 301
Neomethymycin, 29
Nepatalactone, 221
Nepodin, 81
Neurosporene, 298
Ngaione, 98
Nicotinic acid, 31
Nidulin, 65, 67
Nootkatin, 98
19-Norandrostenedione, 359
Norbornyl carbonium ion, 259
Norcaperatic acid, 99
Norfarnesinic ester, 261
30-Norlanosterol, 313
Nornidulin, 67
6-Nor-5,7-seco-5-keto-7-carboxy-
  cholestane, 306
19-Nortestosterone, 347, 359
Novobiocin, 159
Nyctanthic acid, 278

Obscurines, 117
Ocimene, 207
cis,cis-2,6-Octadiene, cyclization of,
  261

trans,trans-2,6-Octadiene, cyclization of, 261
Odyssic acid, 137
Oleandomycin, 29
Δ^{18}-Oleanene, 263
from Δ^3-friedelin, 263
Oleanolic acid, 287
from mevalonate, 287
Oleic acid, 134
Oleylmethyl ketone, 62
Onocerin, 265, 266
Ononetin, 59, 103
Ononis spinosa, 59
Oösporein, 64
Opsin, 301
Orcinol, 62
Orientin, 53
Orobol, 58
Orsellinic acid, 3, 16, 62, 132, 143, 166
derivatives, 19, 62
Osthenol, 109
Osthruthin, 111, 114
Ostruthol, 111, 112
Oxaloacetate decarboxylase, 179
Oxidative coupling, 25
Oxygen, 134
Oxygen attachment, sites of, 11, 28
Oxypeucedanin, 111

Palitantin, 73, 164
Palmitic acid, 125
Palmitoleic acid, 134
Pannaric acid, 67
Paracotoin, 31, 105
Parasorbic acid, 30
Parietin, 88
Parietinic acid, 88
Patulin, 168
Pelanjuaic acid, 62
Peltogynol, 74
Penicillic acid, 166
Penicillium brevi-compactum, 64, 165
charlesii, 165
cyclopium, 166
gladioli, 71
griseofulvum, 12, 81
islandicum, 89, 144, 152
patulum, 143, 167
Penicillium species, 71

Penicillium urticae, 143
n-Pentylorcinol, 71
Peonol, 41
Perilla-ketone, 98
Perlatolic acid, 67
Peucedanium, 111
Peucedanum species, 111
Peucenin, 44, 111
α-Phellandrene, 213
Phellopterin, 109
Phenanthraquinone, 88
Phenethylbiguanide, 322
Phenylacetic acid, 58, 103
Phenylalanine, 20
Phenylalanine deaminase, 157
α-Phenylbutyric acid, 191
Phenylcoumalin, 31
Phenyllactic acid, 157
Phenylpropane skeleton, 32
Phenylpropanol, 33
Phenylpyruvic acid, 20
Phloridzin, 162
Phloroacetophenone, 41
Phloroglucinols, substitution of, 22
Phoenicin, 64
Phomarizin, 153
Phyllocladene, 244
Phyllodulcin, 73
Physcion, 88
Physiological conditions, 13
Physodic acid, 65, 68
Phytocholic acid, 340
Phytoene, 298
from geranyl-geranyl pyrophosphate, 295
from mevalonate, 294, 297
from terpenyl pyrophosphates, 295
Phytoene synthesis, effects of nicotinamide adenine dinucleotide phosphate on, 295
Phytofluene, 289, 296, 298
Phytol, 241
Piceid, 160
Picrolichenic acid, 69
Picromycin, 29
Pimaradiene, 243
Pimaricin, 30
α-Pinene, 217
from acetate, 218
from mevalonate, 218

β-Pinene, from myrcene, 218
Pinobanksin, 53
Pinocembrin, 53, 55
Pinoresinol, 34
Pinostrobin, 55
Pinosylvin, 73, 105
Pinselin, 49
Pinus cembra, 105
Pinus species, 53
Piperic acid, 31
Piperitenone, 215
Piperitone, 215
Plastoquinone, 303
Pleuromutilin, 255
Plumbagin, 78, 79
Podophyllotoxin, 34
Polyacetyl compounds in simulated
    biosynthesis, 155
Polyene macrolides, 30
Polygodial, 237
Pongamol, 57
Porphyrilic acid, 68
Pratensein, 58
Pregnanediol, from cholesterol, 341
5α-Pregnanolone, 306
Δ⁵-Pregnen-17α,20β-diol-3-one, 352
Pregnenolone, 344, 345, 354, 358, 364
    from 22-hydroxycholesterol, 345
4-Pregnen-20α-ol-20-one, from pro-
    gesterone, 351
Δ⁵-Pregnen-3β,11α,20α-triol, 351
Δ⁵-Pregnen-3β,17α,20β-triol, 351
Prephenic acid, 20
Progesterone, 347, 354, 358, 362
    from acetate, 342
    from cholesterol, 8
    from pregnenolone, 346
Prolycopene, 301
Propionate in macrolide biosynthesis,
    30, 138
Propionyl carboxylase, 138
Propionyl coenzyme A, 337
Protoaphin, 80
Protocotoin, 47, 105
Protohypericin, 89
Protokosin, 44
Protolichesterinic acid, 99
Protomagnamycin, 29
Protopine, 147
Prunetin, 58

Psoromic acid, 65, 171
Pterocarpus species, 59
Pterostilbene, 73
Puberulic acid, 169
Puberulonic acid, 169
Pulegone, 213, 215, 247
    from dimethylacrylic acid, 209, 215
Pulvic acids, 35
Pungenin, 157
Purine biosynthesis, 185
Purpurin, 90
Purpurogenone, 81
Pyrethrolone, 97
Pyrethrosin, 236
Pyrophosphatases, in tumor cells, 197
Pyrromycinones, 93
ε-Pyrromycinone, 154

Quadrilineatin, 71
Quassin, 98
Quercetin, 53, 161
Quinic acid esters, 157

Rapanone, 64
Rauwolfia serpentina, 119
Δ⁴-Reductase, 356
5α-Reductase, 356
Renghol, 62
Reptiles, 339
Resistomycin, 94
α-Resorcyclic acid, 160
β-Resorcyclic acid, 163
Retinene, 301
Retinene isomerase, 301
Rhapontin, 160
Rhodocladonic acid, 89
Rhodocomatulins, 92
Rhodomycinones, 93
Rhodopsin, 301
Ricinoleic acid, 134
Rimuene, 244
Rosenonolactone, 253, 286
    from acetate, 254
    from mevalonate, 188, 254
Rotenoids, 51, 59
Rotenone, 109
Rotiorin, 86, 104, 149

Rottlerin, 54
Rubiaceae species, anthroquinones, 89
Rubiadin, 90
Rubiginic acid, 97
Rubriogliocladin, 150
Rubrofusarin, 83
Rubropunctatin, 76, 86, 149
Rubroskyrin, 90, 152
Rubber, 7, 302
  from isopentenyl pyrophosphate, 194
  from mevalonate, 188

Salvia species, 155
Samidin, 109
Sanatal, 58
β-Santalene, 227
Santonin, 231
Sclareol, 242
Sclerotiorin, 76, 86, 149
Scopoletin, 158
Selagine, 117
Sennidines, 89
Sequence of biosynthetic steps, 14, 21
Shark, 339
Shikimic acid, 21, 33, 50, 96, 118, 155
Sinapic acid, 157
Siphulin, 94
β-Sitosterol, 287
  from mevalonate, 287
Skyrin, 90, 152
Solanidine, 363
Solanochromene, 303
Solorinic acid, 92
Sorigenins, 78
Soyasapogenol, 286
  from mevalonate, 188, 286
Spinochromes, 78
Spinulosin, 64
Squalene, 7, 287
  cyclization of, 273
  by dimerization of farnesyl pyrophosphate, 201
  from isopentenyl pyrophosphate, 194
  from mevalonate, 190, 287
  relation to lanosterol, 174
  stereochemistry of, 264
Squalene oxidocyclase, 280

Stearic acid, 127
Δ^{22}-Stigmasten-3β-ol, 287
  from mevalonate, 287
Stilbenes, 73
Stipitatic acid, 169
Stipitatonic acid, 169
Strepsilin, 67
Streptimidone, 104
Streptomyces, 93, 104
Streptovitacin, 104
Strobopinin, 55
Strychnine, 118
Sucrose, 161
Sulochrin, 47, 49, 81
Swertiamarin, 223
Swertianol, 49
Swertia species, 48
Sylvestrene, 213
Syringaldehyde, 156
Syringyl alcohol, 33

Tannins, 96
Taraxasterol, 265, 270, 271
Taraxerol, 265, 272
Tasmanone, 44
Taurine, 338
Taurocholic acid, 330, 338
  from cholesterol, 330
Taxifolin, 53
Teak constituents, 88
Teloschistin, 88
Tenuazonic acid, 165
Tenulin, 233
Tephrosia lanceolata, 57
Terpene synthesis, control of, 177
α-Terpinene, 213
Terramycin-X, 93
Terrein, 97
Terrestric acid, 100
Testosterone, 352, 354, 358
  from 17α-hydroxyprogesterone, 354
  inhibition of hydroxylation by, 348
Tetracycline, 93
Tetracycline biosynthesis, 154
Tetrahydrocannabinol, 71
Tetrahydroxycinnamic acid, 103
3α,7α,12α,26-Tetrahydroxycoprostane 336

Tetronic acids, 99, 165
Thelephoric acid, 36, 171
Thujaplicin, 98
(α)-Thujene, 219
Thujic acid, 216
Thujone, 219
Tirucallol, 265, 267, 268
Tocopherols, 70, 71, 114
Tolbutamide, 322
Tomatidine, 363
Torquatone, 42, 47, 109
Trachelogenin, 102
Trichothecin, 238
    from acetate, 238
    from mevalonate, 188, 238
Tricin, 162
3α,6α,7β-Trihydroxycholanic acid, 336
3α,6β,7α-Trihydroxycholanic acid, 335
3α,6β,7β-Trihydroxycholanic acid, 335
3α,7α,12α-Trihydroxycoprostane, 332,
    336
3α,12α,16α-Trihydroxycholanic acid,
    340
Trihydroxycoprostanic acid, 336
    from cholesterol in the alligator, 332
    as an intermediate in bile acid
        formation, 332
3α,17α,21-Trihydroxy-pregnane-20-
    one, from acetate, 343
2,4,4-Trimethylcyclopentanone, 97
Triparanol, 320
Triton-WR 1339, 185
Tropic acid, 59
Tropinone, 10
Tropolones, 99, 168
Tryptamine, 118
Tryptophan, incorporation into
    lysergic acid, 197
Tuberculostearic acid, 29
Tumor cells, sterol synthesis in, 196
Tyrase, 157
Tyrosine, 20

Ubichromene, 303
Ubiquinones, 302
    from mevalonate, 189
Umbelliprenin, 114
Unsaturated fatty acids, 133

Ursolic acid, 287
    from mevalonate, 287
Urushiol, 62
Usnic acid, 25, 44
Ustic acid, 64

Vaccenic acid, 137
Valeraldehyde, 309
Valeric acid, 309
Vanillin, 156
Variolaric acid, 68
Veatchine, 249
Veratric acid, 161
Verbenalin, 222
β-Vetivone, 235
Virensic acid, 67
Visnadin, 109
Visnagin, 44
Visnamminol, 44, 109
Vitamin A, 241
Vitamin B$_{13}$, 182
Vitamin K, 108, 115, 303
Volucrisporin, 35, 156

Wagner-Meerwein migrations, 259

Xanthoaphin, 80, 90
Xanthones, 47
Xanthophylls, 296
Xanthopurpurin, 90
Xanthoria fallax, 88
Xanthorrhea species, 41
Xanthostemone, 44, 47
Xanthotoxol, 109

Yangonin, 32
Yeast, 135, 137
Yohimbine, 10, 118, 223

α-Zeacarotene, 299
β-Zeacarotene, 299
Zeaxanthin, 290
Zerumbone, 228
Zierone, 233
Zingerone, 32
Zymosterol, 316
    to cholesterol, 329